Principles

of

Second Edition

W. B. Saunders Company

Philadelphia   *London*

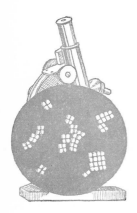

MICROBIOLOGY

WALTER W. KRUEGER
Formerly Department of Biology, Grand Rapids Junior College

KARL R. JOHANSSON
Division of Research Grants, National Institutes of Health, Bethesda, Maryland; Formerly Associate Professor of Bacteriology and Immunology, University of Minnesota

Preface to the Second Edition

In the preparation of this edition the book has undergone thorough revision to keep it abreast of the new developments and points of view in the science of microbiology. The general organization of the previous edition, however, has been retained. In addition to changes necessary to bring the subject matter up-to-date, other alterations have been effected for the improvement of the book. In many of the chapters new illustrations have been introduced.

A discussion of sexual reproduction as it is believed to occur in bacteria has been included in Chapter 4. Chapter 6 has been almost completely rewritten to bring it into conformity with the 7th edition of Bergey's Manual of Determinative Bacteriology. Much new material on viruses has been included in Chapter 9. Changes have been made in the chapter dealing with genetics and a discussion of the genetics of viruses has been included. Because of the important role played by the nucleic acids in life processes, they have been given prominence in the chapters in which they are considered. Improvements have been introduced into Chapter 3 to broaden the students' perspective of protoplasm and its functions.

To enable the student to gain a more complete understanding of the chemistry of enzymes and the nutrition and metabolism of microorganisms, as well as the environmental factors that influence their lives, Chapters 10 and 12 have been altered considerably and Chapter 11 has been completely rewritten. In the study of microbiology the student can now learn the basic facts of enzymes, nutrition, metabolism, reproduction and genetics.

In this edition the senior author has been joined by a co-author, Dr. Karl R. Johansson, who is responsible for the revision of Chapters 3, 10, 11, 12 and 17 and who also suggested changes in other chapters.

We wish to thank Drs. Herman C. Lichstein, S. G. Bradley and Leroy C. McLaren for their many criticisms and suggestions, which were helpful in the preparation of certain sections of the second edition.

Although the book has undergone extensive revision, much of it remains unchanged, and its level of presentation is comparable to that of the first edition.

WALTER W. KRUEGER
KARL R. JOHANSSON

Preface to the First Edition

This book is intended primarily as a text for an introductory course in general microbiology or bacteriology for college students. It represents an attempt to present the basic principles, concepts and viewpoints of the subject in a volume of moderate dimensions. The writer has endeavored to attain a logical sequence of subject matter and to cover the general field of microbiology without placing particular stress on any special branch of the subject. He has also made a definite effort to be accurate in factual statements and to keep the discussion abreast of modern developments.

The approach to the subject is biological; microorganisms are interpreted as biological entities, i.e., as physicochemical agents. This approach is essential to an understanding of the principles underlying microbiological phenomena.

The sequence of treatment is indicated in the titles of the nine parts into which the book is divided. The first part, consisting of three chapters, provides a general survey of the subject as well as an historical introduction to assist the student to become oriented in the field of microbiology. A chapter dealing with protoplasm has been included chiefly for those students who have had no previous training in the field of biology. For those who have had such training this chapter may serve to refresh their memory in regard to protoplasm and its properties.

In the second division of the book the student is introduced to the principal types of microorganisms—bacteria, fungi, protozoa, rickettsiae and viruses. A discussion of bacterial taxonomy and nomenclature is included.

Part III is concerned with the general physiological aspects of microorganisms. It includes a discussion of (1) enzymes and their role in microbial activities; (2) the nutrition and respiration of microorganisms; (3) environmental factors affecting their growth; and (4) bacterial heredity and variability.

The first three divisions of the book cover the fundamental points concerning the structure, taxonomy, physiology, nutrition, respiration, reproduction, ecology and heredity of microorganisms. This basic information is essential for any further study of the subject. After these parts have been covered, the sequence of treatment need not necessarily follow that of the book but may be altered at the discretion of the instructor to suit his own plan of presentation. In some instances eliminations may be necessary to fit the time limits of the course.

Microbiologic techniques and methods are treated in Part IV. Chapter 14 deals with the cultivation and laboratory study of microorganisms. It includes a discussion of culture media, culture techniques and methods, microscopes, dyes and staining procedures. This chapter has been designed chiefly to assist the student in his laboratory study of microorganisms. Some of the information it contains will be needed by the student at the very beginning of his laboratory work; other parts will be of help to him later. Thus the various parts of the chapter may be taken up at different times. This section of the book also includes chapters dealing with the inhibition and destruction of microorganisms by physical and chemical means and a chapter on chemotherapeutic agents.

Considered in Parts V, VI and VII are the applications of microbiology to agriculture, the dairy and fermentation industries, community water supplies, sewage treatment; and to the preservation, spoilage and processing of foods. Included is a discussion of the microbiological assay of food products for certain vitamins and amino acids. The aim of this part of the book is to give the student a broad view of the role microorganisms play in the world of life and in our everyday practical economy.

Since disease is an important aspect of human life, the tremendously important role microorganisms play as agents of disease has not been neglected. Part VIII treats of the disease-producing activities of microorganisms, body defenses against infection, immunity and immunization, and hypersensitivity. The value of immunization in civil defense as a protective measure in the event of biological warfare is given some consideration.

The four final chapters, which constitute Part IX, are devoted to a discussion of diseases caused by bacteria, fungi, protozoa, rickettsiae and viruses. There are differences of opinion regarding the emphasis to be placed on this phase of the subject in a course in general microbiology. Since the majority of the students upon completion of the course do not pursue the subject further, it appears desirable that they acquire some understanding of infectious diseases and the progress that has been made in their control. An adequate conception of the world of microorganisms is scarcely possible if the diseases they produce are completely ignored. More diseases have been included than can be ordinarily covered in the course. This permits the instructor to choose for consideration those he desires to include in his course. The final chapter of the book deals with microbial diseases of plants. It has been included chiefly for students whose special interests lie in the field of agriculture.

The illustrations are closely correlated with the text. They have been chosen chiefly to clarify the student's understanding of the subject matter. Many of the structural features of microorganisms are illustrated by line drawings, photomicrographs and electron micrographs.

A representative list of questions has been added to each chapter. The list may be augmented by the instructor with additional questions adapted to his particular group.

Each chapter concludes with a brief list of selected references. These may be of interest to students who wish to pursue further the study of certain phases of the subject.

The writer wishes to express his sincere gratitude to those who reviewed the manuscript and offered constructive suggestions. He extends his thanks also to the various authors, publishers, manufacturers, commercial establishments and other organizations for making available to him original photographs and other illustrative material.

WALTER W. KRUEGER

Grand Rapids, Michigan

Contents

II • The Microscopic World

Contents

IV • Microbiologic Techniques and Methods

V · Useful Activities of Microorganisms

VI · Microbiology of Sewage and Water

VII · Microbiology of Foods

VIII · Infection and Body Defenses

Contents **xxi**

Contents

Tuberculosis 467
    TUBERCLE BACILLUS 468
    TUBERCULOSIS IN HUMAN BEINGS 469
    BOVINE TUBERCULOSIS 471
    DETECTION OF INFECTED PERSONS 472
        The Tuberculin Test, 472. Roentgenogram of the Lungs, 473.
        Demonstration of Tubercle Bacilli, 473.
    IMMUNITY AND IMMUNIZATION 473
    TREATMENT 474
Tetanus 474
    THE ORGANISM 474
    THE DISEASE 475
    IMMUNIZATION AND TREATMENT 476
Diphtheria 476
    THE ORGANISM 476
    THE DISEASE 477
    IMMUNITY AND IMMUNIZATION 478
        The Schick Test, 479.
Brucellosis 479
    THE ORGANISM 479
    BRUCELLOSIS IN ANIMALS 480
    BRUCELLOSIS IN MAN 481
    PREVENTION AND TREATMENT 482
Plague and Tularemia 482
    PLAGUE 483
        The Causative Organism, 484. The Disease, 484.
    TULAREMIA 485
        The Causative Organism, 485. The Disease, 486.
Syphilis 487
    THE CAUSATIVE ORGANISM 487
    THE DISEASE 488
        Primary Stage, 488. Secondary Stage, 488. Tertiary Stage, 489.
        Congenital Syphilis, 489. Laboratory Diagnosis, 490. Immunity,
        491. Treatment, 491.
Questions 491
References 492

33 · Diseases Caused by Organisms Other Than Bacteria 493

Fungous Diseases 493
    RINGWORM INFECTION 493
    BLASTOMYCOSIS 496
    CANDIDIASIS 496
Protozoan Diseases 497
    AMEBIASIS 497
        Causative Organism, 498. Pathogenesis, 499. Transmission, 499.
    MALARIA 499
        Etiological Agents, 500. Vivax Malaria, 501.

I · Introduction

1 • Introductory Survey

The living things of the world may be grouped into two main categories on the basis of size: (1) macroorganisms, which constitute the larger forms, and (2) microorganisms, which include those forms visible only when highly magnified.

It is members of the latter group that comprise the subject matter of the science of microbiology. These minute forms of life, lying beyond the sphere of unaided human sight, constitute a world of unceasing activity—an enchanting world in which the drama of life is performed upon a microscopic stage.

Although man's environment abounds with microorganisms, he is scarcely aware of their presence since they carry on their activities quietly and for the most part unobtrusively. The existence of these minute life entities presents problems to man as well as a challenge to understand their nature. From whence do they come? What is their relationship to the rest of the living world? Do they have a bearing on the life of man? Do they minister to his needs? Are they detrimental? Can they be utilized by man? What role, if any, do they play in the scheme of nature? The answers to these questions and many other related or subsidiary ones lie within the province of the science of microbiology. The attempt on the part of man to probe the mysteries of the microscopic creatures of his environment has given rise to knowledge that has become of inestimable value to him.

DISCOVERY OF MICROORGANISMS

The world of microorganisms was unknown to man before the invention of the microscope. The first microscopes, however, lacked sufficient magnifying power to bring these minute organisms within the range of observation. Probably the first microscopist to see these small forms of life

3

was Antony van Leeuwenhoek (1632–1723) of Delft, Holland, who devoted his leisure time to the hobby of grinding lenses and constructing microscopes. He developed astonishing skill in grinding lenses of high magnifying power. The type of lense he made was exceedingly small and was practically the same as the front lens of the modern oil immersion objective. His microscopes were remarkable instruments with sufficient magnifying power to reveal microorganisms of various kinds. Each microscope (Figure 2) contained but a single lens mounted between two thin metal plates. The object to be examined was placed in front of the lens on the point of a short metal rod, which could be moved (laterally and vertically) into focus by means of a screw. Leeuwenhoek made many

Figure 1. Antony van Leeuwenhoek. (From Garrison: History of Medicine. 4th edition.)

such microscopes during the course of his long life, some of which magnified as much as 270 times. He never disclosed the methods he used in grinding his lenses and was suspicious of those who came to see his instruments, which he guarded jealously.

Although not widely educated, Leeuwenhoek became an ardent microscopist, examining such things as rain water, decaying matter, blood, cheese and scrapings from his teeth. In the course of his observations, which were largely of a random nature, he discovered the existence of microorganisms and thus opened a new realm of the biological world for exploration by man. He referred to the organisms he saw as "animalcules" because he believed that they were little animals.

Through the encouragement of his friend Regnier de Graaf, the distinguished anatomist, he communicated his discoveries in the form of letters to the Royal Society of London, a scientific organization patronizing research. The Royal Society, whose membership included such illustrious men as Isaac Newton, Robert Boyle, Christopher Wren and Samuel Pepys, later elected Leeuwenhoek a Fellow of its organization.

His letters to the Royal Society, although rambling and discursive, contained accurate, detailed accounts of what he saw. His first communication in 1674 was followed by others, some 200 in all, over a period of many years. These letters were written in Dutch rather than Latin, the language of the learned at that time. Many of his letters are still preserved in the archives of the Royal Society. Some have been translated into Eng-

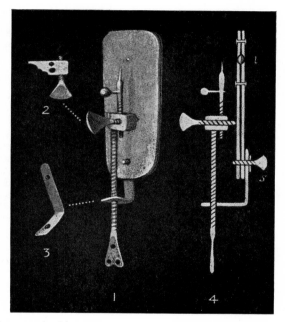

Figure 2. Leeuwenhoek's microscope. (From Clifford Dobell: Antony van Leeuwenhoek and His Little Animals. Reproduced by permission of Harcourt, Brace and Company, Inc.)

lish and Latin. He also sent a number of communications to the French Academy of Sciences.

Among the microscopic organisms which he first observed were protozoa, the lowest forms of animal life. Later he observed bacteria in water and in material from the human mouth and intestine. Figure 3 shows drawings of bacteria made by Leeuwenhoek and included in one of his letters. These drawings were the first published illustrations of bacteria.

In his thirty-ninth and most famous letter to the Royal Society, written in 1683, Leeuwenhoek described organisms found in scrapings from his teeth. He wrote as follows:*

* From Dobell, Clifford: Antony van Leeuwenhoek and His Little Animals. Quoted by permission of Harcourt, Brace and Company, Inc.

T'is my wont of a morning to rub my teeth with salt, and then swill my mouth with water: and often, after eating to clean my back teeth with a toothpick, as well as rubbing them hard with a cloth. . . . Yet notwithstanding, my teeth are not so cleaned thereby, but there sticketh or groweth between some of my front ones and my grinders a little white matter, which is as thick as if it were batter. On examining this, I judged that there yet were living animalcules therein. I have therefore mixed it, at divers times, with clean rain-water, and also with spittle, that I took out of my mouth, after ridding it of air bubbles: and I then most always saw, with great wonder, that in the said matter there were many very little animalcules, very prettily a-moving. The biggest sort had the shape of Fig. A: These had a very strong and swift motion, and shot through the water like a pike does through the water. These were most always few in numbers.

The second sort had the shape of Fig. B. These ofttimes spun round like a top, and every now and then took a course like that shown between C and D: and these were far more in number.

To the third sort I could assign no figure: for at times they seemed to be oblong, while anon they looked perfectly round. These were so small that I could see them no

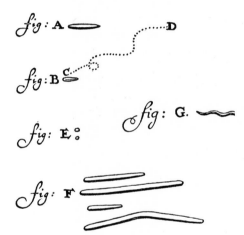

Figure 3. Leeuwenhoek's drawings of bacteria from the human mouth. (From Clifford Dobell: Antony van Leeuwenhoek and His Little Animals. Reproduced by permission of Harcourt, Brace and Company, Inc.)

bigger than Fig. E: yet therewithal, they went ahead so nimbly, and hovered so together, that you might imagine them to be a big swarm of gnats or flies, flying in and out among one another. These last seemed to me e'en as if there were, in my judgment, several thousand of 'em in an amount of water or spittle no bigger than a sand-grain; albeit there were quite nine parts of water, or spittle, to one part of the matter that I took from betwixt my front teeth, or my grinders.

Furthermore, the most part of this matter consisted of a huge number of little streaks, some greatly differing from others in their length, but of one and the same thickness withal; one being crooked, another straight, like Fig. F, and which lay disorderly ravelled together. . . . The biggest sort (whereof there were a great plenty) bent their bodies into curves in going forwards, as in Fig. G.

Leeuwenhoek's descriptions and drawings leave no doubt that he saw some of the larger bacteria, including forms we now describe as cocci, bacilli and spirilla. His quaint, simple descriptions, almost entirely free from speculation, are remarkable for their objectivity, which should give them enduring value. He was chiefly an observer rather than a theoretician. Nevertheless, he was interested in the meaning of the organisms he observed.

Thus Leeuwenhoek's painstaking observations opened up the vast world of microscopic life to the mind of man and marked the beginning of our knowledge of microorganisms. Many became interested in exploring this world, but no one at that time had any conception of the tremendous importance of these diminutive creatures. The discovery of the existence of microorganisms laid the foundation for the brilliant achievements which were to follow, achievements which made possible our modern manner of living.

In addition to his discovery of microorganisms, Leeuwenhoek investigated the microscopic anatomy of higher forms of life. He gave the first accurate description of red corpuscles and demonstrated the capillary connection between arteries and veins, thus confirming the findings of the Italian anatomist Malpighi. He also studied the structure of bone, teeth, muscle, and legs of insects and the structure of the crystalline lens of the eye.

Although Leeuwenhoek's discovery of microorganisms evoked great interest in the scientific world, it did not directly lead to an understanding of their significance. This was due to the absence of basic knowledge of chemistry and physiology and the lack of the necessary techniques to subject microorganisms to experimental investigation. It was not until the advent of Louis Pasteur and Robert Koch in the nineteenth century, nearly two centuries after Leeuwenhoek's discovery, that important advances were made.

KINDS OF MICROORGANISMS

The world of microorganisms embraces a large number of highly diversified forms which vary considerably in size as well as in their activities. Besides the bacteria, the organisms commonly included in the subject of microbiology are the protozoa, unicellular algae, certain fungi (yeasts and molds), the rickettsiae and viruses.

Bacteria

The bacteria receive the greater share of attention in the science of microbiology. They are widespread, successful organisms, highly efficient in development, multiplication and survival. Bacteria constitute a versatile and hardy group of organisms capable of utilizing an extremely wide range of materials as food. They occur in diverse habitats. In form bacteria are rodlike, spheroid, spiral or threadlike. Each bacterium, in the group known as "true bacteria," is a minute, undivided mass of protoplasm analogous to a single cell of higher forms of life. Figure 4 is a drawing of common forms of bacteria.

Through their numerous activities bacteria affect the life of man in many ways. Although some are inimical to man's welfare, the vast majority carry on activities which are of value to man. Together with molds and yeasts, bacteria are nature's great agency for the dissolution of organic matter and thus are indispensable for the very existence of green plants and, hence, of animals, including man himself. A number of species are utilized by man in the manufacture of important industrial products.

Bacteria are classified as members of the plant kingdom, not because of any one character they possess, but largely because as a group they show more resemblance to the blue-green algae, the simplest forms of green plants, than to the protozoa. In form these two groups are strikingly similar, and both reproduce by transverse fission. Bacteria differ from the blue-green algae in that some are motile by means of hair-like appendages

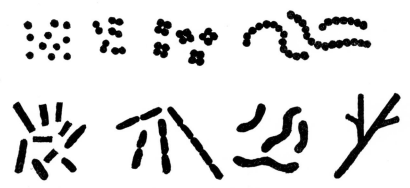

Figure 4.   Various kinds of bacteria.

(flagella). The blue-green algae contain chlorophyll, which enables them to utilize the energy of sunlight in the synthesis of organic compounds from inorganic substance. With a few exceptions, bacteria lack chlorophyll or chlorophyll-like compounds. It should be noted that the dividing line between plant and animal is an entirely arbitrary one, and in the realm of microscopic life it is often vague and indeterminable.

Protozoa

The protozoa are the most primitive forms of animal life and comprise a large group of unicellular organisms characterized by great diversity of

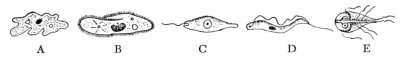

| A | B | C | D | E |

Figure 5.   Various kinds of protozoa. *A*, Ameba; *B*, Paramecium; *C*, Euglena; *D*, Trypanosoma; *E*, Giardia.

form. Some have irregular changing shapes; others have a definite body outline, being spherical, oval or elongate. Certain types have developed a high degree of structural complexity. Protozoa inhabit most of the waters of the earth, and certain types are abundant in the soil. The majority are free-living, but a few species lead parasitic lives in the bodies of higher organisms, including man. *Amoeba* and *Paramecium* are examples of free-living protozoa, whereas those causing malaria, amebic dysentery and African sleeping sickness represent disease-producing forms. Figure 5 illustrates five different kinds of protozoa. The branch of biological science that deals exclusively with the study of the protozoa is known as *protozoology*.

Fungi

The fungi included in the science of microbiology are chiefly those forms that are commonly referred to as yeasts and molds. Yeasts are somewhat larger than most bacteria and are generally ovoid, spheroid or, at times, elongated in form. They are structurally more complex than bacteria and multiply by a characteristic manner of budding. Yeasts are

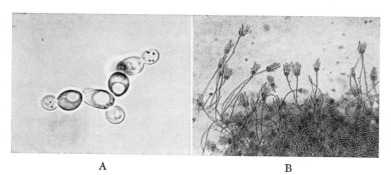

A   B

Figure 6. Fungi. *A,* Yeast cells; *B,* a mold (*Penicillium.*) (*A,* courtesy of the Fleishman Laboratories of Standard Brands Incorporated. *B,* courtesy of V. B. D. Skerman, University of Queensland, Brisbane, Australia.)

important in some industrial fermentation processes. A few species produce disease.

The molds constitute a large, heterogeneous group of organisms which have developed a considerable degree of specialization. They consist essentially of branched threads and have special structures for the production of spores which serve as a means of reproduction. Each organism is usually composed of many units (cells). Molds play an important role in nature as agents of decay. Some species are important in industrial fermentation processes. A few species cause disease. Figure 6 shows two kinds of fungi, a yeast and a mold. The biological science concerned with the study of the yeasts, molds and other fungi is known as *mycology*.

Rickettsiae

The rickettsiae (singular, rickettsia) constitute a group of microorganisms which resemble certain bacteria in being spherical and rodlike in form. They are of smaller dimensions than most bacteria, lying near the lower limit of visibility of the optical microscope. They are named for their discoverer, Howard Ricketts, an American microbiologist. They live as parasites in ticks, mites, fleas and lice and are the cause of certain human diseases, the two most important of which are Rocky Mountain spotted fever and typhus. The science which deals exclusively with the rickettsiae is known as *rickettsiology*.

Viruses

Viruses are incredibly small. With a few exceptions, they are too small to be seen under the optical microscope, but can be observed with the electron microscope (see Chapter 14). Apparently all viruses lead a parasitic mode of life, multiplying only within living cells. They are the infectious agents of many diseases of man, animals and plants. A large number of human diseases, many of them exceedingly serious, are due to viruses. A few examples of such infections are smallpox, influenza, poliomyelitis, rabies and the common cold.

Long before the electron microscope was invented it was known that viruses existed. Although they could not be seen, they were known by their behavior. The science concerned with the study of viruses is known as *virology*.

THE SCIENCE OF MICROBIOLOGY

The science which deals with living systems, i.e., with matter in the living state, is called *biology*. The two major divisions of biology are *zoology*, the science of animal life, and *botany*, the science of plant life. The term *microbiology* designates that branch of biological science which is concerned with the study of microorganisms. However, the field of study to which this term is commonly applied deals with those forms of microscopic life that are of particular importance to man. Certain groups, such as the algae, are usually given very little consideration. Microbiology, therefore, may be defined as the science which is concerned with the bacteria and those members of other groups of microorganisms that have a bearing on human welfare. The term *bacteriology* is also used as a name for this science. Neither term is entirely suitable—"bacteriology" is too restricted, since it implies only a discussion of the bacteria, and "microbiology" is too general for the science that does not include all the various microscopic forms of life. In this text the term "microbiology" will be used in preference to "bacteriology."

The science of microbiology deals with the composition, structure and activities of microorganisms, the forces that operate within and upon them, the ways in which they affect human life, and methods for their control. Our present-day understanding of microorganisms is the result of painstaking labor and countless trial and error experiences, as well as innumerable observations of their behavior under different circumstances. Although microbiology is one of the youngest divisions of biological science, it has made contributions of tremendous importance to the welfare of mankind.

The study of microbiology has contributed notably to our knowledge of life in general. Because of their rapid metabolism and the similarity of their metabolism with that of higher organisms, microscopic forms of life are frequently used in the place of larger forms in the solution of problems pertaining to organisms in general. At the present time much research into the principles of general biology is being carried on with bacteria, yeasts and molds as the immediate objects of investigation in the attempt to obtain information concerning the general problems of living things. Because of their small size, large numbers of them can be readily used as experimental and control groups.

THE HAUNTS OF MICROORGANISMS

Microorganisms are everywhere about us; they occur wherever life is tenable; and they are an inescapable part of our immediate environment. They float in the air we breathe and are present on the objects we handle and in the food we eat. They are abundant in the soil and in bodies of water, such as lakes and streams. Most species are highly cosmopolitan, being found wherever suitable habitats exist. Some are found only in aquatic situations, others are strictly soil organisms. As a group, these forms of life are adapted to live through a wide range of environmental conditions. When soil becomes dry many soil organisms, along with minute soil particles, are lifted into the air by air currents and are thus transmitted with the greatest facility from place to place. Bacteria and the spores of yeasts and molds have been found in the air at altitudes above 20,000 feet. Although these organisms do not flourish in the air, their ability to survive the atmospheric environment for a relatively long time facilitates their wide dissemination. They differ in distribution from higher forms of life in that any particular species of these forms usually has a limited geographic range.

Microorganisms are not only common inhabitants of our environment but are found also on, and in, the bodies of human beings, animals and plants. Some have become adapted to live on the human skin and in the various body cavities that open to the exterior, such as the mouth, nose, ears and intestines. These organisms are normally harmless, subsisting on the cellular secretions or the intestinal contents without attacking body cells. A relatively small number of species cause diseases in man, animals and plants.

THE ROLE OF MICROORGANISMS IN NATURE

In spite of their minuteness, certain groups of microorganisms play a role of gigantic importance in the great panorama of life. A vast complex of microscopic life is unceasingly active in the soil, vigorously attacking and transforming the organic substance of dead plant and animal material into simple inorganic compounds such as nitrates, phosphates, sulfates, carbon dioxide and water, and thus restoring to the soil the chemical compounds upon which the existence of plant life depends. Microorganisms thus are the medium through which a steady supply of the inorganic compounds needed by plants enters the soil.

The organisms that take part in these activities increase in numbers with extraordinary rapidity and consist chiefly of bacteria, molds and yeasts. By disintegrating the organic refuse of the world, they serve as nature's chief agency of decay and constitute an essential link in the endless chain of interdependent life. The number of microorganisms engaged in this task defies human comprehension. A grain of soil may contain as many as a hundred million. It is upon the activities of this vast horde of microscopic creatures that the continued existence of higher forms of life depends. Without them the soil would not be replenished and plant life would cease. Without plant life there could be no animal life. Microorganisms thus are indispensable for the survival of the rest of the living world.

MICROORGANISMS AND HUMAN WELFARE

Because of the manifold roles that microorganisms play, they are intimately related to many fields of human activity and are inseparably associated with the health of man, animals and plants, and with community sanitation, agriculture and various industrial processes as well as household management. Much of our knowledge of microscopic life has been put to practical use.

The early developments of microbiology were chiefly in the field of applied rather than theoretical science. The part played by microorganisms as causative agents of disease became an important field of inquiry early in the history of the science. The knowledge thus gained has had a marked influence on the welfare of mankind. It has enabled man to parry the blows of many of his microbial foes. Although the total number of species capable of disease production is relatively small, these organisms are man's most dangerous enemies. Disease-producing microorganisms are referred to as *pathogens.* Much of man's history has been influenced by pathogenic microorganisms which in past centuries caused extensive epidemics, often with catastrophic results. The greatest struggle the human race has had has been its struggle to cope with microscopic aggressors.

One of the greatest achievements of modern times has been the subjugation of many of the infectious diseases which in former times took a heavy toll of human lives. This accomplishment has had a decided effect in reducing the death rate and increasing the average duration of life. In 1800 the average length of life in the United States was only about thirty-five years, while at present it is about seventy years. It is in the control of disease-producing organisms that man has achieved his greatest conquest over his environment. Many problems still remain to be solved, however, before man will have in his hands the necessary weapons to combat effectively all the microscopic agents of disease.

Although some are pathogens, thinking of microorganisms as being predominantly disease-producers represents a distorted view of the significance of these forms of life. The vast majority are either beneficial or do not affect the life of man to any great extent. Knowledge of the diverse activities of both harmful and beneficial microorganisms has been of immeasurable value to man.

Agriculture has benefited enormously from an understanding of the important relationships of microorganisms to soil fertility and to the diseases of domestic animals and cultivated plants. For the sanitary control of milk and milk products, the dairyman needs knowledge of those forms that produce changes in milk and dairy products. Dairy microbiology embraces also the study of those bacteria, yeasts and molds that are utilized in the making of butter and cheese. The canner of vegetables, fruits and meats, the packer of meat products, the baker—these and others who are engaged in the handling of foods are helped in their enterprises by an understanding of the principles of microbiology. The homemaker profits by knowing how microorganisms affect food, the conditions that are favorable to their growth and the underlying factors that serve as a basis for our methods of food preservation.

In many instances the activities of microorganisms can be utilized in the industrial production of chemical products of great value to man. Certain species are used in the production of acetone, butanol, ethyl alcohol, lactic acid and many other commodities of great importance in modern life.

From certain bacteria that inhabit the soil (chiefly filamentous varieties) and a few molds, man has succeeded in obtaining substances known as antibiotics, which in extremely low concentration are capable of inhibiting the growth of other organisms. Some of these are effective in inhibiting the growth of certain pathogens within the body and, therefore, can be used to combat infectious diseases. Examples of antibiotics are penicillin, streptomycin and chloramphenicol. These are now produced in large quantities for the treatment of certain diseases.

The varied activities of microorganisms have given rise to a number of divisions of applied microbiology, including medical microbiology, agricultural microbiology, dairy microbiology, sanitary microbiology and industrial microbiology. In each division a different set of scientific facts is needed, but the student of any particular branch needs an understanding of the fundamental principles of general microbiology.

QUESTIONS

1. Why is Leeuwenhoek entitled to recognition as having made an important contribution to the field of microbiology? When did he live? What kind of microscope did he use?

2. Why did nearly two centuries elapse after the discovery of microorganisms before anything was learned about their significance in the world of life?

3. What are microorganisms? Name and characterize briefly the principal groups of microorganisms.

4. Define: (*a*) biology, (*b*) microbiology, (*c*) bacteriology, (*d*) protozoology, (*e*) mycology, (*f*) rickettsiology, (*g*) virology.

5. (*a*) Of what importance is microscopic life?

   (*b*) What unique role do certain groups of microorganisms play that makes them indispensable in the world of life?

6. Where can microorganisms be found?

7. In what ways may an understanding of microorganisms be of value to you in everyday life?

8. Name some of the divisions of applied microbiology.

REFERENCES

Bulloch, W.: The History of Bacteriology. London, Oxford University Press, 1938.

Clay, R. S., and Court, T. H.: The History of the Microscope. London, Charles Griffin & Co., Ltd., 1932.

Dobell, C.: Antony van Leeuwenhoek and His Little Animals. New York, Harcourt, Brace and Company, Inc., 1932.

Garrison, F. H.: Introduction to the History of Medicine. 4th ed. Philadelphia, W. B. Saunders Company, 1929.

Kluyver, A. J., and van Niel, C. B.: The Microbe's Contribution to Biology. Cambridge, Harvard University Press, 1956.

Rahn, O.: Microbes of Merit. New York, The Ronald Press Co., 1945.

2 • History of Microbiology

Mankind owes an immeasurable debt to the scientific workers who, through painstaking toil, have made possible today's fund of knowledge of microorganisms. Men of many nations have sought out the basic truths of the world of microscopic life. Their labors laid the foundation for the giant forward strides that have been made in medicine and sanitation and in the foods and fermentation industries. In no other field of science have investigators made greater contributions to the health and well-being of mankind.

As pointed out in the preceding chapter, man's knowledge of microscopic forms of life had its beginning in the latter part of the seventeenth century with the observations of Leeuwenhoek. For a period covering nearly two hundred years after their discovery by Leeuwenhoek, these minute forms of life were looked upon merely as microscopic curiosities. Nothing of great significance was learned about them until the middle of the nineteenth century, when the Frenchman Louis Pasteur subjected them to experimental investigation.

THE DOCTRINE OF ABIOGENESIS

After the discovery of the world of microscopic life, speculation arose concerning the origin of microorganisms. Do they come from preexisting forms of life, or are they generated spontaneously from lifeless matter? The idea that some plants and animals could originate by abiogenesis, i.e., by spontaneous generation under certain conditions, was generally accepted by the earlier naturalists. This theory was supported by Aristotle (384–322 B.C.), who believed that worms, insects, crabs, mollusks and other forms of animal life could come into being spontaneously out of the moist earth or the slime and mud of rivers. The overwhelming authority of Aristotle gave credence to the belief in spontaneous generation.

15

Aristotle's teachings, in general, dominated man's thinking for many centuries. The belief in abiogenesis persisted throughout the eighteenth century and until the middle of the nineteenth century.

Since the belief in spontaneous generation was still widely held when the world of microscopic life was discovered, the concept that these small forms of life could originate by abiogenesis readily gained ground. There were some men, however, who doubted that life could be generated from lifeless matter. An interesting controversy developed over this point between scientists of several nations. Experiments of many sorts were devised. The controversy dragged on for more than a century before it was finally settled.

One of the first of these experimental investigations was carried on by John Needham (1749), an English clergyman and naturalist. Needham heated some meat broth in cork-stoppered vials and took the precaution to cover the vials with hot ashes to destroy any bacteria that might be in the air above the liquid in the vials. Notwithstanding his precautions, in a few days the flasks were found to teem with microorganisms. Needham concluded that the microorganisms in his vials originated spontaneously. He believed that there was inherent in every particle of organic matter a "vital force" capable of causing it to become transformed, under suitable conditions, into living substance. It was his opinion that this so-called "vital force" was the same force that created Eve out of Adam's rib. His Bible-based reasoning gave rise to many arguments.

Lazzaro Spallanzani (1765), an Italian ecclesiastic and naturalist, became interested in the problem of abiogenesis. He repeated the experiments of Needham, but, instead of corking his flasks, sealed them hermetically, thus definitely preventing the entrance of air from the outside. He kept the broth at boiling temperature for three-quarters of an hour. Although the results were somewhat irregular, the majority of his flasks remained sterile. The irregular results undoubtedly were due, at least in part, to the fact that certain bacteria can undergo a reversible change into heat-resistant forms known as spores, which, however, was not known at that time. Spallanzani criticized Needham's work by contending that his vessels were not heated sufficiently and that the corks he used did not hermetically seal them. Adherents of abiogenesis raised objections, however, claiming that the prolonged heating Spallanzani used destroyed what they called the "vital principle" in the organic substance and also vitiated the air in the containers; therefore the conditions favorable to spontaneous generation no longer existed. Thus the experiments of Spallanzani were inconclusive.

A few years after these experimental investigations were made, Lavoisier (1775) established the fact that oxygen, one of the components of air, is consumed in the process of respiration. Consequently doubts arose whether in the experiments of Spallanzani the air had not been altered by the operations to which the organic fluids had been subjected so that it became unfit for the support of life.

Franz Schultze (1836) took up the problem of the relation of air to spontaneous generation by devising an experiment in which he sterilized some broth in a flask and admitted air which had been passed through concentrated sulfuric acid to destroy any microorganisms it might contain. In most cases the flasks remained sterile. He set up controls by exposing some flasks to air untreated by passage through acid. Organisms developed in these flasks. Proponents of abiogenesis maintained that passing air through sulfuric acid destroyed its "life-maintaining properties."

Two workers, Schroeder and von Dusch (1854), resorted to a simple type of experiment in which flasks containing boiled broth were provided with cotton plugs. The cotton plugs permitted air to enter and served as filters, freeing the air of any floating particulate matter. The flasks remained free from putrefaction. It could not be argued that the mechanical passage of air through a cotton plug produced any change in the properties of the air. Although this was a carefully devised experiment to refute the doctrine of abiogenesis, it was not completely convincing because it could not always be repeated and produce the same results. At times putrefaction occurred in some of the flasks. This was due, as we now know, to the presence of spores which resist heating to 100° C. even when the heating is prolonged. The work of Schroeder and von Dusch, however, demonstrated the usefulness of the cotton plug, which is now in universal use in microbiological laboratories.

The controversy was revived by Pouchet (1859), a member of the French Academy of Sciences, who was an ardent supporter of abiogenesis. He carried on many experiments which convinced him that microorganisms were able to originate spontaneously.

Louis Pasteur (1864) became interested in the spontaneous generation controversy. He devised a series of experiments in his attempt to solve the problem. In one experiment he poured broth into a flask and then drew out its neck into a long slender tube in the form of the letter S, as illustrated in Figure 7. The broth was then boiled. The tube remained open, providing direct contact of the broth with the outside air. It could not be argued that air was excluded or that the air in the flask became vitiated. The broth remained sterile. Dust and bacteria in the air that entered the flask settled out in the bent portion of the tube; consequently the air that entered the flask was free from microorganisms. When the flask was tilted momentarily so that some of the broth entered the bend of the tube and then was permitted to flow back into the flask, the broth quickly developed a growth of microorganisms. Thus Pasteur sounded the death knell of the concept that microorganisms can arise spontaneously.

In a lecture in which Pasteur pointed out the fallacy of spontaneous generation he said: "No, there is no circumstance known in which it can be affirmed the microscopic beings came into the world without germs,

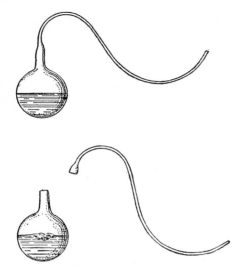

Figure 7. Swan-neck flask used by Pasteur in his studies on spontaneous generation. (From Duclaux: Pasteur: The History of a Mind.)

without parents similar to themselves. Those who affirm it have been duped by illusions, by ill-conducted experiments, spoiled by errors that they did not perceive or did not know how to avoid."

Tyndall (1876), an English physicist, also became interested in the problem and produced scientific evidence refuting the hypothesis of spontaneous generation. He constructed a small wooden chamber (Figure 8) with a glass front and a small glass window at each side. In this chamber floating particles in the air could be made visible by passing a beam of

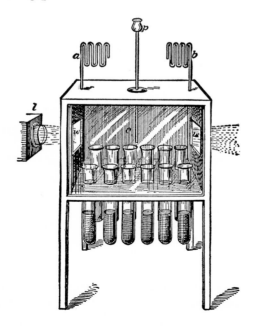

Figure 8. Tyndall's chamber.

light through the lateral window. The interior of the chamber was coated with glycerin to catch the dust particles present in the air of the chamber. After a few days, when a beam of light passed through the box showed the interior to be free from floating particles, tubes of sterile broth were introduced into the chamber. The tubes remained sterile for months, demonstrating that air free from particles will not contaminate sterile broth exposed to it. Tubes of sterile broth placed in the chamber before the dust particles had settled out soon swarmed with living organisms. This ingenious experiment furnished additional evidence that microorganisms do not arise spontaneously.

The overthrow of the concept of the spontaneous generation of microorganisms took the mystery out of their origin and suggested to investigators that definite scientific progress could be made in the study and control of these minute forms of life. The concept of abiogenesis gave way to the concept of biogenesis, which maintains that life comes only from pre-existing life.

The concept of biogenesis, however, does not exclude the possibility that during the early periods of the earth's history living matter gradually emerged from nonliving matter under conditions that probably differed greatly from those that exist at present. With increasing complexity some of the evolving substance of the earth may have become gradually infused with the type of organization we call life. The earlier stages of living entities, it may be assumed, were relatively simple, pre-cellular forms. Thus the step from nonlife to life may have been a very gradual process, as well as an inevitable one, due to the interplay of the forces of nature.

LOUIS PASTEUR

In addition to his work on spontaneous generation, Pasteur carried on many other investigations involving microscopic life. Born in 1822 at Dole, France, he was the son of a tanner who had been a soldier under Napoleon. After graduating from the Ecole Normale in Paris (1847) as a chemist, Pasteur held a number of teaching positions, notably at the college of Strasbourg (1852–1854), the University of Lille (1854–1857), the Ecole Normale in Paris (1857–1863) and the Ecole des Beaux-Arts (1863–1867).

Pasteur started his scientific investigations in the field of chemistry. His first important research was concerned with the crystals of tartaric and paratartaric acids. He found that paratartaric acid was a mixture of two kinds of tartaric acids which differed from one another optically in that one deviated the plane of polarized light to the right, the other to the left. Pasteur's activity in the field of chemistry, however, was of short duration, for he soon turned his attention, almost by accident, to microbes.

Pasteur was an ingenious experimenter and an astute observer. He used daring imagination in formulating hypotheses and in devising experiments to test them. He was scrupulously precise in his methods and highly

critical in the interpretation of the results of his experiments. His attitude
in this respect is indicated by his remark, "In experimental science it is
always a mistake not to doubt unless facts compel one to affirm." His
work paved the way for scientific advances which contributed tremendously to the welfare of mankind. His contributions to microbiological
science benefited winemakers, silkworm cultivators, vinegar manufacturers, brewers and farmers. They also had a profound influence on
medical science.

Pasteur captured the popular imagination as no scientist had previously
done. It was of Pasteur that Sir William Osler remarked, "He was the most
perfect man who ever entered the kingdom of science."

Fermentation

While at Lille, the center of the fermentation and distilling industries
of France, Pasteur became interested in the process of fermentation. The

Figure 9. Louis Pasteur
(1822–95). (From Garrison:
History of Medicine. 4th edition.)

most commonly accepted theory of fermentation at that time was the one
proposed by the German chemist Justus von Liebig, who regarded it as a
purely chemical process brought about by the presence of unstable compounds. Pasteur studied various kinds of fermentation, alcoholic, lactic,
acetic, butyric and others. He reached the conclusion (1857) that fermentation is a biological process brought about by the normal growth and
activities of living organisms and that the different types of fermentation
are caused by different kinds of organisms. He isolated these organisms
and obtained pure cultures with which he was able to initiate specific
fermentations at will. Liebig, however, remained unconvinced, maintaining that the microorganisms usually associated with fermentation were
the result, rather than the cause, of the process.

Pasteur's investigation in connection with the hypothesis of the spontaneous generation of microorganisms, discussed in a previous section of
this chapter, followed his work on fermentation.

Spoilage of Wine

Another problem which claimed Pasteur's attention (1864) was the spoilage of wine. The wine industry of France was losing many francs each year because the wine frequently turned sour, bitter or ropy. Pasteur solved the difficulty when he found that certain microorganisms were causing the trouble. By further investigations he found that the spoilage could be prevented by heating the wine for a short time to a temperature of 60° to 65° C. after it was bottled. This killed all harmful organisms, but did not alter the flavor of the wine.

He also investigated the spoilage that occurred in beer during storage and found that this was due to microorganisms and could be prevented by the same procedure that was effective in the prevention of the spoilage of wine. This process of heating, universally applied to milk at the present time, as well as to wine and beer, is now known as "pasteurization." The wine and beer industries of France were immediately benefited by Pasteur's discoveries.

Silkworm Disease

A call came (1865) from southern France for help in combating a disease of the silkworm which was threatening to do serious damage to the flourishing silk industry. Pasteur accepted the call and with his assistants worked on the problem for five years. He discovered that the silkworms were afflicted with two diseases (*pébrine* and *flacherie*) and that both were due to microorganisms. He devised a procedure for the detection of infected worms and thus, by their elimination, helped to control the spread of the disease. The discovery that these diseases were due to microorganisms gave a tremendous impetus to the germ theory of disease.

During this investigation Pasteur was stricken (1868) with a cerebral hemorrhage. Fortunately for mankind, he made a remarkable recovery and soon was at work again.

Fowl Cholera

Pasteur (1877) undertook an investigation of fowl cholera, a disease that was causing heavy losses among the domestic fowl of France. This work was to have far-reaching results. The causative organism of fowl cholera had been previously identified. Pasteur cultivated the organism in broth and demonstrated its infectivity for fowls. One day he inoculated hens with an old culture that had been kept at room temperature for a number of days. The hens did not acquire the disease. The lapse of time had destroyed the disease-producing power or virulence of the germ. He applied the term "attenuated" to such altered organisms. Some days later he inoculated the same hens with virulent fowl cholera germs. The fowls remained well. Thus by chance he found that attenuated germs when inoculated into fowls conferred immunity. He thus discovered that the same microorganisms which cause a disease may be utilized to provide protection against it; i.e., he discovered the principle of preventive inoculation. This was a discovery of great fundamental importance, and Pasteur was quick to realize its significance.

Although Edward Jenner in the previous century (1796) had discovered the technique of preventive inoculation (vaccination) for smallpox, he had not understood the underlying principles of the procedure; consequently nothing further developed from this isolated discovery. Pasteur surmised that his own discovery was not an isolated phenomenon but was applicable to other diseases as well as chicken cholera. He immediately made plans to test this hypothesis.

Anthrax

Pasteur's success with fowl cholera led to an attempt (1881) to apply the principle of preventive inoculation to anthrax (*charbon*), a disease which was taking a terrific toll of cattle and sheep in France and throughout Europe. Human beings also fell victim to it. The first difficulty to overcome was to attenuate the anthrax germ. This posed a problem, since the virulence of this organism could not be reduced by the simple procedure of cultivating it at room temperature as was done with the chicken cholera organism. Pasteur soon discovered that when grown at a temperature of 42° to 43° C., the anthrax germ lost its virulence.

A large scale public demonstration was arranged on a farm near Melun to test the efficiency of Pasteur's vaccine. The Melun Agricultural Society placed sixty sheep at Pasteur's disposal for the demonstration. Ten were used as a control group. Twenty-five were vaccinated with two inoculations about two weeks apart. Several weeks later, they and twenty-five more were inoculated with virulent anthrax germs. The results were most dramatic. All the unvaccinated animals died, while the vaccinated ones remained well. The demonstration was a striking success; the grip of this devastating disease was broken.

Rabies

Pasteur next attempted to apply the principle of preventive inoculation to rabies, a terrifying affliction for which there was no cure. There was no hope of recovery for those it attacked. He was unable to isolate the causative agent, which is now known to be a virus. The infective agents now referred to as "viruses"* were unknown at that time. By experiments with animals Pasteur demonstrated that the causative agent of rabies attacks the central nervous system. He found that if saliva from a rabid dog picked up on the streets of Paris (street virus) was injected into rabbits, they succumbed to the disease in fifteen to sixteen days. He found also

* The term "virus," however, was in use at that time. It was used as a general term for disease-producing organisms. Later, when filter-passing disease-producing agents were discovered, they were referred to as "filtrable viruses." The unmodified term "virus" is now used in a restricted sense, referring to those pathogenic agents that readily pass through bacteriological filters.

that if material from the brain of an infected rabbit was transferred directly to another rabbit's brain, the potency of the virus for rabbits was increased. By successive transfer from rabbit to rabbit, after twenty-five or more serial passages, death occurred regularly on the sixth or seventh day. This was the maximum potency that he could obtain. The virus thus became stabilized and was then referred to as "fixed virus." Although the fixed virus was much more highly potent for rabbits than was street virus, its virulence for dogs and man was greatly reduced.

The fixed virus was Pasteur's starting point in making the vaccine. To further decrease the potency of the virus for dogs and man he subjected the spinal cords of infected rabbits to drying for various lengths of time, from a maximum of fourteen days to a minimum of one day. He found that after fourteen days of drying the spinal cords were no longer infectious for rabbits.

In the attempt to immunize dogs against rabies, Pasteur carried on extensive experiments in which he injected material from dried spinal cords mixed with sterile water. He succeeded in developing a procedure which involved the building up of immunity by a series of small daily doses of vaccine, starting with material from a cord which had dried fourteen days and ending with one that had dried for only one day. Dogs treated in this way did not acquire rabies when bitten by a rabid dog. He discovered also that, owing to the long period of incubation (fourteen to ninety days) characteristic of this disease, dogs could be effectively immunized after they were bitten by a rabid dog.

On July 6, 1885, a nine-year-old boy, Joseph Meister, who had been severely bitten by a rabid dog, was brought into Pasteur's laboratory for treatment. Death seemed inevitable. Pasteur, after consulting with a number of physicians, arranged to have one of them treat the boy by the method he had found to be successful with dogs. The boy's life was saved. This case marked the birth of what we now know as the Pasteur treatment for rabies. Soon many persons bitten by rabid dogs came to Pasteur's laboratory to receive preventive inoculations. Additional physicians were required to treat the large number of patients.

The conquest of rabies was a great achievement that won world renown for Pasteur. In appreciation of this accomplishment and his other outstanding contributions to the welfare of mankind, a movement was started to collect funds by popular subscription for the erection of an institution for the treatment of rabies and other diseases for which vaccines had been developed. Funds were received from all over the world. The institution, known as the Pasteur Institute, was opened in Paris in 1888. Its scope has been broadened, and it now serves also as a center for the study of infectious diseases. At the present time there are similar institutes scattered throughout the world.

It is apparent from the preceding discussion that Pasteur established the broad general principles of the science of immunity in the discovery that the virulence of some infecting agents can be reduced to the point where they are no longer capable of producing disease, and that the inoculation of such material into animals or man produces immunity. He laid the foundation for freeing mankind from thralldom to infectious disease.

Pasteur is rightly called the "father of microbiology," since his work led to the birth of microbiology as a science. He had great faith in the value of laboratory work. On one occasion he remarked: "Take interest, I implore you, in those sacred dwellings which one designates by the expressive term: Laboratories. Demand that they be multiplied, that they be adorned. These are the temples of the future—temples of well-being and of happiness. There it is that humanity grows greater, stronger, better."

Pasteur died in 1895 and was buried in a marble crypt beneath the Pasteur Institute. He left a splendid legacy of bacteriological discoveries. Time has not dimmed the luster of his name.

ROBERT KOCH

No science can develop without suitable methods and techniques. The science of microbiology owes much to Robert Koch (1843–1910), a German physician and a contemporary of Pasteur, who introduced many of the procedures and techniques in present-day use. He developed methods for isolating bacteria in pure culture and devised improved techniques for staining bacteria for microscopic examination. He also developed a procedure for studying the infectivity of pathogens and made a series of discoveries of specific disease-producing bacteria. The painstaking and meticulous work of Koch gave the science of microbiology a discipline and standard which contributed greatly to its orderly development.

The period during which Pasteur and Koch were the leading investigators in the field of microscopic life is often referred to as the "golden age of microbiology" because scientific knowledge of microorganisms developed with amazing rapidity. Koch and his disciples made great progress in the isolation and identification of microorganisms and in discovering the microbial agents of many of the infectious diseases, whereas the French school of microbiology under the leadership of Pasteur became chiefly concerned with the problem of immunity. A bitter scientific rivalry developed between the French and German research men which was as intense as the national feeling between the two countries.

Anthrax

Koch's first studies (1876) dealt with anthrax, a disease of cattle and sheep for which, as mentioned in the preceding section of this chapter, Pasteur later developed a method of immunization. Koch isolated the anthrax bacillus, which Pollender and Davaine had seen as early as 1849 in the blood of animals dying of the disease. Koch injected blood obtained from animals infected with the anthrax bacillus into mice and found that the organism invaded the tissues of these animals. As a result he was able to obtain pure cultures of the organism from the tissues of the mice. During the course of this work he discovered the spore stage, observed the spores developing into the active rod-shaped cells, and also saw the cells forming long filaments.

Koch injected organisms from his cultures into experimental animals, reproduced the disease, and recovered the organisms from the inoculated animals after they had acquired the disease. He thus established beyond reasonable doubt that the organism in question was the causative agent of the disease. His work was so complete that little of importance has been added since then to our knowledge of the anthrax organism and its pathogenic properties. His published report of his work on anthrax served

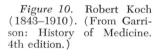

Figure 10. Robert Koch (1843–1910). (From Garrison: History of Medicine. 4th edition.)

as a model for other investigators because of its clear exposition and detailed account of his observations.

Staining Technique

The following year (1877) Koch published a paper in which he described a technique for staining bacteria by spreading them on a cover glass in the form of a thin smear which, when it became dry, formed a film on the glass. The film was fixed in alcohol and stained. He made use of the newly discovered aniline dyes. Later he fixed the film by heating it gently instead of using alcohol. Koch also devised a method for staining the flagella (hairlike structures) of bacteria. The methods now in vogue for staining bacteria are essentially the same as those developed by Koch.

Wound Infections

In 1879 Koch published a notable memoir on the etiology of wound infection in which he described the experimental production of infections in animals by the subcutaneous introduction of microorganisms from various sources. The infections were comparable to the wound infections observed in man. He also described in detail the causative agents of six different kinds of infections developing in surgical incisions. Koch thus showed that microorganisms were the causative agents in wound infections.

The Pure Culture Technique

Koch realized that the lack of a convenient method of isolating bacteria and obtaining pure cultures was a great handicap to progress. The solution of the problem was at hand when he introduced (1881) a liquefiable solid medium by adding gelatin to beef broth. This medium, known as nutrient gelatin, solidifies at room temperature but can be liquefied by the application of heat. Koch found that this medium could be used in two different ways in the isolation of bacteria. In the procedure known as the "streak plate method" he poured liquefied nutrient gelatin on sterile glass plates, where it quickly solidified. Using a sterilized needle, he transferred material from a mixed culture to the medium by streaking it over the surface. He then covered the plates with sterile bell jars. After a few days some isolated colonies (small masses visible without magnification) were present, each consisting of but one kind of organism. To secure a pure culture it was necessary only to transfer bacteria from a colony to a tube of fresh sterile medium.

In the method known as the "pour plate method" Koch added a small amount of a mixture of bacteria to a tube of liquefied nutrient gelatin. Being a dilute culture, the bacteria were for the most part widely separated from one another in this medium. He then poured the medium on sterile glass plates to become solid. The separation of the bacteria was much better by this procedure, and many of the colonies present developed from single organisms which became separated from others and became fixed in place as the medium solidified. To obtain a pure culture, bacteria from any of the colonies could be transferred to other media and then subjected to thorough investigation.

In the place of gelatin Koch later used agar-agar (a gelatin-like product of certain seaweeds) to make the liquefiable solid medium. This type of medium is known as nutrient agar. It has advantages over nutrient gelatin in that it can be incubated at body temperature without liquefying and thus can be used for the growth of pathogens, many of which will not grow at room temperature. Also, there are some bacteria which can digest and liquefy gelatin, thus making this medium useless for their isolation. Petri, one of Koch's assistants, devised (1887) a glass dish, the Petri dish, to be used for plate cultures in place of glass plates and bell jars. These are now in common use.

Koch's technique for isolating bacteria was an important contribution that attracted world-wide attention. It simplified the securing of pure cultures of bacteria from the mixtures in which they generally occur under natural conditions. With this method available many kinds of bacteria were soon isolated and identified by various investigators. In rapid succession the causative organisms of many diseases were isolated and identified.

Discovery of the Tubercle Bacillus

In 1882 Koch announced his discovery of the tubercle bacillus, the causative organism of tuberculosis. This was an important discovery, for tuberculosis was the major cause of death at that time. Koch devised a special method for staining the organism since it could not be stained by the usual staining procedure. After repeated efforts to grow the organism outside the body, he succeeded in obtaining pure cultures on solidified blood serum. By inoculating guinea pigs with bacteria from his pure cultures he was able to produce tuberculosis at will in these animals.

In his published report of this work, which is considered a classical masterpiece of biological research, he laid down the conditions that must be fulfilled before an organism can be recognized as the causative agent of a specific disease. These conditions or rules were first suggested by Jacob Henle, but were amplified by Koch and are known as "Koch's Postulates." They provide that (1) the organism in question must always be associated with the disease; (2) it must be isolated in pure culture from the infected individual; (3) the organism in pure culture must be inoculated into a susceptible animal and give rise to the disease; and (4) it must be recovered in pure culture from the experimentally infected animal. Fulfilment of these conditions constitutes positive evidence concerning the etiological relationship of a given organism to a specific disease.

Koch's postulates played an important role in the study of infectious diseases in that they exerted a restraining influence, keeping investigators from drawing false conclusions. It is now recognized that the fulfilment of these postulates is not always possible since certain diseases of man, such as syphilis, gonorrhea, scarlet fever, bacillary dysentery and whooping cough, do not occur in animals. However, the newer methods of immunology can now be utilized in many instances to furnish proof of the etiological relationship of a suspected microorganism to a given disease. The procedure is based on the detection of specific antibodies (counteracting substances) in the blood of the host, which are absent in normal individuals.

In 1890 Koch reported the preparation of tuberculin, a liquid containing the growth products of the tubercle bacillus when cultivated in glycerol broth. When injected into the skin of a patient with tuberculosis, tuberculin produces a specific reaction and for that reason is a valuable diagnostic agent. Koch announced that it had curative properties in certain cases of tuberculosis, but subsequent experience did not support his claim.

After the epoch-making discoveries just related, Koch was sent (1883) to Egypt and India as director for the German Cholera Commission. He carried on a painstaking investigation of Asiatic cholera and discovered the causative organism, a comma-shaped bacterium now known as *Vibrio comma.*

PAUL EHRLICH

Paul Ehrlich (1854–1915) was one of the brilliant workers attracted to Koch's laboratory. He applied dyes to the study of the cellular contents of blood and developed a technique for staining blood films. In his attempt to explain the process of immunity he formulated a theory known as "the side-chain theory of immunity," which, although no longer regarded as a satisfactory explanation of the process of immunity, served a useful purpose in that it stimulated research and provided a terminology, some of which is still in use at the present time.

Ehrlich, in his search for chemical agents which would have a toxic effect on pathogens without having a deleterious effect on the host, produced (1910) a synthetic compound which he called "salvarsan," but which is now known as "arsphenamine." It proved to be very effective in the treatment of syphilis and a few other diseases. Arsphenamine and its derivatives (neoarsphenamine, and the like) held the field in the treatment of syphilis until 1943, when penicillin was found to be a superior chemotherapeutic agent for the treatment of this disease.

JOSEPH LISTER

Joseph Lister (1827–1912), an English surgeon, became interested in Pasteur's early work on fermentation. He saw a similarity between the formation of pus in wounds and the process of fermentation and formulated the hypothesis that microorganisms were responsible. There was no proof at this time (1865) that pus was the result of microbial activity. However, Lister's reasoning by analogy had far-reaching effects.

The death rate in surgical cases at that time was appalling. Pus formation in surgical incisions was considered unavoidable; some even believed that it was a necessary step in the healing process. No particular precautions as to cleanliness were taken. Surgeons wore street clothes in the operating room and, to keep their clothing from being soiled, wore an apron which was usually soiled with blood from previous operations.

Lister attempted to prevent microbes from entering surgical incisions. He disinfected his instruments and sprayed the air about the operative field with a mist of carbolic acid solution. After the operation he applied an antiseptic dressing to the incision. His adoption of antiseptic surgery reduced surgical mortality in his hospital to a small fraction of what it had been previously.

Lister's hypothesis that pus formation in surgical incisions is due to microorganisms revolutionized surgical practice. It gave rise to antiseptic surgery. Modern surgery has become aseptic; i.e., it attempts to prevent microorganisms from entering incisions, thus alleviating the necessity of applying antiseptics to the incisions. The essential points of our modern aseptic technique developed between 1880 and 1890 in Germany, where bacteriological research was making rapid progress.

OTHER CONTRIBUTORS

The outstanding contributions made by Pasteur, Koch, Ehrlich and Lister inspired other men to carry on research in the field of microbiology. Many valuable discoveries followed in rapid succession. Elie Metchnikoff (1883) discovered the role of white blood corpuscles in the process of immunity. Edwin Klebs (1883) isolated the diphtheria bacillus, and Frederich Loeffler (1884) established it as the cause of diphtheria. Emil von Behring (1890) demonstrated the protective action of diphtheria antitoxin. Kitasato (1889) isolated the tetanus bacillus, and von Behring and Kitasato (1890) produced an antitoxin for tetanus.

The first indication of the existence of viruses appeared in 1892 as the result of experimental work on the transmission of tobacco mosaic disease. The Russian microbiologist Iwanowski found that the sap of infected plants was capable of inducing the disease in uninfected tobacco plants after it had been passed through bacteria-retaining filters (bacteriological filters). Beijerinck of Holland later confirmed this discovery and concluded that the fluid itself was infectious. He formulated the hypothesis that the cause of the disease was a living contagious fluid (*contagium vivum fluidum*). It is now known that tobacco mosaic disease and many other diseases of plants and animals are caused by filter-passing particles known as viruses.

Important advances were made in the study of soil microorganisms. Two German chemists, Hellrigel and Wilfarth, noted (1887) that bacteria living in the root nodules of leguminous plants, such as clover and alfalfa, were capable of assimilating atmospheric nitrogen, giving rise to compounds which plants could utilize. These bacteria were later observed and described by Beijerinck and have since been placed in the genus *Rhizobium*. Beijerinck also isolated two species of bacteria which live independently in the soil and can fix appreciable amounts of atmospheric nitrogen. He created the genus *Azotobacter* for these organisms. In 1893 the Russian microbiologist Winogradsky, who made many important discoveries concerning the activities of soil microorganisms, found that certain soil bacteria were capable of converting ammonia, which forms in the soil by the decay of nitrogenous organic matter, into nitrogen salts (nitrates) which are necessary for plant life.

The discoveries of Hellrigel, Wilfarth, Winogradsky and Beijerinck attracted widespread attention in the realm of agriculture and revealed the significant role of bacteria in the nitrogen cycle of nature.

Alexander Yersin and Kitasato (1894) simultaneously discovered the plague bacillus. Sir Ronald Ross (1897) proved that the Anopheles mosquito transmits malaria. Kiyoshi Shiga (1898) discovered the bacillus of dysentery (*Shigella dysenteriae*). The causative organism of syphilis was discovered by Schaudinn and Hoffmann (1905). Von Behring (1913) introduced the use of toxin-antitoxin in the prophylactic immunization against diphtheria. BCG vaccine, developed by Calmette and Guérin (1926), is now being used by the World Health Organization in the most extensive campaign ever undertaken to stamp out tuberculosis.

AMERICAN CONTRIBUTORS

A number of Americans have made substantial contributions toward the development of the science of microbiology. One of these was William Welch (1850–1934), who, although chiefly interested in pathology, did some important work in the field of microbiology. He spent several years in Germany studying under famous pathologists during the time Robert Koch was a professor in the University of Berlin. On his return he introduced the Koch techniques to America. In 1884 he became professor of pathology at Johns Hopkins University. Together with G. H. Nuttal he isolated and described (1892) one of the causal agents of gas gangrene. They called the organism *Bacillus aerogenes capsulatus* because it produced gas and was surrounded by a capsule. It is now known as *Clostridium perfringens,* although at one time it bore the name *Clostridium welchii.*

Much progress was made in the field of plant diseases. Thomas Burrill discovered (1881) that fire blight of apple and pear trees was a bacterial disease. He isolated the causative organism and gave it a name. Burrill was the first person definitely to associate a specific bacterium with a plant disease. He investigated many important crop diseases. It remained, however, for Erwin F. Smith to do most of the pioneer work in the field of plant pathology. He discovered the causative organisms of many plant diseases and wrote many articles reporting his research work.

Theobald Smith (1859–1934), internationally known for his researches, demonstrated (1890) that Texas cattle fever was transmitted from infected to well cattle by the bites of ticks. Among his other noteworthy contributions was the differentiation of the tubercle bacillus into the human and bovine types (1896).

George Sternberg (1838–1915) entered the army at the time of the Civil War and later became Surgeon-General of the United States Army. He was one of the first investigators to observe and describe (1881) the organism (pneumococcus) that is the most common cause of pneumonia. He made a comparative study of disinfectants and wrote one of the first books on this subject.

During the Spanish American War many cases of yellow fever occurred among American troops stationed in Cuba. Military authorities sent a commission of American Army officers to Havana (1900) in the attempt to solve the yellow fever problem. Major Walter Reed was the chairman of the commission. Reed and his associates, with the aid of soldier volunteers, succeeded in proving beyond all doubt that yellow fever was transmitted from man to man by the bite of *Aedes aegypti,* a species of mosquito. This knowledge made possible an effective means of control and enabled General William Gorgas, four years later, to institute the necessary sanitary measures in Panama that made possible the construction of the Panama Canal.

QUESTIONS

1. Explain the terms "abiogenesis" and "biogenesis."
2. State briefly the more important experimental investigations that were carried on in the controversy that arose over the concept of the spontaneous generation of microorganisms.
3. Why was it important for man to know that microorganisms do not arise spontaneously?
4. If the concept of spontaneous generation had proved tenable, how, in your opinion, might that have influenced the development of the science of microbiology and man's control and utilization of microorganisms?
5. Do the results obtained from these experiments permit us to conclude that no forms of life ever originated spontaneously at any time in the earth's history? Explain.
6. Describe Pasteur's discovery of the cause of fermentation.
7. Explain how Pasteur discovered the principle of protective inoculation against disease.
8. Summarize the work of Koch and point out its importance in the development of the science of microbiology.
9. State Koch's postulates.
10. Indicate briefly the part played by each of the following persons in enlarging our knowledge of microorganisms:

Ehrlich	Beijerinck	Burrill
Lister	Winogradsky	Erwin Smith
Metchnikoff	Hellrigel and Wilfarth	Theobald Smith
Iwanowski	Ross	Reed

REFERENCES

Bulloch, W.: The History of Bacteriology. London, Oxford University Press, 1938.
Compton, P.: The Genius of Louis Pasteur. New York, The Macmillan Company, 1932.
De Kruif, P.: Microbe Hunters. New York, Harcourt, Brace and Company, Inc., 1926.
De Kruif, P.: Hunger Fighters. New York, Harcourt, Brace and Company, Inc., 1928.
Dubos, R. J.: Louis Pasteur, Free Lance of Science. Boston, Little, Brown & Company, 1950.
Duclaux, E.: Pasteur: The History of a Mind. Philadelphia, W. B. Saunders Company, 1920.
Ford, W. W.: Clio Medica: Bacteriology. New York, Paul B. Hoeber, Inc., 1939.
Garrison, F. H.: Introduction to the History of Medicine. 4th ed. Philadelphia, W. B. Saunders Company, 1929.
Grainger, T. H.: A Guide to the History of Bacteriology. New York, The Ronald Press Co., 1958.
Oparin, A. I.: The Origin of Life on the Earth. New York, Academic Press, Inc., 1957.
Roddis, L. H.: Edward Jenner and the Discovery of Smallpox Vaccination. Menasha, Wis., Banta, 1930.
Vallery-Radot, R.: The Life of Pasteur. New York, Garden City Publishing Co., Inc., 1923.
Wood, L. N.: Louis Pasteur. New York, Julian Messner, Inc., 1948.

3 • The Protoplasm of Microorganisms

In order to interpret the activities carried on by microorganisms, it is necessary to understand their chemical and physical organization. Although microorganisms are comparatively simple in appearance, they have a complex chemicophysical structure. Living matter in general is endowed with a complexity which cannot be completely explained on the basis of our present knowledge.

The phenomenon referred to as life is associated with a particular kind of matter, a unique, semifluid, jelly-like translucent substance called protoplasm (Greek, *protos,* primary; *plasm,* formed substance). Protoplasm is matter in the living state; it serves as the material substratum in which the varied phenomena of life stage their play. It is a highly organized and coordinated, heterogeneous system of chemical compounds which has the unique power of being able to form more of its own substance from material taken in from the environment. Protoplasm is the seat of innumerable coordinated chemical reactions concerned with transformations of matter and energy, processes referred to collectively as metabolism. It exists in the form of miniature units known as cells.

Viruses, however, are a unique form of protoplasm, being possessed of essentially no measureable metabolism and being relatively homogeneous in chemical composition. It is uncertain, however, whether they should be classified as living entities or regarded as aggregations of molecules on the threshold of life. Some investigators look upon them as connecting links between the world of the living and the realm of inanimate substance. This topic will be treated more completely in Chapters 9, 13 and 33.

Protoplasm is not a single chemical compound but is a mixture of many compounds. Because of its complexity an adequate, integrated picture of the chemistry of protoplasm has not been obtained, but many facts concerning its make-up have been disclosed.

The protoplasm of microorganisms does not differ fundamentally from that of other organisms. In its general chemical pattern the protoplasm of all organisms is basically alike. Because of this there is a remarkable oneness of the life processes wherever they occur, whether in bacteria, protozoa, whales or human beings. The protoplasm of one kind of organism is not identical, however, with that of another kind, there being subtle differences that produce the distinction between species. There could be but one kind of organism if all protoplasm were exactly alike.

DETERMINATION OF CHEMICAL COMPOSITION

In determining the chemical composition of microorganisms, two techniques may be used: one is a microscopic method, while the other involves direct chemical analysis. The technique performed wholly or in part under the microscope requires the use of certain chemical reagents which, because of their selective action, produce colored complexes with certain constituents without affecting others. Dilute iodine solution, for example, will color *starch* granules blue and *glycogen* a red-brown, without coloring other protoplasmic components. Zinc chloriodide colors *cellulose* blue and *chitin* violet. *Fat* globules are colored black by osmic acid. Certain dyes are selective in their action. The dye Sudan III, for example, stains fat globules red. Polychrome methylene blue has a selective affinity for *volutin* (minute granules of organic and inorganic phosphate compounds found in the cells of some species of bacteria). These various microchemical tests are qualitative rather than quantitative and are limited to the identification of certain protoplasmic components.

Direct chemical analysis provides a means of identifying the various cellular constituents. This type of analytic process cannot be carried on without causing the death of the protoplasm. The process of death is apparently associated with chemical change; thus the analysis deals with protoplasm that has lost the properties of life. It gives an indication, however, of the elements and many of the compounds present, as well as their relative abundance. Since microorganisms are small, it is necessary to grow them in large quantities to obtain an ample amount of material for analysis. This may be achieved by: (1) propagating the organisms on a solid culture medium and then removing the growth for analysis or (2) growing them in a liquid medium and then separating them from the medium by centrifugation. The centrifuged organisms become massed at the bottom of the culture tube. After pouring off the supernatant fluid, the microbial mass is washed to free it of extraneous material, after which it is subjected to analysis. The analysis involves titration, extraction with various solvents, and so forth, until the fundamental components have been separated. The supernatant fluid may be analyzed for metabolic by-products, e.g., organic acids, alcohols, antibiotics, toxins, etc.

CHEMICAL ELEMENTS IN PROTOPLASM

The elements composing microbial cells are those which occur in all protoplasm. The most abundant ones are carbon (C), hydrogen (H), oxygen (O), nitrogen (N), sulfur (S) and phosphorus (P). These are often referred to as the *essential* or *indispensable elements* because they constitute well over 90 per cent by weight of the substance of protoplasm and are ubiquitous in living matter. These elements are abundant also in the nonliving matter of the world. The remaining percentage consists of relatively small quantities of more than 20 *trace elements,* most of which can be detected in all cells. Some of the trace elements are iron (Fe), potassium (K), sodium (Na), chlorine (Cl), calcium (Ca), manganese (Mn), magnesium (Mg), cobalt (Co), zinc (Zn), silicon (Si), aluminum (Al), iodine (I) and copper (Cu). It will be recognized that these elements, too, are widely distributed in inanimate matter.

COMPOUNDS OF PROTOPLASM

The elements composing protoplasm are organized into compounds of various kinds, some of which are relatively simple (i.e., they contain a small number of atoms per molecule), whereas others are characterized by a complexity which far exceeds that of any of the compounds found in the inorganic world. The protoplasm of microorganisms, like that of macroorganisms, is an intimate association of *inorganic* and *organic* compounds. The inorganic components are chiefly water and inorganic salts. The organic constituents may be classified chiefly in three major groups: proteins, carbohydrates and lipids (fats and fat-like substances). In addition, smaller quantities of a variety of other organic compounds, many of great importance to the cell, are found.

INORGANIC COMPONENTS

Water

The water content may be determined by noting the loss in weight on drying protoplasm in air at about 100° C., or in a vacuum oven at a lower temperature. Water is, by far, the most abundant ingredient, constituting between 70 and 90 per cent of the total weight of living cells. The average for bacteria is about 80 per cent, while yeasts average about 75 per cent and molds 85 per cent.

Water is responsible for the fluid nature of protoplasm. In it are dissolved, or otherwise dispersed, all the other constituents of protoplasm. Water is unique in many of its properties. It has remarkable solvent powers; it dissolves a greater variety of substances than any other liquid. Water dissociates to a slight extent into the highly active hydrogen (H^+) and hydroxyl (OH^-) ions.

Water plays an essential role in the activities of protoplasm. Both the chemical and the physical reactions characteristic of living substance require water as a medium. By ionizing many of the chemical substances dissolved in it, water promotes chemical reactions among them. Water is essential, also, for the activity of enzymes, which, as will be pointed out later, play an important role in many life activities.

Water has a high surface tension—higher than any other liquid except mercury. This property is important in the function and integrity of the protoplasmic membranes which form the boundaries of cells. The significance of this will be made clear in a later chapter. Water also serves as a carrier in the taking in of materials from the environment and the elimination of waste products.

Water is present in protoplasm, not only in the "free" state, but also in physicochemical combination with organic compounds. Some of the water is tied to protein molecules which have numerous side chains, some of which have hydrophilic (water-loving) polar groups such as: $-OH$, $-NH_2$, $-SH$. Water is tied to these groups by hydrogen bonds. Such water is known as *bound water*. Bound water, unlike free water, does not act as a solvent. These and other unique properties make water an indispensable component of all living substance.

Minerals

Minerals in various forms of combination enter into the formation of protoplasm. When a dried sample of protoplasm is incinerated in a platinum crucible, the organic components are oxidized and volatilized, leaving an ash of incombustible constituents. The amount of ash corresponds roughly to the quantity of minerals present in protoplasm. The total ash content varies considerably for different organisms, ranging from 2 to 30 per cent. Ash analysis has indicated the presence of more than twenty different elements. Those most commonly found in the ash of microorganisms are phosphorus, potassium, sodium, magnesium, calcium, silicon, sulfur, chlorine and iron, phosphorus being the most abundant. Some of the mineral constituents are in chemical union with organic compounds such as proteins, carbohydrates and lipids; others occur as salts usually dissociated into positive and negative ions which are capable of combining chemically with many of the other constituents of protoplasm.

ORGANIC COMPONENTS

All substances described as "organic" contain the element carbon. On the other hand, carbon is a constituent of a few inorganic chemicals, e.g., carbon dioxide and carbonate salts. Organic compounds are further differentiated from inorganic by being readily combustible. In other words, organic molecules react with oxygen, provided the temperature is high enough, and burn, yielding carbon dioxide and other oxidized inorganic products. Characteristically, all cells contain organic substances. At one time it was believed that organic compounds could be made only by living systems. While it is true that the overwhelming bulk of organic substances originates in plant and animal cells and that without life there would probably be no organic matter on this or any planet, there exists a vast array of synthetic (artificially made) organic compounds, some of which are also found in living matter or in the products and residues of organisms. While the organic chemist can synthesize but a small fraction of those organic molecules indigenous to animate matter, a great deal is known of the atomic configuration of such molecules in spite of the fact that they defy artificial synthesis.

Proteins

Proteins are the most abundant of the organic constituents, making up about 15 per cent of the weight of protoplasm. They are giant molecules of great complexity, composed of large numbers of amino acids linked together in an orderly sequence. Proteins and amino acids contain the elements carbon, hydrogen, oxygen, nitrogen and sulfur. Other elements may be found in those proteins combined with non-protein substances. The word "protein" is derived from the Greek word *proteios,* meaning to take first place, chosen because of the importance of this group in the structure and activities of protoplasm. Biologically, proteins are of great significance. Their great complexity of structure enables them to serve as the framework about which the chemistry of life is built. Directly, or indirectly, they are involved in most of the chemical and physical reactions occurring in protoplasm. They thus play a crucial role in the processes that constitute life.

There are many different kinds of proteins, all of which contain carbon, oxygen, hydrogen and nitrogen. Many contain small amounts of sulfur, and some have phosphorus. A few contain small amounts of other elements. The isolation of proteins in a very pure, unaltered state is extremely difficult because they so readily undergo denaturation. Thus, isolated proteins usually are amorphous, although some can be crystallized under carefully controlled conditions.

As mentioned previously, the protoplasm of one kind of organism differs in some respects from that of other kinds. This appears to be due chiefly to the proteins present. Each species contains proteins that are different from those of all other species. Proteins thus confer individuality to the protoplasm of each kind of organism. Even the proteins of different individuals of the same species are not necessarily completely identical.

Types of Proteins.   Proteins are organized aggregates of amino acids, sometimes united to other groups such as nucleic acids, carbohydrates or lipids. They may be classified as simple proteins, conjugated proteins and derived proteins.

Simple proteins are those which, on complete hydrolysis* with acids, alkalis or enzymes, yield only amino acids. The albumins, globulins,

---

* Hydrolysis involves chemical decomposition in which water enters into the reaction. It is the opposite of condensation.

histones and protamines are examples of simple proteins. Certain globulins present in blood play an important role in the natural defense mechanism the body has against disease-producing microbes. This subject is discussed in Chapter 28.

Conjugated proteins contain a simple protein in combination with another substance called the prosthetic (additional) group. To these compounds belong the nucleoproteins, in which the prosthetic group is nucleic acid; glycoproteins, in which carbohydrates constitute the prosthetic group; phosphoproteins, in which phosphoric acid is present; lecithoproteins, whose prosthetic group is a phospholipid such as lecithin; and chromoproteins, in which the nonprotein group is colored.

Nucleoproteins are of particular interest because of their function in the transmission of heritable characteristics. They are conjugated proteins consisting of a basic protein combined with *nucleic acids*. These acids are of two types: *deoxyribonucleic acid* (*DNA*) and *ribonucleic acid* (*RNA*). Upon mild treatment with acid or alkali, nucleic acids hydrolyze to form *nucleotides*. The latter molecule contains a nitrogenous base (purine or pyrimidine), a pentose (5 carbon atoms per molecule) sugar and phosphoric acid. The sugar in DNA is deoxyribose; in RNA it is ribose. DNA contains the four nitrogenous bases, guanine, adenine, cytosine and thymine. In RNA, thymine is replaced by uracil. It is apparent that the structure of nucleic acids is rather complex. Their structure can be portrayed by a simplified diagram of a *tetranucleotide,* the basic unit of nucleic acids:

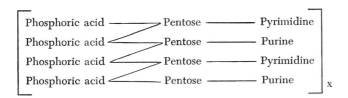

Actually, in the natural state the tetranucleotides polymerize (join together) into sizeable molecules (nucleic acids) and may or may not unite with basic proteins. RNA is found mainly in combination with protein in the cytoplasm and influences the synthesis of proteins. DNA, localized almost exclusively in nuclear material, is an essential, if not the sole, constituent of genes, hence exerts genetic control. The strong affinity of nucleoproteins for basic dyes is responsible for the *basophilic* staining reaction of nuclei and of other sites within the cell which contain nucleoprotein.

Derived proteins include various degradation products, usually derived by partial hydrolysis of proteins. These products are classified as (1) primary protein derivatives (coagulated proteins, proteans, metaproteins) and (2) secondary protein derivatives (proteoses, peptones, peptides).

Since proteins are so varied and abundant in protoplasm, it is not surprising to find them integrated into certain cellular structures, e.g., flagella (whip-like appendages of many bacteria), the cytoplasmic membrane and the nucleus. In some species of bacteria the outer covering, or capsule, is composed of polypeptides. A variety of proteins are dispersed throughout the fluid phase of protoplasm, sometimes being secreted into the extracellular environment. These include such substances as enzymes and toxins.

Amino Acids

The hydrolysis of a simple protein yields a variety of soluble organic acids known as *amino acids*. As their name suggests, these organic acids contain one or two *amino groups* ($-NH_2$); they also contain one or two *carboxyl groups* ($-COOH$). A protein molecule contains several hundred to several thousand amino acid units linked together in an orderly pattern by chemical bonds between amino and carboxyl groups, resulting in a molecular weight of thousands or millions. More than 25 different amino acids have been identified. The proteins of microorganisms contain the same kinds of amino acids as do other organisms, although they have but few proteins in common since the individuality of a protein is dependent upon the sequential arrangement of the component amino acids as well as the types and relative abundance of the amino acids comprising the molecule. Amino acids can be linked together in so many different patterns that, theoretically, an almost infinite number of proteins exists. Some proteins contain nearly all of the known amino acids, while others are known which are composed of fewer than 12 different amino acids.

The primary structural basis of the protein molecule is the *peptide bond,* a chemical linkage between the amino group of one amino acid moiety and the carboxyl group of the adjacent amino acid, the formation of which results in the liberation of one molecule of water. Conversely, the hydrolysis of proteins occurs when molecules of water are induced to split some, or all, peptide bonds to result in the liberation of peptides or all of the amino acids in the free state. The amino group imparts basic properties and the carboxyl group acidic characteristics to the molecule. Therefore, amino acids and proteins can behave as both acids and bases. Such substances are said to be *amphoteric.* The final reaction (acidic or basic) of an amino acid will depend upon which of these groups dominates. Those amino acids containing equal numbers of amino and carboxyl groups will be neutral, those with more amino groups will be basic and those with more carboxyl than amino groups will be acidic, although this is influenced by the pH of the dispersion medium.

Glycine, the simplest of the amino acids, is one of the neutral type, whereas lysine is basic, and aspartic acid represents the acidic type. An inspection of the formulas will show why.

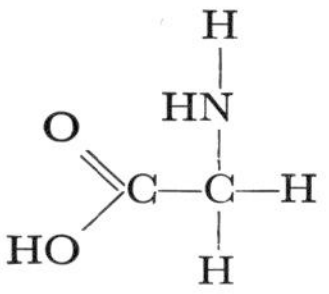

Glycine 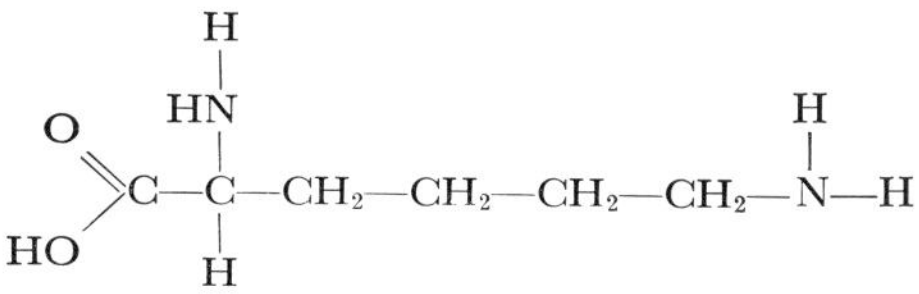   Lysine

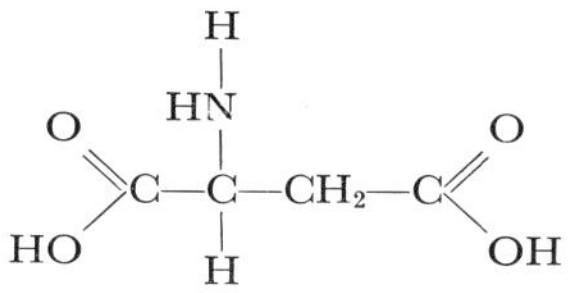

Aspartic acid

Proteins also may be acidic, basic or neutral, depending upon the assortment of the different types of amino acids in their make-up. A large number of amino acids of the acidic type and a smaller number of the basic or neutral type would combine to form a protein with slightly acid properties. Such a protein could neutralize more base than acid.

Enzymes

A large variety of proteinaceous catalytic agents termed enzymes are formed by protoplasm. Enzymes are produced only by living matter and, at exceedingly low concentrations, exert specific stimulatory effects on biochemical transformations. More simply, enzymes are organic catalysts. A catalyst is a substance which alters the rate of a chemical reaction, usually increasing it, without itself being consumed in the process. Since practically all chemical reactions carried out by protoplasm are mediated by enzymes, enzymes have been referred to as the "key chemicals of life." Because of the enzymes it contains, protoplasm can synthesize all of its primary organic constituents, e.g., proteins, carbohydrates, lipids, nucleic acids, etc. Also, enzymes are responsible for the degradation of nutrients for the release of energy so essential in the maintenance of life. This topic will be expanded in Chapters 10 and 11.

Carbohydrates

The elemental composition of most carbohydrates can be represented by the empirical formula, $C_m(H_2O)_n$, although compounds of this composition exist which are not true carbohydrates. Some carbohydrates contain nitrogen. Carbohydrates are most conveniently classified, on the basis of the number of carbon atoms they contain, into two broad groups: the *sugars* and the *polysaccharides*. The least complex carbohydrates are the simple sugars (*monosaccharides*), which contain one saccharide (sugar) unit and cannot be hydrolyzed. The monosaccharides contain from 2 to 7 carbon atoms per molecule, although those with 5 or 6 carbon atoms (*pentoses* and *hexoses*, respectively) are the most common and of greatest importance to protoplasm. The hexoses, with an empirical formula $C_6H_{12}O_6$, can be exemplified by glucose and fructose:

Glucose

$$
\begin{array}{c}
H \\
| \\
C{=}O \\
| \\
H{-}C{-}O{-}H \\
| \\
H{-}O{-}C{-}H \\
| \\
H{-}C{-}O{-}H \\
| \\
H{-}C{-}O{-}H \\
| \\
H{-}C{-}O{-}H \\
| \\
H
\end{array}
$$

Fructose

$$
\begin{array}{c}
H \\
| \\
H{-}C{-}O{-}H \\
| \\
C{=}O \\
| \\
H{-}C{-}O{-}H \\
| \\
H{-}C{-}O{-}H \\
| \\
H{-}C{-}O{-}H \\
| \\
H{-}C{-}O{-}H \\
| \\
H
\end{array}
$$

Although each of these sugars has the same empirical formula, certain spatial differences in their atomic structure are apparent.

Complex sugars, or *oligosaccharides,* are condensation products of from two to four molecules of simple sugars, generally hexoses, and are classified as *disaccharides, trisaccharides* and *tetrasaccharides.* The *polysaccharides* are formed by the condensation of many molecules of simple sugars with a loss in water. Those that yield pentoses upon hydrolysis are termed *pentosans* and have the empirical formula $(C_5H_8O_4)_n$; the *hexosans,* $(C_6H_{10}O_5)_n$, are complexes of hexoses. Still other polysaccharides yield mixtures of pentoses and hexoses when hydrolyzed. The subscript in the empirical formulae indicates that the multiples of sugar residues in the molecule are either unknown or variable, usually of an order of magnitude of thousands. A simplified scheme of the more common carbohydrates follows:

I. Monosaccharides (simple sugars)	Pentoses $C_5H_{10}O_5$	Arabinose Xylose Ribose
	Hexoses $C_6H_{12}O_6$	Glucose (Dextrose) Fructose (Levulose) Galactose Mannose
II. Oligosaccharides	Disaccharides $C_{12}H_{22}O_{11}$	Sucrose (glucose + fructose) Maltose (glucose + glucose) Lactose (glucose + galactose) Cellobiose (glucose + glucose)
	Trisaccharides $C_{18}H_{32}O_{16}$	Raffinose (galactose + glucose + fructose) Melezitose (glucose + fructose + glucose)
III. Polysaccharides $(C_5H_8O_4)_n$ or $(C_6H_{10}O_5)_n$	Starch Dextrins Glycogen Cellulose Lignin	Hemicellulose Pectin Agar Chitin Inulin

Compound carbohydrates are also found in protoplasm. These substances result from the combination of a carbohydrate with another type of compound, frequently protein or lipid. One such substance, *mucin*, is a *glycoprotein* (carbohydrate joined with protein) which forms a protective layer around certain types of cells.

Through the enzymatic activities of protoplasm, carbohydrates are important sources of energy for many organisms. Also, enzymes are capable of synthesizing oligosaccharides and polysaccharides from monosaccharides as well as hydrolyzing the complex carbohydrates into their component monosaccharides. Many waste products, resulting from metabolic activities of protoplasm, are formed directly or indirectly from carbohydrates. Examples of such products are ethyl alcohol, lactic acid, acetic acid and carbon dioxide.

Polysaccharides are important constituents of the cell wall and cytoplasmic membrane of microorganisms. The slime layer which invests many bacterial cells is usually composed of polysaccharides. Within the cells of microorganisms polysaccharides are found as amorphous granules called inclusions. Glycogen is especially abundant in yeasts. Certain pathogenic bacteria form well developed capsules composed of polysaccharide which protect the cells from the destructive or neutralizing forces of the animal body being parasitized.

It can be concluded that carbohydrates are extremely important constituents of protoplasm, being found in the material structure of cells, as well as being a reserve source of food. By and large, carbohydrates are the principal source of energy for living creatures.

Lipids

The lipids include the fats and certain other compounds more or less closely related chemically. They are relatively insoluble in water, but soluble in organic solvents such as benzene, ether, chloroform and acetone. Three types of lipids occur in protoplasm: simple lipids, compound lipids and derived lipids.

The *simple lipids* include the fats and waxes. They contain carbon, hydrogen and oxygen, the proportion of oxygen being relatively small. Fats (*glycerides*) are products of the combination of fatty acids and the trihydroxy alcohol, glycerol (glycerine). Fats usually exist in the *triglyceride* state, i.e., three fatty acids linked to one molecule of glycerol. The hydrolysis of a triglyceride by an enzyme (lipase) or by superheated steam can be depicted as follows:

$$
\begin{array}{c}
\text{H} \quad\ \text{O} \\
|\ \ \ \ \ ||\\
\text{H}-\text{C}-\text{O}-\text{C}-\text{R}_1 \\
|\ \ \ \ \ \text{O} \\
|\ \ \ \ \ || \\
\text{H}-\text{C}-\text{O}-\text{C}-\text{R}_2 \ +\ 3\,\text{H}_2\text{O} \\
|\ \ \ \ \ \text{O} \\
|\ \ \ \ \ || \\
\text{H}-\text{C}-\text{O}-\text{C}-\text{R}_3 \\
| \\
\text{H}
\end{array}
\longrightarrow
\begin{array}{c}
\text{H} \\
| \\
\text{H}-\text{C}-\text{O}-\text{H} \\
| \\
\text{H}-\text{C}-\text{O}-\text{H} \\
| \\
\text{H}-\text{C}-\text{O}-\text{H} \\
| \\
\text{H}
\end{array}
\ +\
\begin{array}{c}
\text{O} \\
|| \\
\text{R}_1-\text{C}-\text{O}-\text{H} \\
\text{O} \\
|| \\
\text{R}_2-\text{C}-\text{O}-\text{H} \\
\text{O} \\
|| \\
\text{R}_3-\text{C}-\text{O}-\text{H}
\end{array}
$$

(Triglyceride)   (Glycerol)   (Fatty acids)

Generally, two or three different fatty acid moieties will be found in a triglyceride. Fats are often seen dispersed as minute globules in the protoplasm of microorganisms. Certain species of yeasts and molds store large quantities of fats in their cytoplasm, particularly if glycerol is present in the environment. The function of these fat deposits is unknown. Since some of the fatty acids are needed in the metabolism of protoplasm, fats may serve as one of the sources of fatty acids. Small quantities of glycerides are also found in chemical union with proteins in cells. *Waxes* are esters of fatty acids with alcohols other than glycerol. Some bacteria, particularly the tubercle bacillus, contain relatively large quantities of wax-like substances.

The *compound lipids* have a more complex structure than the simple lipids. The most common type of compound lipids are the phospholipids which, upon hydrolysis, yield fatty acids, a nitrogenous base, phosphoric acid and glycerol. The best known phospholipids are the lecithins and cephalins. Phospholipids appear to be present in all microorganisms. They are regarded as being important in the structure and functioning of protoplasm. Some of the lecithins in cells are combined with proteins.

The *derived lipids* consist of a heterogeneous group of compounds derived from, or chemically related to, other lipids. Among them is a group of compounds very important in the physiology of higher forms of life. These substances, the *steroids,* are represented by such pharmacologically active products as the sex hormones, vitamin D, ergosterol and cholesterol. Yeast cells contain relatively large quantities of ergosterol which, upon exposure to ultra-violet rays, is converted to vitamin D. This process is used by industry for the production of vitamin D.

Vitamins

The compounds so far considered are not the only constituents of protoplasm. Certain other compounds are necessary to the economy of organisms. Among these are the *vitamins,* a group of metabolic regulators which are present in minute concentrations in all protoplasm. The fat-soluble vitamins (A, D, E, K) are not common in microorganisms, nor is the water-soluble vitamin, ascorbic acid (vitamin C). However, members of the water-soluble vitamin B complex, e.g., thiamine, riboflavin, pantothenic acid, pyridoxine, niacin, folic acid, biotin and cobalamin, are produced by microorganisms. In fact, certain microorganisms serve as a commercial source for riboflavin and cobalamin. Some bacteria produce vitamin K, although this vitamin appears to have no importance in the metabolism of bacteria.

PHYSICAL ORGANIZATION OF PROTOPLASM

Physically, protoplasm is a semifluid, translucent substance resembling raw egg white in some respects. It is slightly more dense than water and almost colorless. Some of the constituents are in true solution, i.e., dispersed in the molecular or ionic state, while others are not actually in solution but are present in the form of discrete particles larger than ordinary molecules. These particles are usually small aggregates of molecules; they vary in size, but are too small to be seen with a standard microscope. A system containing dispersed particles of this type is known as a *colloid* or a *colloidal system*. The colloidal particles, sometimes called *micelles,* are referred to as the *disperse phase,* while the medium in which they are dispersed is appropriately designated the *dispersion medium.* In protoplasm the dispersion medium is water.

Protoplasm is both a true solution and an extremely complex colloidal system. The protoplasmic constituents in true solution include mineral salts, sugars, amino acids and other compounds of relatively small molecular size. The important protoplasmic micelles are proteins, polysaccharides and lipids. Since proteins are the most abundant organic constituents of the cell, they are chiefly responsible for the colloidal character of protoplasm.

In a colloid the dispersed particles are either aggregates of large numbers of small molecules or of comparatively few large molecules. It is probable that in some cases a micelle consists of a single large protein molecule—a molecule that falls within the colloidal range in size. Colloidal particles range in size from approximately 1 to 100 millimicrons in diameter. A liquid system containing particles larger than 100 millimicrons is a suspension. Particles of such dimensions tend to settle out of a liquid system.

Colloidal particles may carry either a positive or negative electric charge and, hence, behave like ions. When an electric current is passed through a colloid, the positively charged micelles will move toward the cathode (negative electrode), while the negatively charged micelles migrate to the anode (positive electrode). Under certain conditions a positively charged particle may acquire a negative charge, and vice versa. A positively charged particle may give off hydrogen ions (H^+) and thus become negatively charged; or wandering positive ions may adhere on the surface, and thus a negatively charged particle may acquire a positive charge. The electric charge of the colloidal particles is an important property of a colloid such as a protoplasm.

Micelles with little or no attraction for the dispersion medium are termed *lyophobic* (solvent-hating), whereas those with a strong affinity for the dispersion medium are *lyophilic* (solvent-loving). Most proteins have a strong affinity for water and are therefore lyophilic (more specifically *hydrophilic*—water-loving); however, they will be lyophobic in alcohol. Each micelle in a hydrophilic colloid can *imbibe* a certain number of water molecules within or upon it and thus may become swollen with water. This applies also to certain carbohydrate particles. A lyophilic colloid has the property of being able to alter its consistency (viscosity) from a so-called *sol* state, in which it may be almost as fluid as water, to that of a semisolid elastic mass known as a *gel*. Protoplasm can change freely from one form to the other. These reversible changes are believed to be due to the release or absorption of water and other substances from one phase of the colloid to the other. Various factors, such as changes in temperature, acidity, and increase or decrease in the amount of mineral matter present, seem to initiate these changes.

Because protoplasm can alter its viscosity, it may be quite fluid at times and extremely viscous at other times. In any unit of protoplasm (cell) one portion may be in a state of low viscosity, while an adjacent portion may have a much greater viscosity.

Substances in the colloidal state exhibit properties different from those in true solution. The colloidal state is of great importance in protoplasm because of the vast amount of surface the disperse phase exposes to the dispersion medium. The sum of the surfaces of the innumerable micelles is large in comparison to the mass of the material present. Since the two phases meet at the surfaces of the particles, both phases have many boundary surfaces. The boundary between a particle of the disperse phase and the continuous phase is called the *interface*. It is at the interfaces that the characteristic physical and chemical reactions that constitute life take place. Colloidal particles have a tendency to hold firmly on their surfaces certain substances with which they come in contact. This surface phenomenon is known as "surface holding" or *adsorption*. It plays an important role in life activities, since it culminates in chemical reactions between the adsorbed substance and the micelle. In a colloidal system such as protoplasm many different kinds of chemical reactions can occur simultaneously at the immense number of interfaces without interfering with one another. It is the colloidal nature of the highly organized physicochemical forces in protoplasm that furnishes the basis for life.

Although colloidal particles are too small to be seen with the ordinary optical microscope, their presence can be detected by means of an ultramicroscope. This instrument operates on the same principle as the darkfield microscope. It resembles an ordinary microscope except that the object under observation is illuminated by a horizontal beam of light rather than a vertical one. A scattering of light occurs (Tyndall effect), which causes the colloidal particles to appear as bright specks (usually in noticeable movement) against a black background. The particles are detectable because they reflect some of the light vertically into the objective of the microscope, but their size and shape cannot be determined. By means of the electron microscope (see Chapter 14), the size and shape of the colloidal particles can be ascertained.

The motion of colloidal particles was first observed and described by the botanist Robert Brown and is known as *brownian movement*. It is brought about by the bombardment of the particles by the molecules of the dispersion medium. This molecular movement, characteristic of all matter, generates energy in the form of heat, hence its intensity is indicated by temperature.

Particles of colloidal size will not diffuse through membranes which permit inorganic salts and other substances of low molecular weight to pass through. Such membranes, usually made of cellulose, are called *dialyzing membranes*. They may be used as filters to separate inorganic salts, and other substances in true solution, from micelles. This method of separation is known as *dialysis*.

DISTINGUISHING MANIFESTATIONS OF LIFE

Protoplasm is characterized, not only by its composition and structure, but also by its activities. The phenomena of life are not found in atoms and molecules as such, but in the organization and cooperation of all the constituent parts of the living substance. Protoplasm is a dynamic, physico-chemical system involving a type of organization entirely different from that existing in inanimate matter. Because of the extreme complexity of protoplasm, the chemistry of all its activities is not completely understood. Life manifests itself by such attributes as adaptation, metabolism, growth and reproduction. These functions will be defined briefly but will be discussed more completely in Part III of this book.

Adaptation

All living organisms have the inherent capacity to receive and respond to stimuli. The technical term for sensitivity to stimuli is *irritability*. The basis of irritability is the instability of the complex physicochemical protoplasmic system. Because of its irritability, living matter is capable of adjusting itself to various stimuli. The result is adaptation, which involves continuous adjustment between the organism and its environment. Even the simplest of living organisms are capable of responding to environmental changes. Protoplasm can change its responses to stimuli to meet new conditions and, in so doing, become altered. The resulting variations may involve changes in structure as well as in function. Living matter thus has the property of *modifiability*. Without the properties of irritability and modifiability living matter would be unable to adapt itself to, and cope with, environmental factors.

Metabolism

Protoplasm is constantly in a state of flux, building up and breaking down compounds of various sorts. Materials for these reactions are obtained from the environment. The entire series of chemical changes constantly in progress within protoplasm is known as *metabolism,* which occurs in two phases: (1) *anabolism,* or synthesis, by which the higher molecular weight substances are synthesized from the simpler compounds absorbed by the cell to participate in normal functions of protoplasm; and (2) *catabolism,* or degradation, by which compounds are split into simpler molecules. Both these processes go on simultaneously and continuously during the life of every organism. In anabolism, *kinetic energy* (energy in its active manifestations) is required and transformed into *potential energy* (bound energy), which becomes a part of the new compound. In catabolic processes the potential energy of complex compounds is transformed into kinetic energy. The life process does not result in the creation of energy but brings about its transformation from one form to another. Protoplasm is a delicate, dynamic system which continuously strives to maintain and propagate itself through anabolic and catabolic activities. Actually, metabolism is a manifestation of irritability; moreover, many components of metabolism are highly adaptable, being sensitive to alterations of the environment. All metabolic processes apparently are mediated by enzymes.

Growth

Protoplasm has the ability to produce more protoplasm, i.e., to increase the volume of its mass. It can transform environmental materials into its own substance and thus has the property of growth. This process results from the coordination of diverse metabolic functions which change as the organism ages until the process becomes one of maintenance. While it is true that anabolism is responsible for the synthesis of protoplasmic substances, catabolism is essential for anabolic activities to proceed.

Reproduction

In the strict sense, reproduction is the property of protoplasm which enables an organism to produce more members of its own kind so as to assure continuity of life, generation after generation, and to perpetuate its species' characteristics. In many of the unicellular organisms, notably bacteria, reproduction occurs simply by the asexual process of division of the protoplasm or cell into two like organisms. The cells of multicellular organisms reproduce similarly, while the entire organism reproduces only by a sexual process initiated by the specialized germ cells, *gametes*. It is apparent, therefore, that growth and asexual reproduction are intimately related and set the stage for subsequent sexual reproduction. Most microorganisms rely upon asexual modes of reproduction for propagation, although many can, under suitable conditions, form gametes and reproduce sexually.

CELLULAR ORGANIZATION OF PROTOPLASM

Protoplasm is organized into minute units called *cells*. The vast majority of cells are of microscopic dimensions. In most of the microorganisms the entire organism consists of a single microscopic cell which is completely equipped for the maintenance of life; i.e., the cell and the organism are one.

Each cell has a compartmentalized internal organization of structural units which have certain specific functions. A typical animal cell, illustrated in Figure 11, is usually differentiated into a *nucleus* and a surrounding structure called the *cytosome*. The protoplasm of the cytosome is known as *cytoplasm*. Each cell has a limiting membrane in the form of a delicate film. It is known by several terms, namely, *cytoplasmic membrane, plasma membrane* or *cell membrane*. This membrane exercises control over the exchange of food material and waste products between the cell and its environment. Immediately surrounding this membrane in plant cells, bacteria, yeasts and molds is an external protective layer, the *cell wall*. A similar structure occurs in some animal cells, particularly in

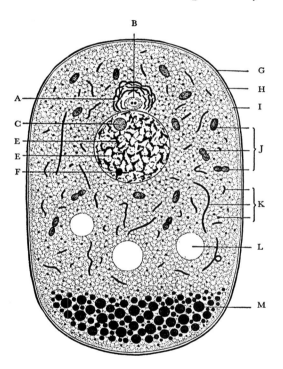

Figure 11. Diagram of an animal cell. *A,* Golgi body; *B,* centrosphere; *C,* nucleolus; *E,* chromatin granule; *F,* karyosome or false nucleolus; *G,* cell wall (pellicle); *H,* cytoplasmic membrane; *I,* cortical cytoplasm; *J,* plastids; *K,* chondriosomes; *L,* vacuole; *M,* cellular inclusions (stored food materials). (From E. B. Wilson.)

some protozoa, and is known as a *pellicle*. The cell wall and pellicle are formed from substances synthesized within the cytosome and secreted to the surface. The cell wall of plant cells usually consists chiefly of cellulose.

The cytosome contains various specialized structures, usually in the form of minute granules, rods or fibrils, which can be seen in cells that have been subjected to differential staining procedures. The role of many of these structures in the living cell is still unknown. The cytosome of many cells contain (1) *chondriosomes,* minute granular (*mitochondria*) or rod-shaped (*chondrioconts*) structures with a membrane (semipermeable), which contain an intense concentration of enzymatic systems; (2) a *Golgi body,* which is usually in the form of a network of fibrils located near the nucleus; (3) *vacuoles,* which are spherical vesicles filled with fluid material, frequently containing granules; (4) one or two dotlike *centrioles* in an ovoid *centrosphere,* adjacent to the nucleus (centrioles take part in cell division); (5) *plastids,* spherical or oval in form, which are structures that control certain synthetic chemical processes (the chloroplasts of green plants, which contain chlorophyll, are examples); (6) cell *inclusions,* which are granules consisting usually of stored food materials, such as glycogen, starch, nucleic acid, protein or fatty material. In addition to the microscopically visible structures just considered, one finds a vast array of *submicroscopic particles,* some of which approach the size of extremely large molecules. Among such minute particles are the *microsomes* and *submicrosomes,* which are believed to play an important role in the synthesis of proteins. No doubt these and other particles are a part of a highly organized submicroscopic cellular organization and constitute the disperse phase of the colloidal system of protoplasm.

The nucleus is bound by a thin membrane, the nuclear membrane, and has a complex internal structural organization. An important structure is a system of delicate threads (linin fibrils) containing irregular granules of material known as *chromatin,* which stain deeply with basic dyes. Chemically, chromatin consists of nucleoproteins. Chromatin granules form structures known as *chromosomes* during cell division. At cell division the chromosomes become duplicated, each of the two new cells receiving a complete set. Thus there is an equal qualitative and quantitative distribution of chromatin material. Within the nucleus is a spherical body, the *nucleolus,* which can be made visible by acid dyes. At times two spherical bodies are present, but one can be stained with acid dyes; the other becomes visible when treated with basic dyes and is sometimes referred to as *karyosome.*

The nucleus exerts a controlling influence over all activities of the cell, including metabolic as well as reproductive processes, by virtue of hereditary factors (*genes*) in the chromatin material. A number of enzymes are found in nuclei, although many more are found in the cytosome, particularly in mitochondria and microsomes.

Many of the structures just considered can be made visible in the cells of certain microorganisms. The cells of most kinds of microorganisms, however, exhibit only a few of these structures. The structural features of the cells of microorganisms will be considered in subsequent chapters.

QUESTIONS

1. Expand the statement, "In its general chemical pattern the protoplasm of all organisms is basically alike."

2. What are two methods of obtaining masses of microbial cells for chemical analysis?

3. Name the essential chemical elements of protoplasm. Which ones are found in proteins? In carbohydrates? In lipids? In nucleic acids?

4. Distinguish between organic and inorganic substances. Cite several examples of each.

5. What are the properties of water that make it indispensable to protoplasm? What is bound water?

6. (*a*) What are proteins?

(*b*) Define and give examples of (1) simple proteins, (2) conjugated proteins, (3) derived proteins.

(*c*) Of what particular importance are nucleoproteins? Are they found only in nuclei?

7. What are enzymes? Of what importance are they?

8. (*a*) What are carbohydrates?

(*b*) Name and define the three main classes of carbohydrates. Give examples of each.

(*c*) What are compound carbohydrates?

9. (*a*) What are lipids?

(*b*) Differentiate between simple lipids and compound lipids and cite examples of each.

(*c*) Name several fat-soluble vitamins.

10. (*a*) Differentiate between a true solution and a colloid.

(*b*) Name some protoplasmic constituents which exist in the colloidal state.

(*c*) Define: (1) hydrophilic colloid, (2) viscosity, (3) sol, (4) gel, (5) interface, (6) adsorption, (7) brownian movement, (8) dialysis, (9) micelle, (10) dispersion medium.

11. Indicate several characteristics of colloidal systems that support the statement, "It is the colloidal nature of protoplasm that furnishes the basis for the fundamental life processes."

12. Explain the following characteristics exhibited by protoplasm: (1) adaptation, (2) metabolism, (3) anabolism, (4) catabolism, (5) growth, (6) reproduction.

13. (*a*) Name the structures characteristic of a cell.

(*b*) What is the role of the nucleus in the cell?

(*c*) Of what importance is the cytoplasmic membrane (consider structural as well as functional properties)?

REFERENCES

Brachet, J.: Biochemical Cytology. New York, Academic Press, Inc., 1957.

DeRobertis, E. D. P., Nowinski, W. W., and Saez, F. A.: General Cytology. 2nd ed. Philadelphia, W. B. Saunders Company, 1954.

Dubos, R. J.: The Bacterial Cell. Cambridge, Harvard University Press, 1945.

Gerard, R. W.: Unresting Cells. New York, Harper and Brothers, 1949.

Giese, A. C.: Cell Physiology. Philadelphia, W. B. Saunders Company, 1957.

Knaysi, G.: Elements of Bacterial Cytology. 2nd ed. Ithaca, N. Y., Comstock Publishing Co., 1951.

Wilson, E. B.: The Cell in Development and Inheritance. New York, The Macmillan Company, 1928.

II • The Microscopic World

4 • The Bacteria

The bacteria comprise a large and heterogeneous group of microorganisms, occurring abundantly in various habitats and possessing a great variety of activities. For convenience, bacteria may be divided into two main groups: "true bacteria" and "higher bacteria." The true bacteria represent the most primitive members of the group and include those forms which are of most importance to man and which have been studied most extensively. The present chapter deals chiefly with the form and structure (morphology) of the true bacteria. Chapter 6 gives additional information about these bacteria and also contains a discussion of the higher bacteria.

FORMS OF BACTERIAL CELLS

On the basis of form, bacteria are of five types: (1) spherical or ellipsoidal, (2) rod-shaped, (3) spiral, (4) comma-shaped, and (5) filamentous (threadlike). (See Figures 12 and 13.)

Under each of these types occur many species which differ in size and proportions. A bacterium that is spherical, or approximately so, is known as a *coccus* (plural, *cocci*). The origin of the term is the Greek word *kokkos*, meaning a berry. Some cocci are slightly elongated; i.e., they are ellipsoidal in form. The rod-shaped type is known as *bacillus* (plural, *bacilli*). The word is the diminutive of the Latin word (*baculum*) for rod or stick. Bacilli are cylindrical in form and may be short and wide, short and slender, long and wide or long and slender. The ends may be rounded, flat or pointed. Very short bacilli with rounded ends may be easily mistaken for cocci. Such forms are called *coccobacilli*. Some bacilli are slightly curved; others are clubbed at one or both ends.

A bacterium that is coiled in a spiral form is known as a *spirillum* (plural, *spirilla*). It has a helixform; i.e., it is helicoidal or corkscrew-shaped. The cell may have only a few, or many, convolutions. Some are tightly, others loosely, coiled. Some spiral species are without the rigid cell walls characteristic of most bacteria but are flexuous, resembling the protozoa in this respect. A bacterium of this type is known as a *spirochete*. The organism that causes syphilis belongs to this group. Spirochetes are generally placed with the higher bacteria.

A comma-shaped bacterium is known as a *vibrio*. Vibrios are short, slightly curved, cylindrical forms. They appear to be next of kin to the spirilla but have only one curve in the long axis. Upon cultivation on artificial media they tend to become straight rods and are then indistinguishable from bacilli. Not many species are vibrios. The most important organism in this group is *Vibrio comma,* the causative agent of Asiatic cholera.

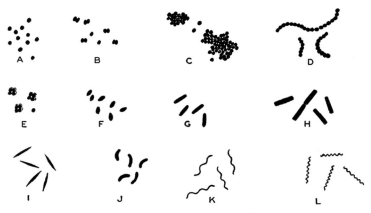

Figure 12.   Morphologic types of bacteria.

Filamentous bacteria are relatively long, slender, threadlike forms, some being branched. They are usually included with the higher bacteria.

SIZE OF BACTERIA

One of the units for measuring microscopic objects is the *micron,* which is a part of the metric system of linear measure and has a value of 0.001 mm., or approximately 1/25,000 inch (more accurately 1/25,400). The micron may be designated by the symbol μ, the Greek letter corresponding to the English *m*. There is a considerable range in size between the smallest and the largest bacteria. Some are so small that they approach the limit of visibility of the optical microscope. It is difficult to visualize the smallness of the micron. A good object of comparison is the human red blood corpuscle, which measures about 7.5 microns in diameter. For the measurement of viruses a still smaller unit is used. This is the millimicron ($m\mu$), which is equivalent to 0.001 micron. This unit is used also for measuring the wave lengths of light and for precision optical work.

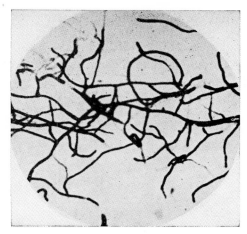

Figure 13. Photomicrograph of filamentous bacteria, × 900. (From Einar Leifson: Bacteriology. Paul B. Hoeber, Inc. Reproduced by permission of the author and publishers.)

Cocci range in size from 0.5 micron to a little more than 1 micron in diameter. Magnified 1000 times, some cocci may appear no larger than a period on a printed page. It would require 25,000 cocci having a diameter of 1 micron and placed side by side to form a line 1 inch long. The bacilli average about 0.5 to 1 micron in width and 1.5 to 4 microns in length. A very short bacillus with rounded ends may approach a coccus in appearance. Such a form, as previously stated, is known as a coccobacillus. Spirilla vary considerably in length from a few microns to about 10 microns. Most of the spirochetes are relatively long, usually more than 7 microns. Vibrios are usually less than 3 microns long. Filamentous bacteria range in length from about 20 to 100 microns or more.

In the stained smears usually prepared for microscopic examination, bacteria appear shorter and thinner than their actual dimensions. The staining procedure causes the protoplasm to shrink. The cell wall does not shrink, but it does not become colored by the ordinary dyes and, therefore, remains invisible.

INTERNAL CELL STRUCTURE

The minute dimensions of bacteria make the study of their internal structure difficult. Much painstaking work has been done in the attempt to disclose the internal structural features of the bacterial cell, and considerable progress has been made in recent years. Their smallness might lead to the inference that they are simple in structure. This, however, is

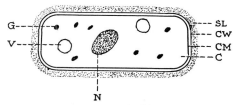

Figure 14. Schematic representation of the structure of the bacterial cell. *SL,* Slime layer; *CW,* cell wall; *CM,* cytoplasmic membrane; *C,* cytosome; *N,* nucleus; *V,* vacuole; *G,* granule.

not true, for they exhibit an amazing complexity both in their structure and activities. Figure 14 is a diagrammatic drawing showing the common structural features of the bacterial cell, and Figure 15 is an electron micrograph of an ultrathin section, showing structural features of the bacterial cell.

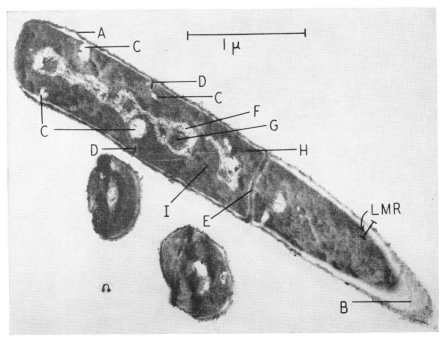

Figure 15. Electron micrograph of an ultrathin, longitudinal section of two adjacent cells and sections of two other cells of *Bacillus cereus.* The sections are less than 0.1 micron in thickness. *A*, cell wall showing evidence of the shrinking of the cytoplasm. *B*, very oblique section of the cell wall. *C*, four peripheral bodies cut at different levels. *D*, beginning of a centripetally growing transverse cell wall. *E*, completed transverse cell wall before thickening. *F*, low-density component of nuclear apparatus. *G*, dense body in nuclear apparatus which may be inclusion of cytoplasmic material. *H*, small dense particles which appear to be main constituent of cytoplasm. *I*, unidentified cytoplasmic inclusions. *LMR*, scale indicating the limit of resolution of light microscope using visible light. (From G. B. Chapman and J. Hillier: J. Bacteriol., Vol. 66. Reproduced by permission of The Williams & Wilkins Company.)

Bacteria are colorless and so nearly transparent that they are rather difficult to see when viewed with a microscope unless they are stained. Dyes are used, however, not only to make bacteria more readily visible but also to display their structural features. Most of our knowledge of bacterial structure has been obtained through the use of dyes. Some dyes, as well as several other reagents, impart color to certain intracellular structures without staining others. This has been of great help in the structural study of cells in general and has been of value, also, in the study of the chemical constitution of cells.

Bacterial cytoplasm consists of translucent protoplasm, which may contain one or more vacuoles, fat droplets and granules of various kinds. A vacuole is a spherical vesicle filled with a fluid containing substances in solution. In young bacteria, vacuoles have been observed in unstained cells.

By the use of differential dyes and other reagents, fat droplets, carbohydrate granules, sulfur granules and various other kinds of granular material have been found to occur in bacterial cells. These cytoplasmic inclusions apparently represent reserve material stored for later use in the metabolic processes of the bacterial cell. They are usually not present in the cells of a young, actively growing culture but accumulate as growth slows down.

Two kinds of carbohydrate granules have been demonstrated. One kind gives a reddish-brown color when treated with a dilute solution of iodine and is interpreted as being glycogen, or a substance closely akin to glycogen. The other kind gives a blue color with iodine and is considered to be starch, or related to starch.

The presence of fat droplets can be recognized by their high refractive power; they can be stained with fat-soluble dyes which color them but lack affinity for nonfatty material. In old cultures the cells often contain large quantities of stored fat.

Many bacteria contain granular bodies known as *volutin granules,* which appear to consist of organic and inorganic phosphate compounds. Because it was found that *Spirillum volutans* usually contained a heavy concentration of such granules, the term "volutin granules" was applied to them. When stained with an old solution of methylene blue (polychrome methylene blue), volutin granules become reddish violet in color due to the methylene violet present in this solution, whereas the cytoplasm stains pale blue. This metachromatism is responsible for the term *metachromatic granules* frequently applied to these granular bodies. Volutin granules may be scattered through the protoplasm or massed at either end of the cell, where they constitute the "polar granules" observable in some bacteria. The presence of such granules is at times an aid in the identification of certain kinds of bacteria, particularly the diphtheria bacillus and related species.

Sulfur granules frequently can be observed in the cells of the so-called sulfur bacteria, which utilize sulfur and sulfur compounds for energy.

Some cytoplasmic granules appear to be *mitochondria,* which are focal points for chemical activities. They contain a complex of enzymes which catalyze chemical reactions. Granules of ribonucleic acid are found also in the cytoplasm of bacterial cells.

BACTERIAL NUCLEUS

In most plant and animal cells the nucleus is a discrete body sharply differentiated from the cytoplasm and contains a large number of chromatin granules which are composed largely of nucleoproteins containing

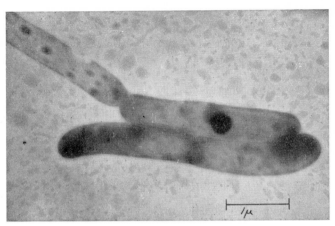

Figure 16. Electron micrograph of *Bacillus mycoides*. The cells show two types of internal bodies characterized by differences in opacity to electrons. The larger, more opaque bodies are believed to be the nuclei of the cells. (From G. Knaysi and R. Baker: J. Bacteriol., Vol. 53. Reproduced by permission of The Williams & Wilkins Company.)

deoxyribonucleic acid. The nucleus regulates many of the cellular activities, undergoes characteristic changes in cell division and serves as a bearer of hereditary determiners known as genes. In cell division the chromatin material is subdivided equally between the daughter cells. Numerous experiments with denucleated protozoan cells have shown that, although such cells survive for several days, they are unable to reproduce and are incapable of synthesizing new substances for growth and maintenance. The nucleus, thus, is an essential part of the cell.

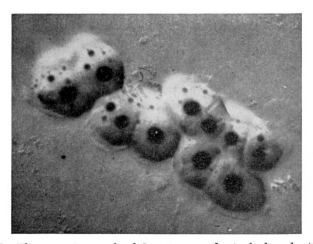

Figure 17. Electron micrograph of *Streptococcus bovis* shadowed with uranium. × 20,000. The large dark bodies appear to be nuclei. (Courtesy of Dr. Jack J. Stockton, Michigan State University.)

The existence of a nucleus in the bacterial cell has long been a disputed question. Since it is characteristic of cells in general to contain both cytoplasm and nuclear material, it was assumed that bacterial cells did not vary fundamentally in this respect from other cells. Until recently, however, attempts to demonstrate the actual presence of a nucleus in the bacterial cell were unsuccessful. The protoplasm of the bacterial cell usually stains uniformly with nuclear dyes and thus gives no indication of the presence of a nucleus. Recent work has revealed that this is due to the high concentration of ribonucleic acid in the cytoplasm of the cell. This acid stains deeply with nuclear stains. It was found that, when it was removed, the cytoplasm no longer became deeply stained. Removal was accomplished by hydrolysis with the enzyme ribonuclease, dilute mineral acids, or by permitting the cells to use the ribonucleic acid as a source of nitrogen by transferring them to a nitrogen-free medium. The nucleus thus became unmasked and could be colored with Giemsa's solution or other nuclear stains. Nuclear structures have been demonstrated in all bacteria which have been examined by suitable techniques. Bacterial nuclei appear as spherical, ellipsoidal or dumbbell-shaped bodies. There may be two, and often four, such bodies in a bacterial cell. Figures 16 and 17 show structures within bacterial cells which are interpreted as being nuclei.

In some bacteria in which the nucleus is unusually acid and the cytoplasm contains little ribonucleic acid, the nucleus can be demonstrated without the removal of ribonucleic acid. Bacterial nuclei are visible also by phase microscopy (see page 234).

CYTOPLASMIC MEMBRANE

The cytoplasm is surrounded by a delicate membrane known by various terms, such as *cytoplasmic membrane, plasma membrane* and *cell membrane*. Because it is only a few molecules in thickness, it is not microscopically visible as a separate structure but can be seen merely as the boundary line of the cell protoplasm. When a bacterial cell is plasmolyzed, i.e., placed in a strong salt solution causing the protoplasm to shrink, the cytoplasmic membrane shrinks with the protoplasm, indicating that it is intimately attached to the cytoplasm. It is an integral part of the protoplasm of the cell and owes its existence to the physical attraction between like molecules. At the surface of a liquid, or a liquid system such as protoplasm, the surface molecules are pulled inward by the force of cohesion. This brings the molecules more closely together at the surface to form a surface film. The tension thus caused at the surface is known as *surface tension*. It is because of surface tension that a glass of water may stand more than level full. Because the cytoplasmic membrane is the result of the phenomenon of surface tension, it is referred to as a surface tension membrane. (See Figure 18.)

Certain substances tend to collect at the surface of the cell and are present there in greater amount than elsewhere in the protoplasm of the cell. This gives the cytoplasmic membrane physical and chemical properties somewhat different from those of the rest of the protoplasm. Microchemical tests indicate that the cytoplasmic membrane is essentially a protoplasmic structure containing inclusions such as lipids and proteins, which seem to be at least partly in chemical combinations as lipoproteins. It appears that lipids are extremely important components of the membranes of all living cells. The cytoplasmic membrane has the remarkable property of differential permeability, which enables it to control the passage of dissolved substances into and out of the cell. This is a function of great importance to the cell; it regulates the intake of materials needed

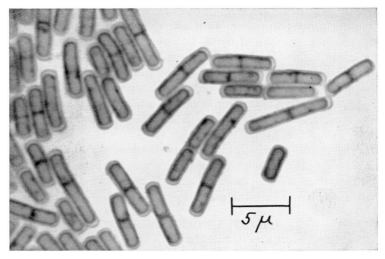

Figure 18. Photomicrograph of *Bacillus cereus,* stained to enhance the contrast between the cell walls, which appear light, and the cytoplasmic membranes, which are darker. (Courtesy of Dr. C. F. Robinow, University of Western Ontario.)

by the cell and the outflow of waste substances that are to be eliminated from the cell.

CELL WALL

Immediately outside the cytoplasmic membrane is an extremely thin, firm, though somewhat elastic, structure known as the *cell wall,* which confers rigidity and the characteristic shape to the bacterial cell. The cell wall normally has a thickness of 10 to 20 mμ and is resolvable only by the electron microscope. It has a low affinity for dyes, and ordinary staining procedures do not color it. It can be dyed, however, by special staining methods. When bacterial cells are placed in a solution of high osmotic pressure, such as a concentrated salt solution, the cytoplasm shrinks, but the cell wall retains its form and position and thus can be observed. With the electron microscope the cell wall can be demonstrated as a structure distinct from the rest of the cell. It can also be observed with the phase microscope. The existence of cell walls can also be demonstrated by mechanically crushing bacterial cells and removing the cytoplasmic material. Both the cell wall and the cytoplasmic membrane can be seen in Figure 18. The cell wall is visible also in Figure 19.

The chemical composition of the cell wall seems to vary greatly in different bacteria. Polysaccharides and proteins are usually present. In some species the cell wall contains large amounts of lipids, and in a few species cellulose is present. The bacterial cell wall is one of the structures through which materials enter and leave the cell.

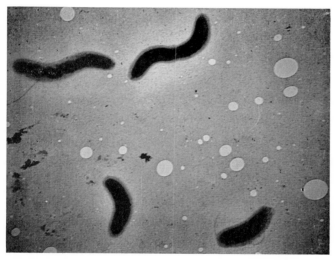

Figure 19. Electron micrograph of *Vibrio fetus* showing comma and S-shaped forms and the cell wall. × 18,000 reduced ¼. (Courtesy of Dr. Jack J. Stockton, Michigan State University.)

SLIME LAYER

The cell walls of many, probably all, bacteria are enveloped by a layer of viscous, gummy material. This *slime layer* is usually thin and difficult to demonstrate; but in some species it forms a relatively large mass around the cell. It is usually not visible in stained smears because it has a low affinity for dyes; but by special staining procedures, either positive or negative staining, its presence can be revealed.

The chief constituents of the slime layer are polysaccharides, but in some cases polypeptides are also present. It is not known whether the slime layer is a product of secretion of the cell or a modification of the outer material of the cell wall. Removal of this layer does not affect the viability of the cell.

When the slime layer is sufficiently thick and firm to form a relatively

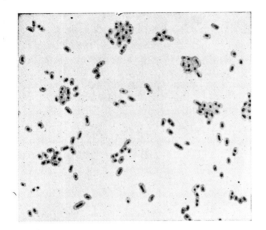

Figure 20. Aerobacter aerogenes stained to show capsules. (Ford: Textbook of Bacteriology.)

large mass around the cell, it is called a *capsule*. (See Figures 20 and 21.) In those species in which grouping occurs, a common capsule may surround the whole group. Environmental factors influence capsule formation. Some species acquire capsules when grown in certain media but are without them in other media. A high carbohydrate content of the medium may stimulate capsule formation in some species, whereas certain pathogens form capsules only in the animal body or in artificial culture media containing blood serum. Loss of the capsule on the part of certain pathogens results in loss of virulence. The capsule of these forms apparently serves as a protection against the defense mechanism of the infected animal.

The capsular substance differs in chemical composition, not only with different species, but also with the subspecies or types that comprise a species. The pneumococcus (*Diplococcus pneumoniae*) is an example of a pathogen with a pronounced capsule and is also an example of a species which has been divided into a large number (more than seventy)

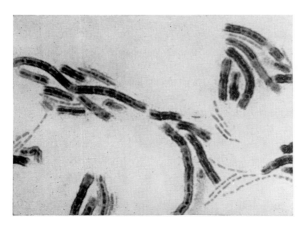

Figure 21. Photograph of a Giemsa stained preparation of virulent encapsulated organisms from a colony of *Bacillus anthracis.* (U. S. Army photograph. Courtesy, Department of the Army Technical Information Division.)

of different types on the basis of the chemical nature of the capsules. These types apparently differ from each other only in the nature of their capsular material, which is type-specific. Only capsulated pneumococci are capable of causing infection.

Some bacteria produce large quantities of slimy material which accumulates in the surrounding medium. Such organisms make solutions in which they are growing extremely viscous or stringy. The slimy substance is probably synthesized extracellularly from environmental substances by means of enzymes secreted by these bacteria. Bacteria of this type are frequently encountered in the sirup vats of sugar refineries, where they give rise to large quantities of a gummy polysaccharide known as dextran,* which interferes with the crystallization of the sugar (Figure 40). The principal dextran-forming organism is *Leuconostoc mesenteroides.*

Certain bacteria which produce large slimy capsules when growing in milk cause it to become ropy. Bread may become ropy when certain capsulated, spore-forming bacteria get into the dough (see p. 314). One of the vinegar-producing bacteria, *Acetobacter xylinum,* produces a slimy material consisting of a loose network of cellulose fibrils. Only one or two other species of bacteria are capable of producing cellulose.

FLAGELLA

A number of kinds of bacteria, including about half of the species of bacilli and most of the spirilla and vibrios, are capable of independent movement. They are equipped with locomotor organelles consisting of extremely delicate, threadlike appendages known as *flagella* (singular, *flagellum*). Flagella are capable of propelling bacteria through liquid media. Very few cocci are motile.

Flagella are usually considerably longer than the cells from which they originate. Being only about 0.03 micron in thickness, they are no thicker than a large protein molecule and are far below the limits of resolution of the optical microscope. They can be observed, however, when stained by a technique in which an opaque substance is precipitated upon their surfaces, thus increasing their apparent thickness sufficiently to bring them within the range of the optical microscope. Flagella can be readily observed under the electron microscope. Each flagellum arises from a small granule in the cytoplasm just inside the cell wall and extends out to the exterior through a minute pore in the wall of the cell.

Some bacteria have only one flagellum, whereas others may have a dozen or more. The number, position and arrangement of the flagella are quite constant for each flagellated species. A cell that has a single polar flagellum is said to be *monotrichous;* if there is a tuft of polar flagella, it is *lophotrichous;* a cell with a single flagellum or a tuft of flagella at each

---

* Dextran has come into use in recent years as a partial substitute for blood plasma and is now produced for that purpose on a large scale by the action of *Leuconostoc* bacteria on sucrose.

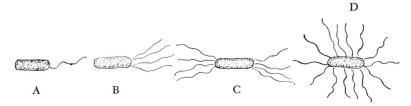

Figure 22.   Diagram showing types of flagellation. *A,* Monotrichous; *B,* lophotrichous;
C, amphitrichous; *D,* peritrichous.

pole is *amphitrichous;* when the flagella are distributed over the surface
of the cell, it is *peritrichous.* Most of the motile rodlike bacteria are peritrichous, whereas spirilla and vibrios are usually monotrichous. In Figure
22 the various types of flagellation are shown. Figure 23 is a photomicrograph of the typhoid bacillus showing the peritrichous arrangement of
the flagella. Figures 24 and 25 are electron micrographs of flagellated
bacteria.

Chemically, flagella consist almost entirely of a type of protein that
belongs to the same group as the contractile protein (myosin) present
in the muscles of animals. Bacterial motion appears to result from a series
of rapid, periodic contractions and extensions running around the surface
helicoidally from one end of the flagella to the other. As the cell moves,
it rotates around its long axis and the flagella trail behind. When a cell has
a number of flagella, they tend to mass together into one or several bun-
dles or fascicles. Motility is most evident in young cultures and can be
observed to best advantage by means of the hanging-drop technique, in
which the bacteria are in suspension in a drop of fluid hanging from the
under side of a cover glass over a small cavity in a slide made for this
purpose.

Under the microscope flagellated bacteria may appear to move at great
speed, but when deductions are made for the magnification, the distance

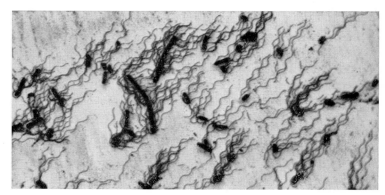

Figure 23.   Photomicrograph of *Salmonella typhosa* (typhoid bacillus) showing flagella.
(Copyright by General Biological Supply House, Inc., Chicago.)

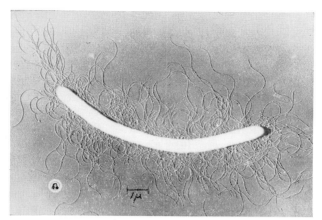

Figure 24. Electron micrograph of *Proteus vulgaris* shadowed with chromium, showing peritrichous flagellation. (Courtesy of C. F. Robinow and J. Hillier.)

traversed is much less than it appears to be. Bacteria which appear to be moving at the speed of 1 inch per second under a magnification of 1000 times are in reality traveling at the rate of only 25 microns per second. However, when one considers the time it takes motile bacteria to traverse a distance equal to their own length, their speed is very rapid.

It is necessary to distinguish true motility from the *brownian movement,* which is a quivering or oscillatory motion. Bacteria, because of their

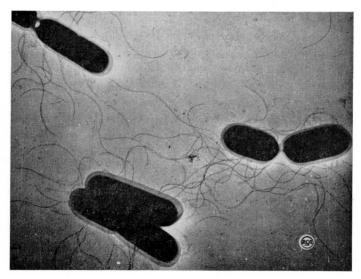

Figure 25. Electron micrograph of *Clostridium tetani* (24 hour culture) showing cell walls, various stages of cell division and peritrichous flagella. (From S. Mudd and T. F. Anderson: J. A. M. A., Vol. 126. Courtesy of the authors and the American Medical Association.)

smallness, are continually jostled about by being bombarded from all sides by the molecules of the fluid in which they are suspended. In this type of movement the bacteria play a passive rather than an active role. Colloidal particles, as mentioned in the preceding chapter, when suspended in a fluid also show the brownian movement.

A few species of bacteria devoid of flagella exhibit a gliding or creeping motion which enables them to move slowly over surfaces. This is true of certain filamentous forms and of members of the group known as myxobacteria. Certain blue-green algae also exhibit this type of motion. No special organelles of locomotion are involved. Gliding motion appears to be due to waves of contraction which cause slight variations in the form and thickness of the cell.

ENDOSPORES

Some bacteria possess the distinctive property of being able to transform themselves into highly resistant bodies known as *endospores*, so called because they are produced within the cell. The endospore is a stage

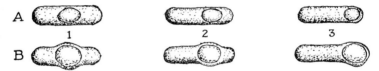

Figure 26. Diagram of bacterial endospores, showing their position within, and their size in relation to, the parent cell. *A,* Cells not swollen; *B,* cells swollen; *1,* central; *2,* subterminal; *3,* terminal.

in the life cycle of certain bacteria, chiefly rod-shaped forms belonging to the genera *Bacillus* and *Clostridium.* Each cell forms but a single spore in the majority of spore-bearing bacteria. Many rod-shaped bacteria whose habitat is the soil are spore formers. Only a few pathogens produce spores; they include *Clostridium tetani,* the cause of tetanus; *Clostridium perfringens* and related forms responsible for gas gangrene; *Clostridium botulinum,* the causative organism of botulism; and *Bacillus anthracis,* the cause of anthrax.

Endospore formation is a process in which the nucleus and a portion of the cytoplasmic material of the cell become organized into a relatively small ovoid, spheroid or beanlike body which becomes surrounded by a highly refractile and relatively impervious coat known as the spore wall. The spore wall of some species appears to consist of two layers, an outer one termed *exine* and an inner known as *intine.*

The endospore appears as a highly refractile body within the wall of the parent cell, which is now known as the *sporangium.* It may be terminal, subterminal or central in position, and may be less, equal to or greater in diameter than the parent cell. (See Figure 26.) When the diameter is greater than that of the parent cell, a bulge occurs at the point where the

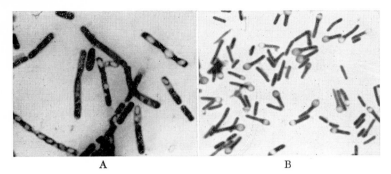

A   B

Figure 27. Photomicrographs showing endospores in a species of *Bacillus* (A) and a species of *Clostridium* (B). (Copyright by General Biological Supply House, Inc., Chicago.)

spore is located. Such cells appear as "drumsticks" (plectridium form) when the spores are terminal (Figure 27,B), or as spindles (clostridium form) when central in location. Bacteria belonging to the genus *Clostridium* produce spores of these two types. The position, size and form of the spores are fairly constant for a given species and in some instances are an aid in identification. When the endospore is mature, the sporangium disintegrates, leaving the spore free. The endospore usually contains two or more nuclei and is usually surrounded by a slime layer. The endospore is

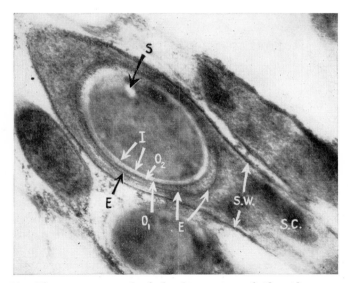

Figure 28. Electron micrograph of ultrathin sections of *Clostridium sporogenes* in the late stages of sporulation. Original magnification × 92,000. S.W., sporangial wall; S.C., sporangial cytoplasm; E, exporium (a thin membrane); O_1, first outer membrane; O_2, second outer membrane; I, inner membrane; S, spot of unknown nature. (From Tadayo Hashimoto and H. B. Naylor: J. Bacteriol., Vol. 75. Reproduced by permission of Tadayo Hashimoto and The Williams & Wilkins Company.)

a bacterial cell in a resting stage. In the active stage the cell is referred to as the *vegetative cell* to distinguish it from the spore stage, in which the life processes are reduced to a minimum. Figures 28 and 29 are electron micrographs of ultrathin sections of a clostridium in the late stages of sporulation.

The conditions governing sporulation are not well understood since, in many instances, the process goes on in young, actively growing cultures under apparently favorable environmental conditions as well as in older cultures in which the environmental conditions have become less favorable for active growth. It is sometimes stated that unfavorable con-

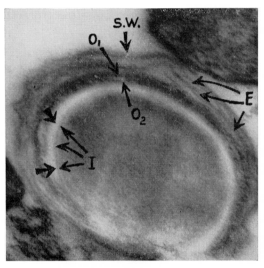

Figure 29. Electron micrograph of cross section of sporangium and spore of *Clostridium sporogenes.* Original magnification $\times$ 92,000. S.W., sporangial wall; E, exporium (a thin membrane); O_1, first outer membrane; O_2, second outer membrane; I, inner membrane. (From Tadayo Hashimoto and H. B. Naylor: J. Bacteriol., Vol. 75. Reproduced by permission of Tadayo Hashimoto and The Williams & Wilkins Company.)

ditions of temperature, partial depletion of nutrient materials, accumulations of metabolic waste products and other adverse conditions govern sporulation. Although these factors may play a role, no reliable evidence to this effect is available. When conditions are unfavorable at the start of growth, or when bacteria are suddenly subjected to harmful influences, sporulation does not occur. The anthrax bacillus, for example, will not sporulate when the culture is kept at 42° C., which is above its optimum temperature. It may be reasonable to assume that the factors that influence spore formation are not the same for all species.

Endospores exhibit extraordinary resistance to many adverse environmental factors. They are highly resistant to heat, desiccation and chemical disinfectants. They are unique in the living world in that no other living organisms can endure the high temperatures endospores are able to withstand. With a few exceptions, vegetative cells are killed when exposed to a temperature of 70° C., but endospores can usually withstand the temperature of boiling water (100° C.), some for five or ten minutes, others for six to eight hours, and a few can be boiled for sixteen to twenty hours without being killed. The spores of *Clostridium botulinum* can withstand boiling for three to four hours.

Many endospores can resist indefinitely the dehydrating effect of air, which is destructive sooner or later to the vegetative forms. Some spores are known to have remained viable for forty years in a dry environment. Spores are also quite resistant to chemical agents that serve as disinfectants for vegetative cells. Their resistance to dyes makes the staining of spores somewhat difficult.

It is generally believed, although not definitely established, that the extraordinary resistance exhibited by bacterial spores is due both to the relative impermeability of the spore wall and the low content of free water. Much of the water in a spore appears to be bound water, i.e., water bound by protoplasmic substances and thus a part of cell compounds, whereas a vegetative cell contains a much greater proportion of free water in relation to bound water. The destructive effect of heat on protoplasm is apparently due to the fact that it coagulates some of the proteins present. A low content of free water reduces the coagulability of proteins; consequently the amount of heat required to produce coagulation is increased. It has been demonstrated that the enzyme system of endospores is inactive. It is assumed that the enzymes become altered in some obscure way and in so doing acquire a high degree of heat resistance.

The existence of spores must be taken into consideration in the canning of food and in methods of sterilization. Temperatures sufficiently high to destroy spores must be utilized. Foods that contain natural acids, such as fruits and berries, can be preserved by heating to 100° C. because, in the presence of acids, this temperature is destructive to spores, but nonacid foods cannot be safely preserved at this temperature except by prolonged boiling. If it were not for spores, canning and sterilization could be carried on safely at temperatures lower than those now required.

Upon return of favorable conditions an endospore becomes transformed into a vegetative cell of the same kind as that from which it originated. This process is known as germination. The first indication of spore germination is swelling of the spore. The spore wall then ruptures and the vegetative cell emerges, shedding the ruptured wall. Endospore formation is not a method of multiplication, since it does not bring about an increase in numbers. The endospores of bacteria are not analogous to the reproductive spores of the molds or yeasts. Figures 30 and 31 are illustrations of germinating spores.

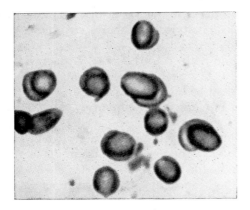

Figure 30. Electron micrograph of germinating spores of *Bacillus megatherium*, × 3,500. (Reproduced by permission of the publishers from Rene J. Dubos, The Bacterial Cell, Cambridge, Mass., Harvard University Press, Copyright, 1945, by The President and Fellows of Harvard College.)

CONIDIA

Certain filamentous organisms belonging to the order of bacteria known as Actinomycetales produce spores known as *conidia* or *conidiospores*. These spores are produced by abstriction at one end of the filament, usually in beadlike chains. They are formed by the development of cross partitions (septa) in the terminal portion of the filament, dividing it into cylindrical segments which later may become spheroid in form or remain cylindrical as they become transformed into spores (Figure 32). Certain

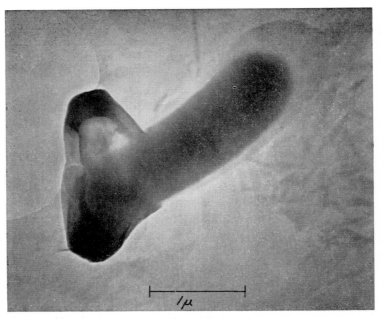

Figure 31. Electron micrograph of germinating spore of *Bacillus mycoides,* showing the vegetative cell growing out through the laterally ruptured spore coat. (From G. Knaysi, R. Baker and J. Hillier: J. Bacteriol., Vol. 53. Reproduced by permission of The Williams & Wilkins Company.)

molds produce spores in a somewhat similar manner. Spore-bearing filaments have a tendency to become spirally twisted. Although the Actinomycetales have some moldlike traits, they have bacteria-like characteristics in that they have an exceedingly small diameter (1 to 2 microns),
lack a readily demonstrable nucleus, and can be infected with bacteriophage.

The function of conidia is chiefly reproductive. They are resistant to
drying, but have only slightly greater resistance to heat than the vegetative cells. In their resistance these spores resemble those produced by
molds. Conidia will be more fully discussed in Chapter 6.

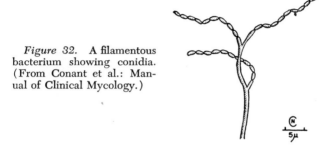

Figure 32. A filamentous
bacterium showing conidia.
(From Conant et al.: Man-
ual of Clinical Mycology.)

REPRODUCTION OF BACTERIA

The usual method of reproduction among the "true" bacteria is an
asexual process known as *binary fission.* The process begins with an inward growth of the cytoplasmic membrane toward the center of the cell,
resulting in the formation of a transverse plate dividing the cytoplasm
into two approximately equal parts. A transverse cell wall continuous
with the outer cell wall now begins to form, probably by secretion, splitting the transverse plate into two layers, one becoming the cytoplasmic
membrane over the newly formed cytoplasmic surface of one of the sister
cells, the other fulfilling a similar function in the other sister cell. When
the transverse cell wall is completed, it becomes separated into two layers,
splitting the two cells apart. There may be a delay in the splitting of the
transverse cell wall. In such cases what may appear as a single cell in a
microscopic preparation may actually be two or more cells which are still
united because the splitting of the transverse walls has not yet been
completed.

In the bacilli and spirilla the plane of division is at right angles to the
long axis of the cell, i.e., transverse. Cocci may divide in more than one
plane, giving rise to characteristic groupings which will be considered
later. Bacilli and spirilla usually elongate somewhat before division,
whereas cocci seldom do, but there is a direction of growth immediately
after cell division.

In some cases, after the process of division has been completed, the cells may form chain-like groups. This is due to extremely fine strands of cytoplasmic material extending from the extremity of one cell to that of the next. The strands pass through pores in the cell wall and are known as *plasmodesmids.* Figure 33 shows rod-shaped bacteria in various stages of division.

Recent investigations suggest that in regard to internal nuclear changes, bacterial cells divide by the same complex process, called *mitosis,* that the cells of higher forms of life undergo. In this process chromatin granules give rise to chromosomes in which genes (the hereditary determiners) are

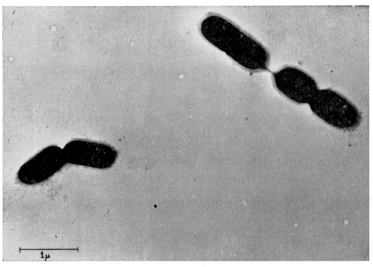

Figure 33. Electron micrograph of *Lactobacillus acidophilus* in various stages of division. Two of the cells are connected by a delicate strand of protoplasm. Note the light cell walls surrounding the dense cytoplasm. (From Archives of Pathology, Vol. 34. Reproduced by permission of Dr. Stuart Mudd and the American Medical Association.)

arranged in linear order. The chromosomes become duplicated and distributed equally between the two sister cells formed from the dividing cell. Our knowledge of the internal changes that go on in the bacterial nucleus at the time of cell division is still too incomplete to permit us to form definite conclusions in regard to this point.

In binary fission the parent organism disappears in the offspring; it has not died and none of its substance is lost. For bacteria, death is not a necessary consequence of life. A bacterium has no ancestors. Because of their mode of reproduction by fission, bacteria are classified as *Schizomycetes,* which means "fission fungi."

Reproduction in the "higher" bacteria will receive consideration in Chapter **6.**

Sexuality in Bacteria

Although bacteria multiply by binary fission, this process may be interrupted occasionally in certain species by a sexual process known as *conjugation.* Conjugation long has been known to occur among the protozoa (Paramecium and other ciliates). In Paramecium two individuals (conjugants) come into contact side by side and exchange nuclear material, following which they separate. After separation both conjugants undergo binary fission in the usual manner. Conjugation occurs only at long intervals after the cells have undergone reproduction through binary fission for a considerable period of time, or when they encounter unfavorable conditions of the environment.

Conjugation on the part of bacteria differs from that of the protozoa in that the transfer of nuclear or genetic material is a one-way passage, a unidirectional transfer in which one of the participating cells serves as donor and the other as acceptor. This indicates that there is a sexual differentiation in the two conjugants, one playing the role of a male (gene donor), the other that of a female (gene acceptor). Only a small portion of the donor cell's genetic substance is transferred to the acceptor cell. Consequently, the progeny of the acceptor cell resulting from the binary fission that follows conjugation receive a larger fraction of their genetic characteristics from the maternal parent than from the paternal parent. It appears that only the acceptor cell (maternal parent) undergoes fission following conjugation. Conjugation as it occurs in the bacteria is often referred to as *gene recombination;* genes of two individuals become reorganized in one of the individuals.

It is now evident that bacteria as a group can no longer be considered as being wholly incapable of sexual reproduction; they take their place with most of the other groups of organisms in being able to resort to sexual reproduction, which is of more or less universal occurrence in the world of life. Fundamentally, sexual reproduction is simply the coming together of two bits of protoplasm which fuse and give rise to a new individual.

Conjugation appears to have a rejuvenating effect on the protoplasm of organisms, enabling them to carry on through the method of binary fission for many generations. It may thus enhance the survival of the species. Since the nuclear material is derived from more than one individual, conjugation makes possible a greater degree of variation among the offspring.

RATE OF REPRODUCTION

Because of their extraordinary powers for converting nonliving matter into living substance, bacteria are capable of multiplying with astonishing rapidity. Under favorable conditions the age of a cell from birth to maturity may be only about twenty minutes. In other words, cell division may take place as rapidly as every twenty minutes. One cell becomes two, two become four, four become eight, eight become sixteen, and so forth.

The increase is a geometrical progression. At this rate of reproduction no bacterium can long maintain its individuality, since it soon disappears in its offspring. If the process of cell division continues without interruption, we soon arrive at figures which are eclipsed only by astronomical distances. A single bacterial cell can theoretically give rise to a vast multitude of cells—more than a billion organisms in a period of ten hours. But conditions do not long remain favorable for reproduction to continue at this rate. Owing to the diminution of the food supply, the accumulation of metabolic wastes and other limiting factors, reproduction slows down or comes to a stop. Some species never multiply as rapidly as others. They may require five to six hours to divide under favorable conditions.

It is because bacteria are capable of producing tremendous numbers of cells in a short period of time that they are of such great significance in the world of life and in the affairs of man. In spite of the small size of an individual bacterium, rapid multiplication produces bacterial populations of enormous numbers. Such a population can give rise to great chemical changes in its environment in a short time.

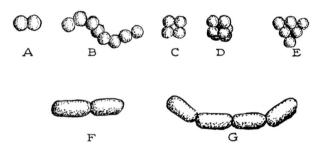

Figure 34.   Drawings illustrating cell grouping. *A*, Diplococcus; *B*, streptococcus; *C*, tetracoccus; *D*, sarcina; *E*, staphylococcus; *F*, diplobacillus; *G*, streptobacillus.

CELL GROUPING

Some species of bacteria exhibit definite, characteristic groupings when the cells remain joined instead of separating after cell division.

Grouping of Spherical Bacteria

When the cells cling together after division, but separate before the next division, they will be grouped in pairs. Such an organism is known as a *diplococcus*. This type of grouping is characteristic of three important pathogens, namely, the pneumococcus (*Diplococcus pneumoniae*), the meningococcus (*Neisseria meningitidis*) and the gonococcus (*Neisseria gonorrhoeae*).

When the cells remain attached through a series of consecutive cell divisions, and if the plane of each successive division is parallel to the previous one, then a chain of cocci results. Such a chain resembles a string of minute beads in general appearance and is known as a *streptococcus*.

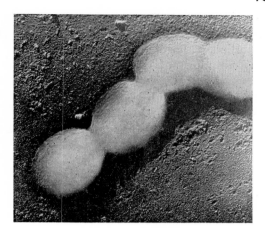

Figure 35. Electron micrograph of *Neisseria catarrhalis*, a spherical bacterium occurring singly or in pairs and occasionally chains of four cells. × 25,000 reduced ⅓. (Courtesy of Department of Physical Chemistry, The Lilly Research Laboratories.)

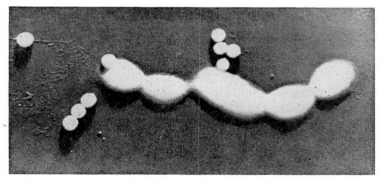

Figure 36. Electron micrograph of a streptococcus. Small white objects are latex globules, 0.2 micron in diameter, included to show scale of magnification. × 35,000 reduced ½. (Courtesy of Division of Laboratories, Michigan Department of Health.)

Figure 37. Electron micrograph of a staphylococcus. × 25,000 reduced ⅓. (Courtesy of Department of Physical Chemistry of the Lilly Research Laboratories.)

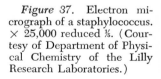

The organism chiefly responsible for the souring of milk, *Streptococcus lactis,* has this form of grouping, which is characteristic also of certain important pathogenic species.

When, after one division, the two daughter cells grow in a direction perpendicular to that of the parent cells, the planes of cleavage of the daughter cells will then be perpendicular to that of the parent cell. This results in a platelike grouping of the four cells, the cells occupying a space that represents a square. A species that has this type of grouping is known as *tetracoccus* or *tetrad.* Few species exhibit this type of grouping.

If, instead of separating after a platelike group of four cells has been formed, a third division occurs at right angles to the second, the result is a group of cells arranged in a cubical octet. Such a group is referred to as *sarcina.* The sarcinae are common in nature.

When the plane of division shifts irregularly after each division and the cells remain attached through a number of divisions, an irregular cluster of cells, resembling a bunch of grapes in form, is the result. An organism showing this arrangement is known as a *staphylococcus.* A common pathogen that has this grouping is *Staphylococcus aureus.*

Grouping of Rod-Shaped Bacteria

Since the plane of division is always at right angles to the long axis in the rod-shaped bacteria, the only kind of grouping that can occur is end-to-end grouping. When the grouping is limited to two cells, the organism is referred to as a *diplobacillus;* whereas a group of many cells arranged end-to-end, forming a filament-like structure, is called a *streptobacillus.* Most of the rod-shaped bacteria separate from one another as they divide and thus occur singly. Figures 34, 35, 36 and 37 illustrate various grouping arrangements of cocci and bacilli.

Grouping of Vibrios, Spirilla and Filamentous Bacteria

In these forms only end-to-end grouping occurs, since the plane of cleavage is always at right angles to the long axis. Vibrios frequently form short groups of three or four cells, while among the spirilla and filamentous forms grouping is uncommon.

COLONY FORMATION

When an isolated bacterial cell is allowed to grow on the surface or within a solid medium, its progeny will soon produce a visible mass called a *colony.* Colonies growing on the surface of a solid medium in many instances have an appearance that is characteristic for a given species. Colony characteristics are governed by the morphology of the individual cells and by their behavior during growth. Colonies of different species may vary in size, form, nature of edge, elevation, opacity, color, texture and other traits. Figures 38, 39, 40 and 41 show various types of bacterial colonies.

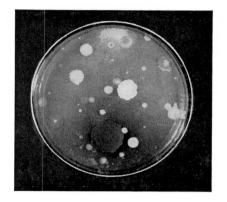

Figure 38. A Petri dish culture showing bacterial colonies of various shapes and sizes which developed on nutrient agar after exposure for 20 minutes to the air of a classroom.

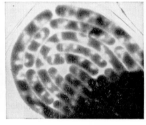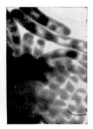

Figure 39. Microcolonies of *Escherichia coli* grown for two and one-half hours at 37° C. on a thin collodion membrane overlying agar. (From S. Mudd and A. G. Smith: J. Bacteriol., Vol. 59. Reproduced by permission of The Williams & Wilkins Company.)

In regard to size, colonies may vary from a small fraction of a millimeter to several centimeters in diameter. Some are just visible to the unaided eye as minute dots (pin-point colonies); others may cover the whole surface of a Petri dish.

In form, colonies may be circular, oval, spindle-shaped or irregular. The edge, under low power magnification, may appear smooth, wavy or angu-

Figure 40. Colonies of *Leuconostoc mesenteroides*, a bacterial species which forms capsules consisting of a gummy polysaccharide known as dextran when grown on a medium containing sucrose. The mucoid appearance of the colonies is due to dextran. (From C. S. McClesky, L. W. Faville, and R. O. Barnett: J. Bacteriol., Vol. 54. Reproduced by permission of The Williams & Wilkins Company.)

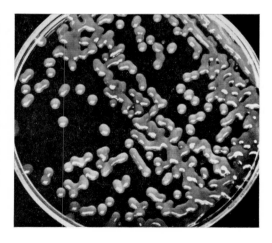

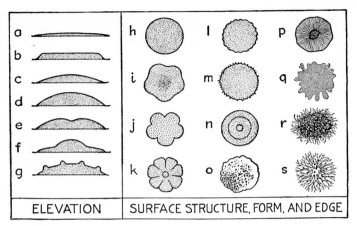

Figure 41. Types of bacterial colonies. Elevation: *a,* flat or effuse; *b,* raised; *c,* low convex; *d,* high convex (dome-shaped or pulvinate); *e,* umbilicate; *f,* umbonate; *g,* papillary. Surface structure, form and edge: *h,* circular, amorphous, edge entire; *i,* irregular, edge undulate; *j,* irregular, granular, edge lobate; *k,* regular, radiate, edge lobate; *l,* regular, edge crenated; *m,* regular, edge dentated; *n,* regular, concentrically ringed, edge entire; *o,* irregular, rugose; *p,* regular, mycelioid; *q,* irregular, curled, edge undulate; *r,* irregular, filamentous; *s,* irregular rhizoid. (From Belding, D. L., and Marston, A. T.: Textbook of Medical Bacteriology. Courtesy of D. Appleton-Century Co., Inc.)

lar and may be curled like a cluster of hair or contain rounded lobes. Elevation refers to the relative thickness of the colony. As for opacity, a colony may be transparent, translucent or opaque. Bacteria with capsules produce colonies that have a slimy consistency, whereas those without capsules give rise to dry, rough-appearing colonies. The colonies of most species are whitish or grayish, but some are yellow, red, blue, green or brown, owing to pigments produced by the bacteria. The pigments, however, are not visible in the individual cells when viewed under the microscope. Colony characteristics are often useful for the purpose of identifying bacteria. In some instances colony differences can be accentuated by growth on media containing certain dyes or other compounds.

It has been determined that some of the morphological features of colonies are due to the movement of bacteria immediately after cell division. When the bacteria separate after dividing and slip past each other, compact colonies with smooth or lobose edges are formed. If the cells adhere instead of separating, irregular (rhizoid) colonies are formed. If they adhere, but tend to fold back, angular edges result.

QUESTIONS

1. (*a*) Name the five types into which bacteria may be grouped on the basis of form. What is a spirochete?

(*b*) Name and explain the units employed for measuring microscopic objects.

(*c*) How many cocci, 1 micron in diameter, arranged in a cube would form a cubic centimeter?

2. (*a*) Is the inference that, owing to their smallness, bacteria are simple in structure, a correct one? Explain.

(*b*) Of what value are dyes in the study of cellular structure?

3. (*a*) What kinds of carbohydrate granules have been demonstrated to be present in the cytoplasm of bacterial cells?

(*b*) What are volutin granules? How can they be demonstrated? Give another term frequently applied to them.

(*c*) How can fat droplets be recognized in bacterial cells?

4. What is the modern conception of the presence of a nucleus in the bacterial cell? How can the nucleus be demonstrated?

5. (*a*) What is the cytoplasmic membrane? What causes it to be formed? Of what special significance is this membrane to the cell? By what other terms is it known?

(*b*) Differentiate between the cytoplasmic membrane and the cell wall. Describe the cell wall.

6. (*a*) Explain what is meant by the "slime layer." What is it chemically? What are bacterial capsules?

(*b*) What are bacterial flagella? Describe the different arrangements of flagella on bacterial cells.

(*c*) Explain creeping motion.

7. (*a*) What are endospores? The production of endospores is carried on chiefly by what kind of bacteria?

(*b*) How do endospores differ from vegetative cells in resistance to (1) high temperatures, (2) the drying action of the air, and (3) chemical agents? To which features of spores may this resistance be attributed?

8. (*a*) Explain how the existence of spores affects our methods of sterilization and food preservation.

(*b*) Which kinds of bacteria produce conidia? How do conidia differ from endospores in the manner in which they are formed? How do they differ in function?

9. (*a*) What is the usual method of reproduction among the "true" bacteria? Explain the process. What is the process called? How rapidly may reproduction proceed? Of what significance is this rapid rate of reproduction?

(*b*) Name and explain the various groupings found among the cocci, bacilli and vibrios.

10. Describe the process known as conjugation as it occurs in bacteria.

11. What is the primary difference between asexual reproduction and sexual reproduction?

12. What is a bacterial colony? How do colonies vary in size, shape, color and other features?

REFERENCES

Bisset, K. A.: The Cytology and Life-History of Bacteria. Baltimore, The Williams & Wilkins Company, 1955.

Bisset, K. A., and Moore, F. W.: Bacteria. Baltimore, The Williams & Wilkins Company, 1952.

Dubos, R. J.: The Bacterial Cell. Cambridge, Harvard University Press, 1945.

Gunsalus, I. C., and Stanier, R. Y., ed.: The Bacteria. A Treatise on Structure and Function. Vol. 1. Structure. New York, Academic Press, Inc., 1959.

Knaysi, G.: Elements of Bacterial Cytology. Ithaca, N. Y., Comstock Publishing Co., 1951.

Miles, A. A., and Pirie, N. W., ed.: The Nature of the Bacterial Surface. Oxford, Blackwell Scientific Publications, 1949.

Spooner, E. T. C., and Stocker, B. A. D., ed.: Bacterial Anatomy. New York, Cambridge University Press, 1956.

Wilson, G. S., and Miles, A. A.: Topley and Wilson's Principles of Bacteriology and Immunity. 2 vols. 4th ed. Baltimore, The Williams & Wilkins Company, 1955.

5 • The Classification and Naming of Bacteria

One of the important problems confronting the biologist is the classification of living things. To deal effectively with the multiplicity of living creatures, a method of grouping or arrangement is necessary. The necessity for classifying bacteria is no less urgent or important than is the classification of other living things.

The classification of organisms belongs to that branch of biological science known as *taxonomy* (Greek *taxis*, arrangement; *nomos*, law). Bacterial taxonomy is often referred to as systematic bacteriology or determinative bacteriology.

The task of systematic bacteriology is to devise a workable system of classification and naming so that each kind of bacterium may be assigned to a definite category and given a specific name by which it will be known by all microbiologists. A system of classification makes possible the construction of clearly defined keys by reference to which an unknown organism may be identified. The classification of organisms in general has had a far-reaching effect in promoting the systematic study of biology.

THE LINNAEAN SYSTEM OF CLASSIFICATION

The foundation of the modern system of classification of plants and animals was laid in the eighteenth century by the Swedish naturalist Carl von Linné, commonly known as Linnaeus, which is the latinized form of his name. In the tenth edition of his book *Systema Naturae*,* published in 1758, he presented the principles of his system as well as a methodical classification of all plants and animals known at that time. His system introduced a rigidly defined grouping based on structural similarities and dissimilarities and included a method of naming plants and animals.

* In the time of Linnaeus, Latin was the accepted language of scholars throughout Europe, and all important scientific books appeared in this language.

Linnaeus subdivided the plant and animal kingdoms into a number of major groups, which he further divided into smaller groups, and each of these into others still smaller on the basis of differential characteristics. He formulated a definite, concise terminology for these groups and assigned a Latin or latinized name of two words to each species. Because of the comprehensiveness and thoroughness of his work, Linnaeus has been termed "the great classifier" and is referred to as the "father of taxonomy." He was the first great systematist. Linnaeus' system was quickly accepted by botanists and zoologists. The modern system of classifying animals and plants, including the bacteria, is an expansion of the system devised by Linnaeus. Linnaeus made no attempt to classify the bacteria, but relegated them along with other unicellular organisms to a group which he called "Chaos."

EARLY ATTEMPTS AT CLASSIFYING BACTERIA

When Leeuwenhoek discovered microorganisms, he grouped them all under the name "animalcula," which means little animals. The early microbiologists made no distinction between the bacteria and protozoa. As knowledge of these forms increased, attempts were made to classify them. One of the earliest attempts to bring order into Linnaeus' Chaos was that of Otto Müller of Denmark, who devised a system of classification in which all microorganisms were placed in the animal kingdom in a group known as "infusoria." He followed the rules of Linnaeus and introduced the terms *vibrio* and *proteus,* which are still used. His classification was published in 1786 in a well illustrated book entitled *Animalcula Infusoria Fluviatilia et Marina.* This book represented a good beginning toward the classification of microorganisms. In 1838 Christian Ehrenberg of Germany published a more extensive classification which recognized five genera of bacteria. For some of his groups he used such terms as *bacterium, spirillum* and *spirochaete.* These terms are still in use today. Both Müller and Ehrenberg considered bacteria to be members of the animal kingdom. In 1857 Karl Nägeli, a Swiss botanist, in a classification he devised, introduced the term *Schizomycetes* (fission fungi), which is still used as the name of the class to which the bacteria belong.

In 1872 a German botanist, Ferdinand Cohn, prepared a classification in which he separated the bacteria from the protozoa and placed them in the plant kingdom. He recognized that bacteria could not be satisfactorily classified according to their morphology alone, but that physiological as well as morphological characters must be considered. He thus made an important contribution to systematic bacteriology.

A more elaborate classification was published by Migula in 1900. This classification described with accurate detail the majority of the species of bacteria discovered up to that time and provided the first comprehensive guide for the recognition of unknown organisms. In 1909 Orla-Jensen proposed a classification in which biochemical activities were stressed.

CURRENT CLASSIFICATION

The classification in current use was originally devised by a committee of the Society of American Bacteriologists, of which David H. Bergey was the chairman. It was published in Bergey's *Manual of Determinative Bacteriology,* the first edition of which appeared in 1923. It is based on the Linnaean system and has gone through several revisions. It is the most comprehensive work on systematic bacteriology that has yet appeared, and although it has not yet been adopted by international agreement, as have the botanical and zoological systems now in use, it has become generally accepted in America and to some extent in England.

In zoological and botanical classifications the individuals are arranged in groups on the basis of their natural or evolutionary relationships, i.e., their phylogeny. A natural classification of the bacteria cannot be devised at the present time since very little is known of their phylogenetic history.

Systematic bacteriology is still in a state of flux and will probably remain so for some time to come. As new facts are brought to light, rearranging and renaming of taxonomic categories and species are inevitable. In spite of its shortcomings, the current classification and nomenclature of the bacteria is a great convenience to the microbiologist.

TAXONOMIC DIVISIONS

The graded series of taxonomic divisions devised by Linnaeus are used in systematic bacteriology, but a few additional ones have been added. Starting with the larger divisions, any particular group, generally speaking, contains several groups of the next lower rank. The taxonomic categories now used include *phylum* (plural *phyla*), *class, order, family, genus* (plural *genera*) and *species.** Frequently intermediate categories are used. Species may be subdivided into smaller groups called *subspecies, varieties, types* or *strains.* A large genus may be subdivided into *subgenera;* a large family into *tribes;* an order into *suborders.* Each of these divisions represents distinctive biological characteristics. The assignment of a given species to a definite category characterizes it as having a definite combination of attributes.

The species is the basic unit in biological classification. Each kind of organism is called a species. A satisfactory definition of this term suited to all cases cannot be formulated since there is no means of determining the limits of the species. Owing to the variations that are characteristic of living things, the organisms of one species may grade into those of another. Where to draw the line between one species and another often cannot be determined. It is frequently impossible to tell whether one is dealing with two different varieties of the same species, or two different species. It must be understood that the categories used in classification are human devices. Nature does not make species, genera, families or

* Species is either the singular or the plural form. The abbreviation of species is sp. (singular) or spp. (plural).

other groups—nature makes only individuals. For practical purposes a species may be defined as a group of individuals having many characteristics in common which distinguish it from other groups. In any species, however, there is a considerable degree of variability grouped around a mean which is typical for the particular species.

A genus constitutes a group of species sufficiently alike to indicate that they have been derived from a common ancestral form. A family consists of a group of genera bearing a certain amount of resemblance; an order is a group of families displaying important similarities; a class is a group of related orders; and a phylum is a group of classes displaying the same general anatomical construction.

NOMENCLATURE

In the Linnaean system each species is given a name known as the *scientific name,* which is composed of the name of the genus, or *generic name,* followed by the name of the species, or *specific name.* The scientific name thus indicates the genus and the species to which the organism belongs. This double-name method of designating an organism is known as the *binomial system of nomenclature.* The terms used are Latin in form, but not necessarily of Latin origin. The generic name is usually a noun based on the organism's morphology or, in some cases, on the name of its discoverer. The specific name distinguishes it from every other member of its genus and usually refers to certain distinguishing points, such as color, source, a physiological property or, in the case of pathogens, the disease the organism is capable of producing. The initial letter of the generic name is always capitalized but that of the specific name is not. In print the scientific name preferably should be in italics.

In zoology and botany the use of the binomial system of nomenclature has become universal; i.e., it has been accepted throughout the civilized world. The scientific names of plants and animals, therefore, are standard throughout the world. In the field of bacteriology this has not yet been achieved.

An example of a scientific name is *Clostridium tetani.* The bacteria placed in the genus *Clostridium* are rod-shaped, spore-forming, Gram-positive, anaerobic organisms. The specific name in this case refers to the disease, tetanus, of which this organism is the causative agent. The organism *Clostridium botulinum* causes a severe form of food poisoning. Since closely related species receive the same generic name, this system of naming indicates relationship and also provides a distinct name for each kind of organism. As for *Salmonella typhosa,* the genus name is based on that of an American bacteriologist named Salmon, while the specific name refers to typhoid fever, the disease this organism produces. Frequently the specific names indicate color, such as *lutea* (yellow) in *Sarcina lutea,* or *rubrum* (red) in *Rhodospirillum rubrum.*

The author of a scientific name is that person who first publishes the name together with a description of the organism, provided he has applied the principles of binomial nomenclature. If a species has been named and described more than once, the earliest name prevails. This is in accordance with the *law of priority*. For purposes of exact reference the scientific name is followed without intervening punctuation by the name, or an abbreviation of the name, of the person (or persons) who first described the organism and gave it its specific name, as, for example, *Diplococcus pneumoniae* Weichselbaum. If the person responsible for the name is well known, his name may be abbreviated. If the species is later transferred to a different genus, the name of the original describer is enclosed in parentheses followed by the name of the author (or authors) responsible for placing the species in the present genus, as, for example, *Corynebacterium diphtheriae* (Flügge) Lehmann and Neumann. The first species described as belonging to a certain genus is designated as the *type species* of that genus. On this basis a genus may be described as containing the type species together with such other species as are closely related to it.

Names of varieties may be applied in several ways. Usually the varietal name is added to the name of the genus and species following the abbreviation "var." (variety), as, for example, *Bacillus cereus* var. *mycoides*. A scientific name of this kind is referred to as a *trinomial*. Certain species contain a number of strains which in some cases cannot be definitely differentiated, but in others differentiation is possible by certain techniques. In the latter case they are usually referred to as *types* and are assigned numerals, as, for example, *Diplococcus pneumoniae* type I. More than seventy types of this organism have been identified.

A scientific name gives some indication of the nature of the organism and helps one to distinguish actual relationships among organisms. The international acceptance of scientific names prevents misunderstanding when publications in foreign languages are consulted. In the field of bacteriology the goal of establishing internationally uniform scientific names has not yet been achieved but undoubtedly will be an accomplishment of the future. Many organisms have common or vernacular names as well as scientific names. Such names are often convenient to use, but when accuracy is required, scientific names should be used. Confusion may arise when common names are used. Such names are often inexact, since a given common name may refer to one species in one region and to another species elsewhere. Examples of common names frequently used are "pneumococcus" for *Diplococcus pneumoniae*, "gonococcus" for *Neisseria gonorrhoeae*, "meningococcus" for *Neisseria meningitidis* and "colon bacillus" for *Escherichia coli*.

It is permissible to abbreviate the generic name, using only its initial letter or several of its letters, provided the complete name has appeared in the preceding discourse. Thus *Bacillus subtilis* may be shortened to *B. subtilis*, *Clostridium tetani* to *Cl. tetani*, *Streptococcus pyogenes* to *Str. pyogenes*.

Taxonomic names are governed by definite, set rules. The names of orders always have the ending *-ales;* suborders end in *-ineae;* family names in *-aceae;* subfamily names in *-oideae;* and the names of tribes have the ending *-eae.* Family and tribe names are derived from the name of one of the genera in the group. This last rule, however, has been violated in some instances.

The following table illustrates the taxonomic position of *Escherichia coli,* a common inhabitant of the intestinal tract of animals and man:

     Phylum, Protophyta
      Class, Schizomycetes
       Order, Eubacteriales
        Family, Enterobacteriaceae
         Tribe, Escherichieae
          Genus, Escherichia
           Species, coli

BASIS OF CLASSIFICATION

The taxonomic characters used in systematic botany and zoology are chiefly morphological. Owing to their small size and limited variety in form and structure, an adequate system for the classification of bacteria cannot be based on morphology alone. Two kinds of bacteria, although morphologically indistinguishable, may exhibit great differences in their cultural characters and biochemical activities. It is impossible, for example, to differentiate between *Escherichia coli* (colon bacillus) and *Salmonella typhosa* (typhoid fever bacillus) on the basis of morphology.

The morphological features used in systematic bacteriology include form and size; presence or absence of spores, flagella and capsules; location of flagella; cell grouping (a highly variable factor upon which not too much reliance should be placed); and the type of colony produced. Although structural features are of fundamental importance in bacterial taxonomy, they fail to provide sufficient diagnostic criteria for an adequate classification. The bacteriological taxonomist utilizes additional characteristics. These include staining reactions, particularly in regard to differential stains; cultural characters; nutritional requirements and metabolic products. In the case of pathogens, disease-producing power and the presence of certain antigenic components* are also considered.

The cultural characters and biochemical reactions are determined by growing the organisms on various culture media such as beef broth, agar slant, agar plate, gelatin, potato slant and sugar broth. The biochemical reactions usually noted include the ability to ferment sugars, particularly glucose, lactose and sucrose; also the ability to utilize simple nitrogen compounds such as ammonia, nitrites or nitrates; liquefy gelatin; or form indole or hydrogen sulfide. Other points such as the *p*H and temperature

*Substances which, when introduced into the body, incite the formation of specific defensive chemical compounds (antibodies).

range in which the organism will grow and whether or not it requires free oxygen in its energy metabolism are additional criteria.

TAXONOMIC POSITION OF THE BACTERIA

In the field of taxonomy bacteria are catalogued with the plants because, as a group, they show more resemblance in their morphologic and developmental characters to the blue-green algae, the lowest of the green plants, than to the protozoa. They also have characteristics that relate

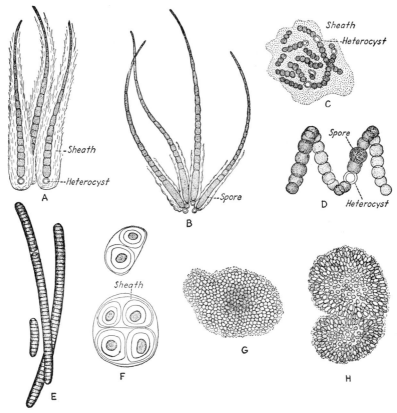

Figure 42.   Types of blue-green algae. *A, Rivularia; B, Gloeotrichia; C, Nostoc; D, Anabaena; E, Oscillatoria; F, Gloeocapsa; G, Microcystis; H, Coelosphaerium.* (By permission from Methods and Materials for Teaching Biological Sciences by D. Miller and G. Blaydes, Copyright 1938, McGraw-Hill Book Company, Inc.)

them to the fungi. Figure 42 exhibits drawings of a few representatives of the blue-green algae.

SUBDIVISIONS OF THE PLANT KINGDOM

The plant kingdom has been subdivided into four phyla by some taxonomists and into five by others. In the former case the bacteria are placed in the phylum *Thallophyta,* in the latter they, along with the blue-green algae, compose the phylum *Protophyta.** The following outline includes five phyla:

Phylum I. Protophyta (primitive plants)

This phylum comprises the bacteria and the blue-green algae. Bacteria have characteristics which relate them to the blue-green algae, although only a few species contain photosynthetic pigments.

CLASS I. SCHIZOMYCETES.   The Schizomycetes, or bacteria, constitute a heterogeneous group of unicellular, rather primitive, organisms. The most numerous kinds are spherical, rod-shaped or spiral. The more highly developed kinds are filamentous, some being in the form of branching threads. Some species are motile and some produce endospores. Multiplication is chiefly of the simplest asexual type, binary fission, or simple cell division. Sexual reproduction, however, occurs in some groups. Certain filamentous forms give rise to reproductive cells known as conidia.

CLASS II. SCHIZOPHYCEAE.   The Schizophyceae, or blue-green algae, sometimes called Cyanophyceae, are the simplest forms of green plants. Each organism is a single cell, lacking a clearly differentiated nucleus. They often form long filaments. The chlorophyll, along with other pigments, particularly a blue pigment (phycocyanin), is diffused through the protoplasm. No flagellated forms occur.

Phylum II. Thallophyta

This is a large aggregation of soft-bodied plants displaying a diversity of morphological types. The thallophytes have a simple body, a thallus, or mass of tissue which is not differentiated into such structures as roots, stems or leaves. They inhabit water or moist places. Many are unicellular, but some are multicellular. Some have chlorophyll (green, brown and red algae), while others (fungi) lack this pigment. Many of the thallophytes have developed some form of sexual reproduction to supplement the asexual method.

Subphylum Algae.   These contain chlorophyll and include the green algae, brown algae and the red algae.

Subphylum Fungi.   These lack chlorophyll. Included are the yeasts, molds, rusts, blights, mildews and mushrooms. Some are unicellular, others are multicellular.

Phylum III. Bryophyta

This includes the mosses and liverworts.

* This term is used in the current (7th) edition of Bergey's *Manual of Determinative Bacteriology.* The term used in previous editions for this phylum was "*Schizophyta.*"

Phylum IV. Pteridophyta

This comprises ferns and allied forms.

Phylum V. Spermatophyta

This includes seed-bearing plants.

The class Schizomycetes is subdivided into orders as indicated in the following key.

KEY TO THE ORDERS OF CLASS SCHIZOMYCETES[1]

I. Cells rigid. Spherical, rod-shaped (straight or curved) or spiral in form. Sometimes in trichomes.[2] Motile by means of polar flagella or nonmotile.

  A. Cells coccoid, straight or curved rods, or spiral in form. Sometimes occur as chains of cells. Cells may contain photosynthetic purple or green pigments. Not in trichomes. Usually motile by means of polar flagella. Occasionally nonmotile.

      Order I. *Pseudomonadales*

  B. Not as above.

    1. Cells in trichomes that are frequently in a sheath. Occasionally motile (swarm spores) or nonmotile conidia are developed. The sheaths may contain a deposit of ferric hydroxide, and the trichomes may be attached to a substrate.

      Order II. *Chlamydobacteriales*

    2. Cells reproduce by a process of budding rather than by ordinary cell division (fission). May be attached to a substrate by a stalk. One genus contains species with photosynthetic pigments (*Rhodomicrobium*).

      Order III. *Hyphomicrobiales*

II. Not as above.

  A. Cells rigid. Spherical or straight rod-shaped cells. Occur singly, in chains or in trichomes. Motile by means of peritrichous flagella or nonmotile. Not acid-fast.

    1. Cells spherical or rod-shaped; no trichomes, although chains of cells may occur.

      Order IV. *Eubacteriales*

    2. Cells in trichomes.

      Order VI. *Caryophanales*

  B. Not as above.

    1. Cells rigid and may grow out into a branching mycelium-like structure which may even develop chains of aerial conidia giv-

---

[1] From Bergey's *Manual of Determinative Bacteriology* (7th ed.) by R. S. Breed, E. G. D. Murray and N. R. Smith. Reproduced by the permission of Dr. H. J. Conn and The Williams & Wilkins Company.

[2] Many-celled filaments in which the multicellular character can be readily observed without staining.

ing colonies a superficial resemblance to mold colonies. In two genera spores develop within sporangia (sporangiospores), and in one of these genera the spores are motile. Where cells occur singly or in simple branched forms, they are frequently acid-fast.

Order V. Actinomycetales

2. Not as above.
   a. Cells rigid, usually large and may occur as coccoid cells or trichomes. Sulfur granules may occur on the surface or within the cells. Move by a gliding, oscillating, or rolling, jerky motion like that of some blue-green algae. No flagella present.

Order VII. Beggiatoales

   aa. Not as above.
      b. Longer or shorter flexuous cells.
         c. Cells flexuous, creeping on a substrate. Frequently pointed at both ends. Fruiting bodies are usually developed from a thin spreading colony (pseudoplasmodium). Slime bacteria.

Order VIII. Myxobacterales

         cc. Cells in the form of longer or shorter spirals. Swim freely by flexion of cells.

Order IX. Spirochaetales

      bb. Nonmotile, highly pleomorphic organisms of a very delicate character. Possess filterable stages.

Order X. Mycoplasmatales

QUESTIONS

1. (a) Who laid the foundation for our present system of classification of plants and animals?
   (b) Give a brief account of the early attempts at classifying bacteria.
   (c) Which book contains the current classification of bacteria now generally accepted in the United States?
2. Why are bacteria classified as plants rather than animals?
3. What are the chief difficulties encountered in classifying bacteria?
4. The classification of bacteria now in use is an "artificial" rather than a "natural" one. Explain what this means.
5. (a) Name in sequence the taxonomic divisions used in biological classification from the largest to the smallest categories.
   (b) What is a species? A genus? A family? An order? A class?
   (c) What is a variety? A strain? A type?
6. (a) What is meant by the term "binomial system of nomenclature"?
   (b) What is the origin of the two terms that constitute the scientific name of an organism?
7. (a) List the morphological features of importance in the classification of bacteria.
   (b) Besides morphological characteristics, which other features are made use of in classifying bacteria?
8. (a) Name the phylum in which the bacteria are placed.
   (b) Into which two classes is this phylum divided?
   (c) Name the orders of the class containing the bacteria.

REFERENCES

Breed, R. S., Murray, E. G. D., and Smith, N. R.: Bergey's Manual of Determinative
    Bacteriology. 7th ed. Baltimore, The Williams & Wilkins Company, 1957.
Editorial Board, International Committee on Bacteriological Nomenclature: Interna-
    tional Code of Nomenclature of Bacteria and Viruses. Ames, Iowa, Iowa State
    College Press, 1958.
Lanjouw, J., ed.: Botanical Nomenclature and Taxonomy. Waltham, Mass., Chronica
    Botanica Company, 1950.

6 • The Class Schizomycetes

As indicated in the key presented in the preceding chapter, the class
Schizomycetes is divided into ten orders. In the present chapter the more
important orders and families will be briefly considered. In taxonomical
nomenclature the ending "ales" denotes an order, whereas the ending
"aceae" denotes a family. The proper pronunciation of the names of the
orders and families is indicated as presented in Bergey's *Manual of De-*
terminative Bacteriology (7th ed.).

PSEUDOMONADALES (pseu-do-mo-na-da'-les)

The order Pseudomonadales embraces rod-shaped, spiral, coccoid and
spherical bacteria. The cells of this order usually are polarly flagellated
but none form endospores. Many of the species are found in water and
soil, and a few are pathogenic. The cells in the first three families described below contain either bacteriochlorophyll or a chemically related
photosynthetic pigment. They also contain red, yellow, purple or brown
carotenoid pigments.

Thiorhodaceae (thi-o-rho-da'-ce-ae)

Morphologically, the bacteria in this family are spheres, short rods, long
rods, spirals or vibrios. They contain green bacteriochlorophyll and yellow
and red carotenoid pigments. In the presence of hydrogen sulfide and
sunlight they are capable of carrying on a photosynthetic metabolism.
They contain sulfur globules and are often referred to as the "purple sulfur
bacteria."

Athiorhodaceae (a-thi-o-rho-da'-ce-ae)

The bacteria in this family are relatively small rods, spheres, vibrios
and spirals. Some are motile by means of polar flagella. They contain

bacteriochlorophyll and a number of different carotenoid pigments causing the cultures to appear in various shades of brown or red, especially when grown in the light. *Rhodospirillum rubrum* (Figure 43), a common inhabitant of stagnant bodies of water, is a representative of this group.

Chlorobacteriaceae (chlo-ro-bac-te-ri-a'-ce-ae)

This family comprises cells of various shapes that are usually of small size. They contain a green photosynthetic pigment which is not identical with chlorophyll, nor with bacteriochlorophyll, and are often referred to

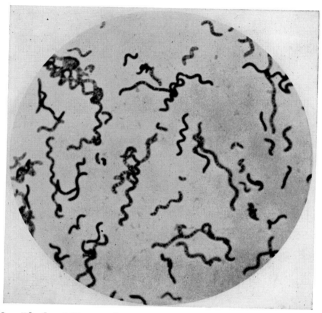

Figure 43. Rhodospirillum rubrum. (Copyright by General Biological Supply House, Inc., Chicago.)

as the green sulfur bacteria. In the presence of hydrogen sulfide these organisms are capable of photosynthesis. Most of the species of this family are widely distributed in mud and stagnant waters containing hydrogen sulfide.

Nitrobacteraceae (ni-tro-bac-te-ra'-ce-ae)

This family comprises rod-shaped, spheroidal and spiral forms. Many species have polar flagella. These organisms derive energy from the oxidation of ammonia to nitrite or from the oxidation of nitrite to nitrate. Endospores are not produced. They are found in soil and in bodies of fresh water. The bacteria of this family are of tremendous importance in the maintenance of soil fertility. They play an important role in the nitrogen cycle (Chapter 18). Three widely distributed genera are *Nitrosomonas, Nitrosococcus,* and *Nitrobacter.*

Thiobacteriaceae (thi-o-bac-te-ri-a'-ce-ae)

This family consists of coccoid forms as well as straight and curved rods. Those that are motile possess polar flagella. These bacteria obtain their energy by the oxidation of sulfur and sulfur compounds. They are commonly referred to as colorless sulfur bacteria. Certain species, such as *Thiobacillus denitrificans, Thiobacillus thioparus* and *Thiobacillus thiooxidans,* are widely distributed in nature and play an important role in the sulfur cycle (Chapter 18).

Pseudomonadaceae (pseu-do-mo-na-da'-ce-ae)

This is a very large family embracing rod-shaped and, occasionally, coccoid forms. These bacteria are usually motile by means of polar flagella

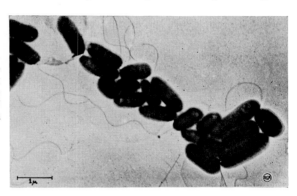

Figure 44. Electron micrograph of *Pseudomonas aeruginosa.* Rods with rounded ends and a single polar flagellum. (Courtesy of Drs. K. Polevitsky-Zworykin and T. F. Anderson.)

which are either single or in the form of tufts. The habitat of most of the species is the soil and bodies of water, including salt water. Yellow, blue, red or green pigments are produced by many members of this family.

The genus *Pseudomonas* contains species which produce a yellowish-green, fluorescent pigment. Their habitat is the soil or bodies of water, including sea water. The best known species of this genus is *Pseudomonas aeruginosa* (Figure 44). Although it is a common saprophyte, it can live as a pathogen. Its pathogenicity, however, is of a low order. It is a common wound contaminant, liberating pigment which contributes a blue color to pus. Its usual habitat is sewage and polluted water.

Members of the genus *Acetobacter* oxidize ethyl alcohol to acetic acid and water. They are used in the production of vinegar. The genus *Photobacterium* comprises species that are luminescent. (See Figure 79, Chapter 11.)

Caulobacteraceae (cau-lo-bac-ter-a'-ce-ae)

This family consists of rod-shaped or kidney-shaped bacteria which

Figure 45. *Gallionella ferruginea.* (From Biology of the Bacteria, by A. Henrici and E. Ordal. Reproduced by permission of D. C. Heath and Co.)

characteristically grow upon stalks attached to submerged surfaces in aquatic habitats. Some species have been found only in marine habitats. The stalks may be short, long and slender, or in the form of twisted bands. The material forming the stalk is secreted from one end of the cell or, in some species, from one side of the cell. In some species the stalks are slender bands composed of ferric hydroxide whereas in other species they are composed of gummy organic matter on which ferric hydroxide is deposited. In some species the young cells are motile by means of polar flagella.

Gallionella ferruginea (Figure 45) is a well known species in which the cells are kidney-shaped, having a length of about 1.2 microns. These

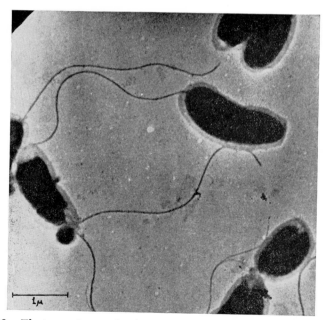

Figure 46. Electron micrograph of *Vibrio comma,* the causative organism of Asiatic cholera. The dense homogeneous cytoplasm of the organisms is shrunken away from the less dense cell wall. The cells have polar flagella which are continuous through the cell wall with the cytoplasm. (Courtesy of Drs. T. F. Anderson and K. Polevitsky-Zworykin.)

bacteria form bandlike stalks by secreting colloidal ferric hydroxide from the concave portion of the cell. The stalks become spirally twisted by a rotary motion of the cells. Cell division causes the stalks to become branched. These organisms may grow in water pipelines and often cause extensive deposits of iron.

Spirillaceae (spi-ril-la'-ce-ae)

The members of this family are vibrio-shaped or spirally twisted. They may adhere end-to-end, forming chains. The cells are rigid and are usually motile by means of a single flagellum or a tuft of polar flagella. In the genus *Spirillum,* volutin granules are usually present. The bacteria of this family are found chiefly in fresh water and also in sea water. Some species are parasitic or pathogenic. *Vibrio comma* (Figure 46) is the cause of Asiatic cholera, and *Vibrio fetus* (Figure 19) causes abortion in cattle and sheep.

CHLAMYDOBACTERIALES (chla-my-do-bac-te-ri-a'-les)

The name of this order means "sheath-forming bacteria." Most of the species grow in long chains or filaments of rod-shaped cells arranged end-to-end and enclosed in a tubular sheath composed of an organic matrix impregnated to varying degrees with iron or manganese oxides. In some species the sheath is entirely organic, and a few species are not ensheathed.

The filaments are usually unbranched but may show false branching when a cell becomes detached from the others and grows into a filament which extends out laterally through the sheath. The filaments may be anchored at one end to a solid object, or they may be free. These bacteria are relatively large and are found in fresh and salt waters.

Reproduction is by fission, by the formation of conidia from the tips of the filaments or by the production of flagellated cells known as "swarm cells." The motile swarm cells are produced by cells at the tip of the filament and escape through the open end of the tubular sheath to start the formation of new filaments. Endospores are not formed.

The order is divided into three families, *Chlamydobacteriaceae* (chla-my-do-bac-te-ri-a'-ce-ae), *Peloplocaceae* (pe-lo-plo-ca'-ce-ae) and *Crenothrichaceae* (cre-no-tri-cha'-ce-ae). Those members of this order whose sheaths are impregnated with iron salts are often called "iron bacteria."

Leptothrix ochracea (Figure 47,A) is a well-known species and a typical representative of the sheathed bacteria. The sheath is unattached to solid objects and is composed entirely of ferric hydroxide in colloidal form. The organism is world-wide in distribution, living in iron-bearing water. The cells measure 1 micron in diameter and have a length of about 15 microns. The filaments may attain a length of 300 microns. Motile swarm cells have been observed. When the sheaths become thick, the filaments may creep out of the opening at the end and secrete a new sheath.

Thus innumerable empty sheaths may accumulate, forming reddish flocculent masses in the water and a reddish-brown slime coating on objects.

Crenothrix polyspora (Figure 47,B) is an ensheathed species which forms long articulated filaments attached at one end to a submerged object. The sheath expands toward the tip, thus forming a funnel-shaped tube, and consists of an organic matrix encrusted with iron, especially at the basal portion. The diameter of this organism, including the sheath, is between 2 and 9 microns. It grows as thick brownish masses in water containing organic matter and iron salts. It may be found in water pipes and drain pipes and frequently causes trouble by clogging water pipes. When the filaments die, they decay, imparting a disagreeable odor and flavor to the water.

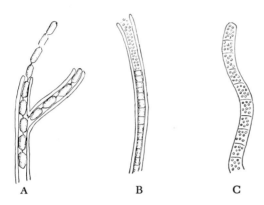

Figure 47. Representatives of the orders Chlamydobacteriales and Beggiatoales. *A, Leptothrix ochracea;* showing false branching and filament creeping out of opening at end of sheath; *B, Chrenothrix polyspora; C, Beggiatoa alba,* showing granules within the cells.

A   B   C

EUBACTERIALES (eu-bac-te-ri-a′-les)

The order Eubacteriales comprises the majority of the common and most familiar bacteria. The prefix *eu* signifies true; thus the members of this order are sometimes referred to as the "true bacteria." They are rigid cells either spherical or rod-shaped. Both motile and nonmotile species are included. Endospores are produced by the members of one family (Bacillaceae). The cells may be single, in chains or in some other grouping arrangement. Certain species are of value industrially, others are important in maintaining the fertility of the soil, and some are parasites of plants and animals. The bacteria of this order are found in the soil, in fresh and salt waters and in the tissues of animals and plants.

Azotobacteraceae (a-zo-to-bac-te-ra′-ce-ae)

These organisms are relatively large rod-shaped or large oval forms (yeastlike), motile by means of numerous peritrichous flagella. They are widely distributed in the soil, where they play a role of some importance in that they are capable of utilizing atmospheric nitrogen in the synthesis of protein molecules. The process of synthesizing free nitrogen into compounds is called "nitrogen fixation." A common species is *Azotobacter chroococcum.*

Rhizobiaceae (rhi-zo-bi-a'-ce-ae)

The members of this family are nonspore-forming rods which are either sparsely flagellated or nonmotile. Some are plant pathogens. This family contains the genus *Rhizobium,* which is of considerable significance in the soil. The members of this genus grow symbiotically in the roots of leguminous plants, including clover, alfalfa, vetch, peas, beans and peanuts. They cause the formation of nodules on young roots. Residing in these nodules, they are capable of utilizing atmospheric nitrogen in the synthesis of cellular compounds; i.e., they can "fix" atmospheric nitrogen.

Achromobacteraceae (a-chro-mo-bac-te-ra'-ce-ae)

These organisms are small- to medium-sized rods which, if motile, have peritrichous flagella. Many members of this family are found in water and soil; some are marine organisms. Some species are plant pathogens and others are parasitic in the intestine of man without being pathogenic. One species, *Alcaligenes viscolactis,* produces ropiness in milk.

Enterobacteriaceae (en-te-ro-bac-te-ri-a'-ce-ae)

This is a large and important family which includes the coliform-dysentery-typhoid group of bacteria. The organisms are homogeneous in morphology, being short, rod-shaped forms. If motile, they have peritrichous flagella. Many animal and plant parasites are included. The species pathogenic for man cause intestinal diseases (enteric fevers).

Those members of the family Enterobacteriaceae which readily ferment lactose with the production of gas (chiefly *Escherichia coli* and closely related forms) are made use of in sanitary water analysis and are referred to as the coliform group.

This family includes *Salmonella typhosa,* the causative organism of typhoid fever, and *Shigella dysenteriae* and several closely related organisms which cause dysentery.

Brucellaceae (bru-cel-la'-ce-ae)

These bacteria are small, motile or nonmotile, coccoid or rod-shaped forms. Some have tapering ends, and some show a tendency to bipolar staining. Included in this family, which contains many species parasitic for man or other warm-blooded animals, is the genus *Brucella,* which contains three species capable of causing brucellosis in man and certain animals. Other species included in this family are *Pasteurella pestis,* the cause of plague; *Pasteurella tularensis,* the causative organism of tularemia ("rabbit fever"); *Bordetella pertussis,* the etiologic agent of whooping cough; *Haemophilus ducreyi,* the cause of the venereal disease known as chancroid.

Micrococcaceae (mi-cro-coc-ca′-ce-ae)

The bacteria of this family are spherical and may occur singly, in pairs, tetrads, packets or irregular masses. Nearly all the members are nonmotile and incapable of producing endospores. Many species are chromogenic, producing yellow, orange, pink or red pigments. These organisms are widely distributed in soil and water. A few species are parasitic.

This family includes *Staphylococcus aureus,** a common pathogen which is capable of causing a variety of infections. The cells of this organism are usually grouped together in irregular clusters. Included also is the genus *Sarcina* which comprises a number of widely distributed saprophytic species. The cells of these organisms are usually arranged in cubical packets.

Neisseriaceae (neis-se-ri-a′-ce-ae)

These organisms are cocci occurring in pairs or masses. They are non-motile and usually nonchromogenic. There are two genera, *Neisseria* and *Veillonella,* the former containing such pathogens as *Neisseria gonorrhoeae,* the cause of gonorrhea, and *Neisseria meningitidis,* the cause of epidemic meningitis. The genus *Veillonella* consists of species which are parasites in the oral and nasal cavities, intestines and urogenital tracts of man and other animals.

Lactobacillaceae (lac-to-ba-cil-la′-ce-ae)

This large family embraces both spherical and rod-shaped organisms which frequently form chains of cells resembling a string of beads or a filament. They ferment sugars with the production of lactic, propionic and other acids. Members of this family may be found in the respiratory tract, oral cavity and intestinal tract as well as in milk and milk products. A few highly pathogenic bacteria are members of this group. Included in this family are *Diplococcus pneumoniae, Streptococcus pyogenes, Streptococcus lactis, Leuconostoc mesenteroides* and *Lactobacillus casei.*

Corynebacteriaceae (co-ry-ne-bac-te-ri-a′-ce-ae)

These are rod-shaped organisms which are usually nonmotile. Some are banded or beaded when stained and some are chromogenic. Many species are animal and plant parasites. Members of the genus *Corynebacterium* have a tendency to be club-shaped. *Corynebacterium diphtheriae* is the causative organism of diphtheria.

---

* In the previous (6th) edition of Bergey's *Manual of Determinative Bacteriology* this organism was called *Micrococcus pyogenes* var. *aureus.* The word "Staphylococcus" was not used as a genus name.

Bacillaceae (ba-cil-la′-ce-ae)

This family comprises rod-shaped bacteria which, when motile, have peritrichous flagella. A distinctive characteristic of these organisms is the ability to produce endospores. The cells usually occur in chains. There are two genera, *Bacillus* and *Clostridium*. *Bacillus subtilis* is widely distributed in the soil and in decomposing organic matter. *Clostridium tetani* is the causative organism of tetanus.

ACTINOMYCETALES (ac-ti-no-my-ce-ta′-les)

The members of this order evidently are somewhat higher in the evolutionary scale than those previously considered. The order includes a variety of morphological types, a few are spherical, some are rod-shaped; many are filamentous (threadlike) with a tendency toward the development of branches and the formation of a mycelium, thus giving rise to moldlike forms. The strands, however, are much thinner than those of the molds, their diameter being no greater than that of ordinary rod-shaped bacteria, i.e., about 1 micron. No cross walls are visible in the strands. In some genera the filaments fragment readily into bacillary or coccoid forms. The members of this order are nonmotile. Endospores are not produced. Conidia may be formed from the tips of the filaments in some genera. Those members of the order that are filamentous are frequently referred to as "actinomycetes." Although they have some of the characteristics of the fungi, they seem to bear a closer relationship to the bacteria. Actinomycetales are primarily free-living soil bacteria which play an important role in the decomposition of organic matter. Some are the source of valuable antibiotics and a few are parasitic.

Mycobacteriaceae (my-co-bac-te-ri-a′-ce-ae)

The members of this family are chiefly slender rod-shaped forms, but some are spherical. The family comprises two genera, *Mycobacterium* and *Mycococcus*. In the genus *Mycobacterium* the organisms are straight or slightly curved rods, but there is a tendency to form short filaments which soon break up into rod-shaped cells. The members of this genus do not stain readily with the basic dyes generally used to stain bacteria, but once stained they resist decolorization with dilute mineral acids and, therefore, are referred to as "acid-fast" bacteria. In the genus *Mycococcus* the cells are usually spherical and are not acid-fast. They are found chiefly in the soil. The genus *Mycobacterium* contains a few pathogenic forms, the most important one being *Mycobacterium tuberculosis*, the etiologic agent of tuberculosis in man. *Mycobacterium bovis* is the cause of tuberculosis in cattle, and *Mycobacterium avium* causes tuberculosis chiefly in birds. *Mycobacterium leprae* is generally accepted as the cause of leprosy.

Actinomycetaceae (ac-ti-no-my-ce-ta′-ce-ae)

These organisms give rise to a branching mycelium during the early stages of growth but later fragment into small bacillary or coccoid segments which look like true bacteria. Some are partially acid-fast. This family contains two genera, *Nocardia* and *Actinomyces*. The genus *Nocardia* contains a large number of species, some of which are parasitic. The genus *Actinomyces* contains only three species, all of which are parasitic. *Actinomyces bovis* is the cause of actinomycosis (lumpy jaw) in cattle.

Streptomycetaceae (strep-to-my′-ce-ta′-ce-ae)

The members of this family are more moldlike than those of the Actinomycetaceae. The organisms grow in the form of a much branched mycelium which does not fragment. Conidia are produced on aerial branches in chains or singly on short stalks. The aerial branches frequently

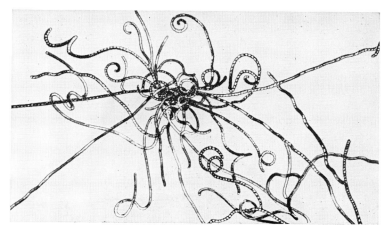

Figure 48. Streptomyces aureofaciens. (Courtesy of Lederle Laboratories Division, American Cyanamid Co.)

have a spiral formation. The members of this family are chiefly saprophytic soil forms. The musty odor of freshly plowed soil is due to the presence of these organisms. This family comprises a very large numbei of species, a few of which are pathogenic for plants. *Streptomyces scabies* is the cause of potato scab. The streptomycetes have become important sources of antibiotics. *Streptomyces griseus* is the source of streptomycin and *Streptomyces venezuelae* produces chloramphenicol (Chloromycetin). *Streptomyces aureofaciens* (Figure 48) is the source of chlortetracycline (Aureomycin) and *Streptomyces rimosus* produces oxytetracycline (Terramycin).

BEGGIATOALES (beg-gi-α-to-α′-les)

The cells of the organisms that comprise this order are arranged in chains, forming filaments which in some cases may be relatively long. One end of the filament may become attached to a solid substrate. Although they lack flagella, many species are capable of a gliding motion when in contact with a substrate. In many respects the organisms of this order resemble blue-green algae but differ from them in that they do not produce photosynthetic pigments. Some biologists regard them as colorless forms of blue-green algae. They contain granules of sulfur and are often called "colorless sulfur bacteria."

A well-known species is *Beggiatoa alba* (Figure 47,C). It grows in waters containing hydrogen sulfide and stores sulfur in the form of granules in its protoplasm. It is commonly found in streams, sulfur springs and bogs and is abundant in sewage-polluted streams. The cells range from 2.5 to 5 microns in diameter and 3 to 9 microns in length.

MYXOBACTERALES (myx-o-bac-te-ra′-les)

This is a curious group of organisms which occupies an intermediate position between the bacteria proper and the slime molds (myxomycetes).

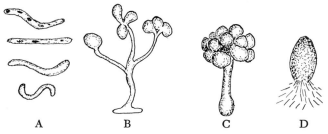

A   B   C   D

Figure 49. Some representatives of the order Myxobacterales. *A,* Vegetative forms; *B* and *C,* fruiting bodies; *D,* a swarm of vegetative rods emerging from a cyst. (Redrawn from Thaxter.)

Because they live in a matrix of slime, they are called "slime bacteria." The life cycle consists of a vegetative stage and a fruiting stage (spore or cyst stage). These stages are illustrated in Figure 49.

In the vegetative stage the cells in most species are rod-shaped, being long and slender, and have a high degree of flexibility. In a few species the cells are spherical or ellipsoidal. In this stage the cells reproduce by binary fission and usually become arranged in groups, lying parallel. The cells are not flagellated but move about in unison in the colony in small parallel groups by means of a crawling or creeping motion. They move away from the center of the colony, thus forming a spreading colony. Because of this characteristic swarming of the cells, the vegetative stage is termed the "swarm stage."

As the colony reaches a certain stage of development, the cells swarm toward definite points in the colony and become heaped up into more or less knoblike masses in which the cells are held together by slime. This is the beginning of the fruiting stage. The masses may develop stalks which usually divide, giving rise to branches on which fruiting bodies are formed at the ends. The fruiting bodies are seldom more than 1 mm. high and may be as large as 100 microns in diameter. They are usually colored, frequently red, yellow or orange. Each fruiting body finally gives rise to an egg-shaped mass surrounded by a wall of slime; i.e., it becomes a cyst. The cells in the cyst become spherical or shortened rods. The slime dries, forming a firm envelope for the cyst. The cells in the cyst are sometimes referred to as spores but are considered by some merely as resting cells. The mature cyst finally becomes detached and can then be disseminated by wind or water. Under favorable conditions a swarm of rod-shaped bacteria emerges from the cyst and the vegetative cycle is repeated. The fruiting stage is absent in some species.

These bacteria live usually as saprophytes and can be found in the soil, on decaying wood and in the dung of animals. Some live in the sea.

SPIROCHAETALES (spi-ro-chae-ta′-les)

The organisms in this order, commonly referred to as spirochetes, are relatively slender, flexuous spirals. Most species exhibit a series of regular, graceful spiral turns, thus resembling a diminutive corkscrew. In some the coils are close together, whereas others are more loosely coiled. The organisms comprising this group vary considerably in size, some being 4 microns long, while others attain a length of 500 microns. Because the artificial cultivation of spirochetes is difficult, many of the species have never been cultivated. Multiplication is by transverse fission. None produce conidia or endospores.

Spirochetes resemble the protozoa and Myxobacterales in that they do not have rigid cell walls. Being flexuous distinguishes them from the genus *Spirillum* (order Pseudomonadales), in which the organisms are rigid spirals.

The spirochaetales have certain structural features which are found in no other bacteria. Some species are equipped with an axial filament, others with a lateral band (crista), and still others show transverse striations. The *axial filament* is a central, elastic, rodlike structure which extends the length of the cell and around which the protoplasm of the cell is spirally wound. The filament may extend beyond one or both ends of the cell, forming flagellum-like extensions. The crista of some members of the group is a thin, flat band or membrane which winds spirally about the organism from end-to-end, one side being free, the other attached to the cell. It is suggestive of the undulating membrane of the trypanosomes among the protozoa (see Chapter 8) and is considered to serve as an organelle of locomotion.

All forms of spirochetes are motile. Movement appears to be brought about by spiral wave motion passing through the cell. In some cases the motion is snakelike, in others the organism revolves screwlike on its long axis. Most species are not readily stained by the ordinary bacteriological dyes. They can be colored with Giemsa's stain or by special silver-impregnation methods. Many of the smaller forms have a refractive index too low to permit them to be observed in unstained preparations under the ordinary light microscope, but they may be demonstrated with darkfield illumination. Figure 50 shows various types of spirochetes.

Spirochetes are responsible for several human diseases, among which are syphilis, yaws, relapsing fever and infectious jaundice. Some are

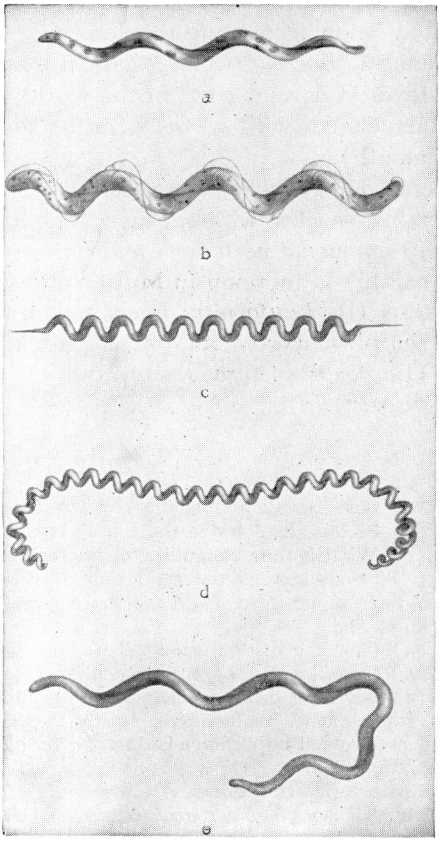

Figure 50. Diagram of various types of spirochetes. *a,* Spirochaeta; *b,* Cristispira; *c,* Treponema; *d,* Leptospira; *e,* Borrelia. (From Frobisher: Fundamentals of Microbiology. 6th edition.)

parasitic in mollusks. A few are saprophytic, living in fresh water or in the sea. Sewage-polluted waters usually harbor large numbers of spirochetes. The order is divided into two families as indicated below:

Family I. Spirochaetaceae (spi-ro-chae-ta'-ce-ae)

The members of this family are relatively long, coarse spirals, varying in length from 30 to 500 microns. The family comprises three genera as indicated below:

Genus I. *Spirochaeta:* free-living in fresh and salt water; common in sewage and foul waters; have well-defined axial filament.

Genus II. *Saprospira:* free-living in marine ooze.

Genus III. *Cristispira:* parasitic in intestinal tract of various mollusks; equipped with crista.

Family II. Treponemataceae (tre-po-ne-ma-ta'-ce-ae)

This family consists of relatively short, slender or coarse, spiral forms, 4 to 16 microns long. Some cells may show fine fibrils at both ends, which appear to be prolongations of the axial filament. Three genera, as indicated below, constitute this family:

Genus I. *Borrelia:* coarse spirals; a number of species cause relapsing fever in various parts of the world; one species, *Borrelia vincentii,* is associated with a fusiform bacillus in Vincent's angina (trench mouth).

Genus II. *Treponema:* exceedingly slender with short kinky coils; contains species which cause syphilis (*Treponema pallidum*), yaws (*Treponema pertenue*) and pinta (*Treponema carateum*). Pinta (or carate) is common in Mexico and Colombia.

Genus III. *Leptospira:* finely coiled, with one or both ends bent into a sharply curved hook when cultivated in liquid media; one species (*Leptospira icterohaemorrhagiae*) causes infectious jaundice (Weil's disease).

QUESTIONS

1. (*a*) Give the distinguishing characteristics of the order Pseudomonadales.
   (*b*) Briefly characterize the family Nitrobacteraceae.
   (*c*) What is the outstanding characteristic of the genus *Photobacterium?*
   (*d*) Briefly characterize the family Spirillaceae.
2. Which group of Pseudomonadales contains bacteria that grows upon stalks? Give an example.
3. (*a*) Give the distinguishing characteristics of the order Chlamydobacteriales.
   (*b*) Describe (1) *Leptothrix ochracea,* (2) *Crenothrix polyspora.*
4. (*a*) Give the distinguishing characteristics of the order Eubacteriales.
   (*b*) Briefly characterize the family Bacillaceae of the order Eubacteriales.
   (*c*) Of what importance is *Azotobacter chroococcum?* Of what importance is the genus *Rhizobium?*
5. Characterize the following families and give examples: (1) Enterobacteriaceae, (2) Brucellaceae, (3) Micrococcaceae, (4) Lactobacillaceae, (5) Corynebacteriaceae, (6) Bacillaceae.
6. (*a*) What are the distinguishing characteristics of the order Actinomycetales?
   (*b*) Briefly characterize the following families and give examples: (1) Mycobacteriaceae, (2) Actinomycetaceae, (3) Streptomycetaceae.
   (*c*) Members of the genus *Streptomyces* are often referred to as being molds. Does the term "mold" correctly apply to them?
7. Give the characteristics of the order Beggiatoales.
8. Characterize the order Myxobacterales. How do the bacteria of this order differ from all other bacteria?
9. Give the distinguishing characteristics and examples of the order Spirochaetales.

REFERENCES

Breed, R. S., Murray, E. G. D., and Smith, N. R.: Bergey's Manual of Determinative Bacteriology. 7th ed. Baltimore, The Williams & Wilkins Company, 1957.

Edwards, P. R., and Ewing, W. H.: Identification of Enterobacteriaceae. Minneapolis, Burgess Publishing Company, 1955.

Lanjouw, J., (ed.): Botanical Nomenclature and Taxonomy. Waltham, Mass., Chronica Botanica Company, 1950.

Waksman, S.: The Actinomycetes. Waltham, Mass., Chronica Botanica Company, 1950.

Waksman, S., and Lechevalier, H.: Guide to the Classification and Identification of the Actinomycetes and Their Antibiotics. Baltimore, The Williams & Wilkins Company, 1953.

7 • The Fungi

The true fungi are the chlorophyll-free organisms constituting one of the two primary divisions of the phylum, *Thallophyta* of the plant kingdom. The other division, the algae, comprises chlorophyll-containing organisms. There is a strong bond of affinity between the fungi and the algae. Although fungi lack chlorophyll, they closely resemble certain green algae in their structure and mode of reproduction. It is possible that the fungi have been derived from green algae and that the earlier forms were aquatic. Many species are still aquatic, but a large number have become adapted for terrestrial life. The fungi are a versatile group tolerant of a wide range of diverse physical and chemical conditions. Many thousands of species have been described.

Included among the fungi are molds, yeasts, rusts, smuts, blights, mildews, mushrooms and toadstools. The branch of biological science specifically concerned with the study of the fungi is known as *mycology*.

The study of certain fungi is included in the science of microbiology because they normally participate in biological processes regularly studied by the microbiologist. This applies chiefly to those that are commonly known as molds and yeasts. Molds are multicellular organisms, each consisting of a network of slender, tubular, branched filaments, termed *hyphae* (singular *hypha*). The entire body (*thallus*) thus composed of hyphae is termed the *mycelium*. Yeasts are typically unicellular—they do not usually produce a mycelium.

RELATIONSHIPS OF YEASTS AND MOLDS

Although it is not difficult to distinguish between a typical yeast and a typical mold, one cannot draw a sharp line of demarcation between these two groups. There are species among the fungi which have the morphology of molds under some circumstances and that of yeasts under others;

106

i.e., they exhibit dimorphism. Among some of the pathogenic fungi the unicellular or yeastlike stage occurs in tissues, and the multicellular, filamentous stage in cultures.

The terms "yeasts" and "molds" do not permit of precise definition since no sharp limits can be set for these terms. They are convenient terms to use but are without taxonomic significance.

Structurally yeasts and molds exhibit greater complexity than the bacteria and occupy a somewhat higher position in the scale of life.

CLASSIFICATION OF THE FUNGI

The classification of the fungi is based on morphology and does not include cultural reactions, as is the case in bacterial taxonomy. The morphological characteristics of most importance are the types of reproductive cells (spores) produced. The fungi occupy the position of a subphylum, which is divided into four main classes, as follows:

1. Phycomycetes—algae-like fungi
2. Ascomycetes—the sac fungi
3. Basidiomycetes—the club fungi
4. Fungi Imperfecti—a heterogeneous group.

Phycomycetes

This is a large group frequently referred to as the "lower fungi." They are believed to be direct descendants of green algae because they resemble them more closely than do any of the other fungi.

One of the distinguishing characteristics of the Phycomycetes is the fact that the mycelium does not contain cross walls or *septa*. A mycelium of this type is referred to as *nonseptate* or *coenocytic*. Some species of algae have a similar structure. Most of the mycelium-producing fungi have a *septate* mycelium. The Phycomycetes are differentiated from other fungi also by the kinds of asexual and sexual spores they produce. Asexual spores are formed in spore cases known as *sporangia*. The sexual spores are of two types, *zygospores* and *oöspores*. Spore formation will be discussed in a subsequent section of this chapter.

The Phycomycetes constitute a diverse group including both aquatic and terrestrial forms. Some are parasitic on fishes and other forms of aquatic life. Molds belonging to the genera *Mucor* and *Rhizopus* are members of this class. The group also includes the downy mildews, which attack potatoes, grapes, melons and other crops.

Ascomycetes

This class represents a large group of organisms distinguished by the production of saclike structures known as *asci* (singular *ascus*) in which sexual spores known as *ascospores* are formed: hence the name Ascomycetes. Besides ascospores, filamentous members of the group produce asexual spores called *conidia*. The mycelium, in contrast with that of the

Phycomycetes, is definitely septate. The group includes certain molds and the yeasts, besides the powdery mildews and the edible truffles and morels. It includes, also, the majority of plant disease fungi, among which may be mentioned apple scab; brown rot fungus, which destroys ripe stone fruits (peach, plum, cherry); and chestnut-tree blight. The Ascomycetes include also the ergot fungus, which grows parasitically on rye and other grains, attacking the grain-bearing heads. At a certain stage in its life history the drug known as ergot is extracted. This drug is used to arrest hemorrhage of the uterus in childbirth.

Basidiomycetes

The members of this group differ from other fungi in that they bear sexual spores externally, typically four in number, each being produced on a club-shaped stalk (*basidium*). The spores are known as *basidiospores*. The mycelium is septate. The class includes the mushrooms; puffballs; bracket fungi, which appear on the outside of tree trunks; smuts; and rusts.

The aerial portion of such fungi as mushrooms constitutes the spore-forming structure and is composed of hyphae bundled together into a compact mass. Beneath the surface of the soil is a ramifying and radiating network (vegetative hyphae) through which the plant is nourished. Smuts are parasitic on cereals such as wheat and corn. Included among the rusts are the blister rust of white pine trees and the black stem rust of wheat and other cereals.

Fungi Imperfecti

This represents a provisional taxonomic grouping for the accommodation of the large number of fungi for which a sexual phase has not been demonstrated. The organisms of this group are known only in the asexual or so-called imperfect stage. From time to time as their sexual stages are discovered, species are removed from this group and placed in one of the previously described classes. Included in the Fungi Imperfecti are saprophytic forms and many of the fungi pathogenic for man. Numerous diseases of plants are caused by members of this group.

THE MOLDS

The term "molds" is applied for convenience to a heterogeneous group of multicellular, filamentous organisms which superficially resemble one another. They are widely distributed in nature, growing within a wide range of environmental conditions. Molds are found chiefly in three of the classes of fungi, the Phycomycetes, Ascomycetes and Fungi Imperfecti.

Morphology of Molds

As previously mentioned, the thallus of a mold consists of an extensively branching mycelium which may be microscopic in size or large enough to be visible to the unaided eye, often forming a cottony mass. In some molds the mycelium is nonseptate or coenocytic, i.e., without septa or cross walls, the protoplasm being continuous throughout the mycelium. In other molds the mycelium is divided into definite cells by cross walls or septa which occur at regular intervals. Each cell of these molds has one or more nuclei, which are relatively small.

In the nonseptate mycelium, nuclei occur at regular intervals. In this type of structure the protoplasm forms a continuous mass. Each nucleus with the surrounding cytoplasm may be considered to represent a cell. A similar nonseptate condition obtains in some of the algae. The nonseptate molds, as previously indicated, are placed in the class Phycomycetes.

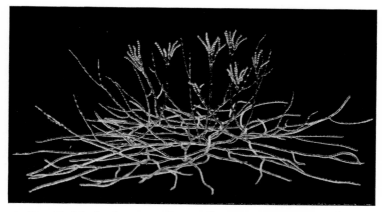

Figure 51. Model of a fragment of *Penicillium notatum* as seen under the microscope. Note the chains of conidia on the upright filaments. (Courtesy of the Chicago Natural History Museum.)

The cells of molds have a cell wall which is relatively thick and rigid and is composed chiefly of chitin, an organic, nitrogen-containing compound. Immediately inside the cell wall is the cytoplasmic membrane forming the boundary of the protoplasm of the cell. The cells of young molds are usually homogeneous in appearance, but in older cells, vacuoles can be seen. The vacuoles contain various reserve food materials, such as granules of glycogen and volutin and globules of fat. These materials appear, not only in the vacuoles, but also in the cytoplasm.

The mycelium of a typical mold consists of *vegetative hyphae* and *fertile hyphae*. The vegetative hyphae are in direct contact with, or permeate, the substrate. The fertile hyphae are aerial in many instances and give rise to reproductive spores. The structure of the spore-bearing parts and the mode of spore formation are characteristics utilized in the identification of molds. Figure 51 shows the general form of a mold.

Reproduction of Molds

Molds reproduce by spores of various kinds, and reproduction in some molds is both sexual and asexual. Some species produce three or even more forms of spores. Spores usually have a tough wall, can endure drying for months or years and remain dormant for a long time. Mold spores are not so resistant to heat as are the bacterial spores. When a suitable environment is encountered, they germinate and form a new mycelium. Asexual spores constitute the chief means of reproduction and are usually produced in countless numbers. Being exceedingly minute and light in weight, they readily float in the air and are carried long distances by air currents. By these spores distribution is efficiently achieved. They are

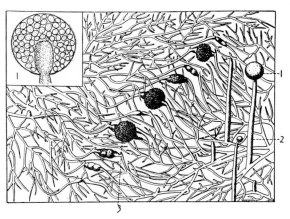

Figure 52. Mucor sp. showing mycelium, asexual spores, sexual spores (zygospores) and development of zygospores. *1,* Sporangium, with spores (inset); *2,* sporangiophore; *3,* zygospore. (Reproduced by permission from Agents of Disease and Host Resistance by F. Gay and associates, Charles C Thomas, publisher.)

usually so abundant in the air that if a suitable culture medium be exposed to the air of a room for a few minutes, colonies of molds will develop within a few days. The sexual type of spore is formed by the fusion of two specialized cells. These spores are produced less frequently and in smaller numbers. In some molds they are rarely encountered, and in many they have not been observed.

Asexual Spores.   There are a number of types of asexual spores. Molds belonging to the class Phycomycetes produce spores in enormous numbers inside globular spore cases known as *sporangia* (singular *sporangium*), which are formed at the tips of fertile hyphae (Figures 52 and 53). The sporangium is separated from the supporting hypha by a transverse wall (*columella*) which has a convexity toward the cavity of the sporangium. The spores are formed by cleavage of the contents of the sporangium and are known as *sporangiospores*. The hyphae from which the sporangia develop are called *sporangiophores* (*spore bearers*). When mature the sporangia burst, releasing the spores, which are scattered like dust into the air. In the aquatic species the sporangiospores usually are motile by means of flagella.

Molds classified as Ascomycetes form spores at the tips of fertile hyphae, which are not encased. Such spores are known as *conidia* (singular *conidium*) or *conidiospores*. They may be single but usually occur in chains like strings of beads. The hyphae that bear them are called *conidiophores*. Conidia are usually formed by the pinching off of a cell at the tip or, in some cases, the side of a conidiophore. This is followed by a second constriction below the first one, thus forming a second cell. The process may be repeated many times, giving rise to a chain of conidia, the

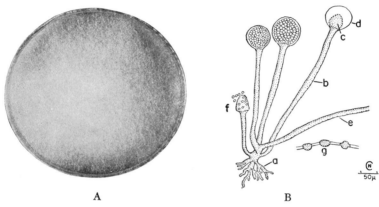

A   B

Figure 53. Rhizopus sp. A, Cottony aerial mycelium in Petri dish; *B*, an individual mold organism; (*a*), rhizoids; (*b*), sporangiophore; (*c*), swollen tip of sporangiophore; (*d*), sporangium; (*e*), stolon. (From Conant et al., Manual of Clinical Mycology.)

one at the end being the oldest one. In some cases, however, the first-formed conidium constricts to form another one, which then repeats the process, giving rise to a chain of conidia in which the youngest cell is the one at the tip. The terminal portion of the conidiophore may be branched; thus many chains of conidia may be formed. The various colors, black, brown, green, yellow, pink and orange, exhibited by molds are due to the sporangiospores and conidiospores they produce.

In many species of molds an occasional cell of the mycelium may acquire a relatively large reserve of food material and thus increase in size. It becomes rounded in shape and surrounded by a greatly thickened wall. This thick-walled, sporelike body is known as a *chlamydospore* (ensheathed spore).

Many species can reproduce by fragmentation of any part of the mycelium into short, ovoid cells known as *oidia* or *arthrospores*. These cells may give rise to other free cells or produce a new mycelium.

Sexual Spores.   The kind of sexual spores produced is used as the main basis for dividing the fungi into classes (*Phycomycetes, Ascomycetes* and *Basidiomycetes*). Fungi not known to produce sexual spores are placed in the *Fungi Imperfecti*. Sexual reproduction is preceded by fertilization, which is a process in which two cells or two nuclei fuse. The cells involved may either be alike or unlike and are known as *gametes*.

In the Phycomycetes two kinds of sexual spores are formed. One kind is produced by the union of morphologically similar gametes (*isogametes*), the other kind by the union of gametes which are morphologically dissimilar (*heterogametes*).

In the terrestrial members of the class, the *Zygomycetes*, sexual spores known as *zygospores* are formed by the fusion of isogametes. In the formation of this type of spore (see Figure 52) two filaments of different organisms lying close together send lateral clublike branches toward each other. These branches (suspensors) gradually approach one another and come into contact end to end. The terminal portion of each branch becomes a separate, multinucleate cell by the formation of a cross wall. These terminal cells are the gametes. The walls in contact dissolve, the contents of the two multinucleated gametes fuse, and the nuclei unite two by two. The resulting zygospore becomes surrounded by a thick, black wall with a warty exterior.

Because the gametes and the two mold organisms that participate in zygospore formation are morphologically similar, they are designated as plus or minus strains rather than male or female. These molds display the rudiments of maleness and femaleness, the plus strain corresponding to one sex, the minus to the other. In these forms there is a physiological differentiation of sex not accompanied by any outward indications.

When the zygospore germinates, it sends out an elongated sporangiophore which bears a sporangium containing asexual spores (sporangiospores). The spores formed in this type of sporangium are of two different kinds; one kind upon germination gives rise to plus organisms, the other to minus organisms.

The aquatic members of the class, the *Oömycetes*, form *oöspores* by the union of a small male gamete and a larger female gamete, i.e., by the fusion of heterogametes. The male and female gametes are usually provided by the same mold organism. The mature oöspore is surrounded by a heavy wall. This method of reproduction is similar to that occurring in the coenocytic green alga known as *Vaucheria*.

The sexual spores of Ascomycetes are known as *ascospores*. They are formed by the union of two cells of the same organism or two separate organisms. Before the nuclei fuse, the number of chromosomes is reduced to one-half the usual number for the species (diploid to haploid). The fusion nucleus undergoes several divisions, ultimately resulting in the formation of a definite number of ascospores, eight being the most common number. The number is constant for the particular species producing them. The spores are set free when the cell containing them, the *ascus*, disintegrates. Each ascospore is capable of producing a new mycelium upon germination. Certain molds and the sporulating yeasts produce ascospores.

THE COMMON MOLDS

Molds are found in all the classes of fungi. A few representatives of those classified as Phycomycetes and Ascomycetes will be described.

Phycomycetes

Some of the most common molds are found in this group. As previously mentioned, the mycelium of the Phycomycetes is nonseptate. This class contains the order *Mucorales,* in which there are two genera of importance: *Mucor* and *Rhizopus.* These molds form a profuse, cottony growth, are widely distributed in the soil, and are found on barnyard manure, fruits and starchy foodstuffs. They are often found growing on old moist bread and are frequent contaminants of laboratory media. Asexual reproduction is by means of sporangiospores and, occasionally, by chlamydospores. When mature, the sporangiospores are black or brown, giving the growth a dark color. Sexual reproduction occurs by means of zygospores.

In *Rhizopus* the sporangiophores grow in clusters, whereas those of *Mucor* arise singly from many parts of the mycelium. Another distinction is that *Rhizopus* sends out *stolons,* or runners, parallel to the surface of the substrate, which produce rootlike hyphae (*rhizoids*) where they touch the substrate. Stolons enable *Rhizopus* to spread rapidly over the substrate.

Rhizopus nigricans is commonly called the bread mold because it is frequently encountered growing on moist bread and as a contaminant of bacteriological culture media. It is responsible for extensive spoilage of fruits and vegetables, particularly strawberries and sweet potatoes. *Mucor mucedo,* another common species, is also a frequent cause of food spoilage.

Many species of Phycomycetes are aquatic. The commonest of the water molds belong to the genus *Saprolegnia.* Aquatic animals, such as fish or frogs (including their eggs), are extensively parasitized by these molds. Many species parasitize aquatic plants. Saprophytic forms live on the bodies of dead crustaceans and water insects. They frequently can be seen in the form of a white fringe of radiating filaments around dead insects floating in water. The tips of many of the filaments contain cylindric sporangia from which, when mature, flagellated spores are liberated.

Filamentous Ascomycetes

A large and important group of molds is included among the Ascomycetes. The mycelium of these molds is septate, consisting of cellular units attached end-to-end. Asexual reproduction is brought about chiefly by conidia. The particular structure of the conidiophore varies in the different families and is an important means of differentiation. At times they reproduce by arthrospores. Sexual reproduction occurs by means of ascospores. The two genera of molds belonging to this group most frequently encountered are *Aspergillus* and *Penicillium*. In a few species of these two genera sexual reproduction occurs. In most of the species, however, sexual spores have not been observed; such species, therefore, are classed as Fungi Imperfecti.

The genus *Aspergillus* includes numerous species which vary considerably in color, some being green, others yellow, pink, orange, brown or black. Each conidiophore has an enlarged globular tip covered more or less completely with closely packed peglike projections called *sterigmata* (singular *sterigma*). The sterigmata bear long chains of conidia which are often so densely packed together that the supporting structure cannot

Figure 54. Colony of *Penicillium notatum.* (Courtesy of Chas. Pfizer & Co., Inc.)

be seen, and the fruiting body then appears as a spherical or, in some cases, columnar mass of pigmented spores.

In sexual reproduction two cells borne at the tips of two hyphae, of the same or separate individuals, fuse to form an ascus. A number of asci are usually produced in close proximity. The group of asci becomes enclosed in a spherical or pear-shaped hull (*perithecium*) formed by a mass of closely woven hyphae. Each ascus usually contains eight ascospores.

Aspergillus niger, a common species, is a black mold which frequently causes the spoilage of food. Two common green species are *A. glaucus* and *A. nidulans.*

Members of the genus *Penicillium,* known usually as the blue-green molds, are common saprophytic forms. They frequently are seen growing on citrus fruits, cheese, cured meats and other foodstuffs. In these molds each conidiophore branches more or less extensively at the tip. At the end of each branch are fingerlike sterigmata from which the conidia extend in parallel chains, forming a brushlike structure from which the name *Penicillium* (Latin *penicillus,* a little brush) has been derived. Figure 54 shows a colony of *Penicillium notatum,* a mold which produces penicillin.

THE YEASTS

The yeasts, first described by Leeuwenhoek in 1680, comprise a large group of fungi which ordinarily do not form a mycelium. They are characteristically unicellular; a few kinds, however, although predominantly yeastlike, under certain conditions produce a rudimentary mycelium. Yeasts of various types are widely distributed in nature, being found in most soils, on the leaves of plants and the skins of such fruits as grapes, apples and pears, and in the nectar of flowers. Many insects harbor yeasts in their alimentary tracts and seem to serve as important agents in their dissemination. Many yeasts have the ability to ferment sugars, with the production of ethyl alcohol and carbon dioxide.

Morphology of Yeasts

In form, yeasts are usually ovoid, but some are spherical and a few have an elongated sausage-like shape. Most species are considerably larger than bacteria. The average diameter of cultivated varieties is 4 to 5 mi-

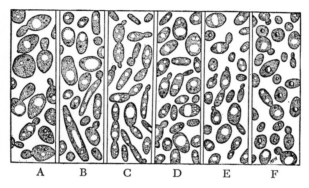

| A | B | C | D | E | F |

Figure 55. Vegetative cells of various species of yeasts: A, *Nadsonia fulvescens;* B, *Hansenula anomala;* C, *Pichia membranaefaciens;* D, *"Torula cremoris";* E, *Rhodotorula glutinis;* F, *Cryptococcus pulcherrimus.* (Reproduced by permission from Henrici's Molds, Yeasts and Actinomycetes by C. Skinner, C. Emmons and H. Tsuchiya, copyright 1947, John Wiley & Sons, Inc.)

crons. A yeast cell does not have flagella or other organelles of locomotion. The cell wall consists of a cellulose-like substance, the exact composition of which has not been determined. A nucleus can be demonstrated near the center of the cell when the cell is treated with nuclear dyes. In a young cell the cytoplasm is homogeneous. Later, one or more fluid-filled vacuoles appear. At times, a large vacuole occupying much of the cell space may be present. Within the vacuoles, granules representing various kinds of reserve foodstuffs become prominent as the cell becomes older. Microchemical tests indicate that both glycogen and volutin granules are usually present.

Cytoplasmic particles possessing the specific staining properties of mitochondria have been observed. Numerous small fat globules are generally present in yeast cells. As the cell matures, these globules become highly refractile and may coalesce to form one large one. Some species, which store relatively large quantities of fat, can be used to produce fat on a commercial scale. In Figure 55 vegetative cells of various species of yeasts are illustrated.

Reproduction of Yeasts

Yeasts multiply by budding or by fission and also by means of ascospores. Budding is an asexual method of reproduction. Because it is the predominant mode of propagation, yeasts are often referred to as "bud-

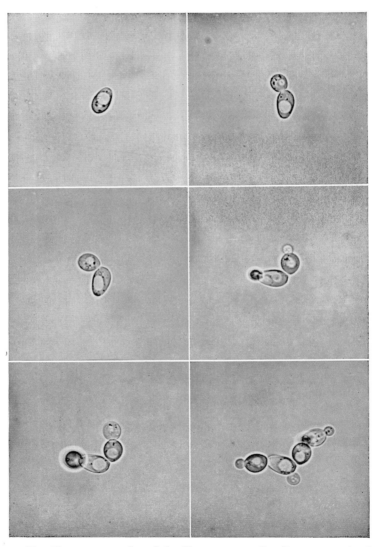

Figure 56. Photomicrographs of budding yeast cells (*S. cerevisiae*), showing growth over a period of 4 hours from a single cell to four adult cells each with a bud. × 1000, reduced approximately one fifth from original photomicrographs. (Courtesy of the Fleischmann Laboratories of Standard Brands Incorporated.)

ding fungi." In the process of budding, a small knoblike projection, resembling a bud in appearance, forms near one end of the cell. The nucleus of the cell divides, forming two nuclei, one of which migrates into the bud. The bud increases rapidly in size and later becomes separated from the parent cell by constricting at its base. During periods of rapid growth, daughter cells may in turn undergo budding before separation from the parent cell takes place, thus forming a pseudomycelial group. Reproduction by budding is illustrated in Figures 56 and 57. A few genera multiply

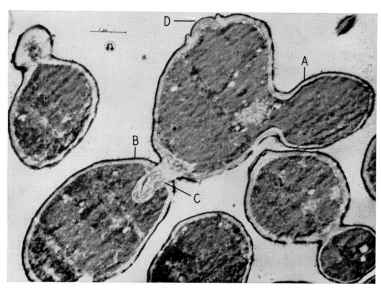

Figure 57. Electron micrograph of thin sections of budding yeast cells. *A*, bud with cytoplasm continuous with that of the mother cell; *B*, mature bud with developing cross wall between mother and daughter cell; *C*, extension of cell wall material into cytoplasm; *D*, bud scar. (From H. D. Agar and H. C. Douglas: J. Bacteriol., Vol. 70. Reproduced by permission of The Williams & Wilkins Company.)

by the asexual method of binary fission, which is similar to the pattern used by bacteria.

Ascospore formation is a sexual mode of reproduction characteristic of many species, but occurs only at intervals. Adverse conditions, such as the dehydration of the medium or exhaustion of the food supply, may serve as a stimulus to the formation of ascospores. In this process the nucleus and cytosome become converted into a definite number of spores, usually four or eight, the number for the cultivated yeasts being four. The cell which contains the spores is called an *ascus*. Upon dissolution of the ascus the spores are liberated.

In some yeasts the first step in ascospore formation is the conjugation of two vegetative cells. In this process adjacent cells extend tubelike protoplasmic projections toward each other. These finally meet and join the cells together. The two nuclei fuse into a single nucleus within the channel formed by these processes, and the fusion nucleus gives rise to four or, in some species, eight daughter nuclei. Each of these becomes invested with cytoplasm, around which a spore wall is formed.

In other species conjugation does not take place until ascospores have been formed. The ascospores are produced *parthenogenetically*, i.e., without the fusion of the nuclei of two cells. In the formation of these spores the chromosome number is reduced one-half, i.e., from the double set (diploid number) of the vegetative cells to a single set (haploid number). The haploid spores, usually four, when liberated from the ascus, conjugate in pairs to form diploid vegetative cells. The common cultivated yeast, *Saccharomyces cerevisiae*, forms ascospores by parthenogenesis. Asci of this species are shown in Figure 58.

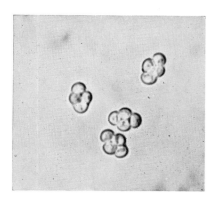

Figure 58. Photomicrograph of asci of S. *cerevisiae*, × 800. (Courtesy of the Fleischmann Laboratories of Standard Brands Incorporated.)

Yeast spores are highly resistant to drying but are not so resistant to heat as are bacterial spores. Sporulation in the yeasts is a method of reproduction as well as a means of surviving adverse conditions.

A few species produce basidiospores, which places them in the class Basidiomycetes, commonly called the club fungi. Those that form ascospores are placed in the group of sac-forming fungi or Ascomycetes. Yeasts that have not been shown to have a sexual stage are grouped with the Fungi Imperfecti.

Cultivated Yeasts

Certain varieties of yeasts have long been cultivated and utilized by man. These yeasts originated from wild yeasts, which have a wide distribution in nature. The natural variability of yeasts enabled man to select strains that showed desirable characteristics. Most of the yeasts used by man are included in the genus *Saccharomyces* (sugar fungi). Because of their ability to ferment sugar and, in so doing, to produce ethyl alcohol and carbon dioxide, these yeasts are of great economic importance. The role of yeasts in alcoholic fermentation of sugar was established by Pasteur in 1859. The cultivated yeasts now include a number of different kinds. Among these are (1) bottom and top fermenting beer yeasts, (2) distillery yeasts, (3) wine yeasts, (4) baking yeasts, and (5) food yeasts. The yeasts used in bread making, brewing and manufacture of ethyl alcohol and distilled liquors are closely related and are regarded as varieties of the same species, *Saccharomyces cerevisiae*. The top yeasts grow principally on or near the surface of the nutrient solution, forming a frothy scum; the bottom yeasts grow chiefly at the bottom of the solutions in which they live.

Saccharomyces ellipsoideus (the wine yeast) is important in wine and hard cider making. There are many varieties of this species. *Saccharomyces fragilis* and *Cryptococcus kefyr* are lactose fermenters used in Asia and eastern Europe in making fermented milk beverages such as koumiss and kefir. Certain species of the genus *Mycoderma* are film-forming yeasts on liquid media, especially those that contain organic acids. They frequently form a white scum on the surface of acid-containing liquids such as pickle brine, sauerkraut and some wines. If undisturbed, the film becomes more than 1 inch thick on tanks of brine pickles.

Certain cultivated varieties of yeasts can be purchased in the form of yeast cakes (compressed or dried) or dried yeast granules. The compressed cakes are made by forming a mixture of yeast and a little starch and molding this into cakes. Dry yeast cakes are made by adding corn meal to yeast, pressing the mixture into cakes and drying the cakes.

RELATION OF FUNGI TO HUMAN WELFARE

Along with the bacteria, fungi perform an indispensable function in the decomposition of dead organic materials in the soil and in bodies of water. They thus play an important role in the maintenance of soil fertility.

Fungi are extensively used industrially (see Chapter 19) for the production of important products. Yeasts are economically important chiefly because of their ability to transform sugar into ethyl alcohol and carbon dioxide. They are used in the production of alcoholic beverages and distilled commercial alcohol. Because they liberate carbon dioxide, yeasts are useful as a leaven in bread making. Bubbles of gas released in the dough cause it to expand, rendering it light and spongy.

Among the molds, the genus *Penicillium* embraces species used in cheesemaking. *Penicillium notatum* and *P. chrysogenum* are the source of penicillin, a valuable antibiotic which is relatively nontoxic for man.

Molds cause much damage to human food in that they are responsible for the spoilage of stored fruits such as apples, pears, grapes and citrus fruits. They also attack various kinds of vegetables and preserved and refrigerated meats. Some species of yeasts and molds are the causal agents of diseases. Fungi are the principal causes of plant diseases. A few are associated with disease in man and animals.

QUESTIONS

1. (*a*) What are fungi? From which forms is it believed that the fungi have been derived?
   (*b*) Which fungi are generally included in the science of microbiology?
2. Name the four classes of fungi and give a brief characterization of each class.
3. Give the general morphology of a mold. Describe the mold cell.
4. Define: (1) mycelium, (2) hypha, (3) vegetative hypha, (4) fertile hypha.
5. (*a*) Explain asexual spore formation in (1) the Phycomycetes and (2) the Ascomycetes.
   (*b*) What kind of sexual spores are produced by (1) the Phycomycetes and (2) the Ascomycetes?
6. Differentiate between (*a*) *Rhizopus*, (*b*) *Penicillium* and (*c*) *Aspergillus*.
7. (*a*) How do yeasts differ from molds? To which class of fungi do they belong?
   (*b*) Give the morphology of a typical yeast.
8. Explain asexual and sexual reproduction in the yeasts.
9. How do the spores of fungi differ from bacterial spores in the purpose they serve?
10. In what ways are molds and yeasts economically important to man?

REFERENCES

Alexopoulos, C.: Introductory Mycology. New York, John Wiley & Sons, Inc., 1952.
Christensen, C.: The Molds and Man. Minneapolis, University of Minnesota Press, 1951.
Cook, A. H., ed.: The Chemistry and Biology of Yeasts. New York, Academic Press, Inc., 1958.
Lindegren, G. C.: The Yeast Cell, Its Genetics and Cytology. St. Louis, Educational Publishers, 1949.
Lodder, J., and Kreger-Van Rij, N. J. W.: The Yeasts; A Taxonomic Study. New York, Interscience Publishers, Inc., 1952.
Raper, K. B., and Thom, C.: Manual of the Penicillia. Baltimore, The Williams & Wilkins Company, 1949.
Roman, W., ed.: Yeasts. New York, Academic Press, Inc., 1957.
Skinner, C. E., Emmons, C. W., and Tsuchiya, H. H.: Henrici's Molds, Yeasts and Actinomycetes. 2nd ed. New York, John Wiley & Sons, Inc., 1947.
Smith, G. M.: Cryptogamic Botany. I. Algae and Fungi. New York, McGraw-Hill Book Company, Inc., 1955.
Thom, C., and Raper, K. B.: A Manual of the Aspergilli. Baltimore, The Williams & Wilkins Company, 1945.
Wolf, F. A., and Wolf, F. T.: The Fungi. New York, John Wiley & Sons, Inc., 1947, Vols. I and II.

8 • The Protozoa

The protozoa (Greek *protos,* first; *zoon,* animal) are unicellular, microscopic, primitive organisms, constituting the lowest primary subdivision (phylum) of the animal kingdom. They are worldwide in distribution, being found in fresh and salt waters, in damp terrestrial environments and as parasites of many species of animals. Nature has produced an immense variety of these organisms, over 15,000 species being known. Although often referred to as simple forms of life, many of the protozoa surpass in complexity any of the cells of the human body. Some have complicated life histories, with alternation of sexual and asexual generations. A few species usually included with the protozoa contain chlorophyll and carry on photosynthesis. Having characteristics of both plants and animals, these forms lie on the borderline between the plant and animal kingdoms. The branch of biological science devoted to the study of the protozoa is known as *protozoology.*

The majority of protozoa are free-living, but a number of species have become adapted to live as parasites in the bodies of plants and animals, including man. Practically every type of vertebrate animal is parasitized by one or more species of protozoa. Some protozoa are parasitic without being pathogenic. In some cases an intermediate host, such as a blood-sucking insect, is necessary for the transmission of pathogenic protozoa to man and other vertebrates. Some of the most devastating diseases of man and animals are caused by protozoa. Among the more common human protozoal diseases are malaria, amebic dysentery, kala-azar and African sleeping sickness.

CLASSIFICATION OF PROTOZOA

The protozoa are usually divided into four classes differentiated chiefly on the basis of morphology. The classification is shown in the following outline:

Phylum *Protozoa*

Class I. *Sarcodina.* Locomotion and food ingestion by means of temporary protoplasmic extensions called pseudopodia

Class II. *Flagellata* (*Mastigophora*). Provided with one or more flagella for locomotion or for securing food

Class III. *Sporozoa.* Mature forms without locomotor organelles; immature forms move by pseudopodia; male gametes have flagella; reproduction usually by spores; all species parasitic; many have complex life cycles

Class IV. *Ciliata* (*Infusoria*). Locomotion by means of short hairlike structures called cilia. A small group has cilia only in the young stages. These are sometimes listed as a separate class called *Suctoria.*

THE PROTOZOAN CELL

The protozoa exhibit great differences in size, shape, structure and methods of reproduction. They are usually microscopic in their dimensions, but there are great extremes in size. Some attain a length of only 3 microns, while a few are large enough to be visible without magnification. Some are relatively simple in structure, while others are complex, having structural differentiation for the performance of special functions, such as locomotion, procurement of food, excretion, protection and attachment to objects. Such structures are analogous in function to the organs of multicellular animals and are referred to as *organelles.*

Many protozoa have a membrane, the pellicle, located outside the cytoplasmic membrane. The pellicle is not composed of protoplasm but consists of organic materials synthesized within, and secreted by, the cell. It is analogous to the cell wall of bacteria and fungi; although it is not so rigid as a cell wall, it gives the body definite form.

In many protozoa the protoplasm of the cytosome is differentiated into a narrow, nongranular, relatively firm surface layer, the *ectoplasm,* and an inner, granular, more fluid area, the *endoplasm.* In some species a definite opening into the cell, known as the *mouth* is present in the ectoplasm.

A remarkable organelle possessed by many protozoa is the *contractile vacuole,* which rhythmically fills with fluid and then discharges it to the outside. Some have only one such vacuole, while others have several. In some the position is fixed, but in others it shifts about within the endoplasm. A contractile vacuole is usually spherical. When filled with fluid, it moves toward the periphery and, by a sudden contraction, discharges its contents to the outside through an opening in the ectoplasm, and thus disappears. It soon re-forms, gradually increasing in size as it fills with fluid. This appearance and disappearance is continuous and rhythmic, the intervals between successive contractions varying from a few seconds to several minutes in different species under conditions of normal activity. The contractile vacuole is characteristic of fresh-water protozoa but is lacking in some of the fresh-water genera and in most of the marine forms as well as in many parasitic species. Figure 59 illustrates the structure of an ameba.

The principal function of the contractile vacuole appears to be the regulation of the water content of the cell. Much water enters the protozoan body with the food taken in and by osmosis through the body surface. By eliminating excess water the vacuolar system keeps the water content within normal limits. It probably also removes some carbon dioxide and other metabolic wastes.

Locomotion in the protozoa is accomplished in three different ways. Characteristic of the Sarcodina is movement by means of a temporary cytoplasmic protrusion, *pseudopodium* ("false foot"), which can be ex-

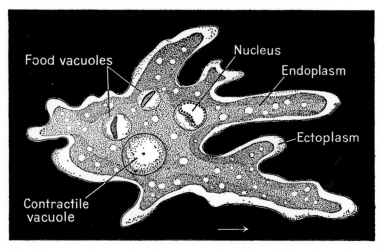

Figure 59.   Diagram of an ameba, showing pseudopodia and internal structures. (From Biology and Human Affairs by J. Ritchie. Courtesy of World Book Co.)

tended from any part of the organism. In the formation of a pseudopodium the ectoplasm is thrust out in one part of the cell, forming a lobular or finger-like projection into which the endoplasm flows. As the pseudopodium is formed, the whole mass of the cell is drawn toward it— thus locomotion is effected. Only those protozoa that lack a pellicle are capable of pseudopodial movement. Because this type of progression is characteristic of the ameba, it is termed ameboid movement. The same type of movement occurs in the white corpuscles (leukocytes) of man and other vertebrates. An active ameba may project a number of pseudopodia at the same time which may be immediately withdrawn without producing movement of the cell. The use of pseudopodia in feeding will be discussed in another section.

In the flagellates the locomotor organelles are permanent structures in the form of slender, flexible, whiplike processes known as *flagella.* They commonly extend from one end of the cell. The number of flagella varies usually from one to four, but a few species have a larger number. Each flagellum pierces the pellicle and arises from a granule, the *basal body,* located in the ectoplasm.

In the class Ciliata movement is by means of *cilia* (singular *cilium*), which, in contrast with flagella, are short, hairlike processes. They are numerous and may be evenly distributed over the whole surface of the cell or restricted to certain regions. Each cilium arises from a granule, the basal body, embedded in the ectoplasm.

Protozoa are usually uninucleated, but the whole group of ciliates is binucleate or multinucleate. Also in the ciliates the nucleus is of two

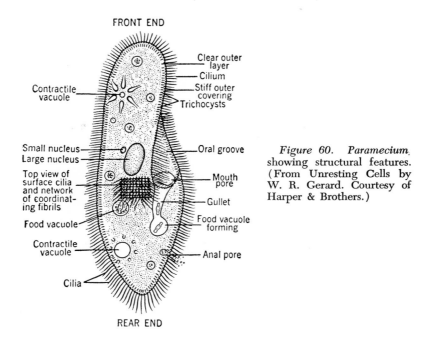

FRONT END

Clear outer layer
Cilium
Stiff outer covering
Trichocysts
Contractile vacuole
Small nucleus
Large nucleus
Top view of surface cilia and network of coordinating fibrils
Food vacuole
Contractile vacuole
Cilia
Oral groove
Mouth pore
Gullet
Food vacuole forming
Anal pore

REAR END

Figure 60. Paramecium. showing structural features. (From Unresting Cells by W. R. Gerard. Courtesy of Harper & Brothers.)

kinds: a single large *macronucleus* and one or more small *micronuclei.* The latter appear to be concerned only with reproduction, while the macronucleus discharges the other functions characteristic of nuclei. Paramecium (Figure 60) is a typical representative of a ciliate protozoan.

LIFE PROCESSES OF PROTOZOA

Nutrition

The majority of free-living protozoa have the capacity to ingest solid food particles, which may consist of bacteria, algae, diatoms, other protozoa or organic debris. In the Sarcodina food particles are taken into the body by means of pseudopodia (Figure 61). By extending pseudopodia around and over a food particle, the particle is taken into the cell. Since water is taken in along with the food, a food vacuole forms as the food and water enter the cell.

Among the ciliates and flagellates special organelles for food taking are usually present. Such protozoa have a cell mouth (*cytostome*) in the ectoplasm for the ingestion of food. They may also have a *gullet* for leading the food into the endoplasm. In the ciliates these structures are most highly developed. Ciliary motion forces food particles along with water into the endoplasm. In *Paramecium*, a common ciliate, a furrow known as the *oral groove* runs diagonally across one side of the cell. It leads to the mouth, from which a short gullet extends to the endoplasm. The beating of the cilia lining the oral groove creates a current of water flowing into the gullet and brings in food such as bacteria, protozoa or particles of dead organic matter.

The endoplasm of an active protozoan usually contains many food

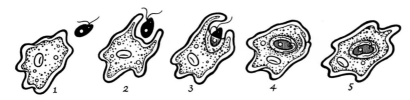

Figure 61. Diagram showing an ameba taking a food particle into its interior to form a food vacuole where it is subjected to the action of digestive enzymes. (From *The World of Life* by W. Pauli. Reproduced by permission of Houghton Mifflin Co.)

vacuoles. Protoplasmic currents cause these vacuoles to circulate through the cytosome. Digestion is accomplished by enzymes synthesized in the endoplasm and secreted into the food vacuoles. The digested food diffuses from the vacuoles into the substance of the cell. When digestion and absorption have been completed, the vacuoles disappear by expelling their contents (water and indigestible matter) to the outside through the cell surface. In some species a permanent anal opening (*egestion pore*) is present for this purpose. Those protozoa that lead parasitic lives may absorb through the cell surface soluble food substances from the body fluids of the host.

Reproduction

Various forms of reproduction are encountered in the protozoa. Both asexual and sexual reproduction are resorted to by some species, but in others no sexual process has been observed. The most common type of reproduction is *binary fission*. In this process the nucleus and the cell elongate, with a narrow constriction in the middle. The nucleus then divides into two nuclei which move to opposite ends of the cell. The constriction of the middle of the cytosome becomes more marked and finally completely separates the two portions, resulting in the formation of two new cells. In the process of fission the division of the nucleus is *mitotic;* i.e., the chromatin granules become organized into *chromosomes,* which divide, forming two groups, each new cell receiving one complete group. Mitosis in unicellular animals differs from that in multicellular forms in that the process is usually accomplished without the disappearance of the nuclear membrane.

In some species the division of the cell occurs at a right angle to the long axis. This is spoken of as *transverse fission.* In others, particularly the flagellates, fission occurs in the plane of the long axis. This is called *longitudinal fission.*

Certain species of protozoa reproduce by *multiple fission (schizogony)* in which the nucleus undergoes a series of divisions, each nuclear mass becoming surrounded by a layer of cytoplasm. Thus one cell becomes transformed into many new ones, which in some instances are referred to as spores.

Budding, or unequal fission, is a less common method of asexual reproduction. When this occurs, one or more smaller cells are produced from portions of the parent cell, which retains its identity.

In many species asexual reproduction is supplemented at intervals by sexual reproduction, which in some cases is of a primitive type known as *conjugation,* involving an exchange of a portion of the nuclear material of two cells. To effect this exchange of nuclear substance, two cells become temporarily attached. After the exchange has occurred they separate and continue their ordinary existence, dividing by binary fission. Conjugation has been frequently observed in *Paramecium caudatum,* a common fresh-water ciliate.

In other instances, particularly in the Sporozoa and colonial flagellates, sexual reproduction occurs through the union (copulation) of two cells which function as *gametes,* comparable to the sex cells of higher animals. Both in conjugation and copulation, a reduction in the chromosome number occurs. The zygotes are diploid, whereas the gametes and the nuclear portions that are exchanged are haploid. Some of the Sporozoa have a complicated life cycle with an alternation of sexual and asexual generations.

Encystment

A characteristic of many of the fresh-water and parasitic protozoa is their ability to enter a quiescent or resting stage known as a *cyst,* within the heavy walls of which they are able to retain viability for a long time outside their normal habitat. Upon entering the cyst stage, the protozoan becomes reduced in size, owing chiefly to the expulsion of water. It becomes spherical. Structures such as flagella, cilia, mouth and food vacuoles disappear. Fresh-water protozoa become encysted only when environmental conditions become unfavorable, but in pathogenic forms, encystment occurs even when conditions are entirely favorable. Encystment is a normal phase in the life cycle of these organisms.

Encysted protozoa are able to resist desiccation and other unfavorable environmental conditions which would kill unencysted or vegetative forms. They can remain dormant for a long time and may be disseminated by the wind or carried great distances on the feet of birds and insects. The ability to encyst is responsible in part for the wide distribution of protozoa. Encystment enables some parasitic protozoa to survive the inhospitable environment outside the body in the passage from one host to another.

The process of encystment often involves a succession of nuclear divisions, giving rise to a number of nuclei, in some cases as many as sixteen. Each nucleus becomes surrounded by a small amount of cytoplasm, and thus the contents of the cyst becomes resolved into as many new cells as there are nuclei. Upon the approach of favorable conditions the cyst ruptures, allowing the cells to escape, and each one by growth and development becomes a cell of normal size and structure. Thus encystment in some protozoa may be a method of multiplication.

THE SARCODINA

As mentioned previously, the members of this class are characterized by the use of pseudopodia in locomotion and feeding. Many species are relatively large, some being visible to the naked eye. Some Sarcodina exhibit temporary flagella.

The common fresh-water ameba, *Amoeba proteus,* is a typical representative of this class. The name "ameba" comes from a Greek word meaning changeful. This name was chosen because the members of this group, being without a limiting pellicle, are continually altering their shape as they move about. The genus *Amoeba* includes a number of species which vary in size and in the type of pseudopodia they project. Under the microscope these organisms appear as grayish or colorless irregular masses containing numerous granules. Reproduction is chiefly by binary fission and in some species also by multiple fission, usually during the encysted period.

The only pathogenic species of importance in this class is *Endamoeba histolytica* (Figure 62), which inhabits the intestinal tract and is the causative agent of amebic dysentery (amebiasis) in man. Other forms which are parasitic, but not pathogenic, in the human intestinal tract are *Endamoeba coli, Endolimax nana, Iodamoeba bütschlii* and *Dientamoeba fragilis. Endamoeba gingivalis* lives as a harmless parasite in the human mouth, feeding on bacteria and loose cells. Apparently many persons harbor this species. Most of these parasitic* Sarcodina produce resistant cysts by which they pass from infected hosts to other individuals.

---

* Parasitic protozoa will be discussed more fully in Chapter 33.

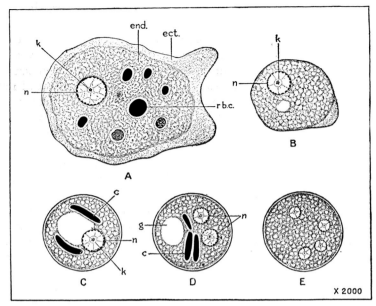

Figure 62.   Endamoeba histolytica. A, Active cell (trophozoite) containing ingested red blood cells; B, precystic stage; C, young uninucleate cyst; D, binucleate
cyst; E, mature cyst with four nuclei. c, Chromatoid body; *ect.*, ectoplasm; *end.*,
endoplasm; *g,* glycogen; *k,* karyosome; *n,* nucleus; *r. b. c.*, red blood cell. (From
Belding, D. L.: Textbook of Clinical Parasitology, 2nd ed., 1951. Courtesy of Appleton-Century-Crofts, Inc.)

THE FLAGELLATA

This class is characterized primarily by the presence of one or more
delicate flagella, which serve for locomotion and food capture. It comprises an immense number of highly diverse species. Inasmuch as certain
Flagellata have ameboid stages in their life cycle and flagella occur temporarily in various Sarcodina, the two classes presumably are closely
related.

The cell body of the flagellates is of fairly definite form (oval, elongate
or spherical), maintained by a rather firm pellicle. Food enters the body
at a definite place in some species, usually at the base of the flagella.

Longitudinal binary fission is the predominating method of reproduction. Some flagellates undergo multiple fission. Many colonial forms multiply by a highly specialized type of reproduction, involving male and
female gametes similar to those produced by multicellular organisms.

Among the flagellates are many fresh- and salt-water species which,
together with Sarcodina and innumerable kinds of minute plants, make
up the microscopic life, *plankton,* of salt and fresh waters. Plankton constitutes the primary food supply of the smaller forms of aquatic animals
which, in turn, are eaten by larger ones; these in their turn, serve as food
for still larger ones. Protozoa thus play a role in the food chain of animal

life. Some of the marine flagellates are phosphorescent, making the sea luminescent at night. Some make the soil their abode, and a number of species live as parasites.

The pathogenic flagellates are found chiefly in four genera, *Trypanosoma, Leishmania, Trichomonas* and *Giardia*. The trypanosomes (Figure 63) are blood parasites of man and other vertebrates. They are carried from one host to another by blood-sucking leeches, ticks and insects. Trypanosomes are elongated in form, pointed at one or both ends, with one flagellum which forms the border of a thin, wavy protoplasmic extension termed the undulating membrane. The attached margin of this membrane is shorter than the free end, throwing the membrane into folds and giving it a wavy appearance. *Trypanosoma gambiense*, commonly, and *T. rhodesiense*, occasionally, are the causative agents of African sleeping sickness; both are transmitted by the bite of the tsetse fly. *Trypanosoma*

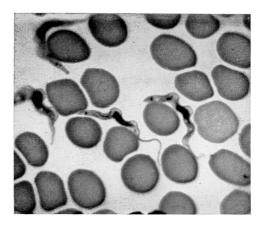

Figure 63. Trypanosomes in stained blood film. (Copyright of General Biological Supply House, Inc., Chicago.)

cruzi causes Chagas' disease in Central and South America, being transmitted by the bite of the blood-sucking reduviid bug.

Closely akin to the trypanosomes, but smaller in size, are the leishmanias, responsible for a number of tropical diseases. These protozoa are spheroid or ovoid and range from 2 to 5 microns in diameter. They attack the cells that form the lining of human blood vessels. An infection caused by these organisms is referred to by the general term "leishmaniasis." *Leishmania donovani* causes a malaria-like disease of man known as *kala-azar*. This disease is epidemic in China, India, southern Russia and the Mediterranean region. *Leishmania tropica* is the cause of a skin disease called "oriental sore."

The flagellates belonging to the genus *Trichomonas* are typically pear-shaped, 10 to 20 microns long, and having four to six flagella springing from the anterior end. One of these extends backward on one side along the edge of an undulating membrane. A stiff supporting rod runs through the cell and projects from the posterior end. *Trichomonas hominis*, apparently a relatively harmless organism, is sometimes found in the intestines of man. *Trichomonas vaginalis* is frequently found in the human vagina, often causing vaginitis.

The genus *Giardia* contains one important pathogenic species, *Giardia lamblia* (Figure 64). It has a bilaterally symmetrical, pear-shaped body provided with a sucker-like depression at the blunt end which gives it the appearance of a spoon when viewed from the side. It has two nuclei and four pairs of flagella. This organism is found in the small intestines of man and animals, where it may give rise to a severe diarrhea. It forms characteristic oval cysts containing four nuclei and a longitudinal dividing

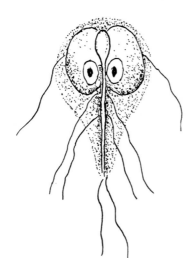

Figure 64.   Giardia lamblia.

line. Giardia infection appears to be common in children in the United States and occurs also in adults.

THE SPOROZOA

The members of this class are without definite organelles of locomotion when mature and undergo sporulation at some stage in their life cycle. The cell body is rounded or elongate and is relatively small; in the early stages it may be ameboid. The organisms of this class are exclusively parasitic. No mouth is present, food being absorbed from the tissue fluids of the host. They do not have contractile vacuoles. Some have a highly complex life cycle in which an asexual generation alternates with a sexual one.

The life cycle involves a period of repeated multiple fission known as *schizogony,* followed by a period of multiple sexual reproduction, occurring within a cyst, which culminates in the formation of sporelike bodies (*sporozoites*). This phase of the life cycle is known as *sporogony*. In some species both phases of the cycle take place in the same host, but in others two different host species, one a vertebrate and the other an invertebrate,

are required for each phase of the cycle. In the Sporozoa causing malaria
the sexual portion of the cycle (sporogony) occurs in anopheline mosquitoes, while the asexual phase (schizogony) takes place in the red blood
corpuscles of man. Examples of disease caused by Sporozoa are *coccidio-
sis* in fowls and rabbits, *pebrine* disease of silkworms and *malaria* in man
and other vertebrates.

The protozoa causing malaria belong to the genus *Plasmodium.* There
are now four recognized species of this genus, each one causing a distinct
type of malarial fever. *Plasmodium vivax* causes tertian malaria, in which
there are recurrent attacks of chills and fever every third day. It is the
common form of malaria in the United States. *Plasmodium malariae*
causes quartan malaria, characterized by recurrence of chills and fever
every fourth day. *Plasmodium falciparum* causes malignant or subtertian
malaria, in which the attack of chills and fever recurs at daily intervals or
is more or less constant. Falciparum malaria is the most deadly type of the
disease. *Plasmodium ovale* is a recently discovered type of malarial organism now recognized as the cause of a distinct, mild tertian type of
malaria.

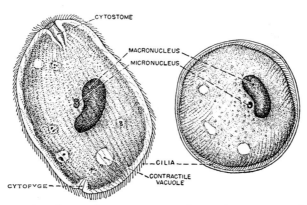

Figure 65. Balantidium coli, active stage and cyst. (From Practical Bacteriology,
Hematology and Parasitology by E. Stitt, P. Clough and S. Branham. Courtesy of the
Blakiston Co.)

THE CILIATA

The class Ciliata is characterized by the presence of cilia for locomotion
and food getting. Most members of this group are free-living, inhabiting
aquatic situations. Each species has a relatively firm pellicle and is of
constant and characteristic form.

The ciliates have attained a high degree of structural complexity within
their single cells, having various organelles for the performance of vital
processes. They include the most highly organized protozoa. As mentioned previously, most members of this group have two kinds of nuclei,
a relatively large one, the macronucleus, and one or more smaller micro-

nuclei. One or more contractile vacuoles are usually present, as well as a highly developed feeding mechanism consisting of an oral groove, mouth and gullet, as previously described.

Paramecium caudatum is the most familiar representative of the ciliates. It is commonly present in fresh-water pools and lakes. It has an elongated body resembling in outline the sole of a slipper and therefore is often referred to as the "slipper animalcule." The forward end is rounded and blunt, while the opposite end is more tapering and pointed. The entire body is covered with cilia. It has two contractile vacuoles, one near each end, which have radiating canals leading into them.

A single genus *Balantidium* contains a species which is an intestinal parasite. *Balantidium coli* (Figure 65) is normally present in the intestinal tract of hogs, from which it is discharged in the encysted form with the feces. Occasionally it infects the large intestine of man, causing a dysentery-like disease.

QUESTIONS

1. What position do the protozoa occupy in the animal kingdom? What different types of locomotion are encountered in this group?

2. (*a*) Give the general characteristics of the protozoa. What different types of reproduction are found among the protozoa?

(*b*) Explain the process of encystment. What is a cyst?

3. Define: (1) pellicle, (2) food vacuole, (3) contractile vacuole, (4) pseudopodium, (5) cilia.

4. (*a*) Describe the class Sarcodina. Give examples.

(*b*) Describe the method of ingestion and digestion in the genus *Amoeba*.

5. What are the distinguishing characteristics of the class Flagellata?

6. Give the characteristics of the class Sporozoa.

7. What are the distinguishing features of the class Ciliata?

8. Indicate the class of protozoa to which each of the following genera belongs:

Trypanosoma	Amoeba	Euglena
Paramecium	Giardia	Leishmania
Plasmodium	Balantidium	Trichomonas

REFERENCES

Chandler, A. C.: Introduction to Parasitology. 9th ed. New York, John Wiley & Sons, Inc., 1955.

Hegner, R. W., and Stiles, K. A.: College Zoology. 6th ed. New York, The Macmillan Company, 1951.

Hunter, G. W., and Hunter, F. R.: College Zoology. Philadelphia, W. B. Saunders Company, 1949.

Kudo, R. R.: Protozoology. 4th ed. Springfield, Ill., Charles C Thomas, 1954.

Villee, C. A., Walker, W. F., and Smith, F. E.: General Zoology. Philadelphia, W. B. Saunders Company, 1958.

9 • The Rickettsiae and Viruses

RICKETTSIAE

The *Rickettsiae* comprise a group of small bacteria-like forms which were first observed by Howard Ricketts, an American bacteriologist. In 1909 he isolated and described the organism causing Rocky Mountain spotted fever. A year later he discovered the causative organism of typhus fever in Mexico and, in the course of his investigation, contracted the disease and died. These and related organisms have been named "rickettsiae," in deference to their discoverer.

Morphologically, the rickettsiae are small rodlike, coccoid or spherical forms, occurring singly, in pairs and sometimes in the form of chains. Many have the form of very short, round-ended rods about 0.3 micron (300 millimicrons) in width and usually less than 0.5 micron (500 millimicrons) in length. They are on the borderline of visibility with the ordinary optical microscope. Electron micrographs show that they have definite cell walls surrounding the internal protoplasm. They are nonmotile, do not produce spores, and have a low affinity for the usual basic dyes, but stain well with Giemsa's stain.

The ability of the rickettsiae to withstand heat, sunlight, dehydration or chemical antiseptics does not differ greatly from that of the bacteria.

The rickettsiae are adapted to a parasitic mode of life and, with one or two exceptions, are not cultivable in the absence of living host cells. They can be grown in the cells of tissue cultures or of animals (mice, rabbits, guinea pigs) and in the cells of developing chick embryos. Some species grow in the cytoplasm, whereas others grow in the nuclei of the infected host cells. One rickettsial species has been cultivated in a medium free of other cells.

Most of the rickettsiae live customarily in the cells of various arthropods (ticks, fleas, lice, mites, bedbugs). They usually live in the cells lining the

133

alimentary tract of these creatures, in many instances as harmless parasites. Many rickettsial diseases are transmitted to man or other vertebrates
by the bite of arthropods. Some species of rickettsiae are transmitted by
ticks to wild rodents (chipmunks, ground squirrels, groundhogs, and the
like) which serve as alternate hosts without being appreciably harmed by
the association. In the human host certain rickettsial organisms are capable of producing severe infection. It appears that the rickettsiae were
originally parasitic only in arthropods and secondarily have become pathogenic for a few vertebrates, including man.

Because they have definite characteristics of their own, such as minute
size, staining reactions, intracellular parasitism and a similarity in the
features of many of the diseases they cause, rickettsiae are recognized as
a special group of microorganisms. In Bergey's *Manual of Determinative
Bacteriology* the rickettsiae are assigned to the order *Rickettsiales.*

RICKETTSIAL DISEASES

The two most important rickettsial diseases affecting man are Rocky
Mountain spotted fever and typhus fever. Rickettsiae are also responsible
for Q fever, tsutsugamushi disease (scrub typhus) and rickettsial pox. A
discussion of a few rickettsial diseases is contained in Chapter 33. Figure
66 shows the rickettsiae responsible for epidemic and endemic typhus
fever.

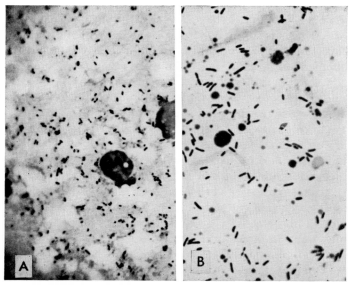

Figure 66. Photomicrographs of rickettsiae. *A, Rickettsia prowazekii,* the etiologic
agent of epidemic typhus fever. *B, Rickettsia typhi,* the causative agent of endemic
(murine) typhus fever. (Courtesy of National Microbiological Institute, Rocky Mountain Laboratory, Hamilton, Montana. Photographs by N. J. Kramis.)

VIRUSES

Viruses are the smallest causative agents of infectious diseases. With a few exceptions, they are below the limits of visibility of the ordinary optical microscope. Their diameters usually measure less than the shortest wavelength of visible light rays. Owing to their small dimensions, they pass through bacteriological filters (see Chapter 15) which hold back even the smallest bacteria. Because of this they are at times referred to as "filterable viruses" or "filter passers." One of the prominent characteris-

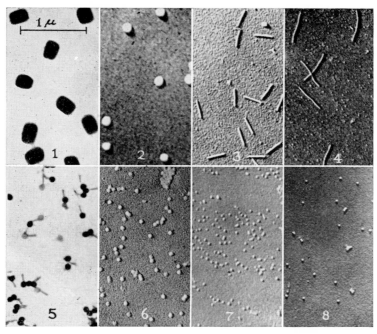

Figure 67. Electron micrographs of eight kinds of viruses enlarged to the same extent. *1,* Vaccinia; *2,* influenza; *3,* tobacco mosaic; *4,* potato-x; *5,* T$_2$bacteriophage; *6,* Shope papilloma; *7,* southern bean mosaic; *8,* tomato bushy stunt. (Revised in 1952 by W. M. Stanley from Stanley, W. M., 1947, Chemical Studies on Viruses, Chemical and Engineering News, 25, 3786–3791.)

tics, shared with rickettsiae, is their inability to live independently of living cells. Viruses are obligate intracellular parasites which can propagate only in the presence of the complex environment of living cells. Some viruses parasitize animal cells, some parasitize plant cells, others attack bacteria. In Bergey's *Manual of Determinative Bacteriology* the viruses are assigned to the order *Virales,* which is subdivided into the three host groups, bacteria, plants and animals. Since this is a tentative grouping it may require revision in the future. Figure 67 shows eight kinds of viruses enlarged to the same extent.

Size and Shape

Viruses vary in size and shape. Some are rodlike in form; others are globular, ovoid or rectangular particles. Some of the globular forms have tail-like processes and are often referred to as being "tad-pole shaped." This shape is characteristic of certain bacterial viruses. With the electron microscope the three-dimensional shape of individual virus particles can

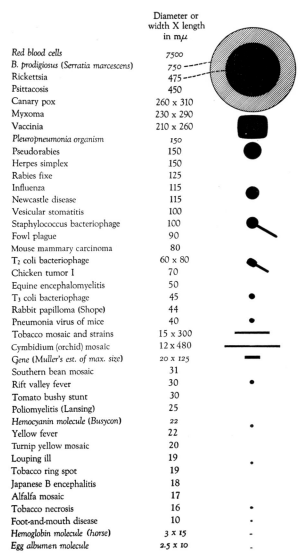

	Diameter or width X length in mμ
Red blood cells	7500
B. prodigiosus (Serratia marcescens)	750
Rickettsia	475
Psittacosis	450
Canary pox	260 x 310
Myxoma	230 x 290
Vaccinia	210 x 260
Pleuropneumonia organism	150
Pseudorabies	150
Herpes simplex	150
Rabies fixe	125
Influenza	115
Newcastle disease	115
Vesicular stomatitis	100
Staphylococcus bacteriophage	100
Fowl plague	90
Mouse mammary carcinoma	80
T₂ coli bacteriophage	60 x 80
Chicken tumor I	70
Equine encephalomyelitis	50
T₃ coli bacteriophage	45
Rabbit papilloma (Shope)	44
Pneumonia virus of mice	40
Tobacco mosaic and strains	15 x 300
Cymbidium (orchid) mosaic	12 x 480
Gene (Muller's est. of max. size)	20 x 125
Southern bean mosaic	31
Rift valley fever	30
Tomato bushy stunt	30
Poliomyelitis (Lansing)	25
Hemocyanin molecule (Busycon)	22
Yellow fever	22
Turnip yellow mosaic	20
Louping ill	19
Tobacco ring spot	19
Japanese B encephalitis	18
Alfalfa mosaic	17
Tobacco necrosis	16
Foot-and-mouth disease	10
Hemoglobin molecule (horse)	3 x 15
Egg albumen molecule	2.5 x 10

Figure 68. Approximate sizes of viruses and reference material. (Revised in 1952 by W. M. Stanley, from Stanley, W. M., 1947, Chemical Studies on Viruses, Chemical and Engineering News, 25, 3786–3791.)

be demonstrated. Although small, viruses are measurable both by direct and indirect methods. These methods include filtration, centrifugation and direct measurement with the electron microscope (see Chapter 14). The results obtained by these widely divergent methods are in close agreement. The filtration method involves the use of specially prepared membranes of collodion or gelatin of graded pore size. By using a series of such membranes, it is possible to determine the smallest pore which will allow the passage of virus. In the centrifugation method high-speed centrifuges, usually referred to as ultracentrifuges, are used. The rate at which particles suspended in a liquid settle to the bottom is determined chiefly by their size. By measuring the rate at which virus particles are thrown out of suspension at a given centrifugal force, the particle size of a virus can be determined. Some of the ultracentrifuges now used for this purpose increase the force of gravity some 50,000-fold.

In recent years a considerable amount of information concerning the size of viruses has been obtained by the use of the electron microscope. The size of some of the larger viruses can be determined with the optical microscope. The size is usually expressed in millimicrons ($m\mu$). Viruses range in diameter, in a more or less unbroken series, from 10 to about 300 millimicrons. This represents an enormous range in size. Those having a diameter of only 10 millimicrons are smaller than the largest protein molecules, whereas the larger viruses approach the size of rickettsiae. Among the smaller ones are those that cause foot-and-mouth disease of cattle, yellow fever and poliomyelitis. The approximate sizes of various viruses and other particulate matter are illustrated in Figure 68.

Discovery of Viruses

The first clues to the existence of viruses resulted from the work of Iwanowski, a Russian botanist, in 1892, when he attempted to find the cause of the mosaic disease of the tobacco plant. In this disease the leaves become mottled in a light and dark green pattern, resembling a piece of mosaic work. Iwanowski failed to find any organisms visible under the microscope as the responsible agent but discovered that juice from infected plants remained infective after passage through a bacteriological filter. Such a filter blocks the passage of bacteria but permits the passage of agents that have the dimensions of viruses. Bacteriologic filters are described in Chapter 15. In 1898 two German investigators, Loeffler and Frosch, demonstrated that the cause of foot-and-mouth disease of cattle was a filter-passing agent. This was the first animal virus to be discovered. Since then many diseases of both plants and animals have been shown to be of virus origin.

General Nature of Viruses

The first clues concerning the nature of viruses came in 1935 from the work of an American chemist, Wendell Stanley, when he succeeded in isolating the tobacco mosaic virus. He purified the virus by ultracentrif-ugation and obtained it in the form of needle-shaped crystals. When the crystals were inoculated into healthy tobacco plants, they produced to-bacco mosaic disease. Soon other viruses that cause diseases in plants were crystallized and studied.

All known viruses contain nucleic acid and protein. Some contain addi-tional substances. The nucleic acid forms a central core around which the protein is arranged in the form of a shell, or protective coat. The nucleic acid is the genetic material of viruses. In some viruses this role is performed by deoxyribonucleic acid (DNA) and in others by ribonucleic acid (RNA). The protein coat provides the mechanism for attachment to the host cell.

Although viruses are now generally placed in the category of living rather than nonliving entities, they are primitive forms exhibiting at least some traits characteristic of living things. They possess a means of multi-plication (reduplication) but can multiply only in living cells. In the process of multiplication viruses occasionally undergo mutation.

Although much remains unknown, many significant facts have been uncovered about certain viruses, especially bacterial viruses (bacteri-ophages), certain plant viruses and the influenza virus.

Virus Replication

A virus particle (extracellular stage) unites chemically with some com-ponent (receptor) on the surface of the host cell. It adheres to susceptible cells because it carries molecules which react appropriately with certain complex compounds present on the surface of host cells. In some cases the entire virus enters the cell, but in other cases (especially bacterial viruses) only the nucleic acid core enters the host cell. A virus cannot enter a nonsusceptible cell because it cannot be adsorbed on the surface of such a cell. It appears that the protein coat determines the specificity of the virus, i.e., whether or not it is capable of attacking a certain cell.

After the virus or its nucleic acid core has entered a susceptible cell, it merges with the substance of the cell and loses its individuality as an identifiable virus particle. Nothing resembling the mature virus can be demonstrated to be present in the invaded host cells; for this reason this stage of the virus cycle is called the *eclipse period*. It is believed that the genetic mechanism of the virus dominates the host cell, diverting its syn-thetic activities to the production of new virus particles out of its own substance. The host cell becomes a virus-producing unit. The manner in which the virus exerts this influence over the metabolism of the host cell apparently is at the genetic level although the details are obscure.

Some time after the virus particle has entered the host cell new virus particles are liberated from the cell. These particles are identical with the extracellular virus particle which infected the cell. In some cases the host cell bursts, i.e., it undergoes lysis, liberating in a group its content of virus particles. In the case of animal viruses it appears that the new virus particles escape from the host a few at a time as they are formed.

Bacterial Viruses

Those viruses that parasitize bacteria are known as *bacterial viruses* or *bacteriophages*. The word "bacteriophage," which literally means "bacteria eater," is frequently used in the abbreviated form of "phage."

Certain bacteriophages can be readily obtained by filtering suspensions of animal feces, ground-up insects or sewage. Phages have been isolated for almost every group of bacteria. Like other viruses, bacterial viruses exhibit a high degree of specificity. In many cases a given phage can

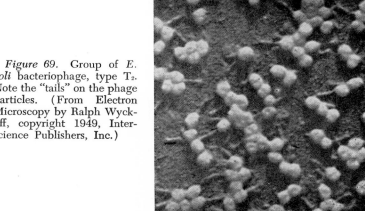

Figure 69. Group of *E. coli* bacteriophage, type T_2. Note the "tails" on the phage particles. (From Electron Microscopy by Ralph Wyckoff, copyright 1949, Interscience Publishers, Inc.)

attack only a certain strain of a species, or several strains, but not all of the strains that compose the species.

Great strides have been made recently in the study of bacteriophages. The most extensive studies have been made on a group of seven phages that attack *Escherichia coli* strain B. These phages are designated by the letter T (for "type") and by numbers (T_1 to T_7).

In the T-series of phages each particle is tadpole-shaped, having a hexagonal head-like part and a structure resembling a tail, as shown in Figure 69. Some strains have relatively long tails, others (T_3 and T_7) have tails that are very short. It has been determined that the phage head contains a central core of deoxyribonucleic acid, the remainder of the phage particle consisting of protein in the form of a protective coat. The protein coat determines the specificity of the phage, i.e., whether or not it is capable of attacking a certain bacterium.

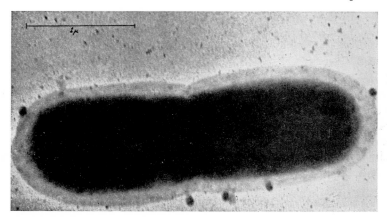

Figure 70. Electron micrograph of *E. coli* with 5 particles of coli phage adsorbed to its cell wall. (From S. Luria, M. Delbrück and T. Anderson; J. Bacteriol., Vol. 46. Reproduced by permission of The Williams & Wilkins Company.)

In the process of infection the phage particle, by means of some property of its protein coat, becomes attached at the end of its tail to the surface of its host, as illustrated in Figures 70 and 73. Apparently an

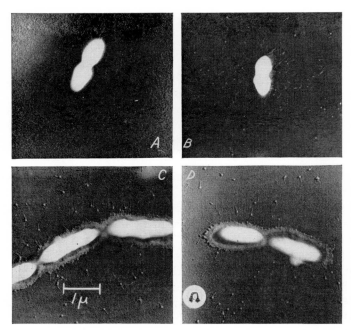

Figure 71. Bacteriophage infecting *Streptococcus cremoris.* A, a pair of normal cells; B, a pair of cells after being exposed to bacteriophage for 15 minutes; C, cells after being exposed to the bacteriophage for 45 minutes (the cells are elongated and appear to have failed to form cross walls); D, cells after being exposed to bacteriophage for 4 hours. (From C. E. Parmellee, P. H. Carr, and F. E. Nelson: J. Bacteriol., Vol. 57. Reproduced by permission of The Williams & Wilkins Company.)

enzyme clears a passage through the tail and forms a hole in the cell wall of the bacterium. The deoxyribonucleic acid in the phage head is then injected into the bacterial cell. The protein coat of the phage is left outside and plays no further role. The bacteriophage thus possesses a highly specialized mechanism for introducing its DNA through the relatively rigid cell walls of bacteria. In a very short time the injected DNA, which is now in the eclipse period, initiates the production of new phage particles by directing the synthetic processes of the host cell. Soon recogniza-

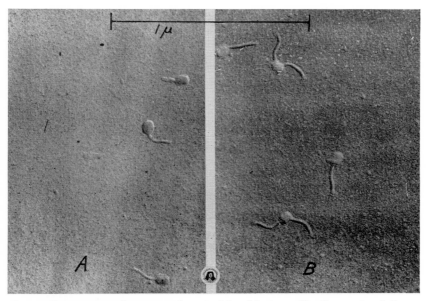

Figure 72. Bacteriophage particles capable of lysing cells of a strain of *Streptomyces griseus.* A, three typical bacteriophage particles; B, four bacteriophage particles, two of which have two tail structures. These double-tailed particles may represent morphological variants of the bacteriophage. (From H. B. Woodruff, T. D. Nunheimer and S. B. Lee: J. Bacteriol., Vol. 54. Reproduced by permission of The Williams & Wilkins Company.)

ble protein coats begin to form and a little later fully formed phage particles, faithful duplications of the parent phage, appear in the cell. Finally the host cell undergoes lysis, releasing into the surrounding medium as many as 200 fully mature phage particles.

Ordinarily a large number of virus particles are formed in a short time in the host cell after it has been invaded by one or more virus particles. In some instances, however, a bacterium which becomes infected with phage continues to grow and divide in a normal manner. The phage responsible for this kind of an infection is termed *temperate phage* in contrast to virulent phage which, in all cases, produces the lytic type of infection. It is believed that the temperate phage becomes anchored to a specific site on the genetic material of the host cell and behaves as if it were a bacterial gene, being duplicated at each bacterial division along with the bacterial genes, and thus transmitted to each daughter bacterium. In this latent form the phage is referred to as *prophage.* As the host cells grow and divide as normal bacteria, each daughter bacterium yields progeny containing prophage. The ability to produce prophage is perpetuated in the bacterial cells. In this state of "peaceful coexistence" there

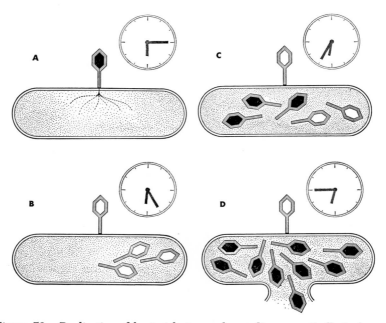

Figure 73. Replication of bacterial viruses shown diagrammatically in four stages. The time required for the process is depicted in minutes. *A,* shows a phage particle attached at the end of its tail to the surface of its host, allowing its inner substance (DNA core) to enter the bacterial cell. The empty protein coat, which plays no further role, remains attached to the cell surface. *B,* the phage DNA induces the synthesis in the host cell of phage protein from which recognizable protein coats are formed. *C,* phage DNA induces the synthesis of more DNA, which enters the protein coats to form mature virus particles. *D,* the host cell bursts and releases into the surrounding medium its content of phage particles which are replicas of the virus which attached itself to the host cell. Only a few of the large number (200 or so) of phage particles usually formed are shown. In these drawings the virus particles are shown much enlarged in relation to the bacterial cell. (From G. S. Stent: Scientific American, May, 1953. Reproduced by permission of Scientific American.)

are no signs of abnormality or disease in the bacterial cells. The genetics of viruses is considered in Chapter 13.

Bacteria containing prophage are called *lysogenic.* From time to time in a population of lysogenic bacteria, the prophage in some of the cells is transformed spontaneously into active virulent phage. The cells in which this occurs undergo lysis and liberate mature phage particles into the surrounding medium. The transformation of prophage into virulent phage may also be induced experimentally by means of certain agents, such as ultraviolet rays, sonic vibration and nitrogen mustard.

Plant Viruses

The virus that causes tobacco mosaic disease has been investigated more extensively than most of the other plant viruses. This virus is a rod-shaped particle which measures 15 millimicrons in width and about 300 millimicrons in length. It consists of a thin, rodlike core of ribonucleic acid enclosed in a cylinder consisting of a spirally arranged wrapping of protein. The protein makes up most of the substance of the virus.

Plant viruses are usually transmitted by insects and are introduced into host cells by the mouth parts of sucking insects. Once the virus has invaded a host cell, it in some way loses its protein coat and multiplies at the expense of the host cell. Experimentally, it is possible to initiate infection with the ribonucleic acid core of the virus after the protein coat has been removed.

Recovery on the part of plants from some virus infections results in the development of immunity to these diseases, although the viruses remain in the plant tissues.

Animal Viruses

The influenza virus has been investigated more thoroughly than any of the other animal viruses. It is composed of ribonucleic acid, protein and lipid. It is spherical in shape and about 28 millimicrons in diameter, but at times long filaments are seen in association with the spherical particles.

Apparently the entire virus enters the host cell, not only its nucleic acid. It seems that entrance is accomplished by an active process of ingestion on the part of the host cell. As is the case with other viruses, the influenza virus upon entering a host cell loses its identity as a particle. Its genetic mechanism influences the host cell, directing it to produce virus particles. Some hours later new virus particles are liberated from the host cell. The spherical particles of the influenza virus are known to be infective, but the filaments are infective only when they have a sphere attached to one end. The power to produce filaments can be lost by mutation. Some kinds of animal viruses contain RNA, others contain DNA.

As in the case of bacteriophages, animal viruses may enter a latent or *provirus* state. There are reasons for believing that some viral diseases of man are the result of the activation of provirus, converting it into virulent virus. Some tumors are caused by viruses. Some investigators are of the opinion that cancer can be caused by viruses.

Cultivation of Viruses

Since viruses develop only in cells that are alive, they cannot be propagated in the ordinary bacteriological media. They can be cultivated, however, in susceptible plant or animal tissues, either in the living plants or animals themselves or in *in vitro** cultures of living susceptible tissues. Bacteriophage is cultivated in bacterial cultures.

Tissue cultures involve the use of balanced salt solutions to which are added other nutrients required by the tissue cells. Tissue cultures of monkey kidney cells are used for the isolation and growth of the polio-myelitis virus and for the preparation of vaccine for immunization against poliomyelitis. Certain animal viruses will multiply in the cells of develop-ing chick embryos. The chick embryo contains a delicate membrane, the *chorio-allantoic membrane,* which lies immediately beneath the inner

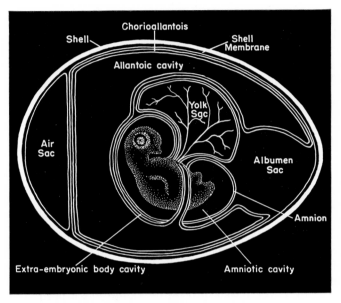

Figure 74. Schematic drawing of the embryonated hen's egg. (From D. T. Smith and N. F. Conant, Zinsser Bacteriology, 11th ed., 1957. Courtesy of Appleton-Century-Crofts, Inc.)

shell membrane (Figure 74). A large variety of viruses inoculated onto this membrane will grow there in abundance. Other parts of the chick embryo (allantoic cavity, yolk sac and the amniotic cavity) are also suitable for the cultivation of certain viruses.

Some viruses will grow well in a certain strain of cancer cells called "HeLa." The name was coined from the first letters of the name of a woman who died of cervical carcinoma and from whom the original cells were obtained.

Bacteriophages are easily propagated in bacteria growing either on

* The term *in vitro* is derived from the Latin word for glass. It is used to describe biological processes or reactions carried on in culture tubes or flasks, i.e., in glass. Processes or reactions carried on in living organisms may be indicated by the term *in vivo.*

solid or in liquid media. By successive transfers phage may be propagated indefinitely in growing cultures of susceptible bacteria. In a turbid broth culture, after several hours of incubation, the phage causes a partial or complete clearing of the medium. If a drop of the cleared culture is examined under the microscope, usually only fragments of disintegrated bacteria can be seen. The phage does not necessarily destroy all the bacteria in the culture because some may have mutated and, thus, become resistant. Phage thus may serve as a selective factor in bacterial varia-

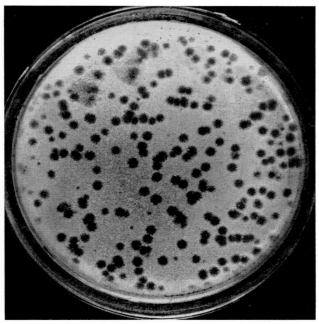

Figure 75. Photograph showing plaques produced by bacteriophage in a Petri dish culture of a bacterium (*Rhizobium* sp.) The light areas represent the bacterial growth, the dark areas the plaques resulting from the destruction and dissolution of the bacteria by the bacteriophage. (From J. Kleczkowska: J. Bacteriol., Vol. 50. Reproduced by permission of The Williams & Wilkins Company.)

tion. On a solid medium the lysis is usually restricted to isolated spots, causing the bacterial growth to become pitted with clear areas which are referred to as *plaques.* Such cultures have been described as having a "moth-eaten" appearance. Figure 75 shows plaques produced by bacteriophages.

Resistance of Viruses to Physical and Chemical Agents

Viruses, like bacteria, can be destroyed by various physical and chemical agents, such as heat, desiccation, ultraviolet rays and chemical disinfectants. Temperatures between 55° and 60° C. will destroy them in thirty minutes or less. Low temperatures are usually not injurious to them. Some viruses have considerable resistance to the drying action of the air, enabling them to survive outside the body of the host for a long time. Many can be dried and frozen and stored in this form for long periods of time. Exposure to ultraviolet rays inactivates viruses in a short time. They vary in their resistance to chemical disinfectants but most do not show a high degree of tolerance for these agents. Viruses are inactivated rapidly by a weak solution of formaldehyde. In the preparation of certain vaccines formaldehyde solution is used to inactivate the virus.

VIRAL DISEASES

Many diseases of plants and animals are caused by viruses. Being destructive to cultivated crops and domesticated animals, viruses cause huge economic losses annually. Potato, corn, bean, beet, tomato and tobacco plants are often severely afflicted by virus diseases. Chapter 34 contains a brief discussion of some plant diseases caused by viruses.

Practically all species of domestic animals are subject to virus infection. Examples of such infections are cowpox, horsepox, cattle plague, dog distemper, sheeppox, hog cholera and foot-and-mouth disease of cattle. Man himself is subject to some forty different types of virus diseases. Among these are smallpox, rabies, influenza, poliomyelitis, yellow fever, the common cold, warts, fever blisters, dengue fever, epidemic encephalitis, mumps, chickenpox and measles. Chapter 33 contains a discussion of a few viral diseases that affect man.

QUESTIONS

1. Give the characteristics of the rickettsiae that differentiate them from other groups of microorganisms.
2. What is their customary habitat? How can they be propagated in the laboratory?
3. How are rickettsial diseases usually transmitted to man?
4. Name some human diseases caused by rickettsiae.
5. (a) How do viruses vary in form and size? What methods may be used to determine the size of virus particles?
   (b) What characteristics do viruses share with rickettsiae?
6. Name the two kinds of chemical compounds all viruses contain.
7. Explain how a virus particle or its nucleic acid core invades a susceptible host cell.
8. Explain the eclipse period?
9. (a) What are bacteriophages?
   (b) In what manner does a bacteriophage become attached to the host cell?
   (c) Which part of the phage enters the host cell?
10. What is meant by: (1) temperate phage, (2) prophage?
11. What are lysogenic bacteria?
12. Describe the tobacco mosaic virus.
13. How does the influenza virus differ from the tobacco mosaic virus?
14. How are viruses cultivated? What is a tissue culture?

REFERENCES

Burnet, F. M.: Principles of Animal Virology. New York, Academic Press, Inc., 1955.
Dalldorf, G.: Introduction to Virology. Springfield, Ill., Charles C Thomas, 1955.

Fildes, Sir P., and Van Heyningen, W. E.: Nature of Virus Multiplication. Cambridge, Cambridge University Press, 1952.

Luria, S. E.: General Virology. New York, John Wiley & Sons, Inc., 1953.

Parker, R. C.: Methods of Tissue Culture. 2nd ed. New York, Paul B. Hoeber, Inc., 1950.

Rhodes, A. J., and van Rooyen, C. E.: Textbook of Virology. 3rd ed. Baltimore, The Williams & Wilkins Company, 1958.

Rivers, T. M.: Viral and Rickettsial Infections of Man. 3rd ed. Philadelphia, J. B. Lippincott Company, 1959.

III • The Physiology of
Microorganisms

10 • The Nature and Significance of Enzymes

The life activities of all organisms—microscopic as well as macroscopic —depend upon chemical reactions. The field of study related to these reactions is labelled *enzymology,* a branch of biochemistry. Such reactions are activated chiefly through the agency of organic catalysts known as *enzymes.* A catalyst is a reagent that alters the rate of a chemical reaction without itself becoming a constituent of the products formed by the reaction, and without being appreciably affected. It does not initiate a reaction, but merely alters the rate (accelerating or decelerating) of one already in progress. Chemists make use of many kinds of inorganic catalysts, chiefly to accelerate various chemical reactions. Enzymes, in contrast to inorganic catalysts, are produced by living matter and are organic in composition. Also, they are more specific in their action than the inorganic catalysts. The compound on which an enzyme exercises its catalytic property is known as the *substrate;* the reaction being catalyzed results in conversion of substrate to one or more *end products.*

FUNCTION OF ENZYMES IN THE CELL

Every cell contains a large assortment of enzymes which enable it to carry on simultaneously many different kinds of chemical reactions at the proper rate to maintain life. These reactions constitute what is known as the metabolism of the cell. Virtually all the chemical reactions going on in cells are activated by enzymes. Usually, the coordinated action of a group of enzymes is required to catalyze a series of interrelated steps. The action of enzymes in metabolic activities is only partially understood. It is because a microorganism is endowed with enzymes that it is able to digest its food, synthesize its protoplasmic constituents and derive energy from materials it takes into its cell.

Some of the chemical transformations catalyzed by enzymes involve the

151

breakdown of complex compounds into simpler ones; others are constructive in that the enzyme catalyzes the synthesis of complex molecules by bringing about the chemical union of simpler ones. Some enzymes cause the reaction they catalyze to be carried to completion; others produce a reaction which goes to a point of equilibrium where both substrate and end products are present in measurable amounts. In the integrated system of protoplasm, however, rates of individual enzymic transformations within a sequence are regulated automatically by the relative abundance of substrate and the demand by the next reaction for the product.

Enzymes exert their effect in low concentration; a very small quantity of an enzyme will alter a relatively large quantity of substrate in a short time. The enzyme sucrase (invertase), for example, can catalyze the breakdown of more than a million times its weight of sucrose. Theoretically, none of the potency of an enzyme is lost in its activities, since it is not consumed in the reactions it catalyzes.

COMPOSITION OF ENZYMES

All the enzymes isolated to date have proved to be protein, of either the simple or conjugated type. The first enzyme to be isolated in pure form was *urease*. This was accomplished in 1926 by James Sumner, an American biochemist. He obtained it in crystalline form and proved it to be a protein of high molecular weight. The work of other investigators soon led to the isolation of many common enzymes in the form of crystalline protein preparations.

Enzymes and Coenzymes

Many enzymes are conjugated proteins, i.e., they contain a low molecular weight, nonprotein compound in chemical union with the protein component. The nonprotein compound is essential for enzymic function and is usually loosely attached, in which case it is termed a *coenzyme.* The simple protein moiety to which the coenzyme is joined is called the *apoenzyme,* while the complete enzyme (coenzyme and apoenzyme united) is sometimes called the *holoenzyme.* Neither the apoenzyme nor the coenzyme by itself is active. The coenzyme, however, is readily dissociable, being able to function with either of two or more different apoenzymes. Thus, the coenzyme may be changed chemically in one reaction and separate from the first apoenzyme to combine with another apoenzyme. The reaction mediated by the second holoenzyme is complementary to the first in that the coenzyme is regenerated. This duality of coenzyme function, of tremendous importance in metabolism, is an elegant example of the dynamic nature of life at the biochemical level.

The coenzymes consist of vitamins, usually phosphorylated derivatives, of the B complex, e.g., thiamine, riboflavin, niacin, pyridoxine, pantothenic acid, biotin and others. They participate in processes concerned with respiration and synthesis.

Metal Ions and Enzyme Function

Many enzymes require minute amounts of certain metal ions, sometimes called activators. The more common ones are iron, magnesium, manganese, potassium and copper. In some cases the ion is tightly bound in the molecular structure of the enzyme; other times it is easily separable by dialysis. The metal may participate directly in the catalysis, or it may serve to unite coenzyme and apoenzyme.

THEORY OF ENZYME ACTION

A vast array of enzymes, each exerting a highly specific coordinated function, is found in protoplasm. Enzymic function is related to molecular structure which, in turn, determines the physicochemical attraction between an enzyme and its substrate. The process can be visualized symbolically (E = enzyme, S = substrate, P = product):

$$E + S \rightleftharpoons E \cdot S \rightleftharpoons E + P$$

Note that two reversible reactions take place: (1) combination of enzyme with substrate, and (2) decomposition of the enzyme-substrate complex to yield enzyme, in unaltered form, and one or more products. The rate at which these reactions take place depends upon (1) the relative amounts of enzyme and substrate, (2) the affinity between enzyme and substrate (physicochemical attraction), (3) the stability of the enzyme-substrate complex, and (4) other factors that can be regulated, such as pH and temperature. Unless more substrate is added or end products are removed, the reaction reaches an equilibrium, usually much in favor of the reaction proceeding from left to right. The course of an enzymic reaction can be depicted pictorially, as in Figure 76. Note in this illustration the combination of coenzyme with the apoenzyme and substrate with the subsequent separation of these components to yield products and free enzyme.

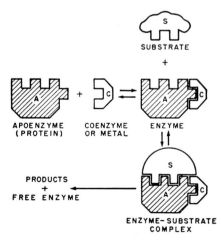

Figure 76. Scheme illustrating the mode by which many enzymes carry out their catalysis. For some enzymes the step involving the combination with coenzyme or an activating metal is not required. (From I. W. Sizer: Science, Vol. 125.)

NOMENCLATURE OF ENZYMES

A convenient system of naming enzymes has been devised. By substituting the suffix "ase" for the last part of the name (or adding it to the
name) of the specific substrate the enzyme acts upon, the name of the
enzyme is obtained. For example, the enzyme that splits maltose is named
"maltase." In some cases the suffix is simply added to the name of the
substrate without dropping any part of the name. This is true of "gelatin-
ase," which acts upon gelatin. A protein-splitting enzyme may be called a
"protease" or a "proteinase." An enzyme that brings about the cleavage of
fats is a "lipase;" one that acts on carbohydrates is a "carbohydrase." This
system of naming does not apply to certain enzymes such as pepsin,
ptyalin and trypsin, which were named before this system was adopted.
These enzymes are involved chiefly in the digestive processes of higher
animals.

Another system of naming enzymes involves the use of an adjective
formed by substituting the suffix "lytic" for the last part of the name of
the substrate. Thus, those that decompose proteins may be called
proteolytic enzymes; those that act on starch (amylum), *amylolytic
enzymes;* and those that break down fats, *lipolytic enzymes.*

Enzymes may be designated also on the basis of the type of chemical
action catalyzed. This terminology is derived by combining the ending
"ase" with the term that indicates the chemical reaction catalyzed by the
enzymes. Thus, enzymes that act by oxidation are *oxidases;* those that
remove hydrogen from the substrate are *dehydrogenases;* those that split
the substrate upon the addition of water are called *hydrolases.* This system is commonly used in conjunction with the name of the substrate.
Thus, the enzyme that removes hydrogen from lactic acid is called *lactic
dehydrogenase.* Another good example of descriptive nomenclature is
cytochrome oxidase, an enzyme which catalyzes the oxidation of cytochromes, a group of respiratory pigments.

CLASSIFICATION OF ENZYMES

Several criteria are used in the classification of enzymes, the major ones
being: (1) the nature of the chemical reaction which is catalyzed, (2)
the site of action of the enzyme (within the cell or outside the cell), and
(3) the dispensability or indispensability of substrate for appearance of
enzyme.

Classification According to Specific Function

Very broadly speaking, enzymes carry out the following types of reactions: (1) splitting, (2) oxidation and reduction, (3) adding (synthesis),
(4) transferring or removing functional chemical groups, and (5) aiding
passage of nutrients across the semi-permeable cell membrane.

The *splitting enzymes* are those which induce a cleavage of a compound upon the addition of water (*hydrolases*) or phosphoric acid

(*phosphorylases*). The hydrolases split such complex substances as proteins, lipids, polysaccharides and peptides into simpler compounds. The phosphorylases assist in the synthesis, as well as the degradation, of polysaccharides. Examples of hydrolytic enzymes are cited in Table 1.

Table 1. Abbreviated Classification of Some Important Hydrolases

Enzyme	Substrate	End Products
I. Esterases:		
Lipase	Fats (Glycerides)	Glycerol + fatty acids
Lecithinase	Lecithin	Lysolecithin + fatty acid
Nucleotidase	Nucleotides	Nucleoside + phosphoric acid
II. Carbohydrases:		
Sucrase (Invertase)	Sucrose	Fructose + glucose
Maltase	Maltose	Glucose + glucose
Lactase	Lactose	Galactose + glucose
Cellulase	Cellulose	Cellobiose
α-Amylase	Starch	Dextrin + maltose
β-Amylase	Starch	Maltose
Pectinase	Pectic acid	Galactose + galacturonic acid
III. Hydrolases specific for nitrogenous compounds:		
Proteinases	Various proteins	Peptones or polypeptides + amino acids
Polypeptidases	Various polypeptides	Amino acids
Deamidases:		
Urease	Urea	Ammonia + carbon dioxide
Arginase	Arginine	Urea + ornithine
Deaminases	Various amino acids	Ammonia + α-keto acid
Ribonuclease	Polyribonucleic acid	Nucleotides

The enzymes concerned with oxidation-reduction reactions and the transfer, removal or addition of chemical groups enable the cell, directly or indirectly, to derive energy from its nutrients or cellular constituents. Therefore, they are important in *intermediary metabolism*, particularly respiration. The many interrelated chemical reactions initiated by these enzymes are not easy to categorize. Nevertheless, a glance at Table 2 will give you a general picture of the scope of the activities of such enzymes. Table 2 is far from complete and does not necessarily reflect the existence of an officially recognized system of classification and nomenclature.

Outside of the phosphorylases and lipases, so little is known about enzymes which initiate the synthesis of the more complex cellular components that nothing can be said about their classification. Likewise, scarcely anything is known about the recently discovered *permeases*, enzyme-like substances which aid the passage of certain nutrients across cell membranes.

Classification According to Site of Action

Some enzymes are confined to the cell, hence are called *intracellular enzymes* or *endoenzymes*. Some enzymes, however, accumulate outside

Table 2. Abbreviated Classification of Some Important Enzymes
Largely Concerned with Intermediary Metabolism

Enzyme	*Substrate*	*End Products*
I. Catalase	Hydrogen peroxide (H_2O_2)	$H_2O + O_2$
II. Peroxidase	H_2O_2 + a reduced compound	H_2O + oxidized compound
III. True Oxidases (use molecular oxygen):		
Cytochrome oxidase	Reduced cytochrome c	Oxidized cytochrome c
Tyrosinase	Tyrosine	Melanin pigments
IV. Dehydrogenases		
A. Transfer hydrogen directly to oxygen:		
Amine oxidases	Various amines	Ammonia + aldehyde + H_2O_2
B. Transfer hydrogen to cytochrome		
Succinic dehydrogenase	Succinic acid	Fumaric acid
C. Transfer hydrogen to coenzyme I or II (DPN or TPN):		
Glucose dehydrogenase	Glucose	Gluconic acid
Lactic dehydrogenase	Lactic acid	Pyruvic acid
D. Transfer hydrogen to riboflavin coenzyme:		
Amino acid oxidase	Amino acids	α-Keto acids
Diaphorase	Reduced coenzyme I ($DPN \cdot H_2$)	Oxidized coenzyme I (DPN)
V. Desmolases (split or form carbon chains):		
Aldolase	Glucose-1,6-diphosphate	Dihydroxyacetone phosphate + phosphoglyceraldehyde
Sucrose phosphorylase	Sucrose	Glucose-1-phosphate + fructose
VI. Transferases:		
Hexokinase	Glucose + ATP	Glucose-6-phosphate + ADP
Transaminases	Glutamic acid + an α-Keto acid	α-Ketoglutaric acid + an amino acid
Transmethylases	Methyl donor + methyl acceptor	Methylated acceptor + demethylated donor
VII. Deaminases:		
Adenase	Adenine	Hypoxanthine + ammonia
Amino acid deaminases	Various amino acids	α-Keto acid + ammonia
VIII. Decarboxylases:		
Amino acid decarboxylases	Various amino acids	Amines or another amino acid + carbon dioxide
Carboxylase	Pyruvic acid	Acetaldehyde + carbon dioxide
IX. Hydrases (add water; mechanism different from hydrolysis):		
Glyoxylase	Methyl glyoxal + water	Lactic acid
Fumarase	Fumaric acid + water	Malic acid

of the cells that produce them. The latter are termed *extracellular enzymes* or *exoenzymes*.

Most of the extracellular enzymes are simple proteins and initiate hydrolytic reactions. Thus they are important in solubilizing (digesting) foods, chiefly proteins, lipids, oligosaccharides and polysaccharides. The intracellular enzymes engage largely in respiration and synthesis. They are of the conjugated protein type molecule. Some hydrolytic enzymes, however, are found in the intracellular site. One would be surprised if this were not true since, presumably, all enzymes originate within the cell, and hydrolytic reactions are very important to the dynamic state of the cell's internal structure and function.

Extracellular enzymes can be found in the cell-free liquid remaining upon removal of the cells from a spent culture. Intracellular enzymes can be released by rupturing the cells with physical agents (grinding, freezing and thawing, ultrasonic waves). Also, penicillin, an antibiotic which inhibits the synthesis of a constituent of cell walls, and lysozyme, an enzyme which degrades a mucopolysaccharide component of cell walls, can be employed to liberate protoplasts (bacteria encased only by the cell membrane, hence lacking cell walls). The protoplasts will burst when placed in a solution containing a low concentration of solutes (hypotonic solution) and liberate their cytoplasm, including the intracellular enzymes. A significant proportion of the intracellular enzymes are found in particulate fractions of the cytoplasm, a characteristic which causes difficulty in their isolation and purification. In fact, the purification of any enzyme is difficult because of the ease with which it becomes denatured, a characteristic of all proteins.

Classification According to Need of Substrate for Formation

Most enzymes are synthesized by the cell regardless of the presence or absence of specific substrates in the cell's internal or external environment. Such enzymes are called *constitutive enzymes*. Another group, the *adaptive enzymes* (termed *inducible enzymes* in recent literature), are formed only when the substrate is present. Adaptive enzymes are particularly common in microorganisms but rare in higher forms of life. Since enzymes are proteins, the study of adaptive enzymes is a useful tool in the hands of biochemists interested in the synthesis of proteins.

SPECIFICITY OF ENZYMES

Enzymes are highly specific, not only for the type of reaction they facilitate (hydrolysis, oxidation, and so forth), but also for the particular compounds they attack. An enzyme which catalyzes the hydrolysis of fats will not break down proteins, and vice versa. Enzymes vary, however, in the degree of their specificity, some being so highly specific that their catalysis is restricted to only one compound (sucrose, for example), while others are specific in the sense that their action is limited to a group of compounds which have a certain molecular configuration. Urease is an example of a highly specific enzyme in that it effects the hydrolysis of only one substance, urea; but many of the lipases, although they hydrolyze only fats, are less specific in that they can act on several kinds of fats.

REVERSIBILITY OF ENZYMIC ACTIVITY

Theoretically, all enzymatically catalyzed reactions are reversible. However, there could be no integration and control of metabolism if these reactions proceeded in one direction as readily as the other. It has been speculated that reversal of hydrolysis, for example, is one way that protoplasm synthesizes complex molecules from the simpler building blocks. This has been difficult to demonstrate experimentally with proteinases and carbohydrases. The lipases, however, convert fatty acids and glycerol into glycerides as readily as they cause glycerides to undergo hydrolysis, depending upon the relative concentrations of end products. The phosphorylases are also readily reversible in action and thus are important in the synthesis as well as the degradation of certain polysaccharides. The vast majority of enzymes exert their catalysis overwhelmingly in one direction only but are subject to dynamic factors in the cell which influence the rate with which the reaction progresses and the extent to which the reaction completes itself.

CONDITIONS AFFECTING ENZYMIC ACTIVITY

The activity of enzymes is greatly influenced by environmental conditions. Among the more important factors that affect the activity of enzymes are (1) temperature, (2) reaction (pH) of the environment, (3) nature and concentration of inorganic ions present, (4) concentration of substrate, and (5) concentration of end products accumulated.

Temperature

Each enzyme has a temperature range within which it can operate. Temperatures near or below the freezing point inactivate enzymes but do not necessarily destroy them. Most enzymes are irreversibly inactivated in liquid media when the temperature rises to 70° C. However, the enzymes of *thermophilic* (heat-loving) bacteria can withstand higher temperatures. In the dried state many enzyme preparations can withstand temperatures as high as 120° C. The enzymes of spores can endure temperatures as high as 100° to 120° C. Each enzyme has an optimum temperature at which, or a temperature range within which, its greatest activity is exhibited. For a large number of enzymes this lies between 30° and 40° C. The rate of enzyme action is approximately doubled for each 10 degree increase in temperature until the optimum is reached, above which there is a decrease in activity because of the denaturing effects of heat on the enzyme-protein. The sensitivity of enzymes to the inactivating influence of heat is often apparent when the length of time of the reaction is considered. Thus, the initial rate of reactions for a given enzyme may be greatest at, let us say, 39° C., but over a longer period of incubation the rate may be greater at a temperature a few degrees lower. This can be attributed, in part, to the slight denaturing effect of the higher temperature on the enzyme. The temperature limitations within which enzymes can operate impose temperature limitations upon organisms, since life processes are activated and sustained by enzymes.

Hydrogen-Ion Concentration

The pH, an exponential expression of the active hydrogen-ion concentration (see page 193 for a fuller treatment of pH), is also very influential on the activity of enzymes. Some enzymes exhibit maximal activity in an acid medium, others in a neutral or alkaline environment. There are upper and lower limits of hydrogen-ion concentration beyond which enzyme activity ceases. For each enzyme there is an optimum pH or pH range. For a large number of enzymes this lies between pH 4 and 7.

Inorganic Ions

Enzyme activity is affected by certain ions. Some metal ions, notably manganese, magnesium, iron and cobalt, serve as activators of certain enzymes. Ions of heavy metals, e.g., mercury, lead, silver and antimony, are injurious to enzymes because of their ability to combine with proteins, thereby destroying their biological activity. In fact, too high a concentration of almost any soluble salt results in denaturation of enzymes as a result of alteration of charges on such molecules.

Concentration of Substrate and End Products

Enzymes will not evince maximal activity unless fully saturated with substrate. Hence, the velocity of an enzymic reaction is proportional to the concentration of available substrate until the saturation point is reached. This may be seen in Figure 77. Of course, the more rapid the conversion of substrate to end products, the greater the tendency for reversal of reaction. Eventually, the concentration of accumulated products will slow down the reaction until the forward and reverse rates reach an

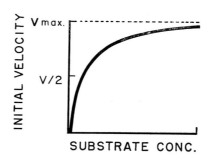

Figure 77. Influence of substrate concentration on the velocity of an enzyme reaction. Velocity calculated as amount of end products produced, or amount of substrate lost, under standard conditions by a constant amount of enzyme (or a preparation containing the enzyme) per unit of time. Vmax. = maximal velocity attainable; V/2 = one-half maximal velocity. Substrate concentration expressed on a molar basis.

equilibrium. Also, end products may alter the pH of the menstruum and the permeability of cell membranes to substrate and further interfere with the progress of the reaction. In a cellular system, however, many of the end products of a single reaction are metabolized by other enzymatically regulated functions. Since the velocity of an enzymic reaction generally decreases with time, particularly under experimental conditions, rates usually are determined during the first 10 to 30 minutes of exposure of enzyme to substrate and called "initial rates." The initial rate of a reaction catalyzed by an enzyme is an indirect measure of the amount of enzyme in the preparation, provided substrate is in excess.

ROLE OF ENZYMES IN HYDROLYSIS

As mentioned previously, the enzymes involved in the digestion of food are hydrolases. (See Table 1.) Included in this category are the *esterases,* which act on fats and other esters; the *carbohydrases,* which break down the various carbohydrates; the *proteinases,* which act on proteins; and the *peptidases,* which break down peptides. Most of the hydrolases are exoenzymes. Some are found within the cell wherein digestion is not their primary function. Energy released by the extracellular hydrolysis of food is not available for the metabolic processes of the cell, the bulk of it being released as heat, thus raising the temperature of the medium.

Hydrolysis of Proteins and Protein Derivatives

Some of the enzymes involved in the hydrolysis of proteins and protein derivatives are *proteinases, polypeptidases, deaminases* and *deamidases*. (See Table 1.) Protein decomposition is sometimes referred to by the term *proteolysis* and is also frequently designated by the less concise term *putrefaction*. The first step in the enzymatic splitting of proteins is the hydrolysis of protein molecules by proteinases to polypeptides. Polypeptides are hydrolyzed to amino acids by polypeptidases. Deaminases remove the amino group from amino acids, i.e., they break the linkage between carbon and nitrogen in these compounds. Some types of deamination are hydrolytic; others involve reactions in which hydrolysis does not occur. (See Chapter 18.) Products resulting from the hydrolytic decomposition of amino acids are fatty acids, alcohols, aldehydes, carbon dioxide and ammonia.

In the course of catabolism of amino acids by animals, much of the amino nitrogen is converted to urea or, in the case of birds, uric acid, and eliminated in the urine. Certain bacteria produce urease, an enzyme which hydrolyzes urea to carbon dioxide and ammonia.

Hydrolysis of Lipids

The hydrolysis of fats is carried on by enzymes known as *lipases*. It is not definitely known whether there is but one lipase or a number of different enzymes capable of hydrolyzing fats. Lipase catalyzes the hydrolysis of fats into *glycerol* and *fatty acids*. Butter and other fat-containing foods may become rancid through the action of bacterial lipase together with oxidation. Phospholipids undergo hydrolytic cleavage by *phosphatase, lecithinase* and other enzymes.

Lipases are not produced in significant quantity by very many microorganisms. Many molds, a few yeasts and some bacteria are lipolytic. Some of these organisms store rather large quantities of fats and oils in their cytoplasm, particularly if some glycerol is incorporated in the culture medium.

Hydrolysis of Carbohydrates

The principal polysaccharides hydrolyzed by microorganisms are cellulose, hemicellulose, starch, pectin and inulin. The most abundant polysaccharide in nature, cellulose, is hydrolyzed by the enzyme *cellulase* to a disaccharide, *cellobiose*, as follows:

$$2\,(C_6H_{10}O_5)n + nH_2O \underset{\longleftarrow}{\overset{\text{cellulase}}{\longrightarrow}} nC_{12}H_{22}O_{11}$$
$$\text{cellulose} \qquad\qquad\qquad\qquad\qquad \text{cellobiose}$$

Some molds and a few bacteria and protozoa are able to digest cellulose.

In this connection it may be noted that cattle, sheep and other ruminants harbor cellulose-digesting bacteria and protozoa in the rumen, one of their four stomachs. Although the food of these animals contains relatively large quantities of cellulose, they do not themselves produce cellulase but are dependent upon the cellulase elaborated by ruminal microorganisms for the hydrolysis of cellulose.

Starch, on hydrolysis by the enzyme *beta-amylase,* yields maltose. The equation given for the hydrolysis of cellulose may be adapted for starch, since both of these polysaccharides have the same empirical formula and both yield disaccharides. Amylase is produced by many molds and some species of bacteria, but not by yeasts. The enzyme *inulase* catalyzes the hydrolysis of inulin to fructose. Many other polysaccharides, such as hemicelluloses, pectins, various gums and mucilaginous substances, are hydrolyzed by bacteria and molds. The breakdown of polysaccharides in nature is an essential part of the decomposition of plant residues.

The hydrolytic cleavage of disaccharides yields monosaccharides. A wide variety of microorganisms, including bacteria, yeasts and molds, are capable of hydrolyzing disaccharides. The enzyme *cellobiase* catalyzes the hydrolysis of cellobiose to glucose:

$$\underset{\text{cellobiose}}{C_{12}H_{22}O_{11}} + H_2O \quad \overset{\text{cellobiase}}{\underset{\longleftarrow}{\longrightarrow}} \quad \underset{\text{glucose}}{C_6H_{12}O_6} + \underset{\text{glucose}}{C_6H_{12}O_6}$$

The hydrolysis of maltose by *maltase* also yields two molecules of glucose. A molecule of sucrose when acted upon by *sucrase* (invertase) yields one molecule of glucose and one of fructose. Lactose is hydrolyzed by the enzyme *lactase* to glucose and galactose.

The *phosphorylases,* a group of splitting enzymes closely related to those which hydrolyze carbohydrates, add phosphoric acid instead of water. Sucrose and starch are split by phosphorylases as follows:

Sucrose + phosphoric acid $\rightleftarrows$ glucose-1-phosphate + fructose
Starch + phosphoric acid $\rightleftarrows$ glucose-1-phosphate + glucose

The phosphorylases are more reversible in their action than the hydrolytic carbohydrases and, therefore, are instrumental in the synthesis as well as the degradation of oligosaccharides and polysaccharides.

The hydrolysis of the more complex carbohydrates enables the cell to derive nutritional benefit from the soluble end products, namely monosaccharides. Many microbial species cannot hydrolyze such polymeric molecules and must be provided with simple sugars in order to live. Within natural ecological systems, microbial species which cannot utilize complex carbohydrates are benefited by those species which produce extracellular hydrolytic enzymes. Carbohydrates are necessary for many microorganisms to derive sufficient energy and carbon with which to carry out their varied life processes.

QUESTIONS

1. (a) Define: (1) catalyst, (2) enzyme, (3) substrate.
   (b) Explain the importance of enzymes in cells and organisms.
2. What is the chemical nature of enzymes?
3. Distinguish between holoenzyme, apoenzyme and coenzyme.
4. Explain how enzymes are named and classified.
5. What is meant by the "specificity" of enzymes? Give examples.
6. How does temperature affect enzyme activity? Which other factors influence enzyme action?
7. Differentiate between intracellular and extracellular enzymes.
8. Discuss the reversibility of enzyme action.
9. (a) What are hydrolases?
   (b) Explain the hydrolysis of: (1) proteins and protein derivatives; (2) lipids; (3) polysaccharides and disaccharides.
   (c) What is phosphorylase?

REFERENCES

Baldwin, E.: Dynamic Aspects of Biochemistry. 3rd ed. Cambridge, Cambridge University Press, 1957.
Boyer, P. D., Lardy, H., and Myrbäck, K., ed.: The Enzymes. Vol. 1. Kinetics, Thermodynamics, Mechanism, Basic Properties. 2nd ed. New York, Academic Press, Inc., 1958.
Dixon, M., and Webb, E. C.: Enzymes. New York, Academic Press, Inc., 1958.
Edsall, J. T.: Enzymes and Enzyme Systems: Their State in Nature. Cambridge, Mass., Harvard University Press, 1951.
Lardy, H. A., ed.: Respiratory Enzymes. Minneapolis, Minn., Burgess Publishing Co., 1949.
Lamanna, C., and Mallette, M. F.: Basic Bacteriology (Its Biological and Chemical Background). 2nd ed. Baltimore, The Williams & Wilkins Co., 1959.
Nielands, J. B., and Stumpf, P. K.: Outlines of Enzyme Chemistry. 2nd ed. New York, John Wiley & Sons, Inc., 1958.
Oginsky, E. L., and Umbreit, W. W.: An Introduction to Bacterial Physiology. 2nd ed. San Francisco, W. H. Freeman and Co., 1959.
Reiner, J. M.: Behavior of Enzyme Systems: An Analysis of Kinetics and Mechanism. Minneapolis, Minn., Burgess Publishing Co., 1959.
Sumner, J. B., and Somers, G. F.: Chemistry and Methods of Enzymes. New York, Academic Press, Inc., 1948.
Thimann, K. V.: The Life of Bacteria: Their Growth, Metabolism, and Relationships. New York, The Macmillan Co., 1955.

11 • Nutrition and Metabolism of Microorganisms

Every organism expends energy in converting materials from the environment into protoplasmic substances. Only two sources of energy are available to living things: *sunlight* and the *chemical energy* releasable from certain elements and compounds. The *radiant energy* of sunlight can be utilized only by organisms that contain chlorophyll or related pigments. Thus, the seemingly intricate and devious biochemical maneuvers of the cell are oriented toward the transformation of radiant energy or chemical energy into biologically usable energy to drive the forces essential for growth and reproduction. As a consequence of these activities, every organism and cell excretes waste products into its environment. A living organism, thus, is a dynamic system requiring a continuous influx and outflow of various kinds of materials.

Basically, then, nutrition and metabolism deal with the physicochemical activities employed by the cell in carrying out transformations of energy. Although microorganisms have many nutritional needs and specific metabolic functions in common with higher plants and animals, their nutrition and metabolism vary widely from species to species.

ABSORPTION OF FOOD

As indicated in a previous chapter, some protozoa engulf or ingest particulate foods (various microbial cells and organic debris) by the use of pseudopodia or a "cell mouth." However, in bacteria, yeasts, molds, algae, higher plants and many protozoa the exchange of materials between the organism and its environment takes place through the cell's surface. Nutrients that enter the cell in this manner cannot be particulate—they must be in solution. Many of the microorganisms secrete hydrolytic en-

163

zymes into the extra-cellular environment, just as higher animals secrete such enzymes into the digestive canal, in order to solubilize food substances.

The physical principle that the smaller the object the greater the ratio of its surface area to its mass or volume has a bearing on microbial nutrition. A young, actively growing microbial cell possesses a relatively large surface area, which enables it to absorb materials from its menstruum at a very rapid rate. The rate of elimination of metabolic waste products is similarly influenced by surface area.

It has been estimated by Rahn that the surface area of *Streptococcus lactis* in a quart of sour milk is approximately 100 square feet, although the volume of cells is less than one-quarter of one per cent of the volume of the soured milk. It is not surprising that microbial cultures dominate and alter their environment so rapidly when one considers the tremendous absorptive and excretory activity of such large surface areas. Also it must be realized, as we shall see in the next chapter, that the increase in numbers of cells during active proliferation of a microbial culture occurs at a geometric rate, not an arithmetic one. It has been estimated that some bacteria, during their phase of most rapid multiplication, will metabolize in one hour an amount of glucose which exceeds twice the weight of the cells.

Semi-permeable Nature of the Cytoplasmic Membrane

While nearly any substance in true solution can pass through the cytoplasmic membrane, not all substances do so with equal facility. In fact, a few very large molecules, such as proteins and polysaccharides, are known to be absorbed or excreted by microbial cells by mechanisms which are obscure. Under some conditions very small molecules or ions will neither leave nor enter the cytoplasm. Therefore, the cytoplasmic membrane is said to be *differentially permeable* (*semi-permeable*) because of its selectivity. Simple osmotic forces (cf. Chapter 12) are not enough to enable the cell to carry out absorption of nutrients and the excretion of waste products or protective materials. In some instances a bacterial culture will absorb a substance against a concentration gradient, i.e., under conditions when the substance being taken into the cytoplasm is present at a lower concentration in the environment than in the cytoplasm. There is evidence that some soluble nutrients are not absorbed until they are enzymatically modified. Recently, biochemists have discovered a group of substances which assist in the transport of specific nutrients across the cell membrane. These substances appropriately have been named *permeases,* although it is not certain that they are true enzymes. Of considerable importance in surface activities of the cell are the electrostatic charges distributed around the entire surface. A negatively charged cell, for example, would have no affinity toward an ion of similar charge, although one must consider the fact that the charge on a cell is a composite of positively and negatively charged sites. It is now evident that the cell must expend some energy (*active transport*) in the absorption of some specific nutrients and, probably, in the excretion of certain products. However, *passive transport*, related to osmotic forces, undoubtedly constitutes a large share of the "traffic" of the cytoplasmic membrane. Whether the exchange of materials between the cell and its environment be of an active or a passive nature, it is the cytoplasmic membrane which controls the intake of all nutrients and the elimination of products of metabolism. See Chapter 12 for a further discussion of forces that govern activities of the cell membrane.

NUTRITIONAL REQUIREMENTS

The gross chemical composition, with some notable exceptions, of microbial protoplasm is not markedly different from that of other forms of life. The essential elements, *carbon, hydrogen, oxygen, nitrogen, sulfur* and *phosphorus,* as well as the so-called trace elements, *calcium, iron, magnesium, manganese, potassium, cobalt, zinc,* etc., are found in all living things. These elements must be available to the cell in a utilizable form to provide suitable materials with which the cell can construct and maintain itself and from which sufficient energy can be derived to sustain these and other activities. The form in which the necessary elements must be provided differs markedly between the various groups of microorganisms, particularly for carbon, nitrogen and sulfur. Some bacteria derive all nutrients from inorganic substances and obtain their energy either from sunlight or from the oxidation of a specific inorganic compound, e.g., sulfur, ammonia, nitrite, methane, etc. At the other extreme are the viruses which are so poorly endowed with metabolic prowess that they depend exclusively on some other cell for all of their nutrients, even inducing the parasitized cell to assist in their reproductive process. In between lie the vast majority of microorganisms, which require from one to many different kinds of organic materials to satisfy their metabolic machinery. By and large, the yeasts and molds have relatively simple nutritional requirements, demanding few organic compounds. The greatest scope of nutritional patterns lies within the bacteria.

Nutritional Types of Bacteria

Bacteria are classified into nutritional groups according to (1) whether they derive the element carbon from carbon dioxide or from organic compounds, and (2) whether they derive energy from sunlight or through the oxidation of certain specific compounds. According to these criteria, the following nutritional categories can be defined:

1. *Photosynthetic autotrophs*

   Obtain energy from sunlight through the process of photosynthesis.
   Inorganic substances serve as hydrogen donors in reducing carbon dioxide to form organic ingredients of the cell.

Example: *Chlorobium limicola;* a species of "green bacteria" which uses H_2S in reducing CO_2.

2. *Chemosynthetic autotrophs*

Obtain energy by oxidizing certain inorganic substrates. Derive all of their carbon from CO_2 and all nutrients are inorganic.
Example: *Nitrosomonas europaea;* oxidizes NH_3 to HNO_2.

3. *Photosynthetic heterotrophs*

Differ from photosynthetic autotrophs in that they depend upon organic compounds as hydrogen donors in the reduction of CO_2 and may have a need for a few organic nutrients (accessory growth factors).
Example: *Rhodospirillum rubrum;* certain organic acids serve as the hydrogen donor for reducing CO_2.

4. *Chemosynthetic heterotrophs*

The great majority of bacteria are in this category. They must satisfy their needs for carbon by metabolizing organic substances.
Example: *Escherichia coli;* usually obtains its carbon and energy from simple sugars or simple organic nitrogenous compounds.

As inspection of the descriptions reveals, *autotrophs* depend solely upon carbon dioxide as the source of carbon, while the *heterotrophs* demand one or more organic substances to serve as hydrogen donors or to serve both as hydrogen donors and sources of carbon. A few autotrophs and heterotrophs can obtain all of their energy from sunlight, hence are termed photosynthetic, while the greater share of autotrophic and heterotrophic species cannot carry out photosynthesis and must satisfy their energy needs by oxidations of inorganic or organic compounds, respectively. As in other synthetic schemes employed in the classification of living things, these four nutritional classes are not sharply delineated. Thus, there exist few *obligate autotrophs*, the majority being facultative, i.e., capable of existing either as an autotroph or a heterotroph. Likewise, many of the photosynthetic bacteria are *facultative autotrophs*, depending upon the nutritional selectivity of the environment. Also, it should be noted that while heterotrophs generally can utilize some carbon dioxide, they cannot rely on carbon dioxide to supply their entire requirement for carbon.

Types of Nutrients

The cell obtains the elements represented in its protoplasmic constituents from a variety of substances which are called *nutrients*. As we have already seen, there are considerable differences among microorganisms in how they satisfy their needs for certain elements. An appreciation of such nutritional diversity can be obtained by examining the composition of culture media designed to meet the minimal nutritional requirements of three different bacteria, one obligate autotroph and two heterotrophs (Tables 3, 4, 5). In spite of such vast differences in nutritional requirements, the protoplasmic components of each of these species of bacteria will differ but slightly, qualitatively and quantitatively. The autotroph, therefore, must be blessed with an amazing metabolic system in order to convert such relatively simple compounds into cellular constituents.

Table 3. Composition of a Defined Medium for the Autotroph, *Thiobacillus thiooxidans**

Water	1,000 ml.
$(NH_4)_2SO_4$	0.2 gm.
$MgSO_4 \cdot 7H_2O$	0.5 gm.
$FeSO_4$	0.01 gm.
$CaCl_2$	0.25 gm.
KH_2PO_4	3.0 gm.
Sulfur, powdered	10.0 gm.

The nutrients can be broadly classified into those that serve as *building blocks* for the synthesis of the various protoplasmic components and those that serve as *energy sources* from which the cell derives the energy required for growth and reproduction. However, metabolism consists of such an array of integrated biochemical transformations that it is frequently impossible to categorically designate a particular nutrient as a building block or an energy source. Many nutrients serve in both capacities. Nutrients can be grouped more precisely into five categories: (1) *water*, (2) *minerals*, (3) *gases*, (4) *organic substances*, and (5) *accessory organic growth substances*. All of the nutrients needed by autotrophs fall in the first three groups. The heterotrophs, however, require organic substances in addition to water, minerals and gases.

Table 4. Composition of a Defined Medium for the Heterotroph, *Escherichia coli*†

Water	1,000 ml.
K_2HOP_4	7.0 gm.
KH_2PO_4	3.0 gm.
Sodium citrate·$3H_2O$	0.5 gm.
$MgSO_4 \cdot 7H_2O$	0.1 gm.
$(NH_4)_2SO_4$	1.0 gm.
Glucose	2.0 gm.

Water. Undoubtedly the demand for water is characteristic of all forms of life. It comprises the most abundant single substance in nearly all cells (most commonly 75 to 85 per cent of protoplasm is water). It is essential as a solvent, as a dispersant of colloidal particles and is necessary for the proper functioning of most biochemical reactions, in some instances being a product of, or an active participant in, such reactions (as in hydrolysis and the reversal of hydrolysis). Water must be in a physiologically available state to function as a nutrient. It must be "free" and

* From, Porter, J. R.: Bacterial Chemistry and Physiology, John Wiley & Sons, Inc., New York, 1946.

† From, Davis, B. D. and Mingioli, E. S.: Mutants of *Escherichia coli* requiring methionine or vitamin B_{12}. Journal of Bacteriology, Vol. 60, p. 17, 1950.

not "bound." For a fuller treatment of the biological significance of water see page 192.

Table 5.   Composition of a Defined Medium for the Heterotroph, *Leuconostoc mesenteroides**

Minerals:				
Water	1,000 ml.	DL-Methionine	0.1 gm.	
NH_4Cl	3.0 gm.	DL-Phenylalanine	0.1 gm.	
KH_2PO_4	0.6 gm.	L-Proline	0.1 gm.	
K_2HPO_4	0.6 gm.	Dl-Serine	0.05 gm.	
$MgSO_4 \cdot 7H_2O$	0.7 gm.	DL-Threonine	0.2 gm.	
$FeSO_4 \cdot 7H_2O$	0.01 gm.	DL-Tryptophane	0.04 gm.	
$MnSO_4 \cdot 4H_2O$	0.02 gm.	L-Tyrosine	0.1 gm.	
NaCl	0.01 gm.	DL-Valine	0.25 gm.	

Energy and carbon source:		Purines and Pyrimidines:		
Glucose	25.0 gm.	Adenine sulfate·H_2O	10 mg.	
Sodium acetate	20.0 gm.	Guanine·$HCl \cdot 2H_2O$	10 mg.	
		Uracil	10 mg.	
Amino acids		Xanthine	10 mg.	
DL-Alanine	0.2 gm.	Vitamins:		
L-Arginine·HCl	0.242 gm.	p-Aminobenzoic acid	0.1 mg.	
L-Asparagine	0.4 gm.	Biotin	0.001 mg.	
L-Aspartic acid	0.1 gm.	Folic acid	0.01 mg.	
L-Cysteine	0.05 gm.	Niacin	1.0 mg.	
L-Glutamic acid	0.3 gm.	Ca DL-Pantothenate	0.5 mg.	
Glycine	0.1 gm.	Pyridoxal·HCl	0.3 mg.	
L-Histidine·HCl	0.062 gm.	Pyridoxamine·HCl	0.3 mg.	
DL-Isoleucine	0.25 gm.	Pyridoxine·HCl	1.0 mg.	
DL-Leucine	0.25 gm.	Riboflavin	0.5 mg.	
L-Lysine·HCl	0.25 gm.	Thiamine·HCl	0.5 mg.	

Minerals.   The cell's need for some of the essential elements and for all of the trace elements is usually met by certain mineral salts and, in some cases, by the element per se (as in the case of sulfur for *Thiobacillus thiooxidans* or gaseous nitrogen for the nitrogen-fixing microorganisms). Whether the organism be an autotroph or a heterotroph, certain mineral salts must be supplied. Commonly, the elements available to the cell in the inorganic state are phosphorus, sulfur, potassium, sodium, magnesium, iron, manganese and calcium. Most of the remaining trace elements are required in such low concentrations that they can be provided as contaminants in the major ingredients of a culture medium. Nitrogen is available to many microorganisms, autotrophs as well as heterotrophs, in the inorganic state, e.g., ammonium salts and salts of nitrate, or simply as N_2 for the nitrogen fixers. Nevertheless, those heterotrophic bacteria with complex nutritional requirements require various organic compounds of nitrogen, as we will see in the subsequent discussion of "organic substances." By definition, autotrophs meet their needs for carbon with inorganic carbon, viz., carbon dioxide or the bicarbonate ion. Heterotrophs can assimilate some inorganic carbon, but not enough to meet all their demands for this element.

* From, Steele, B. F., et al.: Media for *Leuconostoc mesenteroides* P-60 and *Leuconostoc citrovorum* 8081. Journal of Biological Chemistry, Vol. 177, p. 533, 1949.

It is obvious that in the preparation of culture media the mineral composition is of great importance. Frequently the omission of a trace element will not prevent growth but will result in cells that are abnormal in appearance or in metabolism. Advantage can be taken of this fact in the assay of certain minerals. Some mineral salts also serve as buffers (cf. p. 195), i.e., they prevent abrupt alterations of the hydrogen-ion concentration of the extracellular environment. Another consideration is the effects which inorganic salts have upon the osmotic pressure (cf. p. 196). Thus, if the salt content of a culture medium is too great, growth will be inhibited or prevented by the high osmotic pressure, causing water to leave the cells. Minerals, therefore, provide the cell with certain necessary elements and also exert certain important physical effects through reactivity with hydrogen ions and through influences on the cell's semipermeable cytoplasmic membrane.

Gases. Any discussion of the gaseous requirement of microorganisms raises the question of differences in the requirement for *oxygen*. As we shall see in a later section of this chapter, microorganisms differ in their respiratory activities. Respiration is concerned with the transport of hydrogen and electrons. Those microorganisms which can activate molecular oxygen to accept electrons and hydrogen atoms are called *aerobes*. Those microorganisms called *anaerobes* cannot utilize molecular oxygen but must rely upon substances other than oxygen to accept the electrons and hydrogen. In fact, molecular oxygen is toxic toward strict anaerobes. A few microorganisms will not grow in a medium containing the usual atmospheric tension of oxygen but require a reduced oxygen tension. These organisms are known as *microaerophiles*. The majority of microorganisms are *facultative anaerobes,* meaning that they thrive in the presence as well as the absence of air. Some facultative anaerobes, such as fermentative yeasts, possess the metabolic mechanisms for aerobic metabolism. Others carry out anaerobic metabolism regardless of the presence of oxygen, hence are tolerant of oxygen but have no use for it. Anaerobes vary in their tolerance toward oxygen. *Obligate* or *strict anaerobes* cannot thrive in the presence of the least trace of molecular oxygen; others will tolerate traces of oxygen. By the same token, *obligate aerobes* have a strict demand for oxygen. With the outstanding exception of the fermentative yeast, e.g., *Saccharomyces cerevisiae,* the vast majority of fungi (yeasts and molds) are obligate aerobes. The majority of bacterial species, on the other hand, are facultative with regard to their need for or tolerance toward oxygen.

The classification of microorganisms on the basis of oxygen requirements can be summarized as follows:

1. *Aerobes*

Require gaseous oxygen for certain vital metabolic activities. Cannot survive in the complete absence of O_2.
Example: *Acetobacter aceti.*

2. *Anaerobes*

The least trace of O_2 is toxic to these organisms. Therefore, they cannot utilize O_2 in their metabolism.
Example: *Clostridium tetani.*

3. *Facultative anaerobes*

a. Indifferent toward gaseous oxygen
Do not utilize O_2 in their metabolism but are not particularly harmed by the presence of O_2.
Example: *Lactobacillus acidophilus.*
b. Opportunistic toward gaseous oxygen
Possess both aerobic and anaerobic metabolism, thus can get along in the absence of O_2 but utilize O_2 if it is present.
Example: *Escherichia coli.*

4. *Microaerophiles*

The customary atmospheric tension of O_2 is inhibitory; demand a reduced tension of O_2 for best growth. Also, usually demand an elevated CO_2 tension.
Example: *Actinomyces bovis.*

Another gas that is an essential nutrient for many microorganisms is *carbon dioxide*. We have already discussed the essentiality of carbon dioxide for autotrophs and have pointed out that heterotrophs "fix" a certain amount of carbon dioxide. The method by which carbon dioxide is absorbed by the cell is unknown, but it is probable that it is not transported across the cell membrane in the gaseous phase.

Some microorganisms, in the absence of fixed forms of nitrogen, are able to utilize *atmospheric nitrogen* to fulfill their need for this element. These are the so-called *nitrogen-fixing* organisms, e.g., certain genera of heterotrophic bacteria, including chemosynthetic and photosynthetic types, as well as some species of blue-green algae.

A small group of organisms, the *hydrogen bacteria,* oxidize *hydrogen* to water as a means of obtaining energy, some of which is used in the reduction of carbon dioxide to cellular constituents. Many of the photosynthetic bacteria and certain *sulfur bacteria* oxidize *hydrogen sulfide* to sulfur in their respiratory activities. Hydrogen sulfide, incidently, is produced by *sulfate-reducing bacteria* which utilize the sulfate ion as the oxidizing agent in their anaerobic metabolism. Other bacteria may produce hydrogen sulfide as a consequence of their metabolism of sulfur-containing amino acids.

In conclusion, it can be said that the primary gases that serve as nutrients are oxygen, carbon dioxide and nitrogen. Two other gases, hydrogen and hydrogen sulfide, are important nutrients for a relatively small number of bacterial species.

Organic Substances. While the number of organic compounds that serve as nutrients for microorganisms is tremendous, they can be discussed conveniently according to the element which they provide.

Organic forms of carbon are essential to furnish heterotrophic bacteria with some or all of the carbon and energy which they require. Commonly, carbon is furnished as simple sugars such as glucose. Some heterotrophs cannot utilize sugars as a source of carbon and energy but will metabolize one or more of a variety of organic substances, e.g., amino acids, organic acids, alcohols, various aromatic compounds and even hydrocarbons. Many heterotrophs are extremely versatile, being able to metabolize an array of different organic compounds to satisfy their needs.

Organic nitrogen can be supplied to heterotrophs in many forms. For many species, inorganic forms of nitrogen are adequate (most commonly as ammonium salts in culture media). However, the more nutritionally demanding heterotrophs require various organic compounds of nitrogen; others may require only one specific compound of organic nitrogen. The customary forms of nitrogen in the organic state which satisfy the nutritional demands are simple peptides, amino acids, purines and pyrimidines. Many heterotrophs have no minimal demand for organic nitrogen but will derive nutritional benefit from such substances if they are provided in the environment. A few species derive their nitrogen by enzymatically splitting urea into ammonia and carbon dioxide and absorbing the ammonia thus liberated. Organisms that are proteolytic can assimilate such degradation products of proteins as amino acids and peptides to supply their needs for nitrogen.

Sulfur can be furnished in the inorganic state, usually sulfate, but many microorganisms must be supplied with organic molecules which contain sulfur. Frequently the sulfur-containing amino acids will meet the nutritional demand for this element.

Some of the more demanding bacteria require some *phosphorus* in the organic form, although for most organisms this element serves as an excellent nutrient in the inorganic state (phosphate).

Accessory Growth Substances. The metabolic processes in all types of cells require the participation of very small amounts of organic compounds which are derived from, or related to, the accessory growth substances, most of which are *vitamins.* Autotrophs are able to synthesize from their inorganic nutrients all of the vitamins which they require in their metabolism. Heterotrophs are extremely variable in this respect (note the differences in nutritional requirements of the two heterotrophs cited in Tables 4 and 5). With but few exceptions, only vitamins of the water-soluble B complex are important in the metabolism of microorganisms. The importance of vitamins can be appreciated upon the realization that prosthetic groups (coenzymes) of certain enzymes are derivatives of vitamins. This aspect of the subject was treated in the previous chapter and will be expanded in the latter sections of this chapter. In most cases the demand for a specific vitamin may be so great that the microorganism will not grow in its absence. Upon the addition of minute amounts of the vitamin to the culture medium, growth will ensue. In some cases, a concentration of vitamin as low as several micromicrograms ($1 \ \mu\mu g = 1$ x 10^{-12} gram) per milliliter of medium will give a growth response. It is of interest to note that several of the vitamins (biotin, pantothenic acid, niacin, folic acid) essential in human nutrition were first discovered as growth factors for bacteria.

While this discussion has dealt with vitamins as nutrients, it should be pointed out that the *microbial synthesis of vitamins* in the intestinal tract of animals constitutes a source of certain vitamins essential in the metabolism of the host. The complex microflora that exists in the intestinal canal, especially in the large intestine, synthesizes a variety of vitamins, part of which the microorganisms themselves use and part of which are absorbed by the intestinal wall for transport throughout the body. However, this is a very complex ecologic relationship since the microorganisms both synthesize and utilize vitamins, thereby competing among themselves and with the host. Also, the nature and physiological activities of the microflora are readily influenced by the composition of the diet. Therefore, the true significance of the intestinal synthesis of vitamins and other growth factors is uncertain. It is interesting to note that neither vitamin K nor vitamin C are needed by any microorganism, yet intestinal biosynthesis appears to furnish the needs of some animals, including primates, for these vitamins.

Definition of Essential Nutrient

The essentiality of a given chemical compound for a microorganism is assessed in a *synthetic, chemically-defined medium.* (See Chapter 14.) The omission of a single compound from a synthetic medium designed to meet the "minimal" nutritional requirements of a certain strain of microbial species will prevent growth and reproduction. Some nutrients, however, are said to be "stimulatory" since their addition to the minimal medium enhances growth. Moreover, the effects of the omission of one nutrient from a minimal medium oftentimes can be reversed by some other compounds or combinations of compounds.

Growth is the common criterion employed in evaluating the nutritional requirements of microorganisms. Sometimes, however, growth will be prolific in the absence of a given nutrient, but certain metabolic activities, otherwise present, will be impaired. This is sometimes called a "biochemical lesion." Obviously, microorganisms will utilize many nutrients that are not classified as essential. Thus, *Escherichia coli* will grow well in the minimal medium shown in Table 4 but will assimilate many of the substances in more complex media, such as the one devised to meet the minimal nutritional needs of *Leuconostoc mesenteroides* (Table 5).

One must bear in mind that the essential nutrients are those that the organism cannot synthesize for itself. Furthermore, many substances that are essential nutrients for one species can be synthesized by other species of microorganisms. Therefore, *an essential metabolite need not be an essential nutrient.*

THE ROLE OF METABOLISM

The varied interrelated chemical reactions which occur during growth and reproduction of a cell comprise the subject of metabolism. It is convenient to consider metabolism as being the sum of two general types of biochemical activities: (1) *catabolism* or *dissimilation,* and (2) *anabolism* or *assimilation.* Catabolic activities degrade molecules with the liberation of energy, while anabolic reactions initiate the synthesis of larger molecules from simpler substrates with the utilization of energy. Basically then, it is *energy* which is the directing force of metabolism.

Energy

It is customary to speak of energy as the ability to do work. In biological systems, work is required in performing such tasks as the synthesis of new cellular material, cell division, maintaining substances which constantly break down, expanding the cell's surface during growth, motility, etc. The energy expended in such metabolic functions is provided by reactions which yield energy in a useful state. Green plants and a few bacteria are able to transform the *radiant energy* of sunlight into *chemical energy.* This basic reaction, upon which all life ultimately depends, is called *photosynthesis.* The photosynthetic reaction is made possible by virtue of the presence of a pigment called *chlorophyll* (*bacteriochlorophyll* in bacteria). The general reaction can be visualized as follows:

$$CO_2 + 2\ H_2A + light\ (energy) \rightleftharpoons (CH_2O)_x + 2\ A + H_2O$$

$(CH_2O)_x$ represents a carbohydrate product of high potential energy which the plant can divert to do work. H_2A is any inorganic or organic hydrogen donor. In the case of photosynthesis by green plants, the hydrogen donor, H_2A, must be water, while for photosynthetic bacteria it is some other reduced compound, e.g., hydrogen sulfide or an organic compound. It is obvious that by-product A is oxygen in the process as mediated by green plants, while it is sulfur or some other substance in the case of bacteria.

Photosynthetic organisms, therefore, manufacture their own energy-yielding food and are not dependent upon other forms of life to provide this type of nutrient, except for those photosynthetic bacteria which require accessory organic factors or must use organic hydrogen donors in the photochemical reaction. Other forms of life, including the majority of microorganisms, derive energy from the oxidation of various compounds, some organic and some inorganic.

Biological Oxidation-Reduction Activities

Oxidation-reduction reactions are a result of the transfer of electrons between reactants. While it is customary to think of oxidation as the addition of oxygen to a substance and reduction as the removal of oxygen, biochemical activities concerned with transformations of energy carry out oxidation-reduction reactions by the transfer of electrons and hydrogen atoms through the catalytic action of enzymes. Oxygen need not participate in this process, although it certainly does in the case of aerobic microorganisms. *Basically, oxidation occurs when a compound parts with electrons or hydrogen. Conversely, reduction takes place upon the acceptance of electrons or hydrogen.* Whenever an oxidation takes place, a simultaneous reduction occurs upon the acceptance by some substance of the electrons or hydrogen liberated by oxidation. The substance parting with hydrogen is termed the *hydrogen donor* and is the *reducing agent.* The substance which accepts hydrogen is called the *hydrogen acceptor* and is the *oxidizing agent.*

Fundamentally, *respiration* is a series of oxidation-reduction reactions from which the cell derives energy to conduct its other activities. Strictly speaking, respiration is an aerobic process in which molecular oxygen is enzymatically "activated" to accept the electrons and hydrogen atoms from the substrate. Organic compounds, frequently simple sugars, serve as the substrate for respiration by heterotrophic microorganisms, while autotrophs utilize oxidizable inorganic substrates, e.g., NH_3, NO_2, H_2S and even H_2. Many microorganisms, however, cannot activate oxygen. Instead, they resort to an anaerobic mode of energy metabolism called *fermentation.* In the classical type of fermentation, the molecules of substrate are so degraded and rearranged as to provide both organic hydrogen donors and organic hydrogen acceptors. Some microorganisms carry out another type of fermentation in which reducible inorganic compounds other than oxygen act as the acceptor of the hydrogen removed from an organic substrate. (Contrast this with respiration as defined earlier in the paragraph.) One classical form of fermentation, *glycolysis,* is characteristic of various animal tissues, although many species of bacteria dissimilate sugars to lactic acid by mechanisms identical to those of glycolysis.

To sum up, the aerobic biological process concerned with transformations of energy is respiration; the anaerobic process designed for this purpose is fermentation. In either case, the purpose is to release the chemical energy contained in some substrate and trap it in a biologically available form.

Preservation of energy.   Oxidation-reduction reactions are carried out by the cell to release the potential energy available in certain nutrients and metabolites. However, the cell must harness some of this energy or it will be dissipated in the form of heat. Actually, some energy is lost in the form of heat during respiration and fermentation. The rest of the energy released by these processes is "trapped" in certain molecules which readily release energy as it is needed to drive energy-consuming reactions. Thus there exists an *energy pool* of metabolites constantly picking up and releasing energy. These metabolites are characterized by the possession of one or more chemical bonds (linkages between atoms in a molecule) which contain far more potential energy than most chemical bonds. The most important substance involved in energy transfer is the nucleotide, *adenosine triphosphate,* commonly abbreviated ATP. It is composed of ribose (a pentose sugar), three phosphate residues and adenine (a purine). ATP functions as a coenzyme in the transfer of energy by parting with a *high-energy phosphate bond* to make possible those metabolic reactions termed *endergonic* (require energy to proceed). Upon losing a phosphate group, ATP becomes ADP (adenosine diphosphate). ADP, in turn, is capable of forming one high-energy phosphate bond from the energy which *exergonic* (yield energy) reactions release. Also, ADP can furnish one high-energy phosphate bond to promote endergonic reactions and be converted to AMP (adenosine monophosphate), a molecule containing no high-energy bonds. Thus the cell has an amazing self-generating pool of chemical bond energy which shuttles energy back and forth between exergonic (catabolic) and endergonic (anabolic) reactions.

Fermentation.　　Many microorganisms (anaerobes and facultative anaerobes) conduct a type of energy metabolism called fermentation, a process which generates high-energy bonds without the participation of molecular oxygen. It was indicated earlier in this discussion that fermentation can be typed according to whether the final acceptors of the hydrogen atoms arising from the substrate are organic or inorganic compounds. Where organic compounds act as the final hydrogen acceptors, they invariably have come from the substrate. Accordingly, this is often referred to as *intramolecular fermentation.* In contrast, if the final acceptor of hydrogen is inorganic, but not oxygen, the fermentation may be called *intermolecular* since the hydrogen acceptor did not originate from the substrate. Respiration in the same sense is an intermolecular oxidation-reduction sequence. Our discussion of fermentation will be divided on the basis of the source and nature of the hydrogen acceptor.

1. *Intramolecular fermentation.*

The better known fermentations are intramolecular, i.e., the substrate furnishes the final hydrogen acceptor(s).

Commonly, the substrate for intramolecular fermentation is a simple sugar, although other substances, notably amino acids, are fermented by certain microorganisms. A variety of fermentations exist, depending upon the enzymic constitution of the organism. *Homofermentative* organisms yield only one dominant end product while *heterofermentative* organisms produce a variety of products from the substrate. Table 6 cites some of the types of fermentations carried out by microorganisms. Despite the variety of fermentations, they all have the same role; namely, to enable the cells to derive some of the energy contained in the substrate.

It is beyond the scope of this book to delve into the biochemical intricacies of fermentation. However, an appreciation of the subject can be gained from a brief inspection of the "lactic acid fermentation," a fermen-

Table 6.   Examples of Fermentations (Intramolecular) Carried Out
by Microorganisms

Organism	Substrate	End Products
Saccharomyces cerevisiae and *Zymomonas lindneri*	Glucose	Ethyl alcohol and carbon dioxide
Heterofermentative lactic acid bacteria, e.g., *Leuconostoc mesenteroides*	Glucose	Lactic acid, acetic acid, ethyl alcohol, glycerol and carbon dioxide
Homofermentative lactic acid bacteria, e.g., *Lactobacillus acidophilus*	Glucose	Lactic acid
Escherichia coli	Glucose	Lactic acid, formic acid, acetic acid, succinic acid, ethyl alcohol, carbon dioxide and hydrogen
Aerobacter aerogenes	Glucose	Lactic acid, formic acid, acetic acid, succinic acid, ethyl alcohol, acetoin or 2,3-butanediol, carbon dioxide and hydrogen
Clostridium acetobutylicum	Glucose	Formic acid, acetic acid, butyric acid, ethyl alcohol, butyl alcohol, acetone, acetoin, carbon dioxide and hydrogen
Propionibacterium spp.	Glucose	Propionic acid, acetic acid and carbon dioxide
Clostridium butyricum	Glucose	Butyric acid, acetic acid, carbon dioxide and hydrogen
Clostridium propionicum	Alanine (amino acid)	Propionic acid, acetic acid, carbon dioxide and ammonia

tation carried out by a number of species of streptococci and lactobacilli.
The over-all reaction with glucose as the substrate is as follows:

$$C_6H_{12}O_6 \longrightarrow 2\ CH_3CHOHCOOH + 54,000\ calories$$
$$\text{(glucose)} \qquad\qquad \text{(lactic acid)} \qquad\qquad \text{(energy)}$$

Actually, the process is more complex than indicated by this simple equation. Like all fermentations, the substrate is degraded stepwise through
the catalytic action of a sequence of enzymes. An abbreviated symbolic
scheme of the lactic acid fermentation is illustrated in Figure 78. Note
that for every mole of glucose dissimilated, two moles of lactic acid and
ATP are formed. Since each mole of high-energy phosphate contains approximately 8,000 calories of energy, 16,000 of the total 54,000 calories are
made available to the organism, giving an efficiency in terms of recovery
of energy of less than 30 per cent. A more complete picture of net effects
of the dissimilation of glucose to lactic acid may be given as follows:

$$C_6H_{12}O_6 + 2\ H_3PO_4 + 2\ ADP \longrightarrow 2\ CH_3CHOHCOOH + 2\ H_2O$$
$$+ 2\ ATP + 38,000\ calories\ (heat)$$

The 38,000 calories represents an energy loss (as heat), hence are unavailable to do work for the organism.

The key intermediate product in the fermentation of sugars is *pyruvic*

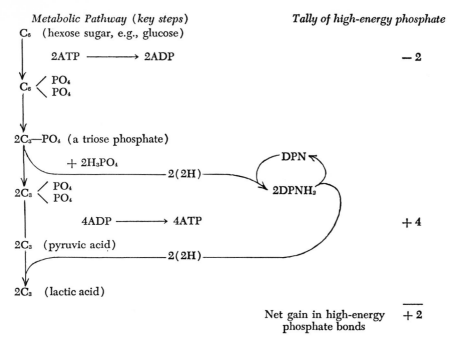

Tally of high-energy phosphate

C_6 (hexose sugar, e.g., glucose)

2ATP ⟶ 2ADP   — 2

$C_6 < \begin{matrix} PO_4 \\ PO_4 \end{matrix}$

$2C_3$—PO_4 (a triose phosphate)

+ 2H_3PO_4

2(2H) — DPN

$2C_3 < \begin{matrix} PO_4 \\ PO_4 \end{matrix}$ 2DPNH$_2$

4ADP ⟶ 4ATP   +4

$2C_3$ (pyruvic acid)

2(2H)

$2C_3$ (lactic acid)

Net gain in high-energy   +2
phosphate bonds

Figure 78. Abbreviated version of the lactic acid fermentation. Actually there are 11 well identified steps in the process, each mediated by a specific enzyme. It is apparent that 2 high-energy phosphate bonds are utilized but that 4 are generated in this dissimilation of glucose. Note the role of the coenzyme, diphosphopyridine nucleotide (DPN), in the transport of hydrogen.

acid, a three-carbon compound which can undergo a number of different enzymic transformations to yield a variety of end products. Thus in the lactic acid fermentation, pyruvic acid is reduced to lactic acid as follows:

lactic
dehydrogenase

$$CH_3COCOOH + DPN\text{-}H_2 \xrightarrow{\hspace{3cm}} CH_3CHOHCOOH + DPN$$
(pyruvic acid)   (lactic acid)

On the other hand, fermentative yeasts such as *Saccharomyces cerevisiae,* produce pyruvic acid via the same pathway as lactic acid bacteria, but transform it into alcohol and carbon dioxide in the following manner:

pyruvic decarboxylase

$$CH_3COCOOH \xrightarrow{\hspace{3cm}} CH_3CHO + CO_2$$
                                        (acetaldehyde)

alcohol dehydrogenase

$$CH_3CHO + DPN\text{-}H_2 \xrightarrow{\hspace{3cm}} CH_3CH_2OH + DPN$$
                                        (ethyl alcohol)

The many other end products which microorganisms are known to produce during fermentation (cf. Table 6) are derived from pyruvic acid. It is thus apparent that the nature of the end products of a fermentation depends on the way the organism metabolizes pyruvic acid.

2. *Intermolecular fermentation.*

In the absence of oxygen some heterotrophic as well as autotrophic bacteria are able to carry out oxidation-reduction reactions in which certain inorganic substances, instead of organic products (as in fermentation) or oxygen (as in respiration), serve as acceptors of hydrogen. An excellent example of intermolecular fermentation, one of particular importance in the nitrogen cycle (cf. Chapter 18), is the *reduction of nitrate.* The first step in the reduction of nitrate is the formation of nitrite coupled with the oxidation (removal of hydrogen) of some organic substance, e.g., sugars, fatty acids, alcohols, etc. This is demonstrated by the following equation:

$$\text{Organic compound} \cdot H_2 + HNO_3 \longrightarrow CO_2 + H_2O + HNO_2 + \text{energy}$$

However, nitrite is rather toxic and its accumulation is prevented by further reductions called *denitrification* to result in the stepwise formation of nitrous oxide (N_2O), N_2 and, sometimes, NH_3. These further anaerobic oxidation-reduction reactions also yield energy to the organism.

Another interesting intermolecular fermentation is carried out by *Desulfovibrio,* an obligate anaerobe able to oxidize organic substrates and reduce sulfur or some of its oxides to hydrogen sulfide:

$$\text{Organic compound} \cdot H_2 + H_2SO_4 \longrightarrow CO_2 + H_2O + H_2S + \text{energy}$$

The production of methane (CH_4) through the reduction of carbon dioxide is carried out by bacteria in the genus *Methanobacterium.* These organisms derive hydrogen from certain organic substances, or utilize hydrogen gas directly to reduce carbon dioxide:

$$4 H_2 + CO_2 \longrightarrow CH_4 + 2 H_2O + 195,000 \text{ calories}$$

Respiration.   The participation of oxygen in biological oxidations results in a form of metabolism called respiration. All aerobes and many facultative anaerobes respire. For heterotrophs the substrate of respiration is some organic substance, commonly a simple sugar. The autotrophs utilize oxidizable inorganic substances as substrates in their respiratory activities. Given an adequate supply of molecular oxygen, the respiring cell will oxidize the substrate completely. Sometimes, however, the substrate will not be oxidized completely, either because of a limited supply of oxygen or because the cell is not constitutionally endowed with the necessary metabolic system to permit molecular oxygen to accept the hydrogen atoms and electrons streaming from the substrate.

1. *Complete oxidation.*

The complete oxidation of glucose as carried out by many microorganisms can be represented symbolically by the following equation:

$$C_6H_{12}O_6 + 6 O_2 \longrightarrow 6 CO_2 + 6 H_2O + 689,800 \text{ calories}$$
$$\text{(glucose)} \hspace{6cm} \text{(energy)}$$

Thus, all of the hydrogen atoms of the substrate are accepted by atoms of oxygen and the substrate's carbon is oxidized to carbon dioxide together with the liberation of considerable energy. Note how much more energy is released by the complete oxidation of glucose then in the lactic acid fermentation. Approximately 38 high energy phosphate bonds are formed in the process of the complete oxidation of glucose, thereby enabling the organism to trap approximately 304,000 calories of the 689,800 total and achieve an efficiency of almost 45 per cent in gaining energy from glucose. This is a higher efficiency of conversion of energy than realized by fermentation. Taking into consideration the transformations of energy in this respiratory oxidation, the following equation can be constructed:

$$C_6H_{12}O_6 + 6\ O_2 + 38\ H_3PO_4 + 38\ ADP \longrightarrow 6\ CO_2 + 44\ H_2O +$$
$$38\ ATP + 385,800\ \text{calories of heat}$$
$$(\text{energy loss})$$

The over-all equation of the process tells us nothing of the sequential intermediate steps by which the hydrogen contained in the glucose is ultimately combined with atoms of oxygen. Suffice it to say that glucose is enzymatically degraded to pyruvic acid, as in fermentation, and the pyruvic acid is then swept into an aerobic cycle to undergo a series of oxidations, reductions and decarboxylations, until only carbon dioxide and water remain. The latter cycle, referred to as Kreb's tricarboxylic acid cycle, constitutes the terminal phases of respiration during which 36 of the 38 high-energy phosphate bonds are generated.

Autotrophic bacteria also may carry out complete oxidations. A notable example are the colorless sulfur bacteria (genus *Thiobacillus*) which are able to oxidize various inorganic forms of sulfur, including elemental sulfur. The complete oxidation of sulfur as carried out by *Thiobacillus thiooxidans* is represented by the following equation:

$$2\ S + 2\ H_2O + 3\ O_2 \longrightarrow 2\ H_2SO_4 + 237,000\ \text{calories}$$

Some of the energy liberated by the complete oxidation of sulfur is trapped in the chemical energy pool of the cells. It has been estimated that less than 10 per cent of the energy released by respiration of autotrophs is kept by the cells. Other examples of the complete oxidation of inorganic compounds by autotrophs are:

Nitrobacter: $2\ HNO_2 + O_2 \longrightarrow 2\ HNO_3 + 35,000\ \text{calories}$
Hydrogenomonas: $2\ H_2 + O_2 \longrightarrow 2\ H_2O + 112,000\ \text{calories}$

Notice that in all cases of complete oxidation the products cannot be oxidized further, meaning that no more energy can be liberated from the substrate.

2. Incomplete oxidation.

Some microorganisms are constitutionally unable to oxidize completely the substrate for respiration. The best known examples of this are the acetic acid bacteria (genus *Acetobacter*). These bacteria are responsible for the product vinegar by virtue of their ability to oxidize ethyl alcohol to acetic acid. This reaction proceeds as follows:

$$C_2H_5OH + O_2 \longrightarrow CH_3COOH + H_2O + 118,000 \text{ calories}$$
$$(\text{ethyl alcohol}) \qquad\qquad\qquad (\text{acetic acid})$$

Given more time, some species of *Acetobacter* will oxidize the acetic acid completely to carbon dioxide and water, liberating an additional 210,000 calories of energy.

Some autotrophs carry out incomplete oxidations. The best illustration of this is the oxidation of ammonia to nitrous acid by members of the genera *Nitrosomonas* and *Nitrosococcus*. These organisms complete the following reaction:

$$2\,NH_3 + 3\,O_2 \longrightarrow 2\,HNO_2 + 2\,H_2O + 66,500 \text{ calories}$$

Respiratory enzymes and the transport of hydrogen. It has already been emphasized that fermentation and respiration consist of a sequence of enzymatically catalyzed reactions which deal basically with the transport of hydrogen from the substrate to a suitable acceptor. A whole battery of enzymes is necessary to regulate the gradual dissimilation of the organic substrates which participate in fermentation and respiration. However, we shall consider only those enzymes concerned more directly with hydrogen transport. The major components engaged in transporting hydrogen are: (1) *dehydrogenases*, (2) certain *coenzymes* (*DPN* and *TPN* and *flavoprotein enzymes*), (3) *cytochrome pigments*, (4) *cytochrome oxidase*, and (5) *oxygen*. DPN (*diphosphopyridine nucleotide*) and TPN (*triphosphopyridine nucleotide*) are derivatives of the vitamin *niacinamide* and function together with various apoenzymes called dehydrogenases. The latter enzymes enable DPN or TPN to remove hydrogen from either the substrate or from degradation products of the substrate. The flavoprotein enzymes contain the B vitamin *riboflavin* and link the transport of hydrogen between DPN or TPN and oxygen. The flavoproteins also donate electrons to the cytochrome pigments. The cytochromes are proteins related to hemoglobin, with a prosthetic group which contains iron in a state able to accept and part with electrons; thus, the iron component of the cytochromes is reversibly oxidized and reduced. Three such respiratory pigments are known; they are *cytochrome a, b* and *c*. Cytochrome oxidase accepts electrons from the cytochromes and passes them on to molecular oxygen. Thus, oxygen is ionized or "activated" by electrons to accept hydrogen atoms from the flavin enzyme resulting in the end product, water:

$$O_2 + 4\,e^- \longrightarrow 2\,O^-$$
$$4\,H^+ + 2\,O^- \longrightarrow 2\,H_2O$$

The major pathways of hydrogen transport by the cell can be summarized as follows:

   1. Anaerobic

Substrate $\xrightarrow{\text{H}^+}$ DPN or TPN $\xrightarrow{\text{H}^+}$ organic acceptor $\xrightarrow{\text{H}^+}$ end product

   2. Aerobic

Substrate $\xrightarrow{\text{H}^+}$ DPN or TPN $\xrightarrow{\text{H}^+}$ flavoprotein $\xrightarrow{e^-}$ cytochromes $\xrightarrow{e^-}$

cytochrome oxidase $\xrightarrow{e^-}$ O_2 $\xrightarrow{e^- + \text{H}^+}$ H_2O

Other variations of the aerobic pathway exist. In some systems of hydrogen transport, the cytochromes do not participate. Instead, the flavoprotein picks up hydrogen from the substrate, DPN or TPN, and transmits it directly to molecular oxygen to result in the end product, hydrogen peroxide (H_2O_2).

Of the aerobic pathways, water is the end product only when the cytochrome pigments participate; otherwise, hydrogen peroxide is formed. Only in the anaerobic pathway does an organic substance serve as the final acceptor of hydrogen. Thus, anaerobic microorganisms do not possess cytochrome pigments. Some anaerobes upon exposure to air accumulate hydrogen peroxide, a compound rather toxic toward cells. While nearly all aerobes and facultative anaerobes also produce some hydrogen peroxide, they prevent its accumulation through the action of *catalase* and *peroxidase,* two enzymes which, by different mechanisms, decompose hydrogen peroxide. It is believed that oxygen is toxic to anaerobes because they lack such enzymes and, thus, cannot prevent the accumulation of toxic concentrations of hydrogen peroxide. This is not the sole explanation for the toxicity of oxygen toward anaerobic species of microorganisms since oxygen is reactive with many cellular substances.

Hydrogen peroxide, sometimes formed during respiration, is not permitted to accumulate because of the ability of *catalase* to initiate the following reaction:

$$2\ H_2O_2 \longrightarrow 2\ H_2O + O_2$$

The *peroxidases* mediate the removal of hydrogen (an oxidation) from organic substances (certain hydrogen donors), and use this hydrogen to reduce hydrogen peroxide:

$$H_2O_2 + 2\ H \longrightarrow 2\ H_2O$$

Some species of bacteria, by means of various enzymes, are able to transport hydrogen from organic substrates to such inorganic compounds as nitrate, sulfate and carbon dioxide. This has already been discussed in the section on fermentation.

Bioluminescence. A few species of marine bacteria, fungi and protozoa possess an unique respiratory mechanism which results in the emission of light. This phenomenon, called *bioluminescence,* is also found in some fish and certain insects (glowworms and fireflys). Some species of fish and squid possess luminous organs especially adapted to harbor luminous bacteria. Colonies of luminous bacteria on solid culture media glow in the dark and emit sufficient light to be photographed (see **Figure 79**).

The luminescent reaction of bacteria occurs only in the presence of oxygen. It results from a chemical reaction employed in the transport of hydrogen and electrons to oxygen. The catalysts, *luciferin* and *luciferase,* serve to transport the hydrogen, resulting in the end products, hydrogen peroxide and light. This respiratory pathway is not known to yield energy to the cell, although it is tied in with high-energy phosphate exchanges since ATP is required for the light emission to occur. Luminous bacteria do not depend upon the luminescent reaction in the transport of hydrogen.

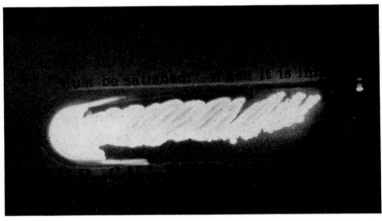

Figure 79. Agar slant culture of luminous bacteria (*Photobacterium fisheri*). The only light used in taking this photograph was that emitted by the bacteria. The exposure was six hours at f/4.5. (Courtesy of Carolina Biological Supply Company.)

Brief summary. The foregoing discussion of oxidation-reduction metabolism touches upon the salient features of the means by which the cell satisfies its most basic need; namely, the transformation of the energy tied up in chemical bonds of various foods (substrates) into a usable form. This is accomplished by dissimilation (catabolism) of these substrates through the catalytic action of a series of enzymes interacting with a pool of high-energy phosphate bonds (the "usable form" of energy). The anaerobic dissimilatory processes are labeled fermentation, while the aerobic ones are called respiration. Both processes are concerned with the sequential transport of hydrogen from a primary substrate to final acceptors of hydrogen. Some of the energy released by fermentation and respiration is lost as heat; some is converted to high-energy phosphate bonds. Also, certain wastes or end products accumulate which may, if not removed, impede or kill the cells.

The energy realized by the cell through dissimilation is used to direct and drive all assimilatory (anabolic) functions. In other words, assimilation is linked to dissimilation through the high-energy phosphate pool. These energy consuming, anabolic activities are (1) the synthesis of various molecules, both large and small, (2) reproduction, (3) maintenance of the cell's structural integrity, (4) locomotion, (5) absorption, (6) excretion, etc. While microorganisms were emphasized in this discussion, it should be remembered that all cells must have energy for their various anabolic functions. Thus, mammalian cells, plant cells or microbial cells possess many similar or identical metabolic pathways.

Some Other Important Metabolic Activities of Microorganisms

Thus far our discussion of metabolism has been confined to the cell's drive to obtain energy from some of its nutrients. Actually, fermentation and respiration represent just some of the metabolic activities classified as catabolic or dissimilatory. Many heterotrophs, for example, secrete enzymes which digest (hydrolyze) complex organic molecules to provide the cell with nutrients that are readily absorbed. Extracellular dissimilatory reactions of this type were discussed in the preceding chapter. Most substances absorbed by the cell undergo intracellular chemical alterations, enzymatically induced. Some of the nutrients are dissimilated directly via a fermentative or respiratory pathway, while others are dissimilated by other metabolic schemes which may, or may not, merge with fermentative or respiratory cycles. Nutrients also enter into anabolic or assimilatory activities, thus serving as "building blocks" for the synthesis of the larger molecules contained in protoplasm. Many molecules are diverted into both catabolic and anabolic paths.

Synthesis. A large portion of the energy realized by oxidation-reduction metabolism is directed into assimilatory paths to result in synthesis. The synthesis of starch from glucose is a good example of such a synthesis:

(1) Glucose + ATP $\xrightarrow{\text{hexokinase}}$ glucose-6-phosphate + ADP

(2) Glucose-6-phosphate $\xrightarrow{\text{phosphoglucomutase}}$ glucose-1-phosphate

(3) n (glucose-1-phosphate) $\xrightarrow{\text{phosphorylase}}$ starch + n (phosphate)

Note that these reactions are reversible and that reaction (1) requires the expenditure of high-energy phosphate. In a sense, the energy is not spent but is merely stored in the starch molecules and can be regained by reversal of the reactions, although there is some loss in the transfer of the energy in ATP to starch. Some bacteria store a starchlike substance, *granulose,* which is presumably synthesized through a mechanism similar to that in the above equations.

A number of low molecular weight compounds can be formed with isolated enzyme systems and ATP. Little is known about the synthesis of such complex biological compounds as proteins and peptides. Recent research has revealed nucleic acids to be the organizing force in the synthesis of proteins. Except for glycerides, syntheses of the common polymeric molecules in protoplasm do not occur merely by the reversal of hydrolysis.

Many bacteria produce a marked slime layer (capsule) composed of polysaccharide or, in a few instances, polypeptide. By and large, these complex molecules are synthesized intracellularly and secreted into the medium and on to the surface of the cells. Some of the polysaccharide slimes are synthesized from sucrose. One bacterium, *Leuconostoc mesenteroides,* produces a *dextran* slime by joining together the dextrose (glucose) component from many molecules of sucrose into a polymeric molecule:

$$n\text{C}_{12}\text{H}_{12}\text{O}_{11} \longrightarrow (\text{C}_6\text{H}_{10}\text{O}_5)_n + n\text{C}_6\text{H}_{12}\text{O}_6$$
$$\quad\text{(sucrose)} \qquad\qquad\qquad \text{(dextran)} \qquad \text{(fructose)}$$

The details of the synthesis of many microbial products is obscure. Such products as *pigments* and *antibiotics* are in this category. Some products of assimilation, e.g., *toxins* and *enzymes,* are proteins or contain protein. In general, much more is known of the nature of dissimilatory reactions than of assimilatory processes.

Heat Production.   It has been emphasized already that all organisms lose some energy in the form of heat. The vigorous growth of microorganisms generates considerable heat. This process is called *thermogenesis.* Its effects are commonly seen in decaying compost or manure heaps and in moist straw or hay. These materials are poor conductors of heat and may attain a temperature as high as 80° C. as a result of the thermogenic activities of the indigenous microflora. Gardeners take advantage of this, maintaining suitable temperatures in hotbeds during the early spring.

Chromogenesis.   A number of species of microorganisms produce *pigments,* i.e., compounds which absorb all waves of the visible spectrum except for a narrow band which transmits the pigment's characteristic color. Chromogenic organisms are widely distributed in nature. Essentially all the colors of the visible spectrum are represented among the pigments produced by microorganisms. Pigment formation is greatly influenced by a number of environmental factors, particularly osmotic pressure, light and temperature. Because of differences in solubility, some pigments are confined to the cell while others diffuse into the extracellular surroundings.

While the chemical composition of many of the pigments has been elucidated, the physiologic significance of most of them has remained obscure. Some of the microbial pigments are *antibiotics* (cf. Chapter 17), e.g., *pyocyanin* (dark blue) from *Pseudomonas aeruginosa, iodinin* (violet) from *Chromobacterium iodinum,* and *chlortetracycline* (bright yellow) from *Streptomyces aureofaciens.* A wide variety of *carotenoids,* red, orange or yellow pigments, are produced by bacteria and yeasts. Since carotenoids are soluble only in certain fat solvents, they are confined to the cell and impart a bright color to colonies of such organisms as *Staphylococcus aureus, Sarcina lutea* and *Rhodotorula* (a genus of yeasts). The function of carotenoids in microorganisms is not understood, except in the photosynthetic species where they assist in the absorption of light.

Probably the most important group of pigments are the *porphyrins,* represented by the *chlorophylls, cytochromes* and *heme.* The latter substance is the active component of hemoglobin, the protein in red blood cells and important in respiration. The cytochromes are vital in the transport of electrons, being found in all cells capable of respiration. Of course, the photosynthetic bacteria possess *bacteriochlorophyll,* a pigment closely related to the chlorophyll of higher plants.

One species of rod-shaped bacteria produces a brilliant blood-red pigment named *prodigiosin.* It has an interesting historical background. In 332 B.C., during the siege of Tyre by the Macedonians under Alexander the Great, bloody spots appeared inside the loaves of bread served to the army. This caused great apprehension among the soldiers, for it was considered an omen of their destruction. Alexander immediately called on his most skillful soothsayer to interpret the phenomenon. He cleverly explained the matter by saying that, since the spots were inside the bread, they meant bloody destruction for those inside the walled city and that, because there were no spots on the outside of the bread, the Macedonians had nothing to fear. This interpretation encouraged the soldiers to continue the siege, and the city of Tyre soon fell.

A number of other instances in later centuries in which blood-red spots appeared in bread are on record. Many attributed this phenomenon to supernatural causes. In the twelfth century a Danish priest noticed "blood" in the "host" used in the church sacrament known as Holy Communion. This caused great consternation among the people. It was feared that it was an ominous foreboding of disaster. A few weeks later an invading pagan army overthrew the state and made slaves of all the inhabitants.

In 1819 an epidemic of spotted polenta (corn mush) occurred in Padua, Italy. The population became so terrified that the government appointed a commission consisting of university professors, police officials and health officers to investigate the phenomenon. This investigation was of considerable importance, since it led to the discovery that a certain rod-shaped bacterium was the true cause of the bloodlike spots. This organism, now known as *Serratia marcescens,* is often referred to as the "miracle organism."

ECOLOGIC TYPES OF HETEROTROPHS

The nutrition and metabolism of an organism in large measure determines its natural habitat. Thus, an obligate aerobe cannot exist in the anaerobic mud of lake bottoms; a halophilic (salt-loving) bacterium is not encountered in fresh waters; autotrophs are not found inhabiting the bodies of higher forms of life; etc. On the basis of the degree of nutritional dependence or independence, heterotrophs are classified into two main groups. Those "free-living" types which obtain food from nonliving organic matter are termed *saprophytes* or *saprophytic* microorganisms. Those that depend on the organic foods of higher plants or animals are called *parasites* or *parasitic* microorganisms. In general, parasitic microorganisms have a less versatile metabolism, hence a more demanding nutrition, than saprophytic forms.

The vast majority of heterotrophs are saprophytic. They are present in enormous numbers in fertile soils and natural bodies of water, where they serve the useful purpose of degrading organic materials which are being deposited constantly in such environs. The reactions they assert on organic compounds are popularly called decay, putrefaction, fermentation and mineralization. The term *decay* is used to denote the decomposition of organic material in general; *putrefaction* refers to the decomposition of proteins, particularly in the absence of air; *fermentation* applies mainly to the decomposition of carbohydrates in the absence of air; *mineralization* describes the sum total of aerobic processes which result in the conversion of organic matter to inorganic matter (for example, the conversion of organic nitrogen to ammonia, nitrite and nitrate). The importance of these processes will be treated in Chapters 18, 21 and 22.

The term parasite embraces those microorganisms living upon or within other forms of life. The parasitized organism is called the *host*. Many microorganisms are able to adopt either a saprophytic or a parasitic existence. The three types of parasitism are:

1. *Commensalism*

This is an innocuous association between parasite and host, one from which the host is neither harmed nor benefited. The parasites are known as *commensals*. The skin and body cavities contain many commensals. Some are more appropriately referred to as opportunists.

2. *Symbiosis*

Symbiosis is a form of parasitism which is mutually advantageous to parasite and host. The parasite is called a *symbiont*. Some of the vitamin-synthesizing intestinal bacteria are symbionts. The classical example of symbiosis is the relationship between bacteria in the genus *Rhizobium* and leguminous plants which results in the fixation of nitrogen. The microflora of the rumen of sheep, cattle and other polygastric animals consists of symbionts inasmuch as they are provided with an excellent habitat for which they compensate the host by converting poor nutrients (hay, grass, silage) into foods suitable for their host's nutrition.

3. *Pathogenesis*

An association in which the parasite inflicts obvious injury (disease) to the host is a pathogenic one. Such *infectious* parasites are known as *pathogens*. Pathogens have shadowed mankind from time immemorial and have taken an enormous toll of life. Pathogens may be *obligate* or *opportunistic*. The former almost always produce frank disease, while the *opportunists* live as commensals until the host is stressed mechanically or physiologically, whereupon they become infectious. The term pathogen applies also to certain obligate saprophytes whose toxins (poisonous products of metabolism) when ingested cause disease. The best example of a disease caused by a saprophyte is botulism, a toxemia caused by eating a food in which *Clostridium botulinum* has grown.

Inevitably, metabolism and pathogenesis are intimately related. Because of certain unique metabolic activities, the pathogen inflicts damage on the host. Because of genetic or physiologic differences in potential hosts, pathogens exhibit host specificity. Thus, the metabolism of both the pathogen and the host are determinants of infectious disease. Metabolic products of the pathogen which are influential in pathogenesis include an array of enzymes that break down various structural barriers of the host's tissues and a variety of other products, some of which are protective toward the pathogen (capsular material, for example) and some of which are directly injurious to the host.

QUESTIONS

1. How are nutrients absorbed by the cell? What is meant by "active transport?" Compare the latter with "passive transport." What structures of the microbial cell regulate the passage of nutrients and wastes?

2. Explain the statement, "Potential metabolic activities determine the nutritional requirements of an organism." Distinguish between an essential nutrient and an essential metabolite.

3. Differentiate between autotroph and heterotroph; between photosynthesis and chemosynthesis. Do autotrophs or heterotrophs have the more intricate metabolism? Explain.

4. What are the different categories of nutrients? Cite examples of nutrients which serve as sources of carbon; of sulfur; of nitrogen.

5. Discuss briefly the role of vitamins. Of what practical significance is the microbial synthesis of vitamins?

6. Define: (1) aerobe, (2) anaerobe, (3) facultative anaerobe, (4) microaerophile. What two types of facultative anaerobes exist?

7. What is meant by the statement, "Energy is the directing force of metabolism?"

8. Distinguish between dissimilation (catabolism) and assimilation (anabolism).

9. Why does all life ultimately depend upon photosynthesis? In the process of photosynthesis, higher plants, but not bacteria, produce oxygen. Explain.

10. What is the role of adenosine triphosphate in dissimilation and assimilation?

11. Define: (1) fermentation (intra- and intermolecular), (2) respiration, (3) complete oxidation, (4) incomplete oxidation. Cite an example of each.

12. Why are aerobic instead of anaerobic conditions employed in the production of baker's yeast?

13. Why is pyruvic acid such an important intermediate product in metabolism?

14. Hydrogen is removed from the substrate during both fermentation and respiration. How does each of these processes handle the transport of hydrogen?

15. Define: (1) dehydrogenase, (2) catalase, (3) peroxidase.

16. Name some pigments produced by microorganisms that are of physiologic significance.

17. Distinguish between a saprophyte and a parasite. What are the major categories of parasitism?

18. What is the relationship between thermogenesis and the efficiency with which microorganisms derive energy from their nutrients?

REFERENCES

Barker, H. A.: Bacterial Fermentations. New York, John Wiley & Sons, Inc., 1956.

Clifton, C. E.: Introduction to Bacterial Physiology. New York, McGraw-Hill Book Co., Inc., 1957.

Fry, B. A., and Peel, J. L., ed.: Autotrophic Micro-organisms, Fourth Symposium of the Society for General Microbiology. Cambridge, Cambridge University Press, 1954.

Gale, E. F.: The Chemical Activities of Bacteria. 3rd ed. New York, Academic Press, Inc., 1951.

Kluyver, A. J., and van Niel, C. B.: The Microbe's Contribution to Biology, Cambridge, Mass., Harvard University Press, 1956.

Lamanna, C., and Mallette, M. F.: Basic Bacteriology (Its Biological and Chemical Background). 2nd ed. Baltimore, The Williams & Wilkins Co., 1959.

Oginsky, E. L., and Umbreit, W. W.: An Introduction to Bacterial Physiology. 2nd ed. San Francisco, W. H. Freeman and Co., 1959.

Porter, J. R.: Bacterial Chemistry and Physiology. New York, John Wiley & Sons, Inc., 1946.

Stanier, R. Y., Doudoroff, M., and Adelberg, E. A.: The Microbial World. Englewood Cliffs, N. J., Prentice-Hall, Inc., 1957.

Stephenson, M.: Bacterial Metabolism. New York, Longmans, Green & Co., 3rd ed., 1949.

Thimann, K. R.: The Life of Bacteria: Their Growth, Metabolism, and Relationships. New York, The Macmillan Co., 1955.

Werkman, C. H., and Wilson, P. W., ed.: Bacterial Physiology. New York, Academic Press, Inc., 1951.

12 • Factors Influencing the Growth of Microorganisms

Microorganisms as well as all other forms of life are subject to the influence of environmental factors. There is a complex interrelationship between organisms and their environment. An organism can exist only within definite and rather narrow limits in regard to environmental factors and can thrive most successfully within still narrower limits. The phase of biological science that deals with the interrelationships between organisms and their environment is known as *ecology*.

Among the factors which exert a more or less direct effect upon the growth and development of microorganisms are the food supply, oxygen tension, temperature, moisture, hydrogen-ion concentration, oxidation-reduction potential, surface tension, osmotic pressure, light and the presence of other organisms. The foods required by microorganisms and the influence of oxygen tension have been considered in the previous chapter.

TEMPERATURE

Environmental temperatures play a significant role in the activities of microbial life. As mentioned in a previous chapter, the metabolic processes of organisms involve chemical and physical reactions. The rate of these reactions is profoundly influenced by the all-pervading factor of temperature, a most important variable of the environment. Metabolic activities are retarded by cold and accelerated by heat up to a certain point, beyond which they gradually cease. The temperatures to which microorganisms are exposed may stimulate their growth; alter their metabolism, morphology, or pathogenicity; or cause their death. Low temperatures retard or prevent growth because they cause metabolic activities to taper off or cease. Temperatures below the freezing point of water are often lethal

189

because of the formation of ice crystals. Temperatures above the optimum for growth of a microorganism also retard or prevent growth. Of course, temperatures excessively greater than those optimum for growth will kill, a fact used to good advantage in the canning of foods, sterilization of laboratory glassware, etc. A knowledge of the effect of temperature on the rate of growth and other processes of microorganisms is essential for such practical matters as (1) the cultivation of microorganisms, be it in the laboratory or in an industrial production plant, and (2) the preservation and sanitary handling of foods.

Some organisms grow best at low temperatures—these are known as *psychrophiles.* Others grow most rapidly at high temperatures—these are called *thermophiles;* whereas those that grow best at moderate temperatures are termed *mesophiles.*

Temperature Ranges of Growth

In general, microbial growth is possible between 0° and about 80° C. No one species, however, can be active within this entire range, each having its own growth range within these limits. At the zero point, the temperature at which water freezes, most species are unable to grow. Certain marine bacteria, however, will grow at −7.5° C., a temperature which is above the freezing point of sea water. Even at 10° C. growth does not occur, or is slow, in most species. Starting at 15° C., growth increases rapidly for the majority of species. This temperature has been referred to as the "threshold temperature" because, starting at this point, each degree rise in temperature (up to a certain maximum) causes a greatly accelerated growth. The temperature of most rapid growth for many species is about 30° C.

The temperature below which a certain organism will not grow is known as the *minimum growth temperature* for that organism. The temperature above which it will not grow is called the *maximum growth temperature.* For many soil bacteria the maximum lies between 30° and 35° C. Pathogens, as a rule, show little growth above 42° C. Certain thermophiles grow at a temperature as high as 80° C. The temperature range between the maximum and the minimum is known as the *growth-temperature range.* Within this range the vital activities of the organism can be carried on. The growth-temperature range of a given species, however, is not necessarily the same in the various media or surroundings in which it can live. A number of environmental factors are capable of affecting the range. For some species the growth-temperature range is narrow, whereas for others it is wide. For most pathogens the range is narrow. The tubercle bacillus, for example, has a range of not more than 10 degrees, while the range of *Escherichia coli* is more than 35 degrees. The ranges for saprophytes vary greatly.

For every microbial species there is a temperature at which growth takes place most rapidly. This temperature lies between the minimum and maximum and is known as the *optimum growth temperature* for that organism. The optimum temperature for a given organism is not necessarily the same in different media. Although the optimum temperature is most favorable for growth, it is not necessarily the most favorable for all the activities carried on by the organism. Certain metabolic functions may proceed optimally at temperatures several degrees removed from the optimum growth temperature. Even the use of growth as the criterion for determining optimum temperature can be misleading, inasmuch as many species in culture produce their greatest final *mass* of cells at a temperature a degree or two below that which is considered to be optimum for supporting the greatest *rate* of growth. Unfortunately, this dilemma cannot be resolved without specifying the criterion employed in designating a temperature as optimum for any given culture. In popular usage, however, the optimum temperature for a microorganism is that which permits the *greatest rate of growth*. Most bacteria pathogenic for man have an optimum growth temperature of 37.5° C., the body temperature of man. Likewise, organisms pathogenic for birds have an optimum of 42° C., the body temperature of birds. As the temperature rises above or drops beneath the optimum, growth continues, but at a slower rate, until the temperature drops beneath the minimum or rises above the maximum, when growth ceases. For many species the maximum temperature is but a few degrees above the optimum.

Psychrophiles. The psychrophilic microorganisms have an optimum temperature usually below 15° C., depending upon the species, with a minimum of 0° C. or below and a maximum of about 30° C. These organisms are endowed with the ability to grow near zero and, in some instances, at subzero temperatures. Psychrophiles are widely distributed, being found in cold lake, spring and ocean waters, and also in the soil of northern regions. In cold storage plants they may cause the decomposition of meats and other foods.

Thermophiles. The thermophilic microorganisms grow best at temperatures above 50° C. They do not grow appreciably at temperatures below 25° C., and their maximum lies between 60° and 90° C. Hence, many thermophiles grow at temperatures above those that will kill psychrophiles and mesophiles. Thermophiles are found in the soil, decaying manure and in certain hot springs, some of which may have temperatures above 80° C. Few other forms of life can carry on their activities at such high temperatures. Because of their ability to withstand high temperatures they are of considerable economic importance, owing to the harm they are capable of doing in the dairy and canning industries. Occasionally they get into milk and increase rapidly in numbers during the process of pasteurization, which is carried on at a temperature (60° to 65° C.) suited to their growth. This temperature kills most bacteria, but is near the optimum for certain thermophiles. They do not give rise to injurious products in the milk but do lower its quality.

Many thermophiles are spore formers, producing spores unusually resistant to heat. They sometimes cause trouble in the canning industry in that the spores survive the processing temperatures. As the food gradually loses its heat, the spores germinate into vegetative forms which multiply rapidly before the food is cooled to room temperature, producing the condition known as "flat souring." Canned foods are now usually cooled in water immediately after being removed from the retort (steam chest) to prevent the spores of thermophiles, should they be present, from germinating.

Mesophiles. Mesophilic microorganisms are those which grow best between 20° and 40° C. The vast majority of microorganisms are mesophiles; only a relatively small number of species thrive at high or low temperatures. Many of the soil bacteria responsible for the decomposition of organic matter are mesophiles. Since the body temperature of warm-blooded animals lies within the mesophiles' range, organisms which parasitize these animals are mesophiles.

It should be understood that the lines of demarcation between psychrophiles, mesophiles and thermophiles cannot be drawn with precision. Some mesophiles grow very slowly in the psychrophilic range. By the same token, certain thermophiles will grow slowly in the mesophilic range.

MOISTURE

Microorganisms require moisture for their activities, not only within their cells, but also in their environment. Their natural habitat is a watery medium in which they can readily maintain the water content of their cells and take in food in solution by diffusion through the cell surface, or, as in some of the protozoa, take in food in the form of particulate matter along with water to form food vacuoles. The importance of water to the cell has been considered previously (Chapters 3 and 11).

Microbes do not necessarily require environs saturated with water. Many microorganisms are able to live in the thin films of water surrounding soil particles. Molds can usually grow in situations containing less water than is required by bacteria or yeasts.

When subjected to the natural process of drying in air, some kinds of microorganisms are readily destroyed, whereas others survive long periods in a desiccated state. Certain pathogenic bacteria, such as the gonococcus and meningococcus, are killed in a relatively short time when dried, but the tubercle bacillus and the staphylococcus can remain viable for a long time in the desiccated state.

Because drying inhibits the activity of microorganisms, man can use desiccation as a method of food preservation. Desiccation was used by primitive man in the drying of meats and fish. Modern man uses it on a large scale to protect foodstuffs from the attacks of microorganisms. Fruits, vegetables, meats, fish, milk and eggs are some of the foods used daily in the dehydrated state. Such foods keep because of their dryness, although spontaneous chemical reactions will affect, in time, the palatability of dried foods.

Under certain conditions, bacteria may be preserved by desiccation. In the process of *lyophilization* a suspension of cells is frozen quickly in a vial and subjected to a high vacuum. This causes *sublimation* of the moisture, i.e., the water goes from the solid phase (ice) to the vapor phase without a transition in the fluid phase. Upon complete removal of the moisture, the vial is sealed without releasing the vacuum. The dried cells which remain can be stored for years without loss in viability and with retention of all genetic characteristics. Not all types of microorganisms can be preserved by lyophilization, but the method is an excellent one for keeping collections of bacteria, particularly the more delicate and nutritionally exacting types which frequently are lost by routine transfers in culture media.

HYDROGEN-ION CONCENTRATION

The *reaction* or *hydrogen-ion concentration* of the environment exerts a considerable influence on all activities of the cell. Some grow best in a medium that is neutral in reaction; others require an acid or alkaline reaction.

Acidity and alkalinity are measured most conveniently in terms of hydrogen-ion concentration. Whether a liquid is acidic or basic in reaction depends upon the relative proportions of positively charged hydrogen ions, (H^+) characteristic of acids, and negatively charged hydroxyl ions (OH^-) characteristic of bases. An excess of hydrogen ions gives rise to an acidic reaction, while an excess of hydroxyl ions produces a basic reaction. A liquid that contains equal numbers of hydrogen and hydroxyl ions is said to be neutral. Pure water is the typical neutral medium (at 22° C.). In water a small degree of ionization occurs, giving rise to a small but equal number of hydrogen and hydroxyl ions.

$$HOH \rightleftarrows H^+ + OH^-$$

An acid, such as hydrochloric acid, ionizes in aqueous solution into positively charged hydrogen ions and negatively charged chlorine ions:

$$HCl \rightleftarrows H^+ + Cl^-$$

A base, such as sodium hydroxide, dissociates into positively charged sodium ions and negatively charged hydroxyl ions:

$$Na\,OH \rightleftarrows Na^+ + OH^-$$

A basic solution always contains some hydrogen ions, owing to the ionization of water. The basic reaction is due to the excess of hydroxyl over hydrogen ions. Likewise, an acidic solution contains hydroxyl ions from the water it contains. The strength of an acidic or a basic solution depends upon the degree of ionization rather than on the total amount of acid or base present.

The acidity of a solution can be expressed in terms of its hydrogen-ion concentration; since a basic solution also contains hydrogen ions, its alkalinity can be expressed in terms of its hydrogen-ion concentration. The hydrogen-ion concentration is one of the important variables in the environment of microorganisms.

To express hydrogen-ion concentration, the so-called *p*H scale is used. On this scale *p*H 7 represents neutrality. This value is based on the hydrogen-ion concentration of a liter of water. Pure distilled water (at 22° C.) has a hydrogen-ion concentration of 0.0000001 gm. per liter. The reciprocal of this fraction is 10,000,000, or 10^7, and the logarithm of the reciprocal is 7. This is the basis for using *p*H 7 to represent neutrality. *The term "pH" may be defined as the logarithm of the reciprocal of the hydrogen-ion concentration.*

The symbol *p*H can be used to designate either acidity or alkalinity, because for any given hydrogen-ion concentration there is a certain definite corresponding concentration of hydroxyl ions. Since *p*H is the logarithm of a reciprocal, *p*H decreases as the hydrogen-ion concentration increases. On this basis a *p*H scale has been constructed extending from *p*H 0 to *p*H 14. The more acidic the solution, the lower the *p*H; the less acidic or more basic, the higher the *p*H. The *p*H of acidic solutions is less than 7, and the *p*H of basic solutions is greater than 7. Since a logarithmic scale of ten is used as a base, each change of one in the *p*H scale corresponds to a tenfold change in the concentration of hydrogen ions. Thus a *p*H of 4 will contain ten times as many hydrogen ions as one of *p*H 5 and a hundred times as many as one of *p*H 6.

The *p*H of solutions may be determined by one of two methods; (1) *electrometrically,* or (2) *colorimetrically.* The electrometric method involves the use of a potentiometer. The colorimetric method, while not as accurate, is frequently used. This method requires the use of indicators (certain organic dyes) which show color changes over certain ranges of *p*H values. What is actually measured in *p*H determinations is hydrogen-ion activity, i.e., the degree of acidity or alkalinity, rather than the total quantity of acid or base present.

Each type of microorganism has a *p*H range as well as an optimum *p*H for growth. The majority of bacterial species have an optimum *p*H which lies between 6 and 8. Some bacteria are restricted to a narrow range, while others can grow over a range as wide as 6 or 7 *p*H units. A few can grow at a *p*H as low as 3, while some rare species require an environment whose *p*H is in the region of 13. Some species of the sulfur bacterium, *Thiobacillus,* lower the *p*H of the medium to less than 0 as a result of the oxidation of sulfur to sulfuric acid, although they cannot initiate growth at such a low *p*H.

Yeasts and molds are more tolerant of acidic environments than are bacteria, although they do not prefer highly acidic conditions. Few bacteria will initiate growth in a medium with a *p*H less than 4.5, while most fungi will grow in a medium with a *p*H as low as 2.5 or 3.0.

Certain foods, such as sauerkraut, do not readily spoil because their *p*H has been reduced by microbial activity to a point where spoilage organisms are unable to grow.

Buffers

Although the metabolic activities of certain microorganisms may give rise to large quantities of acid or alkali, the presence of buffers will prevent rapid changes in the reaction of the environment from occurring. A *buffer* is a substance which can react with either acids or bases and, therefore, tends to prevent any great change in the *p*H of the medium unless its capacity is exceeded. Buffers exert their effect by reactions that bind hydrogen or hydroxyl ions. Certain salts, particularly the phosphates, acetates, carbonates and many organic substances, such as proteins, peptones and amino acids, act as buffers. The amino groups of proteins and their degradation products react with acids and the carboxyl groups with bases (cf. Chapter 3). The bacteriologist frequently adds buffers to culture media to prevent undesirable *p*H changes in these media.

OXIDATION-REDUCTION POTENTIAL

You will recall from the discussion of oxidation-reduction metabolism in Chapter 11 that any chemical reaction which parts with electrons is an oxidation. Conversely, a reaction which accepts electrons is a reduction. Actually, the two reactions occur simultaneously and, in any single system, will reach an equilibrium if conditions which affect the reactions are kept constant. For example, the ionization of hydrogen gas, a reversible oxidation-reduction reaction, takes place as follows:

$$H_2 \rightleftharpoons 2\,H^+ + 2\,e^-$$

(where e^- is the symbol for an electron).

Such a system exerts an electromotive force of an intensity or *potential* related to the ratio of the oxidized form to the reduced form. This potential, called the *O/R potential,* is expressed in volts as measured by a potentiometer. A qualitative measure of the O/R potential can be obtained by employing certain dyes that undergo color changes as they are oxidized or reduced. One such dye is *methylene blue,* which in its oxidized state is blue and in its reduced state (*leuco*-methylene blue) is colorless. The reducing activity of a bacterial culture can be observed by adding a very dilute solution of methylene blue and watching the color gradually disappear.

The higher the O/R potential, the greater the oxidizing activity of the system. Contrariwise, the lower potentials indicate good reducing (acceptance of electrons) activity. Every oxidation-reduction system has its characteristic O/R potential at equilibrium when determined under standard conditions. Several factors, particularly *p*H and temperature, influence the O/R potential.

In the metabolizing cell numerous enzymatically regulated oxidation-reduction reactions are integrated in the transport of hydrogen and electrons. Such biological oxidation-reduction systems impart to the cell and its environment an O/R potential. As a rule, the O/R potential of a microbial culture decreases once growth ensues. Anaerobes lower the potential farther than aerobes. If a *reducing agent* (a substance which will establish an oxidation-reduction system of low O/R potential) is added to the culture medium, it will *poise* the O/R potential of the medium at a low level. This favors the growth of anaerobes, even in the presence of dissolved oxygen. Thus oxygen is not toxic to obligate anaerobes if the O/R potential of the environment is of a low order, although oxygen will tend to raise the potential. Some reducing agents often added to culture media are ascorbic acid, thioglycolic acid, cysteine and glutathione. Bits of meat sterilized with broth media tend to poise the O/R potential at a low point.

OSMOTIC PRESSURE

Osmotic pressure is the force which causes molecules of a solvent (usually water) to pass through a semipermeable membrane in the direction of the higher concentration of solutes (substances in true solution). When two solutions containing different concentrations of solutes are separated by a membrane which is permeable to the solvent, the effects of osmotic pressure cause a greater flow of solvent in the direction of the higher concentration of solute. This process is termed *osmosis*. The osmotic pressure of a solution is proportional to the number of molecules, or molecules and ions, of dissolved substance contained in a given volume of solution. A concentrated solution has a high osmotic pressure. Living cells, in general, are influenced by the osmotic pressure of the surrounding medium, generally an aqueous solution. For many microorganisms the surrounding medium is fresh water; for others, salt water; for parasites it may be body fluids such as blood or lymph or the sap of plants.

If a cell is suspended in a solution having a higher concentration of solute and, consequently, a lower water concentration than its own protoplasm, more water will flow from the less dense solution within the cell to the more dense solution surrounding the cell than in the reverse direction. Theoretically, this will continue until an equilibrium has been established between the cell contents and the medium. The cell will lose water and shrink under these conditions and is then said to be *plasmolyzed*. The process is known as *plasmolysis*. If the cell has a rigid cell wall, the wall maintains its original form, while the protoplasm shrinks. The pellicle of protozoa, being flexible, becomes wrinkled when the protoplasm shrinks. Advantage may be taken of the phenomenon of plasmolysis in the preservation of certain foods. Jellies, jams, sugared fruits and salted foods will not undergo spoilage due to the presence of bacteria or yeasts if their osmotic pressure is sufficiently high to plasmolyze the microorganisms that find their way into them. Molds, however, may occasionally grow in such foods, since they can withstand higher osmotic pressures than can most bacteria and yeasts.

If a cell is suspended in distilled water, more water will flow into the cell than out of it. The cell will thus imbibe water and swell and is then said to be *plasmoptyzed*. The process is known as *plasmoptysis*. This may cause the cell wall to burst, allowing the cell contents to escape. However, the firm cell walls of bacterial cells usually prevent undue swelling under such conditions, since an internal pressure develops to prevent further entrance of water. This high internal pressure, known as *turgor*, is characteristic of the cells of plants, bacteria, yeasts and molds. Human red blood corpuscles, however, when placed in pure water, will swell quickly and burst, because they, as well as animal cells in general, are incapable of developing the condition of turgor. The role of the cell wall of bacteria in maintaining turgor is demonstrated by the behavior of *protoplasts* (cells without cell walls but with an intact cytoplasmic membrane). Certain species of bacteria lose their cell wall upon treatment with lysozyme or penicillin. The protoplasts which form undergo plasmoptysis in solutions of the customary solute concentrations because of the lack of a confining cell wall. This can be prevented by allowing the protoplasts to form in a solution of greater solute concentration than normally employed in cultivating the bacterium.

A solution which has an osmotic pressure higher than that of the cell is said to be *hypertonic*, while one having a lower osmotic pressure is referred to as *hypotonic*. Thus, hypertonic solutions induce plasmolysis while hypotonic solutions encourage plasmoptysis. A solution which has an osmotic pressure equal to that of the cell is termed an *isotonic* solution. The cells of microorganisms vary greatly in their ability to withstand extremes of osmotic pressure. Some species of exceptional microorganisms thrive in habitats of high osmotic pressure. Such organisms are found in oceans (salinity of about 4 per cent), salt lakes (the Dead Sea contains about 29 per cent salts) and sugary or salted foods. Microorganisms which demand high osmotic pressure for their existence are called *osmophiles*. Those osmophiles associated with saline environments are spoken of as *halophiles*, while those which thrive in high concentrations of sugar are commonly called *saccharophiles*. While some microorganisms can adjust to extreme hypertonic conditions, most are inhibited or killed by elevated osmotic pressures. Frequently, certain solutes will evidence specific chemical toxicity in addition to an influence on osmotic pressure, depending on their concentration and the nature of the cells being treated. High osmotic pressure, however, can be used to inhibit the growth of most bacteria, yeasts and molds.

Dialysis

In addition to water, the cytoplasmic membrane permits the passage of many solutes. The cell absorbs nutrients and secretes wastes as the result of the diffusion of solutes of limiting size across the cell membrane in the direction of lesser solute concentration. This process which operates hand-in-hand with osmosis is called *dialysis*. In addition to considerations of concentration gradients of solvents and solutes, the electrostatic charges on diffusible ions and the polar groups of nondiffusible molecules (such as proteins) on either side of the membrane may cause a departure from expected osmotic effects. In other words, the charges on ions and molecules across a semi-permeable membrane attract or repel one another, thereby interfering with the forces regulating dialysis as well as osmosis.

SURFACE TENSION

The molecules at the surface of any liquid are oriented in an orderly manner in contrast to a random molecular distribution throughout the body of the liquid. As a rule, the molecules concentrate at the surface and behave as a fluid membrane, resulting in a force aptly named *surface tension*. It is surface tension that makes it possible to float a needle on the surface of calm water. The crescent-shaped meniscus of water in a narrow tube is a result of surface tension. As a result of surface tension, a small drop of liquid in a gas tends to maintain a minimum surface area by assuming the shape of a sphere. A measure of surface tension can be obtained by determining the force necessary to overcome the tendency of a liquid to minimize its surface area. This measurement is commonly made with an instrument called a "tensiometer." The force is expressed in dynes per centimeter. Surface tension in the strict sense refers to molecular organization of a liquid's surface interposed against some gas. A related type of tension exists at the surface of a solid immersed in a fluid. The latter is called *interfacial tension* and is an important force at the surface of cells. This force cannot be measured very precisely. However, a measure of surface tension is a fairly reliable index of interfacial tension.

A number of substances influence the surface tension of water. Many organic compounds lower surface tension, i.e., impede the efforts of a liquid to maintain a minimum surface area. Such compounds are said to be *surface active*, being popularly referred to as *"surfactants"* or *surface tension depressants*. Since they encourage water to spread better over solid surfaces, surface active substances often are termed *wetting agents*. Examples of surface tension depressants are higher molecular weight organic acids, alcohols, soaps, synthetic detergents, proteins and polypeptides. A group of excellent disinfectants, the quaternary ammonium compounds, are highly potent surface tension depressants. Some substances will raise the surface tension slightly, but it is the depression of surface tension that exerts profound effects against cells.

Some bacteria are more tolerant of decreases in surface tension than others. By and large, the Gram-negative bacteria can withstand greater reductions in surface tension than Gram-positive bacteria. Hence, by lowering the surface tension to a threshold level, media inhibitory to Gram-positive bacteria but not to Gram-negative bacteria can be prepared. Nutrient broth at 20° C. has a surface tension of approximately 60 dynes per centimeter. If its surface tension were lowered to 40, few Gram-positive, but most Gram-negative, species would grow in it.

Many aerobic spore-formers grow on the surface of broth media and form a pellicle or dense mat of cells. However, if the surface tension is decreased a bit, such bacteria will no longer form a pellicle but, instead, will grow diffusely throughout the broth.

SUNLIGHT

As previously pointed out, some bacteria have photosynthetic pigments and require sunlight for their growth and development. Often the production of pigment by chromogenic bacteria is enhanced by light. Most microorganisms, however, do not require light. The growth of some molds is stimulated by diffuse light, but most microorganisms grow best in the absence of light. Direct sunlight is injurious to many, if not all, nonphotosynthetic bacteria. It will usually kill them within a few hours. The destructive effect is due chiefly to ultraviolet rays. In the visible spectrum the blue and violet rays exert an inhibiting effect on microorganisms. The practical use of light for the destruction of microorganisms will receive consideration in Chapter 15.

THE BIOTIC ENVIRONMENT

In addition to the physical and chemical factors just considered, microorganisms are subject to the influence of the other living organisms in their environment. The influence of such biotic factors is often very pronounced. In nature nearly every habitat suited to the growth of microorganisms has a characteristic population consisting usually of a number of species of macro- and microorganisms. There may be competition, antagonism and also cooperation in such a community, since the coexisting populations affect one another to a marked degree. The metabolic by-products of one kind of organism may stimulate or inhibit another, thus limiting the growth and survival of its cohabitants.

Beneficial Associations

An association of two or more kinds of microorganisms in which there is mutual benefit is known as *symbiosis*. This mutually advantageous relationship occurs between microorganisms and animals or plants as well as between different kinds of microorganisms. In many herbivorous animals, such as the cow, cellulose-digesting bacteria break down the cellulose in the food of these animals, which, although much of their food is cellulose, do not produce enzymes that act on this compound. These animals are thus dependent upon bacteria for the digestion of one of their important food components and provide a suitable habitat for the microorganisms. The association is therefore mutually beneficial.

There is an interesting symbiotic relationship between leguminous plants and root-nodule bacteria (*Rhizobium*). The bacteria live in little nodules on the roots of the plants. They utilize (fix) free atmospheric nitrogen, from which they build compounds the plants can use. The bacteria are benefited in that they obtain nutrient materials from the plants. These nitrogen-fixing bacteria play a role in the nitrogen cycle. (See Chapter 18.)

Certain insects known as termites eat wood, which is chiefly cellulose. Like herbivorous animals, they do not produce cellulase but depend upon certain protozoa which they harbor in their digestive systems to hydrolyze the cellulose.

Associations frequently occur in which one kind of microorganism by its growth produces substances that other species can use. An association of this kind, in which one species exerts a favorable effect on another species, is spoken of as *metabiosis*. Obligate anaerobes, when growing in mixed cultures with aerobic organisms, benefit from the association in that the aerobes reduce the oxygen tension in the immediate vicinity of the anaerobes, thus favoring their growth. The aerobes, however, are not benefited by the association. Bacteria which hydrolyze cellulose to glucose benefit those bacteria that require glucose but are unable to break down cellulose. The decomposition of organic matter in general is carried out by a series of organisms which follow each other in close succession as the by-products they can utilize become available. The activities of one type of organism thus benefit another, which in turn benefits the next organism in the series. This topic will be elaborated upon in Chapter 18.

Antagonistic Associations

Certain microorganisms are inimical to the well-being of other organisms in the immediate vicinity. Such an antagonistic activity is known as *antibiosis*. The antagonism may be sufficiently intense to inhibit completely the growth of one kind of organism in the presence of another kind. The antagonistic effect may be due to an increase or decrease in hydrogen-ion concentration, increase or decrease in oxygen tension or carbon dioxide tension, or to the production of specific growth-inhibiting or germicidal substances known as *antibiotics*, which, in extremely small amounts, are capable of inhibiting or causing the death of other organisms. The soil is the habitat of many microorganisms capable of producing antibiotics. Microbial antagonism on the part of soil microorganisms is shown in Figure 80.

Antibiotics have created much interest in recent years, since some have become effective chemotherapeutic agents in the treatment of infectious diseases. Examples of antibiotics are penicillin, streptomycin, tetracycline and chloramphenicol. Chapter 17 contains a discussion of these agents.

The acid produced by carbohydrate-fermenting bacteria exerts an inhibitory effect on numerous other species. In the natural souring of milk, lactic acid-producing bacteria become the predominant organisms. The acid they produce inhibits those bacteria that are capable of attacking the proteins of milk and causing putrefaction. For this reason the first alteration of raw milk when acted upon by bacteria is souring instead of

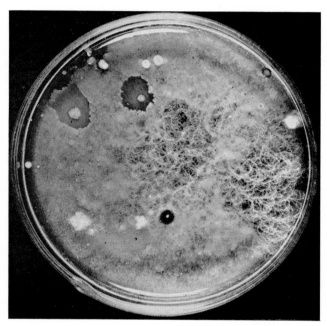

Figure 80. Photograph of an agar plate culture illustrating microbial antagonism. The medium was inoculated with 1 ml. of a 1:10,000,000 dilution of soil. The clear zones surrounding three of the colonies indicate that they produced an inhibitory substance which diffused into the surrounding medium, preventing the growth of the spreading colonies of other species. (Courtesy of Dr. Albert Kelner.)

putrefaction. Later, the acids produced are utilized by other organisms. This finally provides conditions suitable for putrefactive bacteria.

Synergism

An association between microbial species which increases the ability of the participating species to decompose organic matter, or to produce an effect which neither one can produce alone, is known as *synergism*. In some cases the enzyme system of one species supplements that of another. A common form of synergism is the production of gas when two kinds of bacteria are put together in a carbohydrate medium in which neither one alone is able to produce gas. *Streptococcus faecalis,* for example, hydrolyzes sucrose to glucose and fructose and produces acids in the fermentation of glucose or fructose. *Escherichia coli* does not act on sucrose but produces both acid and gas from hydrolyzed sucrose (glucose and fructose). Thus, together these organisms produce gas from sucrose, whereas neither alone is able to bring about this change. Many other pairs of bacteria are known to produce gas from various sugar media when acting together but are unable to do so when fermenting these particular sugars in pure culture. Other types of physiological synergisms exist but are not as readily explained as synergistic gas production.

GROWTH OF BACTERIAL POPULATIONS

The growth of bacteria in a suitable liquid culture medium follows a definite course. If, at regular intervals of time, a series of small samples are removed aseptically from a broth culture and the number of viable cells determined,* data can be obtained with which a growth curve, such as seen in Figure 81, can be drawn.

Lag Phase

Following inoculation of the medium, the bacteria as a rule do not begin to multiply immediately. Often there occurs a decrease in numbers of viable cells at the onset. In most cases they increase in size and their protoplasm becomes more or less homogeneous, owing to the disappearance of granules of glycogen, volutin and other reserve substances. This *lag phase* may last a few minutes or some hours, depending upon the kind of bacterium and the environmental conditions being employed.

Apparently the cells need time to adjust to a new environment before engaging in multiplication. If the culture medium is nutritionally adequate and if the most favorable physical conditions (temperature, osmotic pressure, surface tension, etc.) are utilized, the length of the lag period will be minimized, particularly if the inoculum is large. Moreover, the lag period may not occur if the bacteria in the inoculum were recovered from a culture in its phase of most rapid multiplication.

In the latter portion of the lag phase the cells are said to be in a state

* The most common method for enumeration of viable numbers of bacteria and many other microorganisms is the *plate count*. To prepare a plate count, one makes a series of known dilutions from which measured volumes are transferred aseptically to a series of Petri dishes. A suitable agar medium in the molten state (temperature 42 to 45° C.) is poured into each inoculated plate and gently mixed with the plate's contents. After the medium has solidified, the plates are incubated for a period of time, generally 18 to 72 hours, to allow macroscopically visible colonies to appear. If one assumes that each colony has arisen from an individual cell, the number of colonies multiplied by the reciprocal of the dilution gives a quantitative estimate of the population in the original undiluted specimen. It is also assumed that each viable cell on the plates produced a visible colony. Despite the obvious dangers implicit in these assumptions, the plate count, if conducted carefully, is a fairly reliable, reproducible method of estimating populations of many of the unicellular microorganisms. Care must be taken to carry out the entire procedure with sterile glassware and sterile diluent and as aseptically as possible.

of *"physiological youth"* because their metabolism is so highly active. In fact, most metabolic reactions seem to proceed more rapidly during the late lag phase than at any later stage of the growth cycle. Therefore, a great burst of metabolic activities precedes the next phase, one of a high rate of reproduction.

Logarithmic Growth Phase

After the lag phase the bacteria begin to multiply. The rate of cell division at first is slow, but gradually increases in pace until a maximum speed is reached. Once the maximum rate of increase in population is reached, the culture is said to be in the *logarithmic growth phase*. During this period the population increases at a *geometric* (*not* arithmetic) rate.

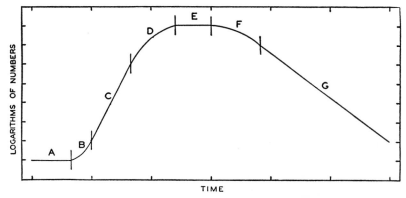

Figure 81. Diagrammatic representation of a bacterial growth curve; logarithms of numbers of viable organisms plated against time of incubation. *A*, Initial stationary phase; *B*, positive growth acceleration phase; *C*, logarithmic growth phase; *D*, negative growth acceleration phase; *E*, maximum stationary phase; *F*, phase of accelerated death; *G*, logarithmic death phase. (From W. Burrows, Textbook of Microbiology.)

Thus, if at time X during the logarithmic growth phase the population were 10,000 viable cells per ml., the concentration of cells at X + 10 minutes would be 20,000 and at X + 20 minutes, 40,000 (*not* 30,000!). If one plots the logarithm of the number of viable cells per unit volume of culture against time, the logarithmic growth phase is represented by a straight line (*C* in Figure 81). During this period, data can be derived with which to calculate the *generation time,* an expression of the time required by one cell, upon first arising from the mother cell, to divide in half. During the phase of logarithmic growth, the generation time is constant, being of an order of magnitude of 20 to 30 minutes for some species, and several hours for the more slowly growing types. The logarithmic phase itself may last for several hours to several days, depending on a number of environmental factors and the nature of the organism being cultured. A suboptimum temperature, for example, would increase the generation time, thereby increasing the length of the logarithmic growth phase. During the logarithmic phase the cells decrease in size, but remain microscopically homogeneous, especially during the earlier part of this phase.

Maximum Stationary Phase

The bacterial count will eventually reach a maximum level with no further increase in numbers. The cells no longer divide rapidly, and the

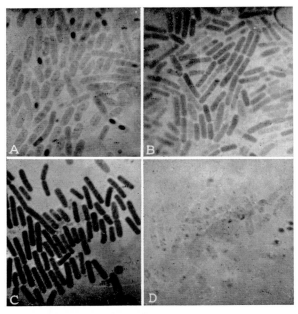

Figure 82. Photomicrographs of *Bacillus cereus* made with ultraviolet light. The organisms in *A* are from an 18-hour agar culture. They do not absorb much ultraviolet light and, therefore, appear very faint. It is assumed that this is due to their low content of nucleotides. A few spores are visible in the preparation. The organisms in *B* are in the middle of the lag phase and are only slightly more dense than those in *A*. The organisms in *C* are in the beginning of the logarithmic phase. They appear much denser than those in the other phases, from which it may be inferred that the nucelotide content is greater and more of the ultraviolet light is absorbed. *D* represents organisms in the phase of decline. The rods appear faint, owing to their low nucleotide content. × 1500. (From Acta Pathologica et Microbiologica Scandinavica, Vol. 24. Reproduced by permission of Berndt Malmgren, Stockholm.)

rate of death balances the rate of reproduction. The bacterial population has now reached the *maximum stationary phase,* which may continue for a number of hours, or days in some instances. Granules of glycogen and volutin, as well as fat globules, now appear in the protoplasm of the cells. If the species is a spore-former, spores will be produced in this phase of development, although some strains of spore-forming bacteria have almost completely sporulated by the time the maximum stationary phase is reached.

Phase of Decline

The aging of the culture is accompanied by a gradual decrease in numbers. The bacterial population is now in the *phase of decline*. Finally, many more cells die than are produced by the cell division still going on, with the inevitable consequence of a rapid decrease, often proceding at a geometric rate (*G* in Figure 81), in the number of living bacteria. With the more rapidly growing species, the phase of decline is reached usually before the twentieth hour of cultivation. During this phase pleomorphism is commonly observed. Bizzare shaped cells appear, and there is no uniformity in either size or shape of the cells. Granulation of the cytoplasm becomes more intense. The cells are aging and unable to rejuvenate themselves without a change in environment. Gradually they die, largely as a result of *autolysis* (self-destruction through the action of their own enzymes and metabolic by-products). Some species of microorganisms succumb more rapidly than others; hence the length of the phase of decline is highly variable. It can be prolonged by a number of procedures, e.g., lowering the temperature, incorporating buffers in the medium to neutralize acids produced by the culture, sealing the culture from air and removing moisture from the menstruum.

Other Aspects of the Growth Cycle

In addition to morphological changes during the growth curve. the cells' resistance to certain adverse physical and chemical conditions changes. For example, during the logarithmic growth phase, the cells are more sensitive to lethal temperatures and chemical disinfectants than during any other period of the growth cycle. On the other hand, they are most resistant to heat during the early lag phase and the phase of decline. Another characteristic which changes with the age of the cell is the reaction to dyes. This is particularly apparent with Gram-positive bacteria (cf. page 240), as they often become Gram-negative early in the maximum stationary phase or upon reaching the phase of decline. Certainly, many of these changes which occur during the course of the growth curve are related to physicochemical changes in the cell and in the cell's environment. Good evidence for this is presented in Figure 82, which relates morphological changes and chemical composition with the age of cells of a common aerobic spore-former, *Bacillus cereus*.

QUESTIONS

1. Define ecology. Name environmental factors that affect the growth of microorganisms.
2. Discuss the effect of temperature on microorganisms. What is meant by the growth temperature range of an organism? Define minimum, maximum and optimum growth temperature.

3. Differentiate between psychrophilic and thermophilic bacteria. In what ways may thermophilic bacteria be a nuisance to man?

4. What are mesophilic bacteria?

5. What is the effect of low temperature on microorganisms? What practical use can be made of the effect of low temperature on the growth of microorganisms?

6. How does drying affect bacteria? Explain lyophilization.

7. Discuss the effect of the hydrogen-ion concentration of the environment on the growth of microorganisms. Define the term pH and its relationship to hydrogen ion concentration.

8. Define: (1) osmosis, (2) osmotic pressure, (3) dialysis. Explain the influence of osmotic pressure on microorganisms. How may man make use of plasmolysis in food preservation?

9. What effect has exposure to direct sunlight on microorganisms? Which rays produce this effect?

10. What is meant by the oxidation-reduction potential? Of what value are reducing agents in culture media?

11. Define: (1) surface tension, (2) surface tension depressants, (3) interfacial tension.

12. In what ways may coexisting populations of microorganisms affect one another? Explain: (1) symbiosis, (2) metabiosis, (3) antibiosis, (4) antibiotic, (5) synergism.

13. Explain the growth curve of a bacterial population in a tube of liquid culture medium. Indicate briefly the course of events in each of the phases. What is meant by "generation time?" Attempt to plot a "growth curve" using logarithms of *total* numbers of cells instead of just *viable* numbers.

REFERENCES

Burrows, W.: Textbook of Microbiology. 17th ed. Philadelphia, W. B. Saunders Company, 1959.

Lamanna, C., and Mallette, M. F.: Basic Bacteriology (Its Biological and Chemical Background). 2nd ed. Baltimore, The Williams & Wilkins Co., 1959.

Porter, R. J.: Bacterial Chemistry and Physiology. New York, John Wiley & Sons, Inc., 1946.

Williams, R. E. O., and Spicer, C. C., ed.: Microbial Ecology. Seventh Symposium of the Society for General Microbiology. Cambridge, Cambridge University Press, 1957.

Wilson, G. S., and Miles, A. A.: Topley and Wilson's Principles of Bacteriology and Immunity. 2 vols., 4th ed. Baltimore, The Williams & Wilkins Company, 1955.

13 • Microbial Heredity and Variability

Although offspring tend to resemble their parents, there is a tendency for living organisms in general to vary and thus acquire traits different from those of their forebears. It is because of this tendency that new varieties of animals and plants come into being. All organisms, including bacteria and allied forms, obey the same natural laws. The individuals that make up a species are not exactly alike. In a pure culture of a bacterial species the individuals are not usually completely identical; there may be slight variations in their morphological and physiological characteristics.

The science that deals with the principles of heredity is known as *genetics*. The science of genetics attempts to account for similarities and dissimilarities (variations) of organisms due to heredity.

THE HEREDITARY MATERIAL

In higher forms of life hereditary continuity is achieved through the transmission by a precise and intricate mechanism of hereditary determiners known as *genes*. Genes are chemical entities responsible, not only for directing the development of the individual, but also for producing variations among the members of a species. A gene is exceedingly small, being composed of either a single or a small number of nucleoprotein molecules.

Genes are located on, and transmitted by, rodlike or threadlike structures, *chromosomes,* formed at the time of cell division from the chromatin granules of the nucleus. They are arranged in linear fashion and are composed of nucleoproteins containing deoxyribonucleic acid. Genes possess the power of self-duplication.

There is good evidence that the specific chemical substance that functions as the genetic determinant is the nucleic acid portion of the gene rather than the protein. It appears that nucleic acids play a central role in the hereditary mechanism of all organisms, including the viruses. The deoxyribonucleic acid of each species appears to be biologically distinctive, even though chemical differences cannot be detected.

In higher organisms each body cell (except mature sex cells or gametes) has two sets of chromosomes, since chromosomes occur in pairs. Such an individual with two representatives of each kind of gene is termed *diploid.* If the genes constituting a pair are identical, the condition is called *homozygous;* if they differ from one another, the condition is termed *heterozygous.*

To avoid a doubling of the chromosome number when reproduction occurs, the number is reduced to one set in the sex cells prior to sexual fusion. Such cells are termed *haploid.* The fusion of two haploid sex cells restores the chromosome number to two sets. Sexual reproduction is invariably accompanied by chromosome reduction (*meiosis*). In many microorganisms the individuals are haploid throughout their life span, reduction of the chromosome number occurring immediately after sexual fusion. Chromosomes cannot be demonstrated in the chromatin material of many microorganisms.

MUTATIONS

Genes exhibit remarkable stability, each reproducing its own kind, generation after generation. It is the stability of genes that causes offspring to resemble their parents. Genes are capable of change, however, and their stability is relative rather than absolute. A change in a gene is known as a *mutation.* Mutations are not frequent occurrences but are of great significance since they are a major cause of hereditary variations. A gene that has undergone mutation reproduces itself in its new form.

Some mutations are difficult to detect because they involve small subtle changes in the organism. Most mutations are minor in nature. Drastic mutations seldom occur. Some kinds of genes mutate more readily than others. Most of the mutations that occur are disadvantageous to the organism. This is probably due to the fact that each species already possesses, because of earlier mutations, a set of genes that satisfactorily fits it to its environment. Most mutant organisms, therefore, are doomed to rapid extinction. A change in environment, however, may change the situation.

The existing conditions in the environment determine whether or not a mutant organism will be able to survive. The environment thus serves as a selective agency, permitting the survival of those organisms with favorable mutations and preventing the survival of those with mutations that are disadvantageous. Because of gene mutations, all species change over a period of time. The evolution of organisms is the outcome of natural selection operating on gene mutations.

The factors that bring about spontaneous mutations in living organisms are unknown. Cosmic rays, which reach the earth from outer space (including areas outside the solar system), have long been suspected as being responsible for mutations that are continuously occurring in the world of life. A number of agents are capable of increasing the rate at which mutations occur. They are referred to as *mutagenic agents,* and the resulting changes are termed *induced mutations.* Such artificially induced mutations are, in general, of the same type as those which occur spontaneously. In other words, these agencies increase the normal frequency of mutations. Examples of mutagenic agents are: x-rays, ultraviolet rays and rays (beta, gamma and others) emitted by radium, uranium, thorium and other radioactive elements. Atomic radiations (products of nuclear fission) emitted by the detonation of atomic weapons have added to the radioactive material in the general environment. Certain chemical substances, such as nitrogen mustard, are also mutagenic.

BACTERIAL GENETICS

Recent investigations indicate that bacterial heredity in general conforms to the same principles that govern inheritance in higher organisms. Although the chromatin bodies of bacteria, like those in more highly developed forms, contain deoxyribonucleic acid, it is not certain whether chromosomes are formed in bacteria. Present evidence indicates that the genes of bacteria are arranged in a definite order on a linear structure, i.e., they exhibit linkage, which suggests that they are a part of intranuclear structures analogous to chromosomes.

Bacterial Variation

In the laboratory, bacteria are cultivated on many different kinds of artificial media. Each kind of medium represents a different kind of environment. When a certain species is subcultured simultaneously on a variety of media, variations are frequently observable. The variations are either morphological or physiological, or both. Many of these changes are transient, i.e., reversible, whereas others may be permanent, similar to the mutations that occur in the higher forms of life. The permanent modifications are transmitted by the modified cells to their progeny, but cells that have undergone transient changes may revert back to the normal type with a change of environment. It is because of morphological variations that the student may find long rods in a stained preparation made from a culture which ordinarily consists of short, plump rods.

The variations that occur may involve loss of certain traits or the acquisition of new ones. Loss of a trait often represents reversion to a less specialized or more primitive state. Flagellated bacteria may give rise to nonflagellated variants. Avirulent variants may arise from virulent pathogenic strains. Capsulated bacteria may lose the property of capsule formation. Pigmented forms may give rise to variants unable to produce pigment. Endospore formation is another characteristic that may be lost. In some cases an accentuation of a certain trait may occur, as, for example, increased ability to produce pigment or to increase in virulence on the part of a pathogen.

It is not always evident whether a variation results from a mutation or is a response to a change in environment. There are certain variations, such as those that occur in the growth stages of a bacterial population in which gene mutations apparently play no role. As mentioned in the preceding chapter, the cells in the lag phase increase considerably in size; this is followed by a decrease in size during the logarithmic and maximum stationary phases. In the phase of declining numbers the cells may become swollen, shrunken or granular, or take on some other decidedly irregular form. When these morphologically altered bacteria of the phase of decline are transferred to a fresh culture medium, they always revert to the original type, suggesting that the altered morphology was an adaptation to changes in the environment and was not due to gene mutations.

When *Escherichia coli*, a short, rodlike bacterium, is grown in a medium containing sodium ricinoleate (a surface tension depressant), it forms long filaments but when transferred to a medium containing calcium chloride, it grows in the form of exceedingly short rods, approaching cocci in appearance. Such noninheritable changes obviously are induced by the environment and are not due to gene mutations. They occur simultaneously in all members of the bacterial population rather than in a few individuals as in the case of gene mutations.

Certain species of bacteria can ferment glucose, producing gas in the process, but are unable to ferment lactose. When such bacteria are inoculated into a medium devoid of glucose, but containing lactose as the only energy source, it frequently happens that after a while the medium will contain acid due to the fermentation of lactose. By careful analysis it has been found that the lactose was fermented, not because the bacteria gradually adapted themselves to the medium and thus acquired the ability to ferment lactose, but because random gene mutations in the original culture gave rise to a small number of variants capable of fermenting lactose. In such a situation it is only the variants that will grow in the medium; the rest perish. The environment (medium) serves as a selective agency, permitting the mutant organisms to survive.

Typhoid fever bacilli recently isolated from a patient cannot grow in a medium in the absence of tryptophane. However, most cultures of this organism will produce a few variants capable of synthesizing this amino acid from other compounds. When a large number of typhoid bacteria are inoculated into a medium lacking tryptophane, growth will usually arise from the variants present. However, if the number inoculated into the medium is small, growth may not occur because the inoculum contained no variants. Because of the large number of individuals in a bacterial population, there are usually a few mutants present upon which selection can act. These few mutant cells become the foci for the development of a variant type.

Pathogenic forms may acquire resistance to inhibitory agents such as penicillin, streptomycin and the sulfonamide drugs. Strains of various pathogens have developed which are resistant to these drugs. The resistance did not result from exposure to the drug but arose spontaneously in some of the bacteria before they were exposed to it. When sulfonamide drugs first came into use in the treatment of disease, it was found that gonorrhea could be successfully treated with one of these drugs. Since then, resistant strains of the gonococcus have developed and become prevalent; consequently, sulfonamide drugs are no longer considered satisfactory agents for the treatment of gonorrhea.

Because variability is a common characteristic of bacteria as well as of other forms of life, there frequently are many strains in a given species which differ from one another in one, or a few, characteristics.

Colonial Variation

Changes may occur also in the morphology of bacterial colonies. Most bacteria can produce several types of colonies, consisting of cells which differ in their morphological and physiological properties. Many species of bacteria which, under usual conditions of growth, produce colonies that are smooth-surfaced, smooth-edged, glistening and moist, will, under certain conditions of growth, produce colonies which are rough-surfaced, rough-edged, dull, dry and irregular in form. The organisms that produce the rough colonies are referred to as the R-type; those that give rise to smooth colonies, as the S-type. An example of this type of variation is the diphtheria bacillus, which ordinarily produces smooth colonies, but may give rise to rough variants. The S-type of this organism is virulent, i.e., is capable of producing disease, but the R-type is relatively avirulent. Here morphological and physiological changes occur simultaneously. Many pathogenic species lose their virulence partly or completely when they change from the smooth to the rough type of colony. In the pneumococcus the change from the S-type to the R-type is associated, not only with loss of virulence, but also with the loss of the capsule characteristic of this organism. Figure 83 shows both smooth and rough colonies of the anthrax bacillus.

It is now known that S and R colonies are manifestations of the operation of certain selective forces in the environment of the bacteria. With some pathogens artificial cultivation permits conditions which favor dominance of cells which arise as colonies of the R-type. Passage of populations of cells from colonies in the rough phase to a susceptible experimental animal creates conditions favorable to the few mutant smooth phase cells which are more resistant to the host's defense mechanisms. Thus, upon primary isolation from the patient or experimental host, the

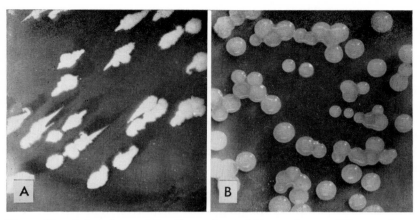

Figure 83. Colony forms of *Bacillus anthracis* (A), rough type; (B), smooth type. (U. S. Army photograph. Courtesy, Department of the Army, Technical Information Division.)

vast majority of colonies will be of the S-type. Prolonged transfer *in vitro,* however, favors the R-type.

Another type of variant colony is one that has a slimy consistency resembling mucus. It is referred to as the mucoid or M-type and consists of cells that are heavily capsulated. For some species the mucoid type of colony is the common form, but for others it represents a variant.

Some flagellated bacteria, such as *Proteus vulgaris,* produce thin, flat, spreading colonies. The cells, being motile, swim out from the edge of the colony in the film of moisture on the medium and thus form a spreading growth. In its flagellated form the organism is referred to as the H-type (from the German word *Hauch,* meaning a film or veil). This organism and other flagellated forms may give rise to nonflagellated variants which produce small, discrete, rounded colonies that show no tendency to spread. These variants are known as the O-(*ohne Hauch*) type (from the German word *ohne,* meaning without).

Another type of colonial variation is the production of exceedingly minute colonies by species which ordinarily do not produce such small colonies. The colonies may be barely visible, having a diameter of about 0.05 mm., and they consist of very small cells. These variants are often designated as the dwarf or D-type.

Transfer of Genetic Material

There are a number of ways in which genetic material can be transferred from one cell to another. In the process of sexual reproduction (conjugation) as described in Chapter 4, nuclear or genetic material is transferred from one of the participating cells, which serves as a male (gene donor), to the other participating cell, which serves as a female (gene acceptor). The bringing together of genetic material within one cell or organism from two parents makes possible a reshuffling of genetic factors. It does not give rise to new characters, but it makes possible the recombining of genes in new ways and is referred to as *genetic recombination.*

Under certain conditions hereditary change may be introduced when an individual comes in contact with deoxyribonucleic acid from a closely related strain. This introduction into a cell of soluble DNA (transforming substance) from a cell of another strain is known as *transformation.* These changes are permanent, i.e., they are transmissible to the progeny of the transformed cell. It appears that DNA is the main genetic determinant in most forms of life. In some species RNA serves this function. Transformation has been demonstrated in pneumococci, the causative organisms of pneumococcal pneumonia. These bacteria ordinarily have well-defined capsules consisting largely of polysaccharides. Variants sometimes occur which are without capsules. It has been found that treatment of nonencapsulated forms with deoxyribonucleic acid extracted from capsule-forming strains transforms the former into the latter. Other transformations have been carried out, both with the pneumococcus and *Haemophilus* spp.

Another process involving the transfer of genetic material from one bacterial cell to another is known as *transduction.* In this process a very minute amount of the genetic material of the bacterial cell becomes incorporated into a maturing bacterial virus particle (bacteriophage) and is transported by the virus into another host cell. Phages which function in this manner, the *temperate phages,* lyse only some of the infected cells. The rest of the cells live symbiotically with the phage, i.e., they are *lysogenic.* The genetic material transferred from one strain of bacterium to another becomes a part of the genetic make-up of the new host. Transduction has been observed in different strains of *E. coli,* the salmonellae group and other kinds of bacteria. The only essential difference between transformation and transduction is that the latter utilizes a bacteriophage vector.

THE GENETICS OF VIRUSES

It is now generally accepted that viruses possess a genetic apparatus which does not differ fundamentally from that of all other organisms. Evidence for this is (1) the capacity of variation in viruses, i.e., the existence of mutations, and (2) the high levels of nucleic acids in viral particles. In the case of bacteriophages and some animal viruses the genetic material is deoxyribonucleic acid, whereas in plant viruses and certain animal viruses it is ribonucleic acid. The smaller viruses consist chiefly of genetic material. There are reasons for believing that a phage particle may contain several dozen genes composed of DNA and arranged in linear fashion.

When a bacterial cell becomes infected with phage, its phage-altered metabolic system fabricates new phage particles from the substance of the cell. It may be inferred that the process is directed by the genetic material (DNA) of the phage while in association with the genetic structure of the host.

When a bacterial cell is infected simultaneously by two related phages differing in several characters, a genetic recombination and rearrangement of genetic factors occurs, giving rise to "hybrid" progeny. This phenomenon is essentially equivalent to a "mating" of the substance of the two related phages.

It has been demonstrated recently that certain plant viruses can be reconstituted upon mixing the two isolated components, protein and nucleic acid, to form typical virus particles. Such *reconstituted viruses* have the ability to infect and multiply in host cells and, in general, display the properties of the original virus. It was also found that the protein of one strain could be united with the nucleic acid of another strain to form biologically active virus particles.

QUESTIONS

1. What is meant by variation of bacterial species? Define: (1) genes, (2) genetics, (3) chromosomes, (4) mutation, (5) selection.

2. What kinds of variations occur among bacteria?

3. Distinguish between mutations and changes due to environmental conditions. Give examples.

4. By what means may mutations be induced artificially?

5. Discuss variations in bacterial colonies. Explain the following types of colonies: (1) S-type, (2) R-type, (3) M-type, (4) H-type, (5) O-type, (6) D-type.

6. Describe the three methods of gene transfer in microorganisms.

7. How does "survival of the fittest" relate to contemporary understanding of mutation.

REFERENCES

Braun, W.: Bacterial Genetics. Philadelphia, W. B. Saunders Co., 1953.

Catcheside, D. G.: The Genetics of Microorganisms. New York, Pitman Publishing Corp., 1951.

Ephrussi, B.: Nucleocytoplasmic Relations in Microorganisms. New York, Oxford University Press, 1953.

Lederberg, J., ed.: Papers in Microbial Genetics, Bacteria and Bacterial Viruses. Madison, Wis., University of Wisconsin Press, 1951.

Wagner, R. P., and Mitchell, H. K.: Genetics and Metabolism. New York, John Wiley & Sons, Inc., 1955.

Weinrich, D. H., Lewis, I. F., and Raper, J. R., ed.: Sex in Microorganisms. Washington, D.C., American Association for the Advancement of Science, 1954.

IV • Microbiologic Techniques
and Methods

14 • The Cultivation and Laboratory Study of Microorganisms

In this chapter the student will become acquainted with the fundamental methodology that has enabled man to attain his present understanding of the structure and activities of microorganisms. The techniques used have gradually evolved from methods originally devised by the earlier microbiologists. The science of microbiology is concerned largely with the behavior of populations of microorganisms rather than with individuals. Aside from certain structural characteristics, the individual microorganism is important chiefly as it contributes to the activities and characteristics exhibited by the population.

CULTURE MEDIA

For the study of microbial populations in the laboratory, substances suitable for the growth of microorganisms are required. Such substances are known as *culture media*, and the growth of organisms in or on a culture medium is called a *culture*. Because different microorganisms differ widely in their cultural requirements, many different types of media are used. Certain media are used not only to support the growth of microorganisms, but also to demonstrate particular growth characteristics and physiological properties such as acid and gas production, liquefaction of certain media and the production of pigments, toxins, indol and other substances. Such media are known as "differential media." Some media are "selective" in that they permit the growth of some kinds of microorganisms and inhibit the growth of others.

In addition to its nutritional constituents, a culture medium must contain an adequate amount of water and must have a suitable osmotic pressure and hydrogen-ion concentration. Many bacteria grow best at a neutral or slightly basic reaction (pH 7.0 to 7.5). Some grow best in a

217

moderately acidic medium, whereas others require a reaction that is moderately basic. All culture media must be sterilized after they have been prepared and before they are inoculated with organisms. Culture media are usually poured into glass containers, such as culture tubes, fermentation tubes, Petri dishes and Erlenmeyer flasks.

Commonly Used Media

One of the first substances used by bacteriologists for the cultivation of bacteria was *nutrient broth.* It is still an important medium and is used also as the basis for the preparation of many other kinds of media. Nutrient broth, as now prepared, contains peptone (a protein derivative) and salt in addition to the soluble constituents of meat. The commercial preparation known as "peptone" which is added to nutrient broth contains proteinaceous substances such as peptides, polypeptides, proteoses and amino acids, in addition to peptone. Some of these constituents serve as essential growth factors for certain organisms. Nutrient broth is suitable for the growth of many saprophytes.

By adding some gelatin to beef broth, Robert Koch prepared the first liquefiable solid culture medium. This medium, known as *nutrient gelatin,* is solid at ordinary room temperature but becomes liquid upon heating. Chemically, gelatin is a protein. It is not a naturally occurring protein but is obtained by the hydrolysis of collagen, which is a protein contained in connective tissue (tendons, ligaments, and the like), and bones. It can be obtained in powdered or sheet form.

Later, Koch used agar-agar as the solidifying agent in place of gelatin. This type of medium is known as *nutrient agar.* The agar-agar used in making this medium is a pectin-like substance derived from certain marine algae. It consists chiefly of a complex polysaccharide chemically related to hemicellulose. Physically, agar-agar has some of the properties of gelatin in that it becomes liquid when heated in water and sets to a firm gel when it cools.

Nutrient agar has definite advantages over nutrient gelatin. It has a higher melting point (about 100° C.) and congeals at about 42° C. It is not ordinarily liquefied by bacteria (except certain marine forms), whereas nutrient gelatin melts at about 28° C. and is subject to digestion and liquefaction by many kinds of bacteria commonly grown in the laboratory. This characteristic, however, can be made use of in the identification of bacteria. Whether or not a certain bacterium can digest gelatin, and thus liquefy a medium containing it, is a cultural characteristic of value in identification.

By the addition of blood or blood serum to either nutrient broth or nutrient agar, media are obtained which are suitable for the cultivation of many species of pathogens. The blood may be defibrinated before adding it to the medium. This is accomplished by thorough shaking in a flask containing glass beads.

Culture media for some heterotrophic bacteria must contain certain

Fluid Media

Fluid media are most commonly used in culture tubes plugged with cotton. These tubes are similar to ordinary test tubes but are without a "lip" and have thicker walls. The cotton plugs permit a free circulation of air and gases and also act as filters, preventing the entrance of contaminating bacteria from the air. Flasks may be utilized if large quantities of medium are to be used. Carbohydrate media in which gas may be produced are used in fermentation tubes, of which there are two kinds: (1) the Smith fermentation tube, which has its closed end bent up into an arm to serve as a trap for gas, and (2) the Durham fermentation tube, which is an ordinary culture tube containing an inverted vial to trap gas that may be formed.

Solid Media

Nutrient agar is frequently used in the form of agar slants. To prepare the slants, tubes of sterilized, liquefied medium are laid down with their mouths slightly raised so that the medium will solidify in an inclined position. This provides a large surface for the growth of bacteria. Nutrient agar is used also to make Petri dish cultures. A Petri dish is a circular glass container with perpendicular sides about ½ inch high. It is provided with a cover of similar design but a little larger in diameter. These dishes are made in various sizes; a type in common use has a diameter of about 10 cm. Petri dishes are often referred to as "plates," and Petri dish cultures as "plate cultures." Plate cultures are used for the study of colonies and also in the isolation of pure cultures, as will be explained later. They are also used in water and milk analysis in determining the number of microorganisms per milliliter.

Nutrient gelatin is usually poured into culture tubes, which are filled one-third full. The tubes are plugged with cotton stoppers, sterilized, and allowed to cool in the vertical position. The medium may then be used for making so-called "stab cultures." The desired bacteria are transferred to the medium with a needle by thrusting it through the center of the medium to the bottom of the tube and then withdrawing it along the needle path. Agar stab cultures are also useful.

Cultures under Diminished Oxygen Tension

Microaerophilic bacteria and obligate anaerobes require media in which the oxygen tension has been reduced. The former require some oxygen, the latter grow in media devoid of free oxygen, but many species are capable of tolerating the presence of a small amount of oxygen. Various methods have been devised for the cultivation of obligate anaerobes; a few representative ones will be considered.

A simple method for providing anaerobic conditions in a tube of liquid medium is to heat the medium to boiling before inoculation to drive out the dissolved oxygen. The medium is then quickly cooled and inoculated.

To maintain anaerobic conditions, the tube is sealed by pouring a layer of sterile, melted petroleum jelly over the medium.

A suitable medium can be made by the addition of minced meat. The meat may be cooked or fresh (aseptically obtained), since either kind will act as a reducing agent, removing the free oxygen from the medium. The addition of reducing compounds, such as glucose, cystine or sodium thioglycolate, to broth usually provides a satisfactory medium.

Another method is to grow the anaerobes in an airtight Petri dish with aerobes, the two being kept apart by a sufficient distance to prevent contamination. The aerobes will reduce the oxygen tension sufficiently to permit the anaerobes to grow.

Still another method is to place plate or tube cultures in a suitable jar which can be tightly closed and then remove the oxygen from the jar, either by chemical or mechanical means. Chemicals used for this purpose are alkaline solutions of pyrogallic acid or self-igniting phosphorus. By means of a suction pump the air may be evacuated from specially constructed jars containing the cultures. The jars are then refilled with an inert gas such as hydrogen or nitrogen.

Cultures under Increased Carbon Dioxide Tension

The growth of certain bacteria is favored when the cultures are incubated in an atmosphere of approximately 10 per cent carbon dioxide. This method of cultivation is used for the isolation of the bacteria that cause brucellosis (undulant fever), as well as of meningococci, the cause of epidemic meningitis, and gonococci, the causative organisms of gonorrhea. Any type of anaerobic jar may be used for this purpose. The so-called candle jar containing a smokeless candle may be used to provide the desired carbon dioxide tension. After the cultures have been placed in the jar, the candle is lighted and the jar tightly closed. The burning of the candle reduces the oxygen tension and increases the carbon dioxide tension. The candle jar is suitable also for the cultivation of some of the microaerophilic bacteria.

Methods of Obtaining Pure Cultures

To determine the nature and activities of microorganisms, they must be grown in pure culture, which is a group of individuals belonging to a single strain. In their natural habitats (soil, water, milk, body discharges, and so forth) many different kinds of microorganisms live together in close proximity. Even very small samples of material from such sources usually contain a variety of different species. To make a study of these organisms, they must be separated physically one from another and obtained in pure culture. As previously pointed out, the basic facts of microbiology are derived through the study of microorganisms in pure culture.

Pure cultures can be obtained by using a technique that will separate the organisms one from another in or on the culture medium so that the resulting growth will contain colonies, each one consisting of but a single species. Two procedures commonly used to accomplish this are the "pour plate" and the "streak plate" methods.

In the pour plate method three tubes of a liquefiable solid medium (nutrient agar, nutrient gelatin or silica-gel medium) are required. The medium is liquefied and cooled to a temperature (about 45° C.) at which it is still liquid but not hot enough to injure or kill bacteria. One tube is inoculated with a loopful or more of the material to be plated and is then rolled between the palms of the hands to distribute the bacteria through the medium. One or two loopfuls of the mixture are transferred from this tube to a second tube and thoroughly mixed. The third tube is inoculated

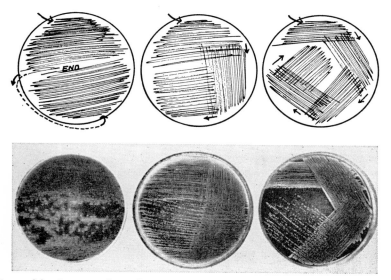

Figure 84. Patterns of streaking that may be used in the isolation of pure cultures. The strokes used are illustrated in the upper diagram. Plates so streaked appear as illustrated in the photograph below. (From Applied Medical Bacteriology by M. Marshall, Lea & Febiger, publishers. Reproduced by permission.)

with several loopfuls from the second tube, and the contents are again thoroughly mixed. The second tube has a higher dilution of bacteria than the first, and the third tube a higher dilution than the second. In each tube the bacteria are well scattered through the medium. The contents of each tube are then poured into a sterile Petri dish; after the medium has solidified, the plates are incubated at a temperature favorable for growth. Usually on one or two of the plates a sufficient dilution is obtained so that the colonies that are formed develop from single bacterial cells and thus contain but one kind of organism. By transferring a small portion of the growth from one of these colonies to an appropriate medium, a pure culture may be obtained. By following this procedure, a pure culture of each kind of organism present in the original material, that will grow on the medium used, can be secured.

In the streak plate method, which is a simpler procedure, parallel streaks are made on a plate of solidified medium with a loop inserted but once into the material to be plated. Most of the bacteria will be removed from the loop during the first few streaks, with the result that in the last series of streaks the bacteria will be deposited far enough apart so that they will give rise to separate colonies of individual species of bacteria from which pure cultures may be prepared. Figure 84 illustrates patterns of streaking that may be used.

In the method known as the single cell technique, a single microbial cell is picked out under the microscope from a suspension of microor-

Figure 85.   Micromanipulator. (Courtesy of E. Leitz, Inc.)

ganisms on the under side of a sterile cover glass. The cell is then transferred to an appropriate medium. This is a rather difficult task, but with the aid of a micromanipulator (Figure 85) it can be accomplished by a skilled operator. A micromanipulator is a device which can be attached to a microscope and by means of which one can control accurately the movements of micropipets and other exceedingly small instruments in the field of vision under the microscope. While looking through the microscope one may draw a single cell from a drop of a bacterial culture into a sterile micropipet and transfer it to a sterile medium.

To obtain a pure culture of a pathogen from a mixture in which there are some nonpathogenic forms in addition to the pathogen, animal inoculation may, in some cases, be resorted to. The mixture is inoculated into an animal susceptible to the pathogen. In the animal body the pathogen will grow, but the nonpathogens will be destroyed. The body of the animal thus serves as a selective medium. After sufficient time has elapsed, material from the animal may be transferred to a suitable culture medium to obtain a pure culture of the pathogen.

The white mouse, for example, is sometimes used for the isolation of the pneumococcus from the sputum of pneumonia patients. Since the mouse is highly susceptible to the pneumococcus, it can be used to function as a highly selective medium from which pure cultures may be obtained. The other organisms normally present in sputum are destroyed by the natural defenses of the mouse.

Incubation of Cultures

Cultures of microorganisms are usually grown in an incubator, which is an insulated cabinet equipped with a heating element (usually electric) and a thermostat to maintain a constant temperature. Pathogenic bacteria are usually incubated at body temperature (37.5° C.). Many saprophytic organisms grow well at 25° to 30° C. Yeasts and molds produce a good growth at the usual room temperature (18° to 22° C.). For the growth of thermophiles a temperature of 65° C. may be used. Media containing gelatin liquefy at temperatures above 25° C. They are usually kept in incubators set at 20° C. Many microorganisms attain their maximum growth when incubated at their optimum temperature for twelve to twenty-four hours. Some species, however, require several weeks for development. In some bacteria, pigment production is prevented or delayed when they are incubated at body temperature.

Maintenance of Pure Cultures

Pure cultures may be kept alive by frequent transfer to fresh culture media. Some cultures can be kept for weeks or months, others only a few days, without being transferred to fresh media. Less frequent transfer to fresh media is required when the cultures are kept in a refrigerator after they have reached the maximum stationary phase of growth.

A satisfactory method for preserving bacterial cultures is to subject them to a process of rapid drying in the frozen state (lyophilization). To carry out the process, the microorganisms are suspended in an aqueous fluid and placed in small glass ampules. They are then quickly frozen at a temperature of $-78°$ C. by being immersed in a mixture of dry ice and alcohol. They are next dried in the frozen state by connecting the vials to a high-vacuum pump. This results in the complete desiccation of the bacterial cells. The vials are then sealed and stored in a cool place. Cultures subjected to this treatment remain viable for many years.

The American Type Culture Collection* of the Society of American Bacteriologists maintains cultures of practically all known species of bac-

* 2112 M Street, N.W., Washington, D.C.

teria, yeasts and molds. Subcultures of any of these organisms are available to educational institutions and industrial establishments. Other type culture collections are the Baarn Collection in Holland and the British Collection of Type Cultures kept at the Lister Institute at Elstres, England.

SYSTEMATIC STUDY OF PURE CULTURES

After an organism has been obtained in pure culture it is possible to determine its characteristics. Microscopic examination is important in ascertaining the morphology of the organism, but many of the characteristics which are of particular importance in identification and classification can be learned only by a study of the behavior of the organism in cultures.

In the systematic study of a bacterial species the following characteristics are important: (1) microscopic morphology, including (a) size, shape and grouping of the organism, (b) presence or absence of spores, flagella and capsules, and (c) staining properties; (2) morphology of colonies on standard or special media, including size, shape, color and texture; (3) appearance of growth in or on different media, including liquid media and slant cultures (nutrient agar, coagulated egg or coagulated blood serum); and (4) physiological or biochemical reactions, including (a) fermentation of sugars (glucose, lactose, sucrose and others), (b) liquefaction of gelatin, (c) formation of indole from tryptophane, (d) reduction of nitrate to nitrite and (e) production of hydrogen sulfide and other products.

A number of other characteristics are made use of in the study of certain kinds of microorganisms. In some cases it may be necessary to determine whether or not the organism will produce disease in laboratory animals (guinea pigs, rabbits, white mice, and the like).

To determine the microscopic morphology of an organism involves staining, which will be discussed in a later section of this chapter. Tests to determine the fermentation reactions of microorganisms are carried out in special tubes, as previously mentioned. The tubes are observed for gas production and acid formation.

MICROSCOPES

Microscopes are instruments designed to obtain greatly enlarged images of very small objects. A number of different kinds of microscopes have been developed. Most of them utilize light and form images by means of glass lenses. To understand the optical principles involved in the use of these so-called "light microscopes," it must be borne in mind that the rays of ordinary daylight travel in straight lines in a homogeneous medium but are bent from their path in passing obliquely from one medium into another of different density. This deviation from a straight course is called *refraction*. Also, each ray is a composite of various colored rays, ranging from red to violet, and each of these differs in re-frangibility, in that it is refracted differently from others when passing obliquely from one medium into another of different density.

The greater the difference in density of the media which light rays traverse, the greater the refraction. A ray of light in passing from air into a plate of glass (Figure 86, A) is bent out of its original course but resumes its original direction as it emerges from the glass on the other side. However, when a light ray passes through a glass prism, it does not resume its former direction but is deviated toward the base of the prism (Figure 86, B). This is a basic factor in the explanation of the performance of lenses. The formation of images by lenses is dependent upon refraction.

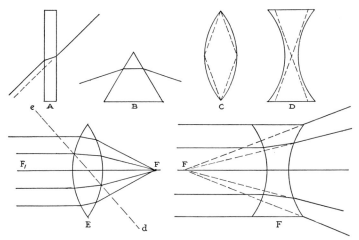

Figure 86. Diagrams illustrating refraction of light rays in passing through a glass plate, prism and lenses.

Lenses

A lens is a portion of a transparent substance, usually glass, bounded by two surfaces, one or both being curved. Lenses are of two chief types, biconvex and biconcave. Each of these functions as though it were constructed of two prisms. A biconvex lens converges rays of light as though it were composed of two prisms with the bases together (Figure 86, C). Such a lens is referred to as a *converging lens*. The biconcave type of lens diverges rays of light as though composed of two prisms with the apices together (Figure 86, D). It thus is a *diverging lens*. Lenses that are not of these two types are modifications or combinations of these types. A planoconcave lens is one which has one plane and one concave side; a planoconvex lens has one plane and one convex side; and a concavoconvex lens has one concave and one convex surface.

If parallel rays of light pass through a biconvex lens (Figure 86, E), they are converged so as to meet at one point, F, termed the *principal focus* of the lens. This point can be readily determined by allowing the sun's rays to pass through the lens to a screen. The distance from the lens to the principal focus is the *principal focal length* of the lens. The greater the convexity of a lens, the shorter its principal focal length. If a source of light be placed at the principal focus, the rays of light after traversing the lens will emerge parallel. Parallel rays of light from the opposite side would form a second focal point, F_1. These two points, F and F_1, are termed *conjugate foci.* They are equidistant from the center of the lens when both sides of the lens have equal curvature.

The ray which passes through the principal focus and the center of the lens traverses what is termed the *principal axis* of the lens. The point on the principal axis through which rays pass without angular deviation is the *optical center* of the lens. In biconvex lenses the optical center is the center of volume. In planoconvex and planoconcave lenses the optical center is the middle point of the curved face. Any straight line (*ed*), other than the principal axis passing through the optical center of the lens, is a *secondary axis.* A ray along a secondary axis undergoes no angular deviation.

A biconcave lens causes parallel rays to diverge (Figure 86, *F*). The principal focus, *F,* of the lens is determined by extending the divergent rays till they meet at a point on the same side of the lens as the source of light. Such a point is known as a *virtual focus,* since it has no actual existence.

Images

When an object is placed more than twice the focal length from a converging lens, the image formed is *real,* inverted and smaller than the object. It is formed at a distance from the lens which is more than once, but less than twice, the focal length. It should be noted that the rays passing through the optical center of the lens are not refracted. An object at a distance of twice the focal length from the lens forms an image the same distance from the lens as the object, and of the same size. When an object is placed so that the distance between it and the lens is more than once, but less than twice, the focal length of the lens, the image will be larger than the object. An object placed at the principal focus of a converging lens does not form a distinct image. An object placed between the principal focus and the lens forms a virtual and an enlarged image which is not reversed. This is the principle upon which the simple microscope, or simple magnifier, operates.

Simple Microscope

A simple microscope—an ordinary converging lens of short focal length, or a combination of lenses—forms a virtual image which is enlarged but not inverted (Figure 87). The rays converge to meet at the conjugate focus, F_1, and an eye at this point would see the image. The image is

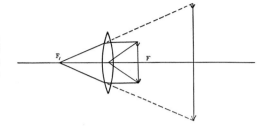

Figure 87. Diagram illustrating the principle of the simple microscope. The image of the object is projected and enlarged.

formed at the intersection of the secondary axes and the imaginary elongation (dotted lines) of the refracted rays. The image is called a *virtual image* because it is not produced by actual light rays. Such an image cannot be projected on a screen as can a real image. The greater the convexity of the lens, the shorter the focus and the greater the magnification.

In using a simple microscope the object must be placed nearer the lens than its principal focus. Objects close to the eyes may be focused clearly. The more the lens magnifies, the nearer it must be placed to the object. Because a device of this type enables one to see details in small objects, it is called a simple microscope.

Compound Microscope

The general principle of the compound microscope is represented in Figures 88 and 89. In its simplest form the compound microscope may be represented as consisting of a converging lens, *CD* (Figure 88), called the *objective* (actually a system of lenses), and another converging lens, *EF*, called the *eyepiece* or *ocular* (actually two lenses). The object, *ab*, lies beyond the principal focus of the objective. A real image, *AB*, is formed slightly nearer the eyepiece than its focal length. This reversed and inverted image formed by the objective, when viewed through the eyepiece, is seen as an enlarged virtual image (A^1B^1). The eyepiece thus acts as a simple microscope, projecting and enlarging the image without reversing it. Figure 89 shows that the real image produced is not brought to focus until the light rays have traversed the lower lens (field lens) of the eyepiece.

Parts of the Microscope

The standard light microscope consists of a number of parts (Figure 89) which may be listed under four divisions: (1) a supporting frame-

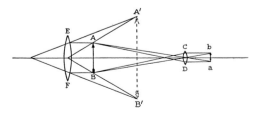

Figure 88. Diagram illustrating the general principle of the compound microscope.

work, (2) an illumination system, (3) a magnification system, and (4) an adjustment system.

The supporting framework consists of the base on which the microscope rests, the pillar, arm and stage. An inclination joint for tilting the microscope is located between the pillar and the arm. The arm is the part which supports the magnifying and adjusting systems and by which the microscope is carried. The stage, on which the object to be examined is placed, is a horizontal shelf with a central opening.

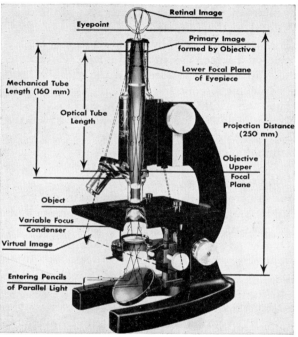

Figure 89. A modern compound microscope showing path of light rays and image formation. (Courtesy of Baush & Lomb Optical Company.)

The illumination system, which is located beneath the stage, consists of a mirror, condenser and diaphragm. The mirror reflects light upward through the opening in the stage to illuminate the object. The condenser, which consists of two or more lenses, is designed to concentrate the rays of light reflected by the mirror so that they will pass through the object, thus assuring ample illumination. By means of the diaphragm the amount of light passing through the object can be modified.

The magnification system is composed of objectives, the body tube and the ocular (eyepiece). Microscopes used in the study of microorganisms are usually provided with three objectives of different magnifying power, which are commonly known as the low-power dry objective, the high-power dry objective and the oil-immersion objective. They are mounted in the revolving nosepiece at the lower end of the body tube and are designated according to their equivalent focal length as 16 mm. (low dry), 4 mm. (high dry) and 1.9 mm. or 1.8 mm. (oil-immersion). The higher the magnifying power, the shorter the focal distance and the smaller the field of view.

Objectives contain a combination of lenses (Figure 90). The purpose of combining lenses is to eliminate certain defects or aberrations (explained in a later section) which are inherent in simple lenses. The greater the magnifying power of the objective, the smaller the diameter of the lenses.

The oil-immersion objective is so-called because, when in use, the lens at the end of the objective dips into a drop of oil placed on the object or the cover glass. The oil used for this purpose has the same refractive index as glass. It prevents the deflection of light rays as they pass from the object or the cover glass to the objective, and thus permits a larger amount of

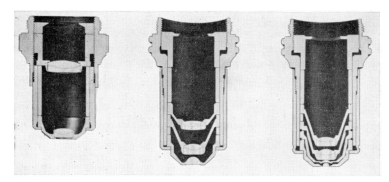

Figure 90. Sectional view of achromatic objectives, 10 ×, 43 × and 97 ×. (Courtesy of Bausch & Lomb Optical Company.)

light to enter the microscope. The oil, together with the substage condenser, assures a well-illuminated field.

The ocular, which is an additional magnifying piece, fits into the upper end of the body tube. The most common type of ocular contains two planoconvex lenses, one at each end. The lower one is known as the *field lens,* the upper one is called the *eye lens.* A fixed diaphragm (a flat piece of metal with a circular opening) is placed between the two lenses at approximately the focus of the eye lens.

The adjustment system is devised to move the body tube up or down for the purpose of bringing the object into focus. The coarse focusing adjustment raises and lowers the body tube over a wide range, while the fine focusing adjustment raises and lowers the body tube by very slight degrees.

Magnification

The total magnification of a microscope, expressed in diameters or times linear, is obtained by multiplying the magnification due to the objective by that of the ocular. Objectives are usually marked with their magnifying power. The low power (10 ✕) magnifies ten times, the high dry (43 ✕) magnifies forty-three times, and the oil-immersion (97 ✕) magnifies ninety-seven times. When these are used in combination with a 10 ✕ ocular, the one most commonly utilized, the low power gives a magnification of 100; the high dry, 430; and the oil-immersion, 970. The usual method of giving a scale indicating the magnification represented by a figure or drawing is to use the sign of multiplication (✕) either followed by, or preceded by, the number which shows the increase in diameter. Thus, ✕ 970 represents a magnification of 970 diameters.

There is a definite limit to the magnification obtainable with the light microscope. This limit is due to the wavelengths of light rays. The visible rays of light have wavelengths of approximately 0.4 to 0.8 micron. A particle that has dimensions less than half the wavelength of the shortest light rays cannot be seen. The limit of magnification with sharp definition is about 1200 diameters. Greater increase is accompanied by blurring.

The degree to which a microscope can distinguish particles that are very small and are separated from each other by very short distances is known as its *resolving power*. It represents the maximum ability of a microscope to reveal fine details of structure and to give distinct images of two points closely adjacent. The limit of resolution of the light microscope is approximately 0.2 micron. Two points closer together than 0.2 micron will appear as one point. Objects less than 0.2 micron in diameter cannot be clearly seen. Actual magnification is of less value (within limits) than high resolving power and clear definition, for it is upon these properties that the quality of the image depends. Because of the smallness of bacteria, it is advisable to use the oil-immersion objective to obtain sufficient magnification and resolution.

Defects in the Image

There are two defects inherent in lenses. These are known as spherical aberration and chromatic aberration. Since light is composed of rays of varying lengths, and since different wavelengths have different indices of refraction, an ordinary lens will not refract to the same degree all rays passing through it. Rays that pass through the periphery of the lens focus on the axis nearer the lens than the central rays, with the result that the image is indistinct and distorted. This defect is known as *spherical aberration.*

The other defect, known as *chromatic aberration,* is due to the fact that light is dispersed into its component colors by the lens. The different colored rays do not come to the same focus. As a result, the image has a fringe of color surrounding it.

Spherical aberration can be corrected by using a combination of lenses having convex and concave surfaces of different curvatures. The lenses are combined so that they will be equivalent to a single lens. Chromatic aberration can be, for the most part, corrected by a combination of several lenses of different dispersive power, made of different kinds of glass. A combination such as a concave lens of flint glass (silicate of potassium and lead) with a biconvex lens of crown glass (silicate of potassium and lime) illustrates this type of correction.

Path of Light through the Microscope

The path of light through a microscope is illustrated in Figure 89. The light, reflected from the mirror, passes through the substage condenser and the object on the stage. It then enters the objective and the field lens, forming a real image in the ocular. The real image is inverted and is converted into a virtual image by means of the eye lens of the ocular.

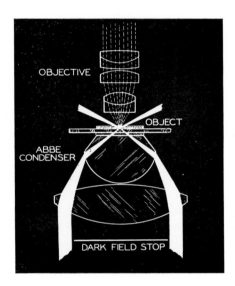

Figure 91. Diagram of darkfield illumination using Abbe condenser with darkfield stop. (Courtesy of Bausch & Lomb Optical Company.)

Darkfield Microscope

In the darkfield microscope the specimen under observation appears brightly illuminated against a dark background. The ordinary compound microscope may be converted into a darkfield microscope by replacing the standard condenser with a substage condenser, which differs from a standard condenser chiefly in that it is provided with a central stop diaphragm that admits only marginal rays (Figure 91). These rays are reflected obliquely and pass through the slide on the stage at such an angle that they do not enter the objective unless reflected upward by some object. The microscope operates on the principle of the Tyndall effect, which is commonly observed when dust particles become visible as a beam of sunlight enters a darkened room. The resolving power of this microscope is not greater than that of the ordinary compound microscope, but bodies below the limit of resolution of the microscope can be seen as luminous

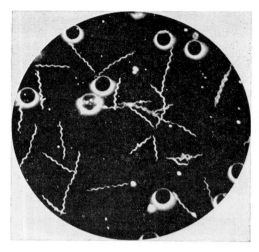

Figure 92. Spirochetes as they appear under the darkfield microscope. (Courtesy of American Optical Company.)

spots. Very slender organisms which are difficult to stain, such as the spirochetes of syphilis, are frequently observed under the darkfield microscope. Details of form and structure, however, are not revealed. Figure 92 shows spirochetes as they appear under the darkfield microscope.

Ultraviolet Microscope

This microscope differs from the ordinary microscope in that it uses ultraviolet rays in place of visible light rays to illuminate the object. Since ordinary glass is opaque to ultraviolet rays, the optical system is made of quartz. Because ultraviolet rays have shorter wavelengths (from 0.1 to 0.4 micron) than visible rays, greater magnification is possible. The limit of resolution is about 0.1 micron, and the useful magnification attainable is about 2000 diameters. Images produced with ultraviolet rays are not visible but can be photographed with plates sensitive to these rays.

Phase-Contrast Microscope

The structures within a cell show little contrast and, hence, are difficult to see under the ordinary microscope. Such structures, unless they are stained, can be observed only if they differ from surrounding structures in light transmission or refraction. In most cases these differences are not sufficiently large to be revealed by the ordinary microscope. In the phase-contrast microscope, contrast is increased by placing a diffraction plate in each objective of the microscope and using a diaphragm with a ring-shaped opening. This arrangement, owing to refraction, retardation of waves and wave interference, selectively modifies the light from the specimen and thus affects the degree of contrast between the different structures within the specimen. Structures such as the nucleus, nucleolus, chromosomes and mitochondria can be seen in living cells.

Electron Microscope

The electron microscope (Figure 93) is an important recent development in the field of microscopy. In place of light this microscope utilizes streams of electrons moving at high speed in a vacuum. The electrons are emitted from a tungsten filament (electron gun) and discharged into a vacuum. The stream of electrons tends to follow a straight path. The vacuum is necessary to prevent air molecules from deflecting the electrons

Figure 93. Electron microscope. (Courtesy of Radio Corporation of America.)

from their course. The microscope is without glass lenses, the electron beam being focused by means of a system of suitably placed electromagnets, or permanent magnets in some models. Such specially designed magnets have the properties of optical lenses, inasmuch as they bend the path of electrons as a lens bends light.

Any small material particle in motion has associated with it a characteristic wavelength. The wavelengths of streams of electrons are exceedingly short—nearly a hundred thousand times shorter than the wavelength of light. The wavelength varies with the voltage used for emitting the electrons. Because of the exceedingly short wavelength of the electron beam, the electron microscope has a high resolving power. It also has great depth of focus.

The electron gun, located at the top of the tubular portion of the microscope, contains a tungsten filament. A high-voltage electric current passed through the filament heats it to a high temperature, which causes the electrons of the tungsten atoms to revolve so rapidly that they fly off into space and are thus permanently lost to the atoms. The electrons pass down the tube in a continuous stream.

The tube of the microscope contains a series of magnetic coils which produce magnetic fields analogous to the glass lenses (condenser, objec-

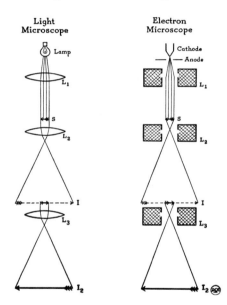

Light Microscope

Electron Microscope

Figure 94. Comparison of the optics of the compound light microscope to that of the RCA electron microscope. A system of magnetic fields in the electron microscope serves the same function as the series of glass lenses in the compound light microscope. In the diagram L_1 is the condensing lens, L_2 the objective lens and L_3 the projector lens. S is the object, I the primary image and I_2 the final, highly magnified image. (Courtesy of Radio Corporation of America.)

tive and ocular lenses) of the light microscope. The magnetic fields focus the electron rays.

On passing through the first magnetic field, the *magnetic condenser* (which corresponds to the substage condenser of the light microscope), the electron beam becomes focused, causing the electrons to converge upon the object. After passing through the object the electrons pass through the magnetic field, known as the *magnetic objective,* which corresponds to the objective of the light microscope. This results in the formation of an intermediate image of the specimen in front of the third electromagnet, the *projector coil,* which corresponds to the eye lens of the ocular of the light microscope. The projector coil forms the final image on a fluorescent screen at the lower part of the tube, where it may be observed. The image may be recorded on a photographic plate by a built-in camera, which is a part of the instrument. Figure 94 shows the path of the electrons. This figure also indicates that the electron microscope is in many ways analogous to the light microscope.

The electron microscope has the advantage of tremendous magnification and extremely high resolving power, which is 100 times that of the ordinary light microscope. Particles smaller than 10-millionth of an inch in diameter can be seen with this instrument. The image may be magnified up to 25,000 times and may be photographically enlarged to a final magnification of 200,000 times without significant loss of detail. Figure 95 illustrates the magnifying power of the electron microscope as compared with the ordinary light microscope.

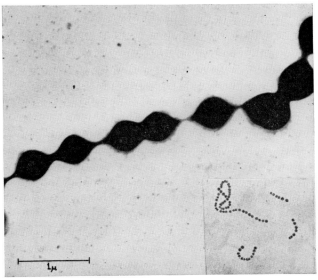

Figure 95. Electron micrograph of a chain of cells of *Streptococcus pyogenes.* (From S. Mudd and D. B. Lackman: J. Bacteriol., Vol. 41. Reproduced by permission of The Williams & Wilkins Company.) Inset is a photomicrograph of streptococci taken with a light microscope. (From Ford, Textbook of Bacteriology.)

By employing a special technique, pictures with a three-dimensional effect can be obtained. This is accomplished by depositing an exceedingly thin layer of vaporized metal, such as gold, chromium or platinum, obliquely on the preparation. Thus one side of the object becomes coated and a shadow is made to appear on the uncoated side, giving a three-dimensional effect. This technique, known as *shadowing,* brings out the depth and shape of the object being examined.

A method has been recently devised for cutting extremely thin sections of bacterial cells with a very delicate microtome. Such ultrathin sections reveal structural features that cannot be observed when whole cells are examined.

The electron microscope has become an instrument of great value in microbiological research as well as in other fields of science and also in industry. It has increased our knowledge of viruses and the structure of bacteria. The instrument, however, has certain limitations. Because the specimens examined must be dry when placed in the microscope, where they are further dehydrated and bombarded by electrons in a high vacuum, microorganisms cannot be observed in the living state.

MICROSCOPIC METHODS IN THE STUDY OF MICROORGANISMS

Microorganisms may be observed in the form of living colonies or cultures, as previously mentioned, or they may be examined as individuals suspended in fluid or in preparations that have been stained.

Observing Living Microorganisms

In the examination of living microorganisms the hanging-drop preparation is usually used. A loopful of fluid containing a suspension of the organisms is transferred to the center of a cover glass, which is then inverted over the concave depression of a slide made for this purpose. Before the cover glass is inverted over the side, a ring of petroleum jelly may be

Figure 96.   Hanging-drop preparation shown in section.

placed around the depression of the slide. This serves to seal the cover glass in place, keeping it from slipping and the drop from evaporating. When completed, a hanging-drop preparation has the appearance shown in Figure 96, the drop hanging suspended from the cover glass into the concave depression of the slide.

The hanging-drop technique permits the examination of microorganisms in their natural state. It is used chiefly for the detection of bacterial motility but may be used also in the study of the shape, size and cell grouping of the organisms and for observing the processes of reproduction, spore formation and spore germination.

Staining Microorganisms

Staining is an important part of microbiological technique. Its value in the study of the structure of the bacterial cell was referred to in Chapter 4. The chemical compounds used in staining are known as *dyes*. The dyes now commonly used in the microbiological laboratory are so-called coaltar dyes, made by the chemical transformation of certain compounds obtained from coal tar. The molecules of these dyes contain groups of atoms known as *chromophores*, which impart the color to the dye. They also contain groups of atoms called *auxochromes*, which are either acidic or basic and which, in some way, make the dye adhere to the material to be dyed. A dye with a basic auxochrome group, such as -NH$_2$, is known as a basic dye; whereas one containing an acidic auxochrome group, such as -OH, is known as an acidic dye. A basic dye is capable of reacting with acids to form salts, while an acidic dye forms salts with bases. Most of the dyes used in staining bacteria are basic dyes. The strong affinity on the part of bacteria for basic dyes appears to be due to the large amount of acid material, chiefly ribonucleic acid, in their protoplasm. Examples of basic coal-tar dyes are methylene blue, crystal violet (gentian violet), basic fuchsin, Bismarck brown and brilliant green.

The Staining Procedure.　　　The first step in making a stained preparation is to prepare a thin film of bacteria on a glass slide. Such a preparation is known as a *smear*. The bacteria may be obtained from cultures on a solid medium or from liquid cultures. In making a smear from cultures which have grown on solid media, a small drop of water is placed on a clean slide with an inoculating loop. Into this is mixed a small amount of the growth removed from the culture with a sterile loop or straight inoculating needle. The material is smeared with a rotary motion over an area about 1 cm. in diameter to form a thin, even film. Smears from liquid cultures may be made by spreading a loopful of the undiluted culture on a slide.

The smear is allowed to dry in the air and is then passed, specimen side up, through the flame of a Bunsen burner, three times in succession. This process of heating, known as *fixing* the smear, kills the bacteria, solidifies their protoplasmic constituents, and causes them to adhere to the slide. Smears are usually fixed by heat, but in some cases methyl alcohol, mercuric chloride, osmic acid or other chemicals are used instead of heat. After fixing, the smear is covered with the staining solution, which is permitted to act usually for a minute or less, depending upon the dye used. The stain is then washed off with a gentle stream of water. The smear is dried by blotting it with absorbent paper and by exposing it to the air. When dry, it is ready for examination under the microscope preferably with the oil-immersion objective. For this purpose the immersion oil may be placed directly on the stained smear; or a cover glass mounted in oil may be placed over the smear and a drop of oil placed on the cover glass.

The technique just outlined is a general staining procedure suitable for staining many kinds of bacteria to make them more readily visible under the microscope. The dyes commonly used in general staining are methylene blue, basic fuchsin and crystal violet.

Usually, when bacterial cells are stained by the foregoing procedure, the whole cell becomes uniformly colored. In some species of rod-shaped bacteria, however, only the ends (poles) of the cell become stained, while the middle portion remains colorless. This constitutes the so-called bipolar staining and is characteristic of certain bacterial species. Some rod-shaped bacteria stain unevenly throughout their length, giving them a barred or beaded appearance. This indicates an uneven distribution of the material for which the dye has an affinity.

Certain dyes, as well as several other chemical reagents, because they impart color to certain intracellular structures without staining others, have been of great help in the study of the chemical constitution of bacteria and of cells in general.

To stain certain structures such as capsules, granules, spores or flagella, special staining techniques are required. Dyes may be used, not only to make bacteria more readily visible and display their structural and chemical nature, but also to aid in distinguishing between different kinds of bacteria which may be similar in general form and size. Certain special staining reactions are highly characteristic of certain groups of bacteria and have attained great importance in differentiating between organisms. Two differential staining procedures of particular importance are the Gram method and the procedure for determining whether or not the bacteria are acid fast. By means of the Gram method, bacteria can be placed into one or the other of two groups—Gram-positive or Gram-negative. The acid-fast staining procedure serves to separate a small group of rod-shaped bacteria (acid-fast group) from all other bacteria.

THE GRAM METHOD.   This staining procedure was introduced by Gram, a Danish scientist, in 1884. It is based upon the fact that certain bacteria, when stained with crystal violet (or gentian violet) followed by the application of an aqueous solution containing iodine, retain the violet stain when subsequently washed with alcohol or acetone. The bacteria that retain the violet stain are said to be Gram-positive, whereas those that are decolorized by the alcohol or acetone are termed Gram-negative. A second stain (counterstain) of a contrasting color—usually safranin or dilute basic fuchsin—is applied after the decolorizing treatment to color the Gram-negative organisms so that they will be readily visible under the microscope. By means of this staining technique, bacteria may be divided into two groups: (1) Gram-positive species, comprising those that retain the violet stain, and (2) Gram-negative species, consisting of those that lose the violet stain and take the counterstain, which gives them a pink or red color.

The Gram method of staining is one of the most important and most widely used differential staining procedures. It is most reliable when applied to young cultures (twenty-four hours old or less). It is an important aid in the differentiation of certain bacterial species, especially the pathogenic cocci. There are species of bacteria that are Gram-variable, but their number is too small to affect materially the value of the Gram method.

The ability to retain the violet dye appears to be due to the presence in the cell of magnesium ribonucleate (a magnesium salt of ribonucleic acid). When this compound is present in the cell, then the crystal violet plus the iodine forms a chemical union with cell constituents which is relatively insoluble in alcohol or acetone. When the magnesium ribonucleate is removed from cells by chemical means or by the action of enzymes, they become Gram-negative.

Gram-positive and Gram-negative bacteria differ from one another, not only in staining characters, but also in other properties, particularly in their resistance to certain antiseptic agents.

THE ACID-FAST PROCEDURE.   The tubercle bacillus and other so-called acid-fast bacteria are difficult to stain by the ordinary staining methods. They can be stained, however, by prolonged action of the dye or by treatment with hot dyes. In the usual procedure (Ziehl-Neelsen technique), hot carbol-fuchsin is used as the staining solution. When once stained, these organisms are not easily decolorized when treated with an acid solution (1 to 3 per cent hydrochloric acid in 95 per cent alcohol): hence the term "acid-fast." After the bacteria have been subjected to the decolorizing process, a counterstain of a contrasting color (usually methylene blue) is used so that nonacid-fast bacteria may be readily seen under the microscope. The property of being acid-fast appears to be due to a high concentration of lipids within the bacterial cell.

This staining technique can sometimes be used to identify the tubercle bacillus when the source of the organism is known. Thus, acid-fast bacilli in the sputum of a suspected case of tuberculosis, or in the cerebrospinal fluid of a person displaying the symptoms of meningitis, may be definitely identified as tubercle bacilli.

OTHER STAINING PROCEDURES.   A number of other staining methods are frequently used. *Negative staining* is a procedure in which the bacteria themselves are not stained, but in which the background is given a dark color with substances such as nigrosin or India ink, which do not penetrate the bacterial cells. The unstained cells are readily visible in the darkened field. Negative staining is of particular value for the observation of bacteria which do not stain well, as, for example, certain species of spirochetes.

By combining indirect and direct staining, the presence of capsules surrounding bacterial cells can be demonstrated. In this procedure the bacteria are stained by the ordinary technique, usually with methylene blue or safranin. The capsules surrounded by the darkened background are seen as clear halos around the stained cells. Another method for showing capsules is to suspend the bacteria in sterile milk or blood serum on a slide and apply a dye after the preparation has dried. The proteins naturally present in milk or blood serum stain faintly when the bacterial cells are stained, thus providing a colored background, but the capsules surrounding the cells remain colorless. It is possible also to impart color to bacterial capsules. By this procedure they appear as faintly stained halos around the more deeply stained bacterial cells.

Bacterial flagella are not visible in ordinary stained mounts, being too thin to be resolved under the light microscope. They become microscopically recognizable, however, when subjected to a procedure in which the dye forms a precipitate on them. This causes the flagella to appear considerably greater in diameter than they are in the living state.

Because of their resistant outer wall, bacterial endospores do not take stains readily. They can be observed, however, in ordinarily stained preparations as colorless bodies which are either free or enclosed within the stained vegetative cells. Endospores can be stained by the procedure used in staining acid-fast bacteria. Once stained, they are acid-fast in that they are not decolorized by weak acid solutions.

QUESTIONS

1. What is a culture medium? What is nutrient broth? How may nutrient broth be converted into a liquefiable solid medium? How do gelatin and agar-agar differ chemically?

2. What are: (1) selective media, (2) differential media, (3) synthetic media, (4) dehydrated media?

3. How may obligate anaerobes be cultivated?

4. (*a*) Describe the "pour plate" and "streak plate" methods for obtaining pure cultures from a mixture of various microorganisms.

(*b*) Describe the single cell technique for obtaining a pure culture.

(*c*) Indicate how animal inoculation may be used to obtain a pure culture.

5. If you had a culture containing two species of bacteria, one of which was a spore-former, what would be the simplest procedure to follow to obtain a pure culture of the spore-forming species?

6. In the systematic study of pure cultures, which characteristics are particularly important?

7. Explain the formation of a real image and a virtual image by a compound microscope. Which parts are included in the illumination system of a compound microscope? Which parts make up the magnification system?

8. Explain what is meant by the resolving power of a microscope or a system of lenses. What factor limits the magnification obtainable with the light microscope? What is the limit of resolution of the light microscope?

9. How does the electron microscope differ from the light microscope? In what ways is it similar to the light microscope? What is the limit of resolution of the electron microscope?

10. What kinds of dyes are commonly used in the microbiological laboratory? Define: (1) chromophores, and (2) auxochromes.

11. Describe the staining procedures commonly used. Point out the essential features of (1) the Gram method of staining, and (2) the acid-fast staining procedure.

REFERENCES

Benford, J. R.: The Theory of the Microscope. Rochester, Bausch & Lomb Optical Company, 1952.

Bennet, A., et al.: Phase Microscopy. New York, John Wiley & Sons, Inc., 1951.

Clay, R. S., and Court, T. H.: The History of the Microscope. London, Charles Griffin & Company, 1932.

Committee on Bacteriological Technic, Society of American Bacteriologists: Manual of Microbiological Methods. New York, McGraw-Hill Book Company, Inc., 1957.

Conn, H. J.: Biological Stains. 6th ed. Baltimore, The Williams & Wilkins Company, 1953.

Hall, C. E.: Introduction to Electron Microscopy. New York, McGraw-Hill Book Company, Inc., 1953.

Schaub, I. G., Foley, M. K., Scott, E. G., and Bailey, W. R.: Diagnostic Bacteriology. 5th ed. St. Louis, The C. V. Mosby Company, 1958.

Society for General Microbiology: Constituents of Bacteriological Culture Media. Cambridge, Cambridge University Press, 1956.

Wyckoff, R. W.: The World of the Electron Microscope. New Haven, Yale University Press, 1958.

15 • Inhibition and Destruction of Microorganisms by Physical Means

Man's knowledge of the nature and activities of microorganisms has enabled him not only to foster the growth of those that are of service to him but also to develop methods for the inhibition and destruction of those that are harmful to him. This development has been of great importance in enabling man to forestall infection and to prevent the spoilage of food and other commodities. The achievements of modern surgery are largely dependent upon efficient methods for the destruction of infectious agents.

In the control of microorganisms man is concerned, not with single organisms, but with microbial populations. Owing to individual differences, some members of a given species are more resistant than others. Also, there are great differences in the resistance of different species to adverse factors.

The various agencies used to check the growth or to kill microbial populations may be divided into two main groups, physical and chemical. The physical agents constitute the topic of the present chapter. The more important of these are high temperatures, low temperatures, light and other radiations, desiccation, osmotic pressure and filtration through specially prepared filters. Most of these agencies can be used to effect sterilization.

The term "sterilization" refers to a procedure which brings about the destruction or elimination of microorganisms of all kinds. Any effective sterilization technique must be destructive to spores as well as to vegetative forms. Sterilization is usually achieved by heat but may be accomplished under certain conditions by other agencies, such as ultraviolet rays, filtration and certain chemicals. The latter, however, usually cannot be relied upon to kill spores.

HIGH TEMPERATURES

Heat is very effective in killing microorganisms and is the most widely used sterilizing agent. It may be used as dry heat or as moist heat. It is believed that heat is lethal to cells because it coagulates some of their proteins and inactivates their enzyme systems. Proteins containing abundant quantities of moisture are coagulated by heat at lower temperatures than those that have had water abstracted from them. It is probably chiefly for this reason that moist heat kills at lower temperatures than dry heat. When cells are exposed to dry heat, they are partially dehydrated before the temperature reaches a sufficiently high point to cause death by coagulation. Cells exposed to moist heat, on the other hand, may absorb rather than lose water, and thus their proteins will be coagulated at a lower temperature.

Of course, the temperature at which a microorganism is killed is a function of time. In addition, heat resistance is affected by (1) the nature of the growth or suspending medium (pH, osmotic pressure, presence of protective organic matter, and other physical and chemical factors), and (2) the nature of the cells (species, age, number, whether spores or vegetative, type of medium from which recovered). Despite these many variables, it is possible to experimentally derive a quantitative expression of heat resistance. Such an expression, defined as the length of time required to kill the cells at a given temperature under certain specified conditions, is called the *thermal death time*. Thus, a suspension of tubercle bacilli in a typical specimen of whole, raw, bovine milk is generally killed in 30 minutes at 58° C. Under identical conditions, most strains of *E. coli* have a thermal death time of 15 or 20 minutes. Heat will not kill simultaneously all cells of a single microbial strain since there are differences in tolerance toward heat from cell to cell. Obviously, the higher the temperature, the shorter will be the thermal death time. Cells in their logarithmic growth phase have a shorter thermal death time than those in their phase of decline. The thermal death time of cells suspended in a substance like milk will be greater than in a simple inorganic isotonic salt solution. Cells succumb to heat more readily in an acidic medium (low pH) than in one of a neutral reaction. Accordingly, acid foods, such as tomatoes, rhubarb and fruits, are more readily preserved by heat than nonacid foods, such as most vegetables (corn, beans, peas, spinach, etc.) and meats.

Excluding spores and vegetative cells of thermophiles, most bacteria in liquid media are killed within one-half hour at 65° C. Bacterial spores are considerably more resistant than this. In some low-acid canned foods, spores of thermophiles may survive 115° C. for over an hour! By and large, yeasts and molds are less tolerant of high temperatures than bacteria, although their spores are about as heat resistant as vegetative cells of bacteria. Most pathogenic bacteria, in customary broth media, are killed in less than 10 minutes at 60° C.

Dry Heat

For the use of dry heat, hot-air ovens are available. Dry heat is used for the sterilization of culture tubes, flasks, pipets, Petri dishes and similar pieces of glassware, as well as other articles not injured by hot air. Certain articles that steam cannot penetrate, such as oils, glycerin and petrolatum, may be sterilized in the hot-air oven. To accomplish sterilization with dry heat, a temperature of 160° to 180° C. must be maintained for an hour or longer.

Another method of using dry heat is by *incineration.* Certain contaminated objects such as swabs, soiled dressings, tongue blades and paper handkerchiefs are usually burned. In laboratory procedures, inoculating loops or needles are sterilized by heating them red-hot in the flame of a Bunsen burner.

Figure 97. The Arnold sterilizer for sterilizing with flowing steam. (Courtesy of Will Corporation.)

Moist Heat

The presence of moisture increases the effectiveness of heat in accomplishing the destruction of microorganisms. Moist heat has greater penetrating power and coagulates protoplasm at lower temperatures than does dry heat. As mentioned previously, dry heat dehydrates cells and thus raises the temperature necessary for coagulation of the proteins of the cells. Moist heat may be applied in the form of boiling water or by exposure to steam.

Boiling. The vegetative forms of microorganisms are killed when heated to 100° C., the boiling point of water. Spores, however, can usually withstand this temperature unless the boiling is prolonged. The spores of some species are able to withstand boiling for fifteen hours or longer. Boiling, therefore, is not a sure means of sterilization.

Fractional Steam Sterilization.   This procedure is carried out in an apparatus known as the Arnold steam sterilizer (Figure 97). In this apparatus "live" steam, i.e., steam at atmospheric pressure, is the sterilizing agent. The lower portion of the sterilizer is in the form of a pan for holding water. When the water is heated, the steam that is generated enters an upper chamber containing the items to be sterilized. Steam continu-

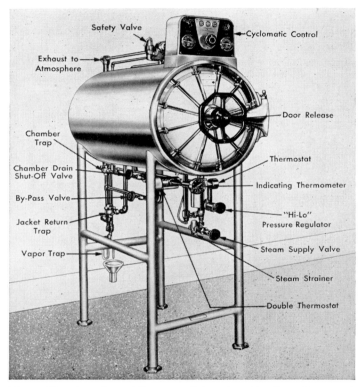

Figure 98.   Autoclave. (Courtesy of American Sterilizer Company.)

ously flows through the chamber, but, being at atmospheric pressure, the temperature never exceeds the boiling point.

The flowing steam sterilizer is used chiefly to sterilize culture media containing milk, gelatin or sugar, which may become chemically altered when subjected to higher temperatures. To be effective for this purpose, a procedure known as *fractional, discontinuous* or *intermittent sterilization* is used. This involves steaming for fifteen to twenty minutes on each of three successive days. The first steaming destroys the vegetative cells. The spores present are not killed but will germinate into vegetative cells by the next day and will be killed by the second steaming. Any spores that were slow in germinating will be killed as vegetative cells by the third steaming. The medium must be kept at about 30° C. during the intervals between steaming, or germination of the spores may be delayed.

This method can be used only for sterilizing materials that are favorable for bacterial growth, i.e., materials in which any spores that may be present will germinate into vegetative forms. It is not always possible to effect sterilization by this method. The spores of obligate anaerobic bacteria may not germinate under the aerobic conditions prevailing during the intervals between steaming and consequently will not be killed. When the medium is later inoculated with bacteria, anaerobic conditions may be brought about by their growth processes, thus providing a suitable environment for the germination of anaerobic spores.

Sterilization by Steam under Pressure.   Steam under pressure is the most efficient method of using steam, because it has a temperature higher than that of free-flowing steam. One heating in the pressure sterilizer or *autoclave* (Figure 98) suffices to bring about complete sterilization. The autoclave is essentially a double-jacketed chamber provided with a means of replacing all the air it contains with steam under pressure. It is fitted with a steamtight door, pressure gauge, thermometer and safety valve. The temperature increases in direct relationship with the increase in steam pressure. The following table shows the relationship at sea level between steam pressure and temperature:

Pounds of Steam Pressure per Square Inch	Temperature	
0	100°C.	212°F.
5	108°C.	226.4°F.
10	115°C.	239°F.
15	121°C.	249.8°F.
20	126°C.	258.8°F.

The usual practice is to permit the pressure to rise to 15 pounds. At this pressure the thermometer reading is 121° C. This temperature, maintained for twenty to thirty minutes, will kill all forms of life, including highly resistant spores. At 15 pounds' pressure the steam is saturated; i.e., it contains as much vaporized water as its temperature allows. At higher pressures, steam is drier (unsaturated) and less efficient as a lethal agent, since its action then is more like that of hot air than of saturated steam.

In operating the autoclave, complete removal of the air from the chamber is necessary, since a mixture of steam and air does not have as high a temperature at a given pressure as pure steam. If some air remains in the chamber, the pressure of 15 pounds will represent a temperature lower than 121° C. If only half of the air has been removed, the temperature will be only 112° C. when the pressure reaches 15 pounds. Air remaining in the chamber does not mix uniformly with the steam but tends to collect in pockets. The sterilizing efficiency of steam is due to the transfer of its latent heat as the steam condenses on the surface of objects having a lower temperature. The rate of condensation is decreased by the presence of air. The sterilizing efficiency of steam is dependent upon its temperature rather than the pressure within the autoclave.

In the laboratory the autoclave is used for the sterilization of culture media, culture tubes, Petri dishes, flasks, pipets and discarded cultures. Substances which cannot be wetted by steam, such as oils, fats and petrolatum, cannot be sterilized efficiently in the autoclave, but their sterilization can be effected by prolonged exposure to dry heat.

The pressure cooker used in the home operates on the same principle as the autoclave. The large steam chests, or "retorts," used in canning establishments for processing food in tin cans or glass jars are essentially autoclaves. Autoclaves adapted for sterilizing instruments and dressings are used in hospitals.

Pasteurization

Pasteurization takes its name from Louis Pasteur, who first used a method of heating wine to a moderate temperature to keep it from spoiling. Later he used the same practice for preventing spoilage of beer. At the present time pasteurization finds its widest application in making milk safe for human consumption and in improving its keeping qualities. Two methods are in use for pasteurizing milk, the low-temperature, long-time, or holding method and the high-temperature, short-time, or flash method. In the holding method the milk is heated to 143° to 145° F. (61.7° to 62.8° C.) and is held there for thirty minutes. In the flash method the milk is heated to 161° F. (71.6° C.) or higher for at least fifteen seconds. In either procedure the milk is immediately cooled to 50° F. (10° C.) or lower after pasteurization. Rapid cooling inhibits the growth of the microorganisms that survive the pasteurization process. Modern pasteurization equipment is provided with a recording thermometer which registers the temperature and time of heating on a rotating disk of paper.

Pasteurization kills the vegetative cells of pathogens and the majority of saprophytes but usually is not effective against bacterial spores. Some saprophytes survive in the vegetative stage. These are frequently referred to as thermoduric (heat-enduring) bacteria. Some of the thermoduric forms are thermophiles, whereas others, although able to endure high temperatures, are unable to grow at these temperatures.

LOW TEMPERATURES

Temperatures far below the minimum for growth, even including temperatures which approach absolute zero,* may be endured by many microbial species, particularly bacteria, viruses and rickettsiae. At temperatures below the minimum growth temperature, metabolism slows down or

* —273° C., the lowest possible temperature permitted by the nature of matter; the temperature at which all atomic and molecular activity ceases.

stops and a gradual decline in numbers of viable organisms occurs, although a certain proportion of the cells remain alive for long periods, especially at temperatures well below freezing. Stock cultures of many microorganisms will remain viable for weeks or months in a standard refrigerator (5 to 10° C.). Slow freezing is rather destructive to microbial cells since the ice crystals which form destroy the cells' integrity by rupturing membranes and disturbing the balance of the colloidal system in the cytoplasm. However, the rapid freezing of cells suspended in certain organic menstrua is far less destructive than a slow freezing process. The relatively small proportion of cells which survive the transition of temperature during freezing are preserved, sometimes for indefinite periods of time, provided thawing does not occur thereafter. When typhoid bacilli are frozen in water or certain foods, a significant number will survive, often for months. Alternate freezing and thawing is particularly lethal.

It is evident that cold environments cannot be used to accomplish sterilization but, owing to their inhibitory effect on microbial metabolism, they may be utilized for the preservation of many foods. A "cold environment" in its practical application means (a) temperatures just above the freezing point of water (0 to 10° C.), (b) temperatures just below the freezing point of water (—10 to 0° C.), or (c) temperatures well below the freezing point of water (—10 to —30° C.). Household refrigerators and commercial cold storage rooms are usually maintained at temperatures of from 1 to 10° C. In this temperature range microorganisms multiply so slowly that foods will remain in good condition for several days or longer. Frozen foods, generally stored at temperatures of from —15 to —20° C., will keep almost indefinitely because microbial activity is completely stopped. Many foodstuffs are now preserved by fast freezing. Foods so treated are not changed appreciably in structure since the ice crystals which form are too small to cause mechanical damage. Slow freezing, however, permits large ice crystals to form which crush or break the tissues and fibers of the food. Such foods do not retain their normal structure and appearance after thawing. The inhibitory effect of prolonged freezing on the growth of microorganisms is illustrated by the frozen bodies of mammoths, dead for thousands of years, that have been dug out of solid ice in the northern latitudes. The flesh of these animals was so well preserved that it was still edible and was readily devoured by the dogs of the exploring parties.

The danger of transmission of disease from frozen foods is illustrated by an experiment in which the investigators froze milk from tuberculous cows and kept it in this state for thirty-two months. When the milk was thawed and injected into guinea pigs, it was found to contain viable tubercle bacilli since the animals acquired tuberculosis. Thus, the tubercle bacillus will survive a minimum of thirty-two months in frozen milk. Because of dangers exemplified by this interesting experiment, foods that are to be frozen should be handled in a sanitary manner. Also, frozen foods should be consumed as soon as feasible after thawing and not left at room temperature for extended periods. In fact, no perishable foods should be left unrefrigerated for more than a few hours.

STERILIZATION BY FILTRATION

Fluids containing microorganisms other than viruses can usually be rendered free from these organisms by passage through specially prepared filters. One type of filter in common use contains a "filter candle" in the form of a hollow, porous cylinder, closed at one end, the open end being mounted on a metal tube. The cylinder is made of diatomaceous earth or

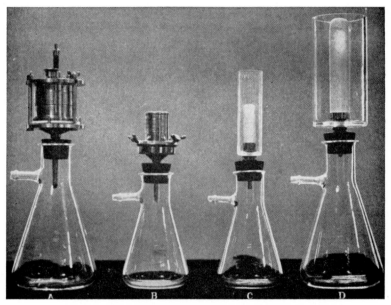

Figure 99.   Some common filters used to remove bacteria from fluids. (From Jordan-Burrows Textbook of Bacteriology.)

unglazed porcelain and is enclosed in a glass cup or mantle. The metal tube passes through a rubber stopper placed in the neck of a special flask (suction flask) containing a side arm for connection to an exhaust pump. Figure 99 illustrates some common types of filters. Since fluids do not readily pass through these filters by gravity, it is necessary to apply positive or negative pressure. Negative pressure (suction) is usually the method used, the fluid being drawn into the suction flask. (See **Figure 100.**)

The three main types of filters in which the filter element is cylindrical are the Pasteur-Chamberland filter, made of unglazed porcelain, and the Berkefeld and Mandler filters, constructed of diatomaceous earth. Another kind, the Seitz filter, has an asbestos disk as the filter element. Some filters are made of sintered* (fritted) glass. Before a filter is used, the entire filtration apparatus, including the suction flask, must be sterilized by heat to prevent contamination of the filtrate.

The filters are manufactured in various grades of porosity, the finest ones being impervious to all bacteria and even to some of the viruses. Pore size, however, is not the only factor that determines the size of the particle that will pass through the filter. Physical and electrical forces play a role in that they may cause microorganisms to adhere to the sides of the pores.

Figure 100. A bacteriological filter in use. (Courtesy of the Fisher Scientific Company.)

Filtration is used for the sterilization of serums, toxins, antitoxins, sugar solutions or other heat-labile (destroyed by heat) substances.

The *membrane filter,* a new, special type of filter, is described in Chapter 22.

LIGHT AND OTHER RADIATIONS

There are various types of radiations, some naturally occurring, others artificially produced. Radiations are forms of energy propagated through space in the form of undulatory waves. Each form of radiant energy has wavelengths within certain narrow limits. Except for their wavelengths, the rays of visible light appear to be essentially the same as other electromagnetic waves. They have the common property of possessing the same velocity, which is approximately 186,000 miles per second. Some forms of radiant energy produce harmful effects on microorganisms and other cells.

* These filters are made of finely ground glass heated just enough to cause the glass particles to become partially fused, leaving minute pore spaces through which liquids may pass.

To produce such effects, the rays must be absorbed by the cells. Those that have wavelengths shorter than those of visible light are of most importance in this respect. The unit of measurement used to express the wavelength of the shorter forms of radiant energy is the Angström unit (A), which has a value of 0.1 millimicron (0.0001 micron).

Visible light constitutes only a small part of the spectrum of the radiant energy transmitted to the earth from the sun. The visible portion of the spectrum lies approximately between 4000 and 8000 Angström units. Beyond the visible red lie the longer, infrared waves (heat waves), and just below the visible violet lies the ultraviolet zone, in which the wavelengths range from 1100 to 4000 Angström units. The most destructive radiations are found in the ultraviolet portion of the spectrum. Those ultraviolet rays having wavelengths of from 2400 to 3000 Angström units are highly lethal, whereas those from 2500 to 2800 Angström units are particularly destructive to microorganisms.

Direct exposure to sunlight is lethal to most pathogens after several hours. Bacterial spores are somewhat more resistant than are vegetative cells. Because ultraviolet rays lack penetrating power, exceedingly small particles of matter may protect microorganisms from these rays. Ordinary glass absorbs ultraviolet rays shorter than 3100 Angström units and, therefore, is opaque to these rays.

Although sunlight is germicidal upon long exposure, it contains a low concentration of the short wavelength ultraviolet rays. Various ultraviolet lamps have been developed which generate a high concentration of those ultraviolet rays that are particularly destructive to microorganisms. Such lamps can be placed in the ducts of ventilating systems, in heating or air conditioning ducts, and in hospital operating rooms, to reduce air-borne infection. They can be used, also, to act on the surface of meats during rapid curing and are of value in refrigerators and cold-storage warehouses.

The cells of microorganisms do not readily absorb x-rays, but some of these rays are absorbed and thus can be used to produce lethal effects. They are not as effective, however, in destroying microorganisms as are ultraviolet rays. The beta and gamma rays emanating from radioactive elements such as radium, uranium and thorium have only slight germicidal power.

Photodynamic Action

A phenomenon of considerable interest is the fact that when certain dyes, such as eosin or methylene blue, are added in low concentration to a bacterial suspension, the bacteria become highly sensitive to visible light and are killed within a few minutes when exposed to the light of a room (which would ordinarily be harmless) but continue to grow when kept in the dark. Viruses react in the same manner. This phenomenon, called *photodynamic action,* appears to be due to a sensitization of the microorganisms by the dye to the rays of the visible spectrum. The dye apparently causes the cells to absorb certain light rays. As stated previously, to produce chemical changes in cells, radiations must be absorbed. Toxins, tuberculin and certain substances (antigens) that play a role in the production of immunity can also be inactivated in this manner.

OSMOTIC PRESSURE

As indicated in a previous chapter, when a cell is placed in a hypertonic solution, i.e., a solution which has an osmotic pressure higher than that of the cell, water will flow from the less dense solution within the cell to the more dense solution outside the cell and the cell will shrink. If the difference in osmotic pressure is not great, the cell may adjust itself to the new conditions and continue to grow; but if the difference is pronounced, the shrinking of the cell will cause its death. High osmotic pressure may be used in the preservation of certain foods. Foods having a high sugar or salt content are partially protected from decomposition by plasmolysis. Examples of such foods are jams, jellies, sugared fruits, sirups and salted meats. The partial desiccation to which prunes and raisins are subjected greatly increases their sugar concentration and thus their osmotic pressure.

DESICCATION

The vegetative forms of most pathogens and many saprophytes can be killed by drying in air. Different species vary considerably, however, in their resistance to drying, some being able to remain alive for a relatively long time, whereas others die within a few days when air-dried. Tubercle bacilli can resist drying for several months, especially when embedded in sputum, but the spirochetes of syphilis can be killed within a few hours by drying. The spores of bacteria, yeasts and molds and the cysts of protozoa remain viable for many years in the dried state.

Preservation of Food by Desiccation

Dehydration may be used as a method of food preservation. The microbial decomposition of food cannot occur in the dried state since active life is impossible without water. Dried foods, however, are not sterile; they usually contain large numbers of living bacteria, yeasts and molds. If placed in moisture-proof containers, the number of microorganisms present will gradually decrease.

SUPERSONIC VIBRATIONS

Sound waves differ from the waves of light rays in that they are longitudinal mechanical vibrations. Those within the audible range are referred to as *sonic;* those that have wavelengths so short that they are inaudible are spoken of as *supersonic* or *ultrasonic.* Although some sonic waves of high intensity have a slight disruptive effect on microorganisms, supersonic vibrations produce more drastic effects. Such vibrations rupture the cell wall and liberate the cell contents (Figure 101). Supersonic vibrations have been found useful in releasing enzymes, antigens and other chemical compounds from bacterial cells in a chemically unaltered state. They are of value also in separating the cell walls from the cell body.

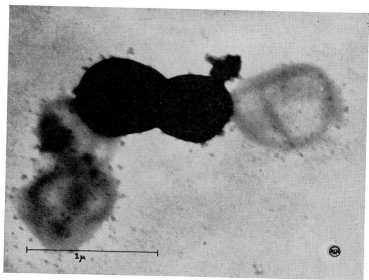

Figure 101. Electron micrograph showing disruptive effect of supersonic vibrations on a chain of five cells of *Streptococcus pyogenes*. Two of the central cells of the chain are intact; they appear black because they contain dense electron-scattering protoplasm; two cells on one end and one on the other end are cytolysed; only the cell walls remain as "ghosts." (From S. Mudd and D. B. Lackman: J. Bacteriol., Vol. 41. Reproduced by permission of The Williams & Wilkins Company.)

QUESTIONS

1. Which physical agents may be used to check the growth of or to kill microorganisms?

2. (*a*) Explain the various ways in which dry heat and moist heat may be used in the destruction of microorganisms.

(*b*) Describe the hot-air oven. For what is it used?

(*c*) Which is the more efficient method of sterilization, flowing steam or steam under pressure? What is meant by "fractional sterilization"? What is an autoclave?

3. What is pasteurization? Why is it so called? Is it a method of sterilization? How does the "holding process" differ from the "flash process"?

4. What practical value have low temperatures in controlling microbial life?

5. How may fluids be rendered free of microorganisms by mechanical means?

6. Discuss the use of light as a lethal agent for microorganisms. What is meant by "photodynamic action"?

7. In what way may osmotic pressure be used to kill microorganisms?

8. Is desiccation an effective sterilization method?

9. Discuss the effects of supersonic vibrations on microorganisms.

10. Define thermal death time and cite some factors which affect it.

REFERENCES
Harris, R. J. C., ed.: Biological Application of Freezing and Drying. New York, Academic Press, Inc., 1957.

Hopkins, E. S., and Schulze, W. H.: The Practice of Sanitation. 3rd ed. Baltimore, The Williams & Wilkins Company, 1958.

McCulloch, E. C.: Disinfection and Sterilization. Philadelphia, Lea & Febiger, 1945.

Perkins, J. J.: Principles and Methods of Sterilization. Springfield, Ill., Charles C Thomas, 1956.

Reddish, G. F., ed.: Antiseptics, Disinfectants, Fungicides and Chemical and Physical Sterilization. 2nd ed. Philadelphia, Lea & Febiger, 1957.

Sykes, G.: Disinfection and Sterilization. Princeton, N. J., D. Van Nostrand Company, Inc., 1958.

Wilson, G. S., and Miles, A. A.: Topley and Wilson's Principles of Bacteriology and Immunity. 2 vols., 4th ed. Baltimore, The Williams & Wilkins Company, 1955.

16 • Inhibition and Destruction of Microorganisms by Chemical Agents

A large number of chemical compounds can be used either to kill or to inhibit the growth of microorganisms. Many of these chemicals have become useful weapons in the prevention and treatment of infection. Chemical agents are used under a wide variety of conditions in the control of microorganisms. They may be applied to inanimate objects, such as surgical instruments, clinical thermometers and eating and drinking utensils; to contaminated body discharges (sputum, feces, urine); and to the body itself. Chemicals differ from one another in their ability to kill microorganisms; also, microorganisms differ widely in their susceptibility to the various chemical agents used as antiseptics and disinfectants. No single chemical agent is suitable for practical use under all conditions. Some are greatly hindered in their action by the presence of organic matter, whereas others corrode metals, or are injurious to fabrics or to living tissues.

Microorganisms cannot be killed so readily in living tissues as they can on inanimate objects because of the fact that agents that kill microorganisms are usually equally destructive to body cells. Certain agents, however, when used in low concentration are of value when used on body tissues because they retard the growth of microorganisms without doing any appreciable damage to body cells.

TERMINOLOGY

A number of terms are used in connection with the inhibition and destruction of microorganisms. Most of these terms apply chiefly to chemical agents, although a few are sometimes applied also to physical agents.

The term *disinfection* refers to the act of destroying agents capable of causing infection. It does not necessarily imply the killing of all kinds of microorganisms or of the spores of pathogens. An agent which accomplishes disinfection is a *disinfectant*. Many chemicals used as disinfectants will kill spores when used in proper concentration—they thus can serve as sterilizing agents. The term as generally used refers to chemical agents applied to inanimate objects, but which may do harm when used on living tissues. The terms *germicide* and *bactericide* are practically synonymous with the term "disinfectant." The ending *-cide* implies a killing action.

The term *sepsis* refers to a local or generalized microbial invasion of the body, especially by pus-producing organisms. *Asepsis* implies the absence of septic matter, or freedom from infective material. Asepsis is achieved in surgery by using only sterile instruments, by applying germicides to the area of the skin where the incision is to be made, and by taking all necessary precautions to keep infectious agents from gaining access to the field of operation. An *antiseptic* is a chemical agent which inhibits the growth and multiplication of infectious agents without necessarily killing them. The term applies especially to substances used on living tissue. Most antiseptics will kill at least a small percentage of pathogens per hour, but death is slow, so that even after several days some of the organisms will still be alive. It is not always possible to differentiate between an antiseptic and a disinfectant. A chemical agent may function as a disinfectant in a certain concentration, but in a lower concentration its action may be that of an antiseptic.

The definition of the term "antiseptic" given here differs from that of the Federal Food, Drug and Cosmetic Act. This act states: "The representation of a drug, in its labeling, as an antiseptic, shall be considered to be a representation that it is a germicide, except in the case of a drug purporting to be, or represented as, an antiseptic for inhibitory use as wet dressing, ointment, dusting powder, or such other use as involves prolonged contact with the body."

The term *bacteriostasis* refers to the retardation of normal bacterial multiplication without necessarily killing the bacteria. The term applies to bacteria in general rather than pathogenic forms alone. A *bacteriostatic* agent is one that is capable of producing bacteriostasis.

MODE OF ACTION OF CHEMICAL AGENTS

Chemical agents act on microorganisms in a variety of ways. Some are known to react with bacterial surfaces. By damaging the cell wall and cytoplasmic membrane, they disorganize the permeability properties of the bacterial surface, allowing cell components to leak out of the cell. The synthetic detergents are examples of surface active bactericides. Other antimicrobial agents owe their germicidal properties to their ability to act as enzyme inhibitors. Examples of agents acting in this manner are mercuric chloride and certain organic compounds of mercury. Another group of bactericidal agents exerts a disrupting effect on the organized colloidal state of the cell protoplasm. Ethyl alcohol belongs to this group. A few act as oxidizing agents, thereby destroying components of the protoplasm: hydrogen peroxide, potassium permanganate and chlorine are the most familiar oxidizing agents. Many disinfectants denature proteins.

A strong selective action is exhibited by some chemical agents in that they act more effectively against some microorganisms than against others. Crystal violet, for example, will kill *Staphylococcus aureus* in concentrations much lower than those required to kill *Escherichia coli*. Owing to their selective action, certain dyes are at times added to culture media to inhibit the growth of unwanted bacteria without interfering with the growth of others.

FACTORS INFLUENCING THE ACTION OF CHEMICALS

The activity of every antiseptic and disinfectant is subject to a variety of influences. The concentration of the chemical agent influences the speed and efficiency of action but not in the same manner for all chemicals. The length of time the agent is permitted to act is important, since a certain amount of time is required for the chemical to penetrate all parts of the material and reach all the microorganisms. If insufficient time is allowed, some of the microorganisms will escape destruction. Owing to individual differences, microorganisms do not all die at once upon exposure to a disinfectant. The largest number is killed in the first time interval, and the number dying decreases rapidly with each succeeding time interval. In many instances the rate of death is logarithmic. By this is meant that if 85 per cent of the microorganisms are killed in the first minute, then in each succeeding one-minute interval there will be an 85 per cent decrease among the survivors, until theoretically only a fraction of one organism remains alive.

When microorganisms are suspended in distilled water, they are usually killed much more rapidly by chemical agents than when extraneous matter is present. In the presence of blood, pus, sputum, urine, feces and other organic substances the action of many antiseptics and disinfectants is greatly reduced. Salts of the heavy metals readily form insoluble compounds with organic matter, whereas phenol and cresol lose little of their efficiency in the presence of organic matter. Mercuric chloride, an effective disinfectant in water, is unsatisfactory for the disinfection of sputum or feces because it combines readily with organic matter.

Temperature plays a role in that the higher the temperature, the more rapid the germicidal action. A rise in temperature increases the activity of some chemicals much more than that of others; consequently the increase in velocity is not the same for all chemicals. The action of many chemicals is hastened two or three times for a 10° C. rise in temperature up to the point where the heat itself is sufficient to cause death. The action of phenol and cresol is increased five to eight times for every ten degree rise.

EVALUATION OF GERMICIDES

A number of methods for evaluating the efficiency of germicides have been devised. At the present time the official method for testing and comparing germicides is the one devised by the Food and Drug Administration of the United States Department of Agriculture. In this test the disinfecting efficiency of a chemical is compared with that of phenol under carefully controlled conditions. From the results of the test the *phenol coefficient* of the chemical is obtained. The phenol coefficient is a number representing the ability of a chemical to kill cultures of test organisms as compared with that of phenol under the same standard conditions.

The phenol coefficient test gives little information concerning the value of a germicide under conditions of actual use. The chief value of the test is that it serves as a yardstick for the evaluation of commercial preparations.

COMMONLY USED CHEMICAL AGENTS

A large number of chemical agents is available for inactivating and destroying microorganisms. Properly used, these agents are of great value to man in the maintenance of a sanitary environment and in the treatment and prevention of disease.

PHENOL AND CRESOL

Phenol

Phenol (C_6H_5OH), also known as carbolic acid, is of historical importance because it was first used by Joseph Lister for the treatment of infected wounds and as an antiseptic agent in surgical operations. Lister's pioneer work with antiseptic agents laid the basis for later studies on antiseptics and disinfectants. Pure phenol occurs as colorless or reddish crystals which have a characteristic aromatic odor and are soluble in water. Phenol is usually used in concentrations of 2 to 5 per cent. A 5 per cent aqueous solution will kill vegetative cells, but is less effective against spores and viruses. Solutions of this strength may be used to disinfect feces, urine, sputum, instruments and utensils.

Phenol is highly toxic, as well as caustic, and relatively dangerous to use on living tissues. It is used chiefly as a bactericidal agent on inanimate objects.

Cresol

What is usually referred to as cresol is a mixture of three related compounds, *ortho*cresol, *meta*cresol and *para*cresol. Cresol has a phenol coefficient varying from two to three. Pure cresol is a yellowish to brownish liquid with a phenolic odor. It has a lower toxicity for human tissue than phenol. It is only moderately soluble in water but readily forms emulsions with liquid soaps and alkalis. In a 2 to 5 per cent concentration it is an effective disinfectant against the vegetative forms of all pathogens.

It is particularly effective against the tubercle bacillus, which is resistant to many of the other chemical bactericides. The presence of organic matter does not interfere appreciably with its germicidal power. Cresol preparations are frequently used for disinfecting sputum or feces or other organic material, as well as glassware, furniture, floors and the walls of rooms.

CHLORINE AND CHLORINE COMPOUNDS

Chlorine and chlorine compounds are used widely as germicidal agents. Chlorine, one of the chemical elements, is a pale yellowish-green, water-soluble gas with a characteristic pungent odor. In the free state and in some combined forms, chlorine is one of the most effective and widely applicable germicides available. The germicidal compounds of chlorine owe their action to chlorine, which, not being firmly bound, is slowly liberated. In the presence of water, chlorine liberates nascent oxygen (oxygen in the atomic form) from the water. Nascent oxygen, being a powerful oxidizing agent, kills microorganisms by oxidation. The germicidal action of chlorine, however, is due not alone to nascent oxygen but also to the direct action of chlorine on the protoplasm of the cell. It replaces some hydrogen atoms in certain organic compounds.

Liquid Chlorine

Chlorine gas can be liquefied by a process of compression and refrigeration. In the liquefied form it is stored in steel cylinders under pressure at ordinary temperatures. Liquid chlorine is used on a large scale for the disinfection of public water supplies, swimming pools and sewage plant effluents. In the proportion of one part of chlorine to one million parts of water it is a highly effective germicide if the water contains little or no organic matter. Since chlorine readily combines with organic matter, its germicidal efficiency is reduced by the presence of such material. The practice of chlorinating drinking water has protected many millions of people from water-borne diseases.

Hypochlorites

The hypochlorites include calcium hypochlorite and sodium hypochlorite. Calcium hypochlorite, $Ca(OCl)_2$, more commonly known as chlorinated lime, is low in cost and one of the most important of the chlorine-liberating compounds used in the control of unwanted microorganisms. It contains about 35 per cent of available chlorine, but slowly loses chlorine upon standing. It bleaches, and is destructive to fabrics, and it corrodes metals. A 1 per cent solution will kill most microorganisms within five minutes. In the presence of much organic matter a stronger solution is required. Chlorinated lime has no rival for the disinfection of body excreta. It is usually used in a 4 per cent solution for this purpose. It is used also for the disinfection of dairies, slaughter houses and outhouses in rural areas.

Sodium hypochlorite, NaOCl, formed by the action of chlorine on sodium hydroxide, is used extensively to disinfect dairy equipment, such as milk cans and bottles and the conveying pipes in creameries. It is used also to keep restaurant equipment in a sanitary condition.

Chloramines

The chloramines are compounds of nitrogen in which one or more of the hydrogen atoms attached to a nitrogen atom are replaced with chlorine. Because they liberate chlorine slowly, the antiseptic action of chloramines is more prolonged than that of the hypochlorites. The simplest of the chloramines is monochloramine (NH_2Cl), one of the active compounds formed when water for drinking purposes is disinfected with chlorine and ammonia. Three commonly used organic chloramines are chloramine-T (sodium *p*-toluene sulfonchloramide), dichloramine-T (*p*-toluene sulfondichloramide) and azochloramide (dichloroazocarbonamidine).

Chloramine-T is employed as a 2 per cent aqueous solution for the treatment of wounds. It is used also to disinfect drinking glasses, eating utensils and various food handling equipment.

Dichloramine-T is only slightly soluble in water but is freely soluble in oils. It is used in the treatment of infected wounds, either as a spray or by direct application.

Azochloramide, also known as chlorazodin, may be used in lieu of chloramine-T or dichloramine-T. It is less irritating and exerts a greater germicidal action in the presence of extraneous organic matter than most chloramines.

IODINE

Iodine is a nonmetallic element occurring as a heavy grayish-black crystalline solid with a metallic luster and a characteristic odor. It is only slightly soluble in water but is freely soluble in aqueous solutions of the iodides and in alcohol and other organic solvents. Iodine is one of the best and most dependable germicides and is widely used in the treatment of superficial wounds and as a skin disinfectant. It is used in surgery to disinfect the skin at the site where the surgical incisions are made. Iodine is widely used in the form of iodine tincture (2% iodine) for the treatment of small cuts and bruises.

HEAVY METALS AND THEIR SALTS

In aqueous solutions the ions of metals are capable of germicidal activity. Salts of mercury and silver, as well as organic compounds of these metals, are in common use.

Mercury Compounds

Inorganic mercury compounds were among the first antiseptics and disinfectants to come into use. A number of organic mercurials have been synthesized in recent years. Among these are Mercurochrome, Metaphen and Merthiolate. These, for the most part, are less irritating, less toxic and more potent than mercuric chloride, the most commonly used inorganic mercury compound. The potency of mercurials has been overrated in the past. They are chiefly antiseptic rather than disinfectant in their action.

Mercuric Chloride.   Mercuric chloride ($HgCl_2$) ionizes in aqueous solution, giving rise to Hg^{++} ions. The use of mercuric chloride is limited, owing to its irritating action on tissues, its toxic effect after absorption, its loss of potency in the presence of an excess of organic matter, and its corrosive action on metals which precludes its use for the disinfection of surgical and dental instruments. It is usually used in a strength of 1:1000 (0.1 per cent). The addition of alcohol enhances its germicidal action.

Mercurochrome.   Mercurochrome (the disodium salt of dibromo-hydroxy-mercurifluorescein) is an organic compound of mercury containing the dye molecule, fluorescein. It is readily soluble in water and alcohol. It is relatively nonirritating and nontoxic and does not precipitate proteins. It is frequently used in the form of a 2 per cent aqueous solution as a skin application. Tests indicate that this solution has a mild antiseptic action and is not as reliable as the 2 per cent iodine tincture. When used as a 5 per cent alcoholic solution, or when dissolved in a mixture of alcohol and acetone, it is more effective.

Metaphen.   Metaphen contains 56 per cent mercury in organic combination. It is insoluble in water, but soluble in dilute aqueous sodium hydroxide solutions. It is used as an antiseptic on the skin and mucous membranes and is sometimes used to disinfect surgical and dental instruments, but it does not kill spores.

Merthiolate.   Merthiolate is used as a skin antiseptic in dilutions of 1:30,000 to 1:5000. It does not appear to be effective against spores. A 1:1000 solution (Tincture of Merthiolate) is sometimes used to disinfect surgical instruments and as a preoperative skin application.

Silver Compounds

Silver compounds such as silver nitrate and colloidal silver preparations are effective antiseptics. The action of these preparations is due to the liberation of silver ions and the affinity of these ions for proteins, which they precipitate as insoluble proteinates. Silver preparations are used as antiseptic agents for application to the mucous membranes of the eyes, nose, throat and urethra. The action of silver preparations is retarded by chlorides, blood and proteins, owing to the formation of insoluble precipitates.

Silver Nitrate.   Silver nitrate is the most widely used silver salt. A solution of 1:10,000 inhibits the growth of most microorganisms. Instilling one or two drops of a 1 per cent silver nitrate solution into the eyes of newborn infants is an effective prophylactic measure against *ophthalmia neonatorum,* a gonorrheal infection of the eyes which usually results in blindness unless promptly and adequately treated. In most states it is required by law that this treatment be administered to the eyes of every newborn infant whether or not there is any reason to suspect that the mother is infected with the gonococcus. This practice unquestionably has saved the sight of thousands of babies born from mothers having gonorrhea.

Colloidal Silver Compounds.   These are preparations of metallic silver or silver oxide in various combinations with proteins. Their action is due to silver ions, but they ionize only slightly in aqueous solution and exert an antiseptic rather than a germicidal action. They have the advantage of being less irritating than silver nitrate.

OXIDIZING AGENTS

Oxidizing agents owe their germicidal action to nascent oxygen, which they give up readily or release from other compounds. Nascent oxygen is capable of rapidly oxidizing organic materials. The chief oxidizing agents are peroxide of hydrogen, potassium permanganate and the chlorine preparations, which have already been considered.

Hydrogen Peroxide

The solution usually used contains 3 per cent of H_2O_2 in water. When applied to a wound, it is rapidly decomposed by tissue catalase into water and oxygen, each molecule liberating an atom of oxygen. The nascent oxygen thus released produces a mild antiseptic action. In addition to its antiseptic effect, it has a secondary action in that it serves as a mechanical cleansing agent, loosening pus and wound debris. This is often of greater importance than its antiseptic action, particularly in wounds and cavities that are difficult of access.

Potassium Permanganate

This compound is an active oxidizing agent but readily combines with organic matter, thereby losing its efficiency. It is used in solutions of 0.1 to 5 per cent strength. It is sometimes used to oxidize organic poisons and was once the recognized treatment for snake bite.

ETHYL ALCOHOL

Ethyl alcohol is widely used as a skin disinfectant and as a cleansing agent for the skin prior to surgical operations and hypodermic injections. It is moderately effective against vegetative forms, but it cannot be relied upon to destroy spores. It was formerly believed to be effective only when the concentration was reduced to 50 to 70 per cent. Recent investigations indicate that higher concentrations are also antiseptic in action against many kinds of bacteria.

SOAPS AND OTHER DETERGENTS

Ordinary soaps (sodium or potassium salts of higher fatty acids) are good detergents or cleansing agents because they remove grease, dirt and loosely adhering bacteria. Soaps also have a definite germicidal action if permitted to act for a sufficiently long time. Many bacteria, however, are resistant to the action of soap. The efficiency of soap as a germicide is considerably increased at higher temperatures. The addition of hexachlorophene (G-11) to liquid soap in sufficient amount so that the soap solution contains 1 per cent of the chemical greatly enhances its germicidal action.

Numerous synthetic detergents, developed in recent years, have come into widespread use. These compounds are excellent wetting agents because they lower the surface tension of water. This enables them to penetrate films of fat and other materials and thus aid in their removal. They form lather and emulsify fats and oils and thus serve as excellent cleansing agents. Some are effective germicides. Many of the laundry powders, dishwashing preparations and shampoos sold on the market at present contain synthetic detergents.

Many of these compounds are ionizable. In some cases the detergent property is present in the anion (negatively charged), in others in the cation (positively charged). The anion-active detergents, although effective cleansing agents, are in general less effective as antiseptics or germicides than the cation-active compounds. Those that show antibacterial activity are more inhibitory or bactericidal against Gram-positive than they are against Gram-negative bacteria.

Certain cation-active detergents belong to the group known as quaternary ammonium compounds. These are complex nitrogen-containing compounds that are effective bacteriostatic and bactericidal agents. They are active in high dilution. They are commonly referred to as "quaternaries" or "quats." A large number of these compounds have been synthesized. Because of their long chemical names they are usually referred to by their trade names. One of these, Zephiran, is frequently used as a skin antiseptic preceding surgery.

DYES

In addition to their use in staining microorganisms so that they can be more readily observed under the microscope, basic dyes, even in high dilution, inhibit the growth of microorganisms. In ordinary concentrations their action is usually inhibitory rather than germicidal and, in many cases, specific in that it is manifested against certain organisms but not against others. Gram-positive bacteria, in general, are more sensitive to dyes than are the Gram-negative varieties. A few dyes, however, are more effective against Gram-negative than Gram-positive bacteria. Among the dyes frequently used as antiseptic agents are crystal violet, methylene blue, eosin, malachite green, brilliant green, acriflavine and proflavine. They are used chiefly on mucous membranes and for the treatment of wounds.

FORMALDEHYDE

Formaldehyde is a gas having a characteristic pungent, penetrating odor. It is soluble in water and is usually marketed as formalin, which is a 37 to 40 per cent solution. It is an efficient disinfectant and is antiseptic in high dilution. The presence of organic matter has little effect in reducing its efficiency. The solution gives off formaldehyde gas, which is very irritating to the mucous membranes of the eyes, nose and throat; this precludes its use as an antiseptic for living tissues. Formaldehyde solutions (10 per cent) are frequently used to disinfect sputum, feces and urine, as well as towels, clothing and similar materials.

AEROSOLS

Aerosols are chemicals which are dispersed in the air in the form of a mist so fine that it cannot be seen. They serve as aerial disinfectants for the destruction of air-borne pathogens. The chemicals most commonly used for this purpose are triethylene glycol and propylene glycol. These chemicals, when dispersed into the air in fine droplets, are effective in high dilution and, apparently, may be breathed without harm. Such mists or vapors are odorless and nonirritating.

The molecules of these compounds are attracted to water and kill the microorganisms floating on minute droplets of moisture coughed, sneezed or exhaled into the air. The germicidal action of these vapors is influenced by temperature and humidity. They are effective only in the relative humidity range of 45 to 70 per cent and are most efficient when the temperature is below 80° F.

QUESTIONS

1. Define: (1) disinfection, (2) disinfectant, (3) germicide, (4) bactericide, (5) sepsis, (6) asepsis, (7) antiseptic, (8) bacteriostasis, (9) bacteriostatic agent.
2. (*a*) What are some of the ways in which chemical agents kill microorganisms?
    (*b*) Mention factors that influence the action of chemicals on microorganisms.
3. What is meant by the term "phenol coefficient"? Of what value is the evaluation of germicides in this manner?
4. Indicate the purposes for which the following may be used: (1) phenol, (2) cresol, (3) chlorine and chlorine compounds, (4) iodine, (5) mercury compounds, (6) silver compounds.
5. Name two oxidizing agents and explain to what they owe their antiseptic properties.
6. Explain the usefulness of ethyl alcohol as an antiseptic agent.
7. Discuss the use of soaps and synthetic detergents as antiseptic agents. What are quaternary ammonium compounds?
8. What is the action of dyes on microorganisms?
9. For what purposes may formaldehyde be used?
10. What are aerosols? How are they used?

REFERENCES
Hopkins, E. S., and Schulze, W. H.: The Practice of Sanitation. 3rd ed. Baltimore, The Williams & Wilkins Company, 1958.

Lawrence, C. A.: Surface-Active Quaternary Ammonium Germicides. New York, Academic Press, Inc., 1950.

McCulloch, E. C.: Disinfection and Sterilization. Philadelphia, Lea & Febiger, 1945.

Rahn, O.: Injury and Death of Bacteria by Chemical Agents. Normandy, Mo., Biodynamica, 1945.

Reddish, G. F., ed.: Antiseptics, Disinfectants, Fungicides and Chemical and Physical Sterilization. 2nd ed. Philadelphia, Lea & Febiger, 1957.

Swartz, A. M., and Perry, J. W.: Surface Active Agents. New York, Interscience Publishers, Inc., 1949.

Sykes, G.: Disinfection and Sterilization. Princeton, N. J., D. Van Nostrand Company, Inc., 1958.

Walter, C. W.: The Aseptic Treatment of Wounds. New York, The Macmillan Company, 1948.

Wilson, G. S., and Miles, A. A.: Topley and Wilson's Principles of Bacteriology and Immunity. 2 vols. 4th ed. Baltimore, The Williams & Wilkins Company, 1955.

17 · Chemotherapeutic Agents

The use of chemical agents which, when introduced into the body, exert an inhibitory or destructive effect upon the causative agents of disease without serious toxic effects on the patient is known as *chemotherapy.* Such chemicals, known as *chemotherapeutic agents,* exercise a specific curative effect in infectious disease. In recent years impressive progress has been made in the field of chemotherapy. Chemotherapeutic agents have become a decisive factor in man's fight against disease. Never before in human history has man had at his disposal so many chemical agents capable of curing infectious diseases.

The most striking success in the early development of chemotherapy was achieved by Paul Ehrlich in the first decade of the present century. Ehrlich, a German physician, synthesized and tested a large number of new compounds in the hope of obtaining an agent that promised a relatively high toxicity for microorganisms that have invaded the body and a relatively low toxicity for the host. The 606th compound he prepared proved to be extremely valuable in combating syphilis. It was an organic compound of arsenic. He named it *Salvarsan,* but it is now usually known as *arsphenamine.* He next improved upon this drug by making *Neosalvarsan* (*neoarsphenamine*), which had a lower toxicity for the patient. Although these chemotherapeutic agents were capable of destroying the spirochetes of syphilis in the body, a long series of treatments was necessary to effect a cure. They were used for many years in the treatment of syphilis but have now been largely replaced by other chemical agents. While the pioneering work of Ehrlich and his students resulted in the discovery of several other chemotherapeutic agents, including antimalarial compounds, chemotherapy progressed little until some twenty-five years after the initial success with Salvarsan.

SULFONAMIDE DRUGS

In 1935 Gerhard Domagk, a German chemist, announced that a red dye known as *prontosil* had a decided curative effect when injected intravenously into mice infected with streptococci. Other investigators later showed that the dye broke down in the animal body with the release of *sulfanilamide* and that this compound produced the therapeutic effect. Sulfanilamide was known to chemists at this time, for it was synthesized in 1908 by Gelmo, but its medicinal possibilities were completely unappreciated. Sulfanilamide is a white crystalline amide of sulfanilic acid. Its chemical name is *para*-amino-benzene-sulfonamide, and its empirical formula is $NH_2C_6H_4$—SO_2NH_2.

After its value as a chemotherapeutic agent was demonstrated, attempts immediately were made to modify its structure in the hope of obtaining compounds effective against many diseases and less toxic to the patient. The quest was successful, since many derivatives of sulfanilamide were soon produced, including sulfapyridine, sulfathiazole, sulfadiazine, sulfaguanidine, sulfamerazine and sulfamethazine, all of which are active antibacterial agents. They have largely superseded sulfanilamide since they are more effective and less toxic chemotherapeutic agents.

The sulfonamides, or sulfa drugs as they are commonly called, vary somewhat in their action against different pathogens. As a group they are useful in a large number of infections. Sulfapyridine has been found useful in the treatment of pneumonia caused by the pneumococcus. Sulfathiazole is effective against staphylococci. Sulfadiazine, one of the most widely used of these drugs because of its high effectiveness and low toxicity for the patient, is especially active against beta-hemolytic streptococci, pneumococci, meningococci and some of the organisms that cause gas gangrene. Sulfaguanidine is effective in bacillary dysentery. The sulfa drugs are of value also in the treatment of infected wounds. By their use many lives were saved among our fighting men on the battlefronts in World War II.

These drugs, however, have disadvantages as well as advantages. They are toxic to the human body, some more so than others. Another disadvantage is the fact that many pathogens are capable of evolving strains that are resistant to these drugs.

MODE OF ACTION OF SULFONAMIDES

The sulfonamides exert their antimicrobial action by interfering with the normal metabolism of susceptible pathogens. This is accomplished by inhibiting the synthesis of folic acid, which is a vitamin needed by microorganisms as well as other forms of life. In the synthesis of folic acid, *para*-aminobenzoic acid is required. The sulfa drugs are closely related structurally to *para*-aminobenzoic acid. Recent investigations indicate that they compete with this acid in the biochemical reactions necessary for the synthesis of folic acid. In so doing they interfere with the production of this vitamin. In other words, they block the utilization of *para*-aminobenzoic acid by combining irreversibly with one of the enzymes involved in the synthesis of folic acid. This kind of biochemical reaction is known as *competitive inhibition*. Many other cases of competitive inhibition are known in biochemical reactions. Those bacteria that do not synthesize folic acid, but require it preformed in their food, are unaffected by the sulfa drugs.

ANTIBIOTIC AGENTS

Certain microorganisms produce, as a unique feature of their metabolism, minute amounts of specific substances which diffuse into the surroundings and inhibit or destroy some other species of microbial life. This form of microbial antagonism is known as *antibiosis* or *antibiotic activity*. It has been known since Pasteur's time that in some cases the growth of one microorganism is inhibited by another. The metabolic products responsible for the inhibition of growth of one microbial species by another are termed *antibiotics*. A large number of infectious diseases can be effectively treated with these agents. Man has tapped the most remarkable of all sources of therapeutic agents in his discovery of antibiotics.

Antibiotics are produced chiefly by microorganisms that inhabit the soil. The major producers of chemotherapeutically useful antibiotics are the filamentous bacteria (actinomycetes in the genus *Streptomyces*), although a number of species of true bacteria and molds are active in this regard. Extremely low concentrations of antibiotics are inhibitory to susceptible microorganisms. Some act mainly against Gram-positive bacteria, while others are more active against Gram-negative bacteria. Some of the antibiotics are termed "broad spectrum" types because they are inhibitory to both Gram-positive and Gram-negative bacteria and even to certain rickettsiae and some of the larger viruses. Only a handful of antibiotics are active against rickettsiae, the larger viruses, yeasts, molds or protozoa. Most of the viruses resist the action of antibiotics.

Many of the antibiotics are superior to the sulfonamide drugs in that they have little toxicity for man, whereas others are too toxic to be used as chemotherapeutic agents. Some, although relatively nontoxic, are ineffective in attacking pathogenic agents within the tissues and fluids of the human or animal body. It is interesting to note that some pathogens resist an antibiotic *in vitro* but succumb to it *in vivo*. Although a number of chemotherapeutically valuable antibiotics are now available, the majority of antibiotics that have been studied have been found to be worthless, because either they were highly toxic or they were ineffective in the body. Antibiotics are primarily bacteriostatic rather than bactericidal. They are believed to produce their effects by interfering in some way with key metabolic processes.

Development of Resistance

Many microorganisms become resistant to increasing concentrations of an antibiotic. This more readily occurs with some microbial species and with certain antibiotics than with others. Occasionally bacterial strains are encountered which exhibit a state of dependency toward an antibiotic to which they were once highly sensitive. Antibiotic resistant strains of microorganisms can arise within the patient undergoing treatment with one of these drugs or they can be "developed" *in vitro* by successive transfers in culture media containing graded increases in concentration of the antibiotic. Such resistance arises because the antibiotic functions as a selective agent, thereby killing or suppressing the nonresistant cells and permitting the survival and subsequent multiplication of the few resistant mutant cells. Apparently the antibiotic does not induce the mutations; rather, the few resistant cells, usually numbering only a few per billion, have resulted from mutations caused by other factors. Through such a selective process it is possible to establish antibiotic-resistant pathogens in the host merely by utilizing a drug to which the vast majority of the initial microbial population would readily succumb.

The most striking example of this situation is the emergence of antibiotic-resistant staphylococci in patients undergoing treatment with one of these drugs. This has resulted in the dissemination in hospitals of staphylococci which are resistant to the more commonly used antibiotics, e.g., penicillin, chlortetracycline, oxytetracycline, chloramphenicol, etc. Likewise, streptomycin-resistant strains of tubercle bacilli arise in patients being treated with this antibiotic.

When two effective but unrelated chemotherapeutic agents are administered simultaneously for treating an infectious disease, there is less danger of resistant mutants surviving than when one drug is given, because mutants resistant to two drugs are uncommon. This principle is sometimes employed in chemotherapy, although indiscriminant use of multiple chemotherapeutic agents predisposes the patient to toxic effects and undesirable side effects. Fortunately, most pathogenic microorganisms, normally sensitive to antibiotics, do not readily become resistant to antibiotics. Thus, penicillin has retained its effectiveness since it was first employed (1940) against infections caused by pneumococci, most streptococci, spirochetes, neisseriae and a few others.

Penicillin

The discovery of penicillin was an accidental occurrence. In 1929 the British microbiologist Alexander Fleming observed the antibiotic action of a mold colony against staphylococci on culture plates in his laboratory. The mold, which gained access to the culture plate as a contaminant, was later identified as *Penicillium notatum*. Fleming later cultivated this mold in peptone broth and found that the broth contained a substance capable of inhibiting the growth of various types of bacteria. He named the active substance *penicillin*. He demonstrated that broth containing penicillin was no more toxic when injected into animals than pure broth. It was not, however, until 1940 that penicillin was obtained in a purer form and its remarkable therapeutic properties were discovered. This was the achievement of H. W. Florey and E. B. Chain at Oxford University in England. They found that it was an acid of low molecular weight and that it could be extracted from the liquid medium in which the mold was growing by

Figure 102. Large fermentation tanks (10,000 gallons) used in the production of penicillin. (Courtesy of Commercial Solvents Corporation.)

means of various organic solvents. A method was developed for purifying the solution thus obtained. It was then frozen and dehydrated from the frozen state. The dehydrated substance was a yellow, amorphous material. At present, owing to improved purification methods, penicillin is a white crystalline material.

Originally produced from surface cultures of the mold *Penicillium notatum*, penicillin is now obtained from submerged cultures growing in a liquid medium in deep aerated tanks which hold from 10,000 to 15,000 gallons of culture medium (Figure 102). The penicillin is extracted from the culture and purified by chemical procedures. A closely related mold, *Penicillium chrysogenum,* is now also used in the commercial production of penicillin. A number of species of molds in the genera *Penicillin* and *Aspergillus* are known to produce penicillin. The strains of *P. chrysogenum* presently used in the industrial production of penicillin are high yielding mutants obtained from cultures exposed to x-rays or ultraviolet rays. Although a number of different types of penicillin are formed by these molds (penicillin F, dihydro F, G, K, O, V, X), penicillin G is the chief one used. Certain chemicals, such as phenylactic acid or phenylacetamide, which can be used by the mold as precursors in the synthesis of penicillin G, are usually added to the medium to assure high yields of the antibiotic. Penicillin is a relatively strong acid from which the sodium salt is most commonly prepared, although a number of therapeutically useful salts are available, some of which have a low solubility.

Penicillin has been used therapeutically for a longer period of time than any of the other antibiotics. The list of infections that it can combat is an impressive one. It is effective against practically all Gram-positive bacteria and the Gram-negative cocci (the gonococcus and the meningococcus). It is very active against spirochetes, notably *Treponema* spp. Penicillin has little tendency to produce serious untoward reactions in the animal body except in those individuals who have developed a state of hypersensitivity to it.

Some bacteria are inherently resistant to penicillin; others may acquire resistance through the selection of mutant strains. In some cases, resistance is due to the production of a specific enzyme, *penicillinase,* which rapidly destroys penicillin. Among the pathogenic staphylococci, resistant strains are encountered which produce penicillinase. Resistant strains of other pathogens have also appeared.

Penicillin is bacteriostatic in low concentrations and bactericidal in higher concentrations. It is known to inhibit cell division of bacteria, a finding undoubtedly related to more recent evidence that it can block the synthesis of some essential component of the bacterial cell wall.

Tyrothricin

Tyrothricin was isolated in 1939 by an American bacteriologist, Rene Dubos, from a culture of an aerobic, sporulating soil bacterium known as *Bacillus brevis.* The isolation of this substance, a mixture of the antibiotics *gramicidin* and *tyrocidin,* was a signal event in the initiation of the antibiotic era because it focused attention on the soil, our richest source of antibiotic-producing microorganisms, and came at a time when the Oxford scientists were attempting to purify penicillin. Gramicidin is, by far, more active than tyrocidin. Unfortunately, both of these compounds are too toxic for parenteral administration because of their hemolytic (lysis of red blood cells) activity. Their use is limited to the treatment of localized infections that can be treated by topical application. Tyrocidin is active in high dilution against both Gram-positive and Gram-negative organisms. The action of gramicidin is restricted chiefly to Gram-positive bacteria, but it is effective also against a few Gram-negative organisms.

Streptomycin

This antibiotic was discovered in 1943 by Selman Waksman and coworkers. It is produced by *Streptomyces griseus,* a moldlike bacterium belonging to the order Actinomycetales. Streptomycin is inhibitory to most Gram-negative and a few Gram-positive bacteria, although its out-

Fig. 103. A partial view of a modern fermentation unit in a streptomycin-manufacturing plant. (Courtesy of Merck & Company, Inc.)

standing attribute is its activity against acid-fast bacteria, e.g. *Mycobacterium tuberculosis.* Thus it is effective in the treatment of tuberculosis and some other diseases not thwarted by penicillin. Streptomycin is toxic upon prolonged use, causing nerve damage to result in temporary or permanent impairment of the sense of balance and coordination and loss of hearing. However, an active derivative, dihydrostreptomycin, has less toxicity. The greatest difficulty with therapeutic application of this antibiotic is the rapidity with which bacteria develop resistance to it. This difficulty has been minimized in the treatment of tuberculosis by the simultaneous administration of one or two other drugs, namely, isonicotinic acid hydrazide and *para*-aminosalicylic acid.

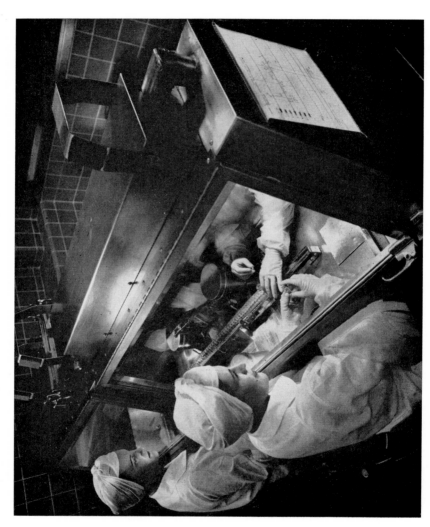

Figure 104. Filling and stoppering vials of dihydrostreptomycin. Operators work through built-in rubber gloves in a sealed cubicle. (Courtesy of Merck & Company, Inc.)

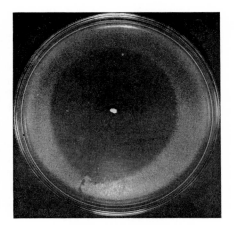

Figure 105. Inhibition of *Staphylococcus aureus* by a colony of *Streptomyces aureofaciens.* Although the plate was heavily seeded with staphylococcus, the bacteria grew only at the edge of the plate, owing to the inhibiting effect of the *Streptomyces* colony growing in the center of the plate. (Courtesy of Lederle Laboratories Division, American Cyanamid Company.)

Chloramphenicol

Chloramphenicol* is produced by *Streptomyces venezuelae,* a bacterium originally isolated in 1947 from a sample of Venezuelan soil. Compared to other antibiotics, the molecular structure of chloramphenicol is not complex and is relatively simple for the organic chemist to synthesize. It is the first and only antibiotic to be commercially produced on a large scale by means of chemical synthesis. This "broad spectrum" antibiotic is effective against many bacteria, both Gram-positive and Gram-negative types, rickettsiae and the larger viruses. It is particularly valuable in the treatment of typhoid fever. There are indications that chloramphenicol is specifically inhibitory toward the synthesis of microbial proteins.

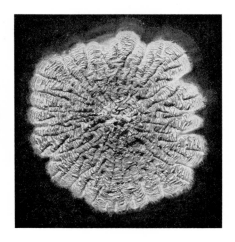

Figure 106. Colony of *Streptomyces rimosus,* the organism that produces oxytetracycline (Terramycin). (Courtesy of Chas. Pfizer Company, Inc.)

* The use of trade names creates much confusion. Chloramphenicol, chlortetracycline and oxytetracycline possess the proprietary names Chloromycetin, Aureomycin and Terramycin, respectively. However, tetracycline has many trade names, e.g., Achromycin, Panmycin, Tetracyn and Polycycline.

The Tetracycline Group*

This group contains the three closely related antibiotics, *tetracycline, chlortetracycline* and *oxytetracycline.* Each one is produced by a different species of *Streptomyces,* although tetracycline is produced commercially by the catalytic hydrogenation of chlortetracycline. All three are naphthacene derivatives. Chlortetracycline and oxytetracycline are derivatives of tetracycline. These antibiotics are of the "broad spectrum" type. They are relatively nontoxic but must be used with caution because they upset the equilibrium of microorganisms in certain parts of the body, especially the large intestine, which results in infections from staphylococci and *Candida albicans,* a pathogenic yeast. Figure 105 illustrates the inhibitory activity of chlortetracycline produced by *S. aureofaciens.* Figure 106 shows a giant colony of *S. rimosus,* the producer of oxytetracycline. These antibiotics inhibit metabolic activities which govern certain transformations of energy.

Other Antibiotics

While it is not feasible to cite all antibiotics having therapeutic value, there exist a number of them which should be added to the list. Members of the genus *Bacillus* produce various polypeptide antibiotics, e.g., *polymyxin* and *bacitracin* (also gramicidin and tyrocidin as discussed on page 272). Since these antibiotics are too toxic to the patient, their primary use is that of topical application, as in ointments. The two closely related antibiotics *erythromycin* and *carbomycin* are produced by streptomycetes and, while having a fairly broad antimicrobial spectrum, are of most value in treating staphylococcal infections which do not respond to penicillin or one of the "broad spectrum" types of antibiotic. *Neomycin,* another antibiotic produced by a streptomycete, is widely employed in the suppression of the intestinal microflora prior to surgery. Antibiotics effective against fungal infections are not common, although a group of chemically related substances produced by various streptomycetes may offer a solution to this difficult problem. *Nystatin* and the more recently isolated *amphotericin B* have been found to be useful in the treatment of some of the mycotic infections. Other newer antibiotics, of promise primarily in the treatment of infections caused by Gram-positive bacteria, are *novobiocin, oleandomycin, vancomycin* and *ristocetin.* The latter one is produced by *Nocardia lurida,* while the first three are elaborated by members of the genus *Streptomyces.*

Other Uses of Antibiotics

While one commonly associates antibiotics with the treatment of infectious diseases of man and other animals, large quantities of antibiotics are being consumed in various ways by the food industry. Thus, feed containing minute concentrations of antibiotics accelerates the rate of growth

* See footnote, p. 275.

of poultry, pigs, calves and lambs. The dipping of freshly dressed poultry in a solution of chlortetracycline or oxytetracycline delays microbial spoilage of the carcass, thereby prolonging the "shelf life." This same principle seems to hold in keeping freshly caught fish. Certain diseases of plants can be prevented or treated by spraying or dusting with one of several antibiotics. The small residue of antibiotics which these practices contribute to the foods we eat is a matter of some concern because of possible toxic effects on the consumer and the likelihood of encouraging an ascendancy of antibiotic resistant microbes in our natural environment. Fortunately, these fears have not materialized. Undoubtedly, agricultural uses of antibiotics will continue to expand.

Unsolved Problems

Inevitably, progress creates new problems. In the years ahead it is hoped that we will learn more about how antibiotics act. We need to know much more about the chemistry of these compounds and how they might be chemically modified to result in other substances with useful therapeutic properties. Although a few antibiotics inhibit tumors, fungi, protozoa and viruses, we can look forward to the isolation of more antibiotics with activity against such agents. Perhaps, too, we may ultimately gain some insight into the question of how and why some organisms synthesize these unique substances termed antibiotics.

QUESTIONS

1. Define: (1) chemotherapy, (2) chemotherapeutic agents, (3) competitive inhibition.
2. Explain the work of Ehrlich in the synthesis of Salvarsan (arsphenamine).
3. What are sulfonamide drugs? What is their usefulness? What is their mode of action?
4. What are antibiotics? Why are they so called? How do they produce their effects?
5. Give the source and usefulness of (1) penicillin, (2) tyrothricin, (3) streptomycin, (4) chloramphenicol, (5) tetracyclines, (6) nystatin.
6. What is the relationship between mutation and drug resistance?
7. Cite several applications of antibiotics in fields other than medicine.

REFERENCES

Cowan, S. T., and Rowatt, E., ed.: The Strategy of Chemotherapy, eighth symposium of the Society for General Microbiology. Cambridge, Cambridge University Press, 1958.
Duthie, E. S.: Molecules against Microbes. London, Sigma Books, Ltd., 1946.
First International Conference on Antibiotics in Agriculture, Proceedings, Publ. 397, National Academy of Sciences-National Research Council, Washington, D. C., 1956.
Flory, H. W., et al.: Antibiotics. Vols. I and II. London, Oxford University Press, 1949.
Grove, D. C., and Randall, W. A.: Assay Methods of Antibiotics, a Laboratory Manual. Antibiotics Monographs No. 2. New York, Medical Encyclopedia, Inc., 1955.
Jukes, T. H.: Antibiotics in Nutrition. Antibiotics Monographs No. 4. New York, Medical Encyclopedia, Inc., 1955.
Karel, L., and Roach, E. E.: A Dictionary of Antibiosis. New York, Columbia University Press, 1951.
Schnitzer, R. J., and Grunberg, E.: Drug Resistance of Microorganisms. New York, Academic Press, Inc., 1957.

Spector, W. S., ed.: Handbook of Toxicology. 2. Antibiotics. Philadelphia, W. B. Saunders Co., 1957.

Waksman, S. A.: Microbial Antagonisms and Antibiotic Substances. New York, The Commonwealth Fund, 1945.

Welch, H., ed.: Antibiotic Therapy. New York, Medical Encyclopedia, Inc., 1954.

Welch, H., and Marti-Ibañez, F., ed.: Antibiotics Annual 1953-1954, 1954-1955, 1955-1956, 1956-1957, 1957-1958, 1958-1959. New York, Medical Encyclopedia, Inc., 1954, 1955, 1956, 1957, 1958, 1959.

V • Useful Activities of
Microorganisms

18 • Soil Microbiology

The soil constitutes the habitat of the vast majority of microscopic forms of life. Tremendous numbers of individual microorganisms representing many species of bacteria, molds and yeasts are almost universally distributed through the soils of the earth. In the pursuit of their normal mode of life these organisms bring about the decomposition of plant and animal residues to inorganic compounds that are essential for the maintenance of soil fertility. The microbes of the soil, thus, play a role of paramount importance in the world of life.

THE SOIL

Soil is composed of disintegrated (weathered) rock mixed with varying proportions of organic matter and water. Much of the disintegrated rock material is in the form of small particles, such as grains of sand. The spaces between soil particles are occupied by air, some of which becomes dissolved in the soil's water. The organic matter consists of the remains of dead plants and animals and of animal excretions, as well as the various products of their decomposition. Chemically, the organic matter is a mixture of different substances, chiefly carbohydrates, proteins and lipids. The mineral particles, the majority of which consist largely of silica or aluminum oxide, are ordinarily coated with colloidal material consisting mainly of organic matter in a matrix of water. Various minerals in finely divided form are also present. This colloidal material serves as a substrate for the growth of microbial populations. The chemistry of this material is of prime importance in soil fertility.

The surface soil, a few inches to a foot or more in depth, is the topsoil. Owing to the presence of considerable quantities of organic matter, it is dark in color. Below the topsoil is the subsoil, which extends down to the underlying rock.

281

MICROORGANISMS OF THE SOIL

The microscopic inhabitants of the soil carry on their activities chiefly in the topsoil; below this layer there is a rapid decrease in the number of microorganisms. The extent of the microbial population depends upon the content of organic matter, the *p*H, temperature, amount of moisture and other conditions. Fertile soil ordinarily has a vast microbial population. Figure 107 shows colonies of soil bacteria that developed in culture media inoculated with small amounts of soil.

The majority of soil bacteria belong to the order Eubacteriales. They are chiefly heterotrophs, but autotrophs are also present. The vast majority are aerobes and facultative anaerobes. A few obligate anaerobes are usually active in certain situations. Most of the soil bacteria in the temperate zone are mesophiles, but the thermophiles and psychrophiles are also

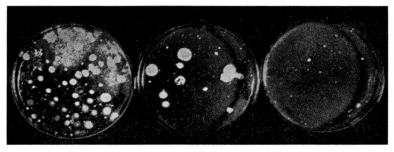

Figure 107.   Plate cultures of soil bacteria. The plate to the right, which has 72 colonies, was inoculated with 0.00001 gm. of soil. This indicates that a gram of soil contains 7,200,000 bacteria capable of growing on the medium the Petri dish contains. (From Otto Rahn: Microbes of Merit. Copyright 1945, The Ronald Press Company. Reproduced by permission.)

represented. Many of the soil bacteria belong to the order Actinomycetales. The genera *Actinomyces* and *Streptomyces* of this order are well represented. These moldlike bacteria, commonly referred to as "actinomycetes," form a large proportion of the microorganisms of the soil. They play an active role in the decomposition of organic matter and are chiefly responsible for the characteristic musty odor of freshly plowed soil. Soils fertilized with stable manure ordinarily contain many thermophilic actinomycetes. Usually, some members of the order Myxobacterales are present also.

Among the molds, species of *Mucor, Rhizopus, Penicillium, Aspergillus* and *Alternaria,* to mention only a few, are widely distributed in the soils of the earth. The decomposition of cellulose and lignin is in large part carried on by molds.

In this connection it is of interest to note that the spores of certain anaerobic pathogens, particularly *Clostridium tetani,* the cause of tetanus or lockjaw, and *Clostridium perfringens,* one of the organisms responsible for gas gangrene, are usually present in soil that has been fertilized with barnyard manure. These organisms live as commensals in the intestinal tracts of many kinds of domesticated animals and thus are present in the feces of animals. *Clostridium botulinum,* whose potent toxin causes botulism (Chapter 25), a type of food poisoning, is present in some soils.

DECOMPOSITION OF ORGANIC MATTER IN THE SOIL

The dead organic matter continuously arising from plant and animal organisms does not remain long in its original condition. It is attacked and dissimilated by microorganisms of various kinds. This never-ending process involves many species and a multitude of individual microorganisms. Each type of organism taking part in the decomposition carries on one step of the process. Different species act successively upon the various intermediate substances as they are formed. Some of the decomposition reactions occur outside the microbial cells and are brought about by enzymes secreted into the substrate; i.e., they are digestive reactions; others take place within the cells.

The simpler carbohydrates and proteins are broken down first, leaving the compounds that are more resistant, such as the polysaccharides, complex proteins, lipids and chitin, as organic residues to form the humus of the soil. Eventually, these are decomposed also. When the process of dissimilation has been carried to completion, the end products are simple inorganic substances. Carbon emerges chiefly as carbon dioxide, hydrogen as water, nitrogen as nitrates, sulfur as sulfates, and phosphorus as phosphates. Because the end products are inorganic, the term *mineralization* is sometimes applied to this process.

The versatility of microorganisms as biochemical agents enables them to attack all types of organic compounds that occur naturally. Not all these compounds, however, are attacked by all species of saprophytic microorganisms. Some are endowed with the ability to break down cellulose, some act on starch, while many soil microbes are actively proteolytic, readily attacking proteins. The specific reactions resulting from the activities of a particular organism depend upon its enzyme system. Yeasts, for example, do not produce cellulase and thus are unable to attack cellulose, but many molds and certain bacteria are able to do so.

The decomposition of non-nitrogenous compounds, such as carbohydrates and fats, on the part of microorganisms is usually called *fermentation.* The term is usually restricted, however, to the decomposition of these compounds under anaerobic conditions. The term is also used at times in a broad sense to indicate the decomposition by microorganisms of all organic compounds. The term *putrefaction* is generally understood to indicate the anaerobic decomposition of proteins and protein derivatives with the evolution of foul odors.

Decomposition of Polysaccharides

The most abundant of the carbohydrates are the polysaccharides—cellulose, hemicelluloses, starch, pectins and lignin. These compounds constitute the bulk of plant structure. Cellulose is the principle component of the cell walls of plants and occurs also as structural material in the stems of plants. The hemicelluloses constitute a group of poorly defined polysaccharides which are intermediate in complexity between the disaccharide sugars and cellulose. Starch is an important storage carbohydrate present in most plant materials. The pectins are associated with cellulose in the cell walls of plants and in the spaces between the cells. They are particularly abundant in certain fruits, such as apples and currants. When these are boiled in water, the pectins dissolve and the fruits become jellified. Lignin is a constituent of the walls of the cells in woody tissues. Wood consists largely of a mixture of cellulose and lignin. The exact structure of lignin is unknown.

Microorganisms utilize polysaccharides by hydrolyzing them extracellularly to simpler compounds. Many of the Eubacteriales, molds and actinomycetes are capable of hydrolyzing polysaccharides. Few yeasts are able to do so. Polysaccharides can be hydrolyzed under either aerobic or anaerobic conditions. When aerobic conditions prevail, the process is carried out by molds, actinomycetes and other bacteria. Under anaerobic conditions, as in waterlogged soil, heavy clay, muck or swamp soil, "lower" bacteria (Eubacteriales) are the active agents.

In soils that are very acid in reaction and in which anaerobic conditions prevail, as in marshy areas, decomposition proceeds at a slow pace. The result is the accumulation of partially degraded vegetable matter with the gradual formation of peat. The coal deposits of the earth were probably formed under similar conditions from luxuriant vegetation growing in swamps during the Carboniferous division of geologic time.

Cellulose is hydrolyzed by the enzyme cellulase to the disaccharide cellobiose. The reaction is indicated by the following equation:

$$2 \ (C_6H_{10}O_5)n + nH_2O \xrightarrow{\text{cellulase}} n(C_{12}H_{22}O_{11})$$

$$\text{cellulose} \qquad\qquad\qquad\qquad\qquad \text{cellobiose}$$

The hemicelluloses, when hydrolyzed by enzymes, yield monosaccharides such as glucose, fructose, galactose, arabinose, mannose and xylose. Many species of microorganisms are capable of hydrolyzing various hemicelluloses. The enzymes involved are referred to as *hemicellulases* or *cytases*.

Starch can be decomposed by many molds and some bacteria. The enzyme *amylase* hydrolyzes starch to maltose. The pectins are hydrolyzed by *pectinases* to monosaccharides and uronic acids. Very little information is available concerning the transformation of lignin. Not many microorganisms are capable of accomplishing its decomposition. However, it undergoes a slow dissimilation in which actinomycetes apparently play an important role.

Decomposition of Disaccharides

The disaccharides, cellobiose, maltose, sucrose and lactose, are hydrolyzed by certain microorganisms into hexose monosaccharides, the general equation being:

$$C_{12}H_{22}O_{11} + H_2O \xrightarrow{\text{enzyme}} 2\ C_6H_{12}O_6$$
$$\text{disaccharide} \qquad\qquad\qquad \text{monosaccharide}$$

A molecule of cellobiose, when acted upon by cellobiase, yields two molecules of glucose. The enzyme *maltase* hydrolyzes maltose to glucose. A molecule of sucrose is hydrolyzed to one molecule of glucose and one molecule of fructose by the enzyme *sucrase*. The enzyme *lactase* hydrolyzes lactose to a molecule of glucose and one of galactose. The monosaccharides thus formed diffuse into the microbial cells and enter into their metabolic processes.

Decomposition of Monosaccharides

The decomposition of monosaccharides is carried on within the cells of microorganisms by intracellular enzymes. These compounds are utilized in microbial respiration, a process which yields energy. Under aerobic conditions monosaccharides may be completely oxidized to carbon dioxide and water, but under anaerobic conditions they are only partially broken down, resulting in the production of by-products, chiefly various organic acids (lactic, acetic, butyric, citric and gluconic), alcohols, carbon dioxide and hydrogen, which are usually excreted as waste products. The fermentation of glucose may follow more than one course. When yeasts attack glucose, ethyl alcohol and carbon dioxide are formed. When bacteria or molds utilize glucose in their energy metabolism, organic acids are produced. Many of the Gram-positive cocci and the lactobacilli produce lactic acid as the sole fermentation product. The following equations represent anaerobic cleavages of glucose:

$$C_6H_{12}O_6 \longrightarrow 2\ CH_3CH_2OH + 2\ CO_2$$
$$\text{ethyl alcohol}$$

$$C_6H_{12}O_6 \longrightarrow 2\ CH_3CHOHCOOH$$
$$\text{lactic acid}$$

The various acids formed in the fermentation of monosaccharides are decomposed into such compounds as methane and carbon dioxide. The following equation represents this type of reaction as it applies to acetic acid:

$$CH_3COOH \longrightarrow CH_4 + CO_2$$
$$\text{acetic acid} \qquad\qquad \text{methane}$$

All the intermediate products, whether they are methane (marsh gas), hydrogen, organic acids or alcohol, undergo further decomposition, usually through the successive action of several different kinds of microorganisms. Ultimately, all monosaccharides are resolved into carbon dioxide and water.

Decomposition of Fats

Many bacteria and molds are capable of dissimilating fats in the presence of moisture, hydrolyzing them to glycerol and fatty acids. The enzymes that catalyze this reaction are *lipases*. The hydrolysis of fats may be illustrated by using tri-stearin as an example:

$$(C_{17}H_{35}COO)_3C_3H_5 + 3\ H_2O \xrightarrow{\text{lipase}} C_3H_5(OH)_3 + 3\ C_{17}H_{35}COOH$$

tri-stearin   glycerol   stearic acid

Glycerol is used in respiration by a number of different kinds of microorganisms. Some break it down to acids and alcohols, others to acids and carbon dioxide. Some anaerobes utilize glycerol, as indicated in the following reaction:

$$2\ C_3H_5(OH)_3 \rightarrow C_3H_7COOH + 2\ CO_2 + 2\ H_2$$

glycerol   butyric acid

Butter may become rancid, owing to changes produced by certain bacteria which bring about the release of butyric acid from compounds known as glycerides (esters obtained from glycerol in combination with acids). The reaction takes place in the minute droplets of water always present in butter. These droplets contain small quantities of lactose, proteins and other compounds which enable bacteria to grow under favorable conditions.

The fatty acids resulting from the hydrolysis of fats are utilized by a few bacteria and molds. The details of the process have not been definitely established.

Decomposition of Protein

Microorganisms differ greatly in the manner in which they decompose proteins and protein derivatives. Some are capable of catalyzing the hydrolysis of conjugated proteins such as glycoproteins (proteins combined with carbohydrates) and lecithoproteins (proteins combined with phospholipids), whereas others can attack only simple proteins. Proteins are broken down step by step, involving the activities of a large variety of microorganisms. Certain species start the process, hydrolyzing the proteins by means of extracellular enzymes (proteinases) to polypeptides. Polypeptidases catalyze the conversion of polypeptides to amino acids.

Amino acids are broken down chiefly by *deamination* and *decarboxylation*. In deamination the amino radical (NH_2) is split off as ammonia

(NH₃). In addition to ammonia, deamination gives rise to organic acids of various kinds. Deamination may occur in several ways and may take place under either aerobic or anaerobic conditions. It may involve hydrolysis, oxidative or reductive reactions. The resulting acids are further degraded by various organisms.

In the process known as decarboxylation, which occurs chiefly under anaerobic conditions, the carboxyl radical is split off, yielding carbon dioxide and amines. Amines are sometimes termed "ptomaines," some of which have poisonous properties. Some of these include histamine, formed from the amino acid histidine; tyramine from tyrosine; and putrescine from arginine. It should be noted here that poisoning due to bacterial products in foods is not due to ptomaines but to specific toxic substances of unknown composition produced by a few species of bacteria. In addition to amines, compounds such as indole, skatole, mercaptans and hydrogen sulfide are formed. The decomposition of the amino acid tryptophane gives rise to indole and skatole, which contribute to the foul odors of putrefying matter. Certain amino acids yield mercaptans, some of which are notorious for their offensive odors. Indole production in a medium containing tryptophane is made use of in the identification of certain closely related bacteria.

The intermediate products formed in protein degradation are completely oxidized under aerobic conditions with the formation of ammonia, carbon dioxide, water and sulfates. Some proteins contain phosphorus which, in the decomposition process, is liberated as phosphoric acid. It readily combines with bases in the soil to form phosphates. Because nitrogen is liberated in the form of ammonia, the dissimilation of proteins carried to the stage of ammonia formation is called *ammonification.*

The dead organic matter of oceans, lakes and streams undergoes dissimilation by microorganisms that normally inhabit bodies of water. In general, the end products are similar to those resulting from the activities of soil microorganisms.

FORMATION OF HUMUS

The partially decayed organic matter present in the soil is known as *humus.* Most of the humus comes from vegetable matter and contains relatively large quantities of organic matter, such as cellulose, hemicellulose, lignin and lipids, which undergo slow microbial disintegration. Lignin resists decay longer than other compounds and may remain for a long time in the humus state. Physically, humus is a dark-colored, amorphous material, much of it in the colloidal state. As the humus gradually undergoes decomposition, it releases simple mineral compounds in forms available for consumption by plants. New humus is continually being formed as part of the old undergoes mineralization. Humus is in effect a storehouse of nutrient plant materials; but it is more than just a source of food materials, since it improves the physical condition of the soil by making it soft, porous and friable. It also increases the water-holding capacity of the soil and holds minerals, such as potassium salts, lime, phosphates, sulfates and nitrates, by adsorption, keeping them from being carried into the subsoil by drainage waters.

SYNTHESIS OF ORGANIC MATTER

The inorganic compounds resulting from the decomposition of organic matter through the agency of microorganisms can be again utilized by green plants in the synthesis of organic substance. The chlorophyll-bearing plants depend for their existence on the presence in the soil—or bodies of water in the case of aquatic forms—of mineral substances such as nitrates, sulfates, phosphates and water. They also require carbon dioxide, the source of which is the atmosphere. These simple compounds constitute the raw materials plants require to build up their substance. Green plants have the faculty of forming sugar from carbon dioxide and water. This is of great significance, since an important energy transformation occurs in the process: the radiant energy of sunlight is transformed into the chemical energy of the sugar molecule. Thus two simple compounds, carbon dioxide and water, of no physiological energy value, are synthesized into a compound of high potential energy. This process of forming carbohydrates from carbon dioxide and water under the influence of light is known as *photosynthesis*. The basic reaction in photosynthesis is the reduction (hydrogenation) of carbon dioxide, which may be summarized as follows:

Carbon dioxide + hydrogen (from water) → sugar + oxygen (from water)

By the combination of many sugar molecules, with the liberation of water molecules, starch, cellulose and other carbohydrates are formed. By adding nitrogen obtained from nitrates, sulfur from sulfates, phosphorus from phosphates, to carbohydrate molecules, amino acid molecules can be synthesized. Amino acids form the units from which plants build protein molecules.

Some of the compounds formed by plants are oxidized and eliminated as carbon dioxide and water, for plants obtain some of their energy from the process of oxidation. Most of the compounds, however, are stored as plant substance, and some are utilized in various metabolic processes. The entire supply of organic compounds for plants as well as animals and most of the microorganisms is dependent upon the synthetic processes of plants. The chlorophyll-bearing plants are the primary source of organic compounds and, directly or indirectly, serve as food for other forms of life with the exception of the autotrophic bacteria. Green plants thus are the fundamental forms of life, and the radiant energy of the sun is the basis of all life.

ROTATION OF ESSENTIAL ELEMENTS IN NATURE

The transformation of matter from inorganic to organic, and vice versa, considered in the previous portion of this chapter, involves the transference of solar energy to living organisms through the agency of chlorophyll-bearing plants and the resolution of organic matter to inorganic through the agency of microorganisms. There is thus a continuous synthesis of organic matter from inorganic and a continuous resolution of organic matter back to inorganic.

Since many of the materials available for organic synthesis, notably simple compounds of nitrogen, phosphorus and carbon, are present only in limited quantities, it is essential that the organic refuse of the living world does not accumulate in large quantities. The decay of this material is essential, since it replenishes the stores of carbon dioxide and mineral salts on which plants depend. The continuous existence of life on the earth is dependent upon the continuous rotation of the elements required by living organisms. The decomposition of organic matter is as essential to the stability of life as its synthesis. Since microorganisms are the agents of decomposition, they play a major role in the world of life; continuity of life is dependent upon their ceaseless activities.

For convenience of study, the cyclic transformations of matter in which death alternates with life can be divided into a number of lesser cycles, each one dealing with a particular element such as carbon, nitrogen or sulfur.

THE CARBON CYCLE

The source of carbon for the synthesis of carbon compounds by green plants and autotrophic bacteria is the carbon dioxide of the atmosphere. Although the percentage of carbon dioxide in the air is low, only 0.03 per cent, the actual amount is large, owing to the immense volume of air enveloping the earth. The atmosphere serves as a reservoir of carbon. Chlorophyll-bearing plants utilize carbon dioxide together with water in the photosynthesis of sugar. Some of the sugar thus formed is oxidized to provide energy for converting sugar into more complex carbohydrates. Sugars also form the basis for the synthesis of proteins, lipids and other organic compounds.

In plant respiration some of the carbon is continually being returned to the atmosphere in the form of carbon dioxide. Some plants are eaten by animals, and the compounds of carbon then become reorganized as animal carbon compounds. Animal respiration returns much of the carbon to the air in the form of carbon dioxide.

Upon the death of plants and animals the carbon compounds are subjected to microbial decomposition in which they are broken down step by step to successively simpler chemical compounds, the end product, as far as the element carbon is concerned, being carbon dioxide. Thus the carbon is restored to the atmosphere in its original form and the cycle of carbon is completed.

The carbon dioxide content of the air would soon be depleted if it were not continuously replaced by the respiratory processes of plants and animals and by the microbic decomposition of organic matter. If there were no microorganisms to decompose dead organic matter, there would be an insufficient return of carbon to the atmosphere, and the supply would soon become too meager for the growth of green plants. A certain amount of carbon dioxide is continuously being released into the atmosphere by the combustion of coal, oil, gasoline and other fuel materials as well as by volcanoes and mineral springs. The amount added from these sources is small in comparison with the total carbon dioxide content of

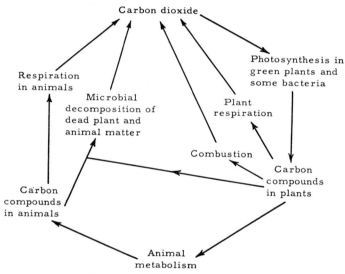

Figure 108.   The carbon cycle.

the air; it does not appreciably raise the percentage of carbon dioxide in the atmosphere.

The various processes involved in the carbon cycle are summarized diagrammatically in Figure 108.

THE NITROGEN CYCLE

Nitrogen is of special importance to living things because it is required in large amounts for the synthesis of essential protoplasmic constituents. Microorganisms participate in various ways in the cycle of nitrogen in nature. Although nearly 80 per cent of the air is nitrogen, plants are unable to use atmospheric nitrogen but procure their nitrogen from certain soil compounds that contain this element.

Soil nitrates constitute the primary source of nitrogen for plants, although some can use ammonium salts. Plants use the nitrogen of these compounds in the synthesis of proteins and other nitrogen-containing organic compounds. The proteins in the plants eaten by animals are hydrolyzed, in the process of digestion, to amino acids, most of which are utilized by animal cells for the synthesis of animal proteins, but some are converted to simpler compounds in the liver. The liver splits off the amino (NH_2) fraction, probably as ammonia, which combines with carbon dioxide to form urea and water. Small quantities of other nitrogenous wastes, such as uric acid and hippuric acid, are also formed and, along with urea, are excreted in the urine.

Ammonification

Upon the death of plants and animals their organic nitrogen compounds (proteins, nucleic acids, etc.) are degraded by various soil bacteria and fungi. Both aerobic and anaerobic microorganisms participate in this process. The inorganic nitrogenous product is ammonia. A variety of intermediate products (polypeptides, amino acids, etc.) are formed before ammonia is liberated. The process is one of *mineralization* and, because ammonia is formed, it is termed *ammonification*. The ammonia thus formed reacts with acids in the soil to form ammonium salts.

The nitrogenous compounds in the urine of animals, as well as those in the feces, undergo a somewhat similar process, resulting in the production of ammonia. A number of species of bacteria produce the enzyme urease, which catalyzes the hydrolysis of urea, as indicated in the following equation:

$$(NH_2)_2CO + H_2O \xrightarrow{\text{urease}} 2\ NH_3 + CO_2$$
$$\text{urea} \qquad\qquad\qquad \text{ammonia}$$

Nitrification

In soil that is well aerated ammonia is rapidly oxidized to nitrous acid by bacteria belonging chiefly to the genera *Nitrosomonas* and *Nitrosococcus*. The former are short, motile rods, while the latter as the name indicates, are spherical organisms. These bacteria are chemosynthetic autotrophs and obligate aerobes. The oxidation of ammonia is their sole source of energy. The reaction may be indicated by the following equation:

$$2\ NH_3 + 3\ O_2 \longrightarrow 2\ HNO_2 + 2\ H_2O + \text{energy}$$
$$\text{nitrous acid}$$

The nitrous acid formed immediately reacts with bases and certain salts to form nitrites (NO_2), i.e., salts of nitrous acid.

Nitrites do not ordinarily accumulate in the soil but are oxidized to nitrates (NO_3) by a group of aerobic autotrophic bacteria of the genus

Nitrobacter (small motile rods). The oxidation of nitrites is the sole source of energy for these chemosynthetic autotrophs.

The process of transforming ammonia to nitrates is known as *nitrification,* and the organisms that take part in the process are called *nitrifying bacteria.* These organisms use the energy they derive from their oxidative reactions in the synthesis of their protoplasmic components. Soil which is slightly basic in reaction favors the process of nitrification.

Nitrifying bacteria are widely distributed in soils throughout the world. The ammonia oxidizers and the nitrite oxidizers are usually found in association with each other. This association prevents nitrites, which are more or less toxic to plants, from accumulating in the soil.

Nitrate Reduction and Denitrification

In soils deficient in oxygen, nitrates may be reduced to nitrites by facultative and obligate anaerobes. These bacteria use nitrates as hydrogen acceptors in the process of oxidation and, in so doing, reduce nitrates to nitrites. The process is called *nitrate reduction.* A considerable number of species can reduce nitrates and thus make them unavailable to plants.

A smaller number of bacterial species reduce nitrates to gaseous nitrogen. This type of nitrate reduction is termed *denitrification,* and the bacteria involved are called *denitrifying bacteria.* Since denitrification liberates gaseous nitrogen, it results in a loss of nitrogen from the soil. When the oxygen supply is adequate, nitrate reduction and denitrification usually do not occur to an appreciable extent, although the organisms capable of catalyzing these reactions may be present.

Nitrogen Fixation

Nitrogen lost from the soil by the process of denitrification may be returned to the cycle through the activities of certain soil bacteria and some of the blue-green algae. These organisms are capable of chemically binding atmospheric nitrogen and utilizing it in the synthesis of protein molecules. This process of combining molecular nitrogen with other elements is known as *nitrogen fixation.* Only a few bacterial genera contain species capable of fixing atmospheric nitrogen. Some live in symbiotic association with plants known as legumes, including clover, alfalfa, vetch, peas, beans and peanuts; whereas others live independently in the soil. Recently certain photosynthetic bacteria have been found to be nitrogen-fixers.

Symbiotic nitrogen-fixing bacteria can infect certain leguminous plants by entering their root system through the root hairs. The plant reacts by the formation of tumor-like nodules on its roots (Figure 109). The nodules contain nutrient plant juices in which the bacteria grow and multiply. The bacteria utilize certain food components present in the plant juices and in return furnish the plant with compounds containing nitrogen obtained from the air. These compounds can be used by the plant to meet its nitrogen requirements. The energy required for the fixation of nitrogen is obtained by the oxidation of carbohydrates contributed by the host plant. Leguminous plants infected with root-nodule bacteria can grow well in soils deficient in nitrogen.

Under favorable conditions leguminous plants in symbiosis with root-nodule bacteria may fix as much as 400 pounds of nitrogen per acre in a growing season. Leguminous plants lacking root-nodule bacteria are unable to use atmospheric nitrogen, and root-nodule bacteria growing independently are incapable of fixing nitrogen.

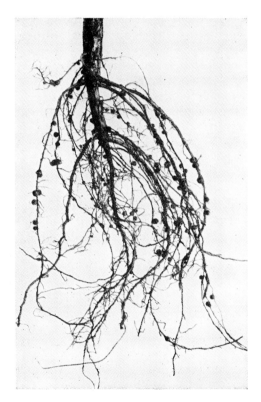

Figure 109. Root nodules on a leguminous plant. (From Farmers' Bulletin No. 1784, U.S. Dept. of Agriculture.)

There are a number of species of symbiotic nitrogen-fixing bacteria, all belonging to the genus *Rhizobium*. The name is of Greek origin, meaning root-growing organism. In young nodules these bacteria occur as small rodlike forms, but in older nodules they take on unusual shapes, becoming branched or club-shaped and, in some cases, resembling the letters Y, T or X. Such forms are known as "bacteroids." For different legumes there are different types of these bacteria adapted to live in their roots. Leguminous plants can be divided into definite groups on the basis of the species of *Rhizobium* with which they live in symbiotic association, as indicated in Table 7.

Table 7.   Symbiotic Nitrogen-Fixing Bacteria

Organism	Host
Rhizobium leguminosarum	Peas, vetches and lentils
Rhizobium phaseoli	Bean plants
Rhizobium japonicum	Soybeans
Rhizobium lupini	Lupines
Rhizobium trifolii	Red, white and crimson clovers
Rhizobium meliloti	Alfalfa and sweet clover

Nitrogen fixation on the part of root-nodule bacteria is of great economic value to agriculture. Growing leguminous crops on land depleted of nitrogen will replenish the soil with a supply of available nitrogenous compounds. A deficiency of soil nitrogen is often a serious problem in agriculture.

Not all soils are supplied with symbiotic nitrogen fixers. This is particularly true when legumes are grown in a soil in which they have never grown before. Also, a soil which has not had a crop of legumes for a number of years may contain few nodule bacteria. In such cases it is usually necessary to supply the proper species of *Rhizobium* if the crop is to succeed. This is known as *inoculation* and is usually accomplished by mixing the seeds just before sowing with a pure culture of the desired bacteria. Cultures of these organisms are now produced commercially on a specially prepared agar medium. Usually, soils in the United States do not need inoculation for clover, but for other legumes it is often necessary.

The nitrogen-fixing bacteria that live independently (nonsymbiotically) are aerobic bacteria of the genus *Azotobacter* and a few anaerobic bacteria of the genus *Clostridium*, as well as a few photosynthetic bacteria. The members of the genus *Azotobacter* are nonspore-forming obligate aerobes. They are relatively large rods, but some are oval in form. *Azotobacter chroococcum* is the most widely distributed member of this genus. It appears to be present in most soils.

The organism chiefly concerned in the anaerobic fixation of nitrogen is *Clostridium pasteurianum*, which is a spore-forming, obligate anaerobic rod-shaped bacterium. It can tolerate acid soil, being able to grow in soil as acidic as pH 5.

Both groups of these free-living nitrogen-fixing bacteria use atmospheric nitrogen in the synthesis of cell proteins. They do not, however, fix large quantities of nitrogen and, consequently, play a less important role in enriching the soil with nitrogen than do the symbiotic nitrogen fixers.

In Figure 110 the main features of the nitrogen cycle are summarized diagrammatically.

Atmospheric nitrogen may become fixed by a number of nonbiological processes. Electrical discharges during thunderstorms cause some of the nitrogen in the air to combine with oxygen to form nitric oxide, which immediately reacts with water to yield nitric acid (HNO_3), which in turn reacts with ammonia to form ammonium nitrate (NH_4NO_3). The ammonium nitrate dissolves in raindrops and is carried down to the soil. Measurements of the annual amount of fixed nitrogen derived from the air in this way indicate that it is relatively small, amounting to only a few pounds per acre.

In recent years man has devised a number of physicochemical processes by means of which he can artificially fix atmospheric nitrogen on a large scale. In one of these processes, the Haber process, nitrogen and hydrogen are forced to combine at a high temperature (200° C.) and high pressure (200 atmospheres) in the presence of finely divided iron, which serves as a catalyst. This results in the formation of ammonia, which is readily con-

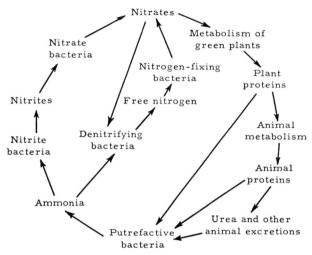

Figure 110.   The nitrogen cycle.

verted into ammonium salts. Several million tons of ammonium salts are produced annually in the United States by this method.

THE SULFUR CYCLE

Sulfur is one of the essential constituents of protoplasm, being present in organic combination in many proteins. Plants obtain their sulfur supply from the soil in the form of sulfates. From plants sulfur is passed on to animals. Upon the decomposition of plant and animal matter by putrefactive bacteria, sulfur is liberated in the form of simple compounds such as hydrogen sulfide (H_2S), thiosulfate ($Na_2S_2O_3$), tetrathionate ($Na_2S_4O_6$) and sulfur dioxide (SO_2). These compounds, as well as elemental sulfur, can be utilized as a source of energy by a number of species of autotrophic bacteria known as sulfur bacteria. In the oxidation of hydrogen sulfide the hydrogen is usually oxidized first, liberating elemental sulfur, which may be stored as reserve food material in the bacterial cells in the form of granules. When the supply of sulfur compounds becomes exhausted, the stored sulfur is oxidized to sulfuric acid. This reaction may be represented by the following equation:

$$2\ S + 3\ O_2 + 2\ H_2O \xrightarrow{\text{enzyme}} 2\ H_2SO_4$$

The sulfuric acid is excreted from the cells and immediately combines with certain soil constituents, such as calcium, magnesium or sodium, to form sulfates. Thus the sulfur is returned to the soil, available again to plants to repeat the cycle. Under anaerobic conditions some bacteria reduce sulfate and sulfur to hydrogen sulfide. The various processes involved in the sulfur cycle are illustrated schematically in Figure 111. The sulfur bacteria constitute a heterogeneous group of autotrophic

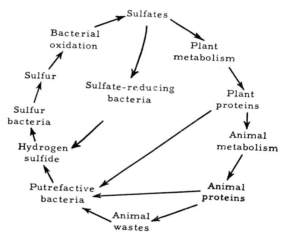

Figure 111. The sulfur cycle

bacteria, including rodlike, spherical, spiral and filamentous forms. Some are chemosynthetic, others photosynthetic. An important genus is *Thiobacillus*, the members of which are small, nonspore-forming, rod-shaped, Gram-negative forms, some being motile, others nonmotile. *Thiobacillus denitrificans* is widely distributed in soils. It oxidizes sulfur, hydrogen sulfide and other sulfur compounds under anaerobic conditions, to sulfuric acid, using nitrates as hydrogen acceptors, reducing them to free nitrogen. *Thiobacillus thioparus* oxidizes sulfur and sulfur compounds aerobically to sulfuric acid. *Thiobacillus thiooxidans* is able to live in strongly acid situations and produces large quantities of sulfuric acid. It usually is found only in soils containing large amounts of sulfur. Sulfur bacteria are found, not only in the soil, but also in the mud of lakes and rivers and in sulfur springs. Some species live only in aquatic habitats.

In addition to the sulfur which enters the soil in plant and animal residues, soil may be enriched with sulfur from other sources. Volcanoes throw large quantities of sulfur dioxide and hydrogen sulfide into the atmosphere yearly. The burning of coal liberates large amounts of gaseous sulfur compounds, and sulfur springs emit volatile sulfur compounds. The sulfur compounds that find their way into the atmosphere are dissolved by rain water and returned to the earth where they are converted into sulfates through the agency of sulfur bacteria.

OTHER CYCLES

Other elements contained in the bodies of plants and animals pass through cycles by the aid of microbial action. One of these is phosphorus, which is present in the protoplasm of nearly all cells as a constituent of nucleoproteins and phospholipids. It is present also in vertebrate skeletons, which consist in large part of calcium phosphate. Phosphorus occurs in the soil in the form of inorganic salts of calcium, magnesium, iron, and so on, which are generally referred to as phosphates. Insoluble phosphates are converted into soluble phosphates through the agency of bacteria. Phosphates absorbed by plants are built into organic compounds. From plants they are passed on to animals. In the process of the microbial decomposition of animal excreta and animal and plant remains, organic phosphorus is converted into phosphates available for plant use.

Many of the minerals utilized by plants and animals retain their inorganic character in living tissue. They are present in the form of salts in solution in the cells and body fluids of animals and in some cases may form loose combinations with proteins. Upon the decomposition of proteins they are restored to their mineral state. This is true of potassium, calcium and a number of other elements. The only role microorganisms play in the cycle of these elements is to liberate them in the process of organic decomposition.

Cycles similar to those discussed in this chapter occur in the natural waters of the earth. Microorganisms play a role in the cycle of elements in the oceans, lakes and rivers of the earth in a manner similar to their role in the cycle of elements in the soil. The species involved, however, are usually not the same as those active in the soil.

QUESTIONS

1. (*a*) What is soil? How is it formed? What is the source of the organic matter in the soil?

(*b*) Where in the soil are microorganisms abundant? What kinds of bacteria are found in the soil? Name some common molds found in the soil.

2. Differentiate between fermentation and putrefaction.

3. (*a*) Discuss the decomposition of polysaccharides in the soil.

(*b*) Explain the hydrolysis of disaccharides by soil microorganisms.

4. (*a*) Are monosaccharides decomposed extracellularly or intracellularly?

(*b*) How does the aerobic decomposition of monosaccharides differ from that carried on under anaerobic conditions?

5. Explain briefly the decomposition of fats.

6. (*a*) What products result from protein decomposition?

(*b*) What is meant by deamination and decarboxylation?

7. What is humus? How is it formed? Of what value is it to crops?
8. Explain briefly the process of photosynthesis carried on by plants.
9. Explain the role played by microorganisms in the carbon cycle.
10. (*a*) Explain the role of microorganisms in the nitrogen cycle.

(*b*) Explain: (1) ammonification, (2) nitrification, (3) nitrate reduction, (4) denitrification, (5) nitrogen fixation.

(*c*) Which bacteria play a role in nitrogen fixation?
11. Explain the sulfur cycle.

REFERENCES

Fry, B.: The Nitrogen Metabolism of Microorganisms. New York, John Wiley & Sons, Inc., 1955.

McElroy, W. D., and Glass, B., ed.: Inorganic Nitrogen Metabolism. Baltimore, The Johns Hopkins Press, 1956.

Nicol, H.: Microbes and Us. Harmondsworth, England, Pelican Books, 1955.

United States Dept. of Agriculture: Soils and Men. Yearbook of Agriculture. Washington, D. C., Government Printing Office, 1938.

Waksman, S. A.: Humus. Baltimore, The Williams & Wilkins Company, 1938.

Waksman, S. A.: Soil Microbiology. New York, John Wiley & Sons, Inc., 1952.

19 • Industrial Utilization of Microorganisms

Knowledge of microbial metabolism has led to the development of fermentation industries in which microorganisms are used to produce a wide variety of useful substances which contribute to man's welfare in many different ways. These products are either definite chemicals resulting from the fermentation of organic compounds, or represent substances that have had their value enhanced by having been changed by the activities of microorganisms. The use of bacteria, yeasts and molds in industrial fermentations has attained great importance in the present-day world and has given rise to a division of applied science known as *industrial microbiology*. Many of the industrial fermentation processes are carried out on a huge scale.

The list of commodities obtained by the industrial use of microorganisms includes ethyl alcohol and alcoholic beverages; various organic acids such as lactic, citric and gluconic; butyl alcohol and acetone, and certain food products, including cheese, sauerkraut, pickles, fermented milk, butter, bread and silage (for cattle). Microbial fermentations are used also in the processing of hides and skins; the retting of flax and hemp; and the curing of tobacco, tea and other products. Some of the chemical compounds obtained by fermentation can be produced also by purely chemical methods, but usually at greater expense or in amounts inadequate to meet the requirements. In many industrial fermentation* processes such farm products as wheat, barley, rye, corn, sugar cane, straw, cornstalks and various vegetables are utilized as raw materials. In this and the following chapter a limited number of important products of microbial activity will be considered.

Certain fermentation processes date back to remote antiquity, although

* In industrial microbiology, the term fermentation is used in a broad sense to indicate the decomposition by microorganisms of all types of organic compounds under either aerobic or anaerobic conditions.

the nature of the fermentative reactions remained unknown until recent times. Among the older industrial processes may be mentioned the production of alcoholic beverages, the making of vinegar, the retting of flax and hemp, and the use of yeast as a leavening agent in the making of bread. It is of interest to note that the preparation of fermented beverages was carried on by the ancient Greeks, Egyptians and Romans and that Greek mythology includes a god of wine called Bacchus.

Anaerobic conditions are necessary for some of the fermentation reactions, while aerobic conditions are required for others. In aerobic fermentations oxygen acts as a hydrogen acceptor, whereas in anaerobic fermentations intermediate decomposition products such as aldehydes, pyruvic acid and other compounds serve as acceptors of hydrogen. Some substrates may be converted to several products, depending on the kinds of microorganisms involved.

Industrial fermentations are usually carried out in large tanks or special fermentation vessels. Tanks with capacities as high as 50,000 gallons may be used. When a large air supply is required, the tanks are provided with stirring devices to aerate the fermenting medium. The metabolic activities of the extraordinarily large number of microorganisms in these tanks may raise the temperature of the medium to a point above the lethal temperature of the organisms. To prevent this from occurring, the tanks are provided with cooling coils.

ETHYL ALCOHOL

Ethyl alcohol, owing to its many industrial uses, is one of the most valuable fermentation products in modern life. Vast quantities are required annually. It is used as a solvent for many drugs and chemicals and also as an antiseptic. It is a necessary reagent in the manufacture of numerous organic compounds. Large quantities are used as a solvent for shellac in making varnishes. Mixed with other liquid fuels it may be used as a motor fuel. It is used in making nonfreezing solutions for automobile radiators. Large quantities have been used in recent years in the manufacture of synthetic rubber. It has many other uses. Much of the industrial alcohol now produced is no longer a product of fermentation but is made synthetically from by-products formed by the "cracking" of petroleum.

Although the art of utilizing the fermentation of sugar to alcohol in the making of alcoholic beverages is ancient, it was not until the middle of the nineteenth century that the role played by microorganisms in the process was recognized.

Ethyl alcohol is obtained by the fermentation of various carbohydrates by yeasts. The raw materials used in the process may be molasses (the residue of sugar manufacture); various grains such as wheat, corn, barley or rice; potatoes; sugar beets; corncobs; or sawdust. In the United States it is made chiefly from so-called blackstrap molasses brought in tankers from Cuba and other Caribbean areas, but grains are used also.

When molasses is used, it is diluted so that the sugar content is 10 to 12 per cent and the reaction adjusted to pH 4.0 to 4.5 by the addition of acid which is favorable for yeasts but too acid for most bacteria. A little ammonium phosphate or sulfate is added to provide nitrogenous matter for yeast growth. To this mixture, known as *mash,* a large quantity of pure culture of a high alcohol-producing strain of the yeast *Saccharomyces cerevisiae* is added. The strain used is referred to as distiller's yeast and is capable of tolerating high alcoholic concentrations. The sugar in the molasses is fermented by the yeast, the chief end products being ethyl alcohol and carbon dioxide. These end products contain less energy than sugar; consequently, energy is liberated in the process.

Alcoholic fermentation is an anaerobic process. However, aerobic conditions are maintained for a time after the yeast culture has been added in order to promote the rapid multiplication of the yeast cells. This is accomplished by aerating the mash. Under aerobic conditions yeast cells multiply rapidly but produce little or no alcohol. After aeration ceases anaerobic conditions soon become established. When the proportion of alcohol in the mash reaches about 15 per cent, the yeast cells die and the fermentation process stops. The process is usually completed within two to three days. The mash is then subjected to fractional distillation, which separates the alcohol from most of the other constituents. The distillation process yields a final product containing approximately 95 per cent alcohol. The carbon dioxide produced is usually collected, purified and compressed in tanks. It is converted into dry ice or used in other ways.

About twelve different enzymes and a number of coenzymes are believed to be involved in the conversion of monosaccharide sugars to ethyl alcohol and carbon dioxide. In the absence of oxygen the yeast cells transform glucose to ethyl alcohol through a series of reactions which are not completely understood. The first enzyme to act upon glucose is phosphatase, which catalyzes the union of phosphoric acid and glucose to form a hexose phosphate. This compound is then broken down through a series of reactions to pyruvic acid. Yeast cells contain an enzyme which catalyzes the decarboxylation of the pyruvic acid molecule with the formation of one molecule of carbon dioxide and one of acetaldehyde, as indicated in the following equation:

$$CH_3COCOOH \rightarrow CH_3CHO + CO_2$$
$$\text{pyruvic acid} \qquad \text{acetaldehyde}$$

In the final reaction the acetaldehyde is reduced to ethyl alchohol by accepting hydrogen from one of the coenzymes involved in the process, which thus becomes oxidized. The following equation represents this reaction:

$$CH_3CHO + 2 H \rightarrow CH_3CH_2OH$$
$$\text{acetaldehyde} \qquad \text{ethyl alcohol}$$

As a final result, each molecule of glucose yields two molecules each of ethyl alcohol and carbon dioxide, as indicated in the equation:

$$C_6H_{12}O_6 \rightarrow 2 \ CH_3CH_2OH + 2 \ CO_2$$

In addition to ethyl alcohol and carbon dioxide, small quantities of a variety of by-products are formed. These include glycerol, organic acids, higher alcohols (propyl, butyl and amyl alcohol), aldehydes and esters. Glycerol constitutes about 3.5 per cent of the end products. The higher alcohols and other substances present which have a higher boiling point than ethyl alcohol are known collectively as *fusel oil.* These are more toxic to the human body than ethyl alcohol. After the process of distillation is completed the remaining mash, now known as "slop," is used as fertilizer or stock feed.

When grains or other starch-containing substances are used as the initial raw material, the starch must be changed to fermentable sugar, since yeasts do not produce amylase. Yeasts can decompose glucose, fructose, galactose, sucrose and maltose but are unable to act on starch. The conversion of starch to sugar may be accomplished either by enzyme or acid hydrolysis. Enzyme hydrolysis may be carried out by the use of barley malt (germinated barley) or certain molds, notably species of *Aspergillus* and *Mucor. Aspergillus oryzae* is frequently used for this purpose. Acid hydrolysis is accomplished by the use of sulfuric acid.

Barley malt is prepared by placing barley that has been previously soaked in water in a warm damp atmosphere so that it will germinate. The germination process brings about the production of amylase (also known as diastase) in the barley. The ground malt is added to the substrate (rye, corn, wheat or potatoes), which has been previously crushed and heated to make a starch paste. The amylase in the malt converts the starch into maltose.

In place of malt, mold amylase is now widely used to hydrolyze the starch to sugar. The mold is usually grown in an acidified mixture of water and wheat bran. The enzyme is extracted from the moldy bran and added to the substrate. In some instances, however, the moldy bran is dried and ground into a coarse powder and added to the substrate. In either case, amylase brings about the saccharification of the starch.

The alcoholic fermentation process can be varied to give a high yield of glycerol. Glycerol is normally obtained as a by-product of soap making but, when necessary, the supply can be augmented by modifying the alcoholic fermentation process. The addition of sodium sulfite to the mash increases the quantity of glycerol produced by five to ten times.

ALCOHOLIC BEVERAGES

The making of beverages of high alcoholic content does not differ essentially from the process used in making industrial ethyl alcohol. The raw materials to be used are chosen with greater care as to quality. Many refinements are introduced to remove offensive-tasting substances as completely as possible to obtain the desired flavor and aroma. The distillation is adjusted so that the concentration of the alcohol does not exceed 50 per cent.

Whiskey may be made from rye, barley, wheat or corn. After distillation it is aged for at least two years in charred oak barrels. The charred inner surface of the barrels absorbs many impurities. Chemical changes take place during the aging process which greatly improve the flavor. This is true of distilled alcoholic beverages in general. Brandy is a distilled liquor made from fruits such as grapes, apples and peaches. Gin usually is made from corn and flavored with juniper berries and other aromatic substances. Rum is prepared from fermented molasses or cane sugar sirup.

Wine is made from fruit juices, chiefly grapes. The raw juice or *must* contains sugar and is acid in reaction. The must may be permitted to undergo fermentation spontaneously by *Saccharomyces ellipsoideus,* the wine yeast, which is always present on the skins of grapes and other fruits. In the United States most wineries eliminate the yeasts and other microorganisms that are naturally present on grapes by pasteurizing the must, which is then inoculated with a culture of a suitable strain of wine yeast.

The alcoholic content of wines varies from 7 to 15 per cent. Most strains of wine yeasts cannot produce more than 12 to 15 per cent alcohol. When the concentration reaches this point, their growth is inhibited and the fermentation comes to a stop. Wines containing a higher percentage of alcohol are fortified with wine spirits (brandy) or alcohol. Wine is usually aged for two years; it may be pasteurized after it is bottled.

Beer and similar beverages (stout, ale, porter) are prepared mainly from barley malt and hops. Usually other malted or unmalted grains such as wheat, corn or rice are added. The brewing of beer is an old industry which, according to historical accounts, was probably invented by the ancient Egyptians. In making beer the malt is ground and suspended in water. Other ground grains are then added. When all the starch has been changed to sugar by the amylase of the malt, the mash is filtered, yielding a straw-colored liquid known as *wort*. The wort is boiled with hops and then run into fermentation vats and inoculated with a culture of a strain of *Saccharomyces cerevisiae,* commonly known as brewer's yeast. The hops adds a bitter taste and also exerts an antiseptic action against lactic acid-producing bacteria. Fermentation is permitted to continue for eight to ten days. The wort is then run into storage tanks, where it slowly continues to ferment. After aging for about two months it is bottled or kegged. Bottle beer is usually pasteurized, but keg beer is not. Beer has an alcoholic content ranging from 3 to 6 per cent.

PRODUCTION OF BAKER'S YEAST

The production of yeast for the baking industry and for use in the home is an industrial operation of considerable scope, over 100,000 tons being produced annually in the United States. The yeast is grown in tanks (Figure 112), and the medium for its cultivation is carefully adjusted in regard to its constituents. The needed carbohydrates are provided by blackstrap molasses diluted so that the sugar concentration will be between 7 and 9 per cent. Ammonium salts are added as a source of nitrogen. Organic nitrogen is also usually added because a yeast culture grows more vigorously if part of the nitrogenous food is organic. Accessory growth

Figure 112.   Pure yeast propagator. (Courtesy of the Pfaudler Company.)

substances containing various vitamins are also included. The medium is acidified to approximately pH 4.5. The desired yeast, a strain of *Saccharomyces cerevisiae* which produces large quantities of carbon dioxide at a rapid rate, is then added to the medium. To obtain a maximum yield of yeast cells, the medium is aerated. Under aerobic conditions, yeasts obtain more energy from the sugar they metabolize since they oxidize most of it to carbon dioxide and water and produce only small amounts of alcohol. More energy is thus available to the yeast cells for use in the synthesis of cell substance. This makes possible a rapid rate of growth and reproduction.

When the culture has reached the maximum stationary phase of its growth, the cells are separated from the medium by a centrifugal separator. The yeast is then run through a filter press to remove the excess liquid. It is then mixed with a small amount of starch or a bland oil and pressed into cakes. Owing to the moisture present in a compressed yeast cake, the cells continue to respire if kept at temperatures above freezing. The reserve foods in the cells are utilized in respiration which, in a short time, results in the death of the cells. After death the cells become autolyzed by their own enzymes, with the result that the yeast cake becomes soft.

Baker's yeast is also placed on the market in the form of an active dry yeast. This is prepared by drying a suspension of yeast cells so that the moisture content is reduced to about 8 per cent. This small amount of moisture does not permit the cells to respire actively but is sufficient to keep them alive. Such yeast can be stored at room temperature for a relatively long time without great loss of viability. It is usually prepared in the form of granules.

PRODUCTION OF FOOD YEAST

Practical and economical methods have been developed for growing yeast for human food in areas such as the West Indies, where carbohydrates, particularly crude molasses, are cheap and plentiful. The yeast most commonly used for this purpose is a strain of *Torulopsis utilis*. The method for growing this yeast on a large scale was developed in England in 1940. It is grown in a molasses medium to which ammonium sulfate and ammonium phosphate are added. The *p*H is adjusted to a suitable value, the temperature is carefully controlled, and the medium is aerated by a mechanical device.

A continuous process has been developed in which fresh culture medium is run in the top of the vat, and medium containing the yeast is drawn off from the bottom. The yeast is centrifuged, washed and dried, yielding pale yellow flakes of inactivated yeast. Great Britain has erected a plant in Jamaica capable of an annual production of 2000 tons of dehydrated yeast.

Food yeast is used by mixing it with other foods. It is an excellent supplement to the dietary, since it is a rich source of proteins and vitamins of the B group. The proteins are of high quality, being similar to those of meat in amino acid content. Food yeast has a pleasant meaty flavor, differing in this respect from baker's yeast, which has a somewhat unpleasant taste, and brewer's yeast, which is bitter unless subjected to special treatment.

Yeast is used also to a limited extent in livestock feed. Brewer's and distiller's yeast are frequently used for this purpose. The production of fodder yeast is economically feasible only when a cheap source of carbohydrate is available for the cultivation of the yeasts.

Some species of yeasts produce large quantities of fat. When fats are in short supply, considerable quantities can be obtained from yeasts such as *Rhodotorula gracilis*. Sweden and Germany used yeasts as a source of fat during World War II. However, a suitable method of obtaining fat economically from yeasts under normal conditions of fat supply has not yet been developed.

PRODUCTION OF VINEGAR

Vinegar can be made from almost any substance capable of yielding alcohol by yeast fermentation. Apple juice is the raw material commonly used in the United States. Grape juice and malt extract are sometimes used. Vinegar making is a two-phase process carried out by two groups of organisms. In the first phase, alcohol is formed anaerobically from fermentable sugar by yeasts; in the second phase, alcohol is oxidized to acetic acid and water aerobically by various bacteria belonging to the genus *Acetobacter*. This genus contains numerous species, two examples of which are *A. aceti* and *A. pasteurianus*. They are rod-shaped forms, occurring singly, in pairs and in long chains. They are widely distributed in nature and are obligate aerobes.

Two methods have been developed for the commercial production of vinegar: the Orleans method and the so-called "quick method."

In the Orleans method large casks or barrels are placed on their sides and partially filled with hard cider or other fermented liquids containing between 10 and 13 per cent of alcohol. This is inoculated with bacteria of the *Acetobacter* genus. As the bacteria grow they form a thick film, commonly called "mother of vinegar," over the surface of the liquid, and the alcohol is slowly oxidized to acetic acid. The film is usually supported by wooden floats to keep it from dropping to the bottom of the cask. Since the process is an aerobic one, the cask must be well ventilated to provide an ample supply of oxygen. After the process is well under way, some vinegar is removed from the cask and additional alcoholic fruit juice added. The process thus is more or less continuous.

Most of the commercial vinegar is now made by the quick method, which requires the use of a tall, wooden, well-aerated tank or "generator." The generator is loosely packed with beechwood shavings that have been impregnated with acetic acid bacteria. The bottom of the generator is perforated, allowing for the entrance of air. The alcoholic solution is sprayed over the top and trickles down over the shavings. The shavings gradually develop a film of acetic acid bacteria. They also provide a large total surface exposed to the alcoholic solution and ensure contact of the organisms with air. Since this is an oxidative process, it is essential that an abundant supply of air be available. The heat generated in the oxidation causes a draft upward, providing an air circulation within the generator. Under these conditions the acetic acid bacteria rapidly oxidize the alcohol to acetic acid and water. The process represents an incomplete oxidation.

The chemical reactions involved may be represented by the following equations:

(1) $$2\ CH_3CH_2OH + O_2 \rightarrow 2\ CH_3CHO + 2\ H_2O$$
ethyl alcohol   acetaldehyde

(2) $$2\ CH_3CHO + O_2 \rightarrow 2\ CH_3COOH$$
acetic acid

The finished product is drawn off at the bottom and contains from 4 to 6 per cent acetic acid in addition to other substances which give it color, flavor and aroma. It is usually pasteurized and then stored in casks or bottles. Like alcoholic liquors, it should be aged before being used.

PRODUCTION OF ORGANIC ACIDS

A large variety of organic acids are formed by the metabolic processes of microorganisms. Only a few of these, however, are produced industrially. Among these are citric, lactic and gluconic acid. Acetic acid, as explained previously, is formed in the process of vinegar production; but vinegar is not the source of industrial acetic acid. Acetic acid for industrial purposes is obtained by the destructive distillation of wood or is made synthetically from acetylene.

Citric Acid

This acid is a natural constituent of many fruits, particularly citrus fruits. It can be obtained from citrus fruits, but most of the commercial supply is now obtained by mold fermentation. Molds of the genera *Aspergillus* and *Penicillium* may be used. The medium employed contains sugar (sucrose or glucose), mineral salts and an inorganic nitrogen compound such as an ammonium salt or a nitrate. The process is aerobic. The submerged-culture technique with forced aeration is usually employed. The citric acid produced can be removed from the medium by various methods.

Citric acid is in considerable demand for pharmaceutical products, chiefly in the form of citrates and effervescent salts. It is used also in the manufacture of flavoring extracts, nonalcoholic beverages, candies and other commodities.

Lactic Acid

Industrial lactic acid is produced by fermentation of various sugars, such as glucose, maltose, sucrose or lactose. The raw materials usually used are molasses, which contains glucose, sucrose and maltose; and whey, which contains lactose. Whey is the liquid part of the milk that remains in the manufacture of cottage cheese, hard cheese or casein. Various lactic acid-producing bacteria may be used, such as *Lactobacillus bulgaricus, L. delbrueckii* or *L. casei.*

The sugar-containing material is sterilized and inoculated with a pure culture of the desired bacteria. The addition of phosphates accelerates the fermentation. Oxygen is not required since the process proceeds anaerobically. The reaction may be represented by the following equation:

$$C_6H_{12}O_6 \rightarrow 2\ CH_3CHOHCOOH$$
$$\text{lactic acid}$$

As the fermentation proceeds, calcium carbonate is added at intervals to neutralize the acid so that the growth of the bacteria will not be retarded. This is continued until all the sugar has been converted. At the termination of the fermentation the acid is chiefly in the form of calcium lactate, which is removed by filtration. Treating the calcium lactate with sulfuric acid liberates the lactic acid and precipitates the calcium as calcium sulfate.

Figure 113.   Fermentation tanks used in industrial fermentation processes. (Courtesy of Commercial Solvents Corporation.)

Lactic acid is used to acidify certain foods, such as canned vegetables and fish products. It is used also in the curing of meat, leather manufacture, the dyeing of silks and other textiles, and the manufacture of textiles. In the form of calcium lactate it is used in the production of baking powders and in the pharmaceutical industry.

Gluconic Acid

Gluconic acid ($C_6H_{12}O_7$) is produced by the oxidation of glucose by certain strains of molds belonging to the genera *Aspergillus* and *Penicillium,* as well as by bacteria belonging to the genus *Acetobacter*. In this process, glucose is oxidized to gluconic acid. Gluconic acid is employed as a medicinal agent in the form of its calcium salt, calcium gluconate.

PRODUCTION OF ACETONE AND BUTYL ALCOHOL

Both acetone and butyl alcohol (butanol) are obtained by the bacterial fermentation of carbohydrates. The organism used, *Clostridium aceto-butylicum,* can ferment various carbohydrates. Corn is frequently used as the raw material. The germ of the corn is removed, and the kernels are then ground to a coarse meal which is mixed with water and cooked in large tanks (Figure 114). This corn mash is then inoculated with a pure culture of the organism. Molasses may be used in place of corn.

Figure 114. Cookers for sterilizing corn meal and water used in the acetone-butanol fermentation process. (Courtesy of Commercial Solvents Corporation.)

The fermentation is carried on in deep tanks under anaerobic conditions for about three days. The chief products are butyl alcohol, acetone and ethyl alcohol in the ratio of 6:3:1. Hydrogen and carbon dioxide are also produced. The fermentation products are separated by distillation. This is an important fermentation process, since both acetone and butyl alcohol are valuable industrial solvents. The gases, hydrogen and carbon dioxide, are combined chemically by the aid of a catalyst to form methyl alcohol, which is also an important industrial solvent.

Butyl alcohol is a solvent for many organic substances. Its most important use is in the manufacture of lacquers for automobiles, airplanes and furniture. It is used also in making synthetic resins and in waterproofing compounds.

Acetone is used in making photographic films, cellulose acetate (artificial silk), airplane dopes, plastics, smokeless powder, chloroform and artificial leather.

By slightly modifying the fermentation process, large yields of the vitamin riboflavin can be obtained in addition to the three primary end products, butyl alcohol, acetone and ethyl alcohol. Butyl alcohol is also obtained as a by-product in the production of gasoline from petroleum.

MICROBIAL PRODUCTION OF VITAMINS

Certain vitamins are produced by fermentation processes. Among these are B_2 (riboflavin) and B_{12}. Two species of yeast, *Ashbya gossypii* and *Eremothecium ashbyii,* are used in the commercial production of riboflavin. In appropriate culture media these organisms synthesize and secrete riboflavin into the surrounding medium. Large yields of this vitamin can be obtained also by slightly modifying the acetone and butyl alcohol fermentation process. Vitamin B_{12} is a by-product in the production of certain antibiotics, particularly streptomycin and the tetracyclines. Vitamin C (ascorbic acid) can be obtained from sorbose, which is produced by bacterial oxidation of sorbitol. Sorbose is used in the chemical synthesis of vitamin C. Nearly all vitamins of the B group are synthesized by yeasts in quantities far above their own needs. Vitamin D can be produced by ultraviolet irradiation of ergosterol, a substance obtained from yeasts.

RETTING OF FLAX AND HEMP

The bast fibers embedded in the stems of the flax and hemp plants are firmly cemented together by pectin. The process used for separating these fibers involves the activities of microorganisms and is known as *retting,* the word meaning "soaking in water." Flax fibers are used in making linen thread and linen fabrics; hemp fibers are used for making coarse fabrics (burlap) and rope. The essential feature of retting is the hydrolysis, on the part of microbial enzymes, of the pectin surrounding the fibers. Retting is essentially a microbial decomposition process which can be carried out under either aerobic or anaerobic conditions.

In the anaerobic method the plant stalks are submerged in water which gradually dissolves some of the plant constituents, thus becoming a good culture medium for many microorganisms. At first, aerobic organisms predominate. By using up the dissolved oxygen, they soon create anaerobic conditions. Anaerobes then become active, chiefly *Clostridium pectinovorum* and *Cl. felsineum,* decomposing the pectin which holds the fibers together. The fibers consist chiefly of cellulose, which decomposes more slowly than pectin. Correct timing of the retting process is important to prevent the fibers from being weakened by cellulose-digesting organisms.

Anaerobic retting is an old process and is often carried on in slow-flowing, warm streams. In Egypt the shallows of the river Nile have been used for this purpose for thousands of years. In China rivers have been used for retting for many centuries. In Belgium the river Lys is famous for flax retting. Retting may also be carried on in bodies of stagnant water such as ponds and in vats containing warm water. When vats are used, a culture of *Cl. felsineum* is usually added to the water, which is kept at about 37° C. for two to three days.

Aerobic retting involves either the use of vats in which the water is aerated or the process known as "dew retting," in which the stalks are spread over vegetation on the ground and kept damp by dew or rain. Dew retting is usually done in the fall of the year when the sun is not too hot to dry out the stalks but the temperature is sufficiently high to promote the necessary microbial activity. Molds, chiefly members of the genus *Mucor,* as well as aerobic bacteria, attack the pectin in this type of retting. Dew retting is carried on in southern England and Ireland.

After the fibers have been freed by the retting process, they are combed, spun into yarns and woven into fabrics.

OTHER USES OF MICROORGANISMS

Microorganisms are used in a number of other ways. The outer coverings of cocoa and coffee beans are removed by fermentation. The flavor of cocoa, coffee and tea is also dependent upon the activities of microorganisms. In the curing of hides and the making of leather microbial action plays a role in the initial steps of the processes. Combustible gases such as methane and hydrogen can be recovered from sewage, garbage, the sulfite waste liquors of pulp mills and other materials undergoing anaerobic decomposition. Butylene glycol, used as an antifreeze in automobiles and in the manufacture of synthetic rubber, is obtained by the fermentation of cornstarch mash or other carbohydrate material by microorganisms.

Some bacteria, particularly *Leuconostoc mesenteroides,* can form dextran from sucrose. Dextran is a gummy polysaccharide composed of a large number of glucose units. It is now produced industrially for use as a substitute for blood plasma in the treatment of shock resulting from severe loss of blood.

QUESTIONS

1. Name some of the products obtained by industrial fermentation processes. In what kinds of containers are these fermentations usually carried out? Which kinds of microorganisms are used in these processes?

2. Which raw materials may be used in making ethyl alcohol? Name the microorganisms responsible for alcoholic fermentation. Is it an aerobic or anaerobic process? Besides ethyl alcohol, which other end products are formed?

3. Describe briefly the industrial production of (1) baker's yeast and (2) food yeast.

4. How is vinegar produced? Is it an aerobic or anaerobic process?

5. Explain the industrial production of (1) citric acid, (2) lactic acid, (3) gluconic acid.

6. Explain briefly the fermentation process that results in the production of acetone and butyl alcohol. Of what importance are these two products?

7. Explain the role microorganisms play in the retting of flax and hemp.

8. Name some other commodities for the production of which microorganisms are used.

REFERENCES

Barker, H. A.: Bacterial Fermentations. New York, John Wiley & Sons, Inc., 1957.

Cruess, W. V.: The Principles and Practice of Wine Making. Westport, Conn., Avi Publishing Company, 1947.

Foster, J. W.: Chemical Activities of Fungi. New York, Academic Press, Inc., 1949.

Frazier, W. C.: Food Microbiology. New York, McGraw-Hill Book Company, Inc., 1958.

Gale, E. F.: The Chemical Activities of Bacteria. New York, Academic Press, Inc., 1951.

Prescott, S. C., and Dunn, C. C.: Industrial Microbiology. 3rd ed. New York, McGraw-Hill Book Co., Inc., 1959.

Rahn, O.: Microbes of Merit. New York, The Ronald Press, 1945.

Smith, G., and Raistrick, H.: An Introduction to Industrial Mycology. London, E. Arnold & Co., 1946.

Woodruff, H. B., and McDaniel, L. E.: Commercial Fermentations. New York, Chemical Publishing Company, Inc., 1949.

20 • Utilization of Microorganisms in Food Production and in Biological Assays

The transformations microorganisms are capable of producing in organic substances can be utilized in some instances in bringing about desirable changes in foods. A number of foods in daily use by man are produced through the agency of microorganisms. Included in this group are bread, butter, cheese, fermented milk and sauerkraut. Microorganisms are used also in the biological assay of vitamins and amino acids.

BREAD

Bread making involves fermentation in which yeasts are active agents, although bacteria may be used for this purpose. Biological leavening agents produce gas which causes the mixture of flour and water (dough) to expand and become porous and spongy in texture. The source of the gas is sugar, which, when yeast is used as the leavening agent, is broken down to carbon dioxide and ethyl alcohol. Present in the dough are proteins (gliadin and glutenin) which, when wet with water, form a sticky mass called gluten. The gluten of wheat and rye has sufficient elasticity to hold the gas in the dough. Grains other than wheat and rye do not have mixtures of proteins satisfactory for the development of a good elastic gluten.

Most flours contain small amounts of amylase, which converts some of the starch they contain to sugar (maltose). Sugar may also be added to the dough. If a flour is deficient in amylase, this may be corrected by the addition of this enzyme or by the addition of malt, which, as previously mentioned, is rich in amylase. The subsequent baking causes the gas in the dough to expand, and thus the loaf increases in size and becomes light and spongy. The alcohol formed during fermentation is evaporated by the heat of baking.

313

Although the primary action of yeast is the production of carbon dioxide, causing the dough to rise, yeast enzymes bring about favorable changes in the proteins of the dough which contribute to the flavor as well as the texture of the bread. Bacteria normally present in the dough give rise to volatile esters and organic acids (chiefly lactic) which contribute characteristic flavors and aromas to the bread. Bread usually has more flavor if sufficient time is allowed for the development of the microorganisms that contribute to the quality of the bread. However, if the fermentation is prolonged, the dough may become sour, owing to excessive amounts of acid formed.

Leavened bread can be made without adding yeast to the dough. In this procedure the dough undergoes spontaneous fermentation due to gas-forming microorganisms, chiefly bacteria, which were originally present in the flour. Bacterial counts indicate that flour contains bacteria in large numbers. The leavening is due to carbon dioxide and hydrogen produced by these bacteria. Considerable time must be allowed for the dough to rise. Bread leavened in this way acquires a characteristic flavor due to the prolonged fermentation the dough undergoes. To hasten the rising the desired bacteria may be introduced from a previous lot of dough. Salt is usually added to the dough to inhibit undesirable organisms. Bread produced in this manner is called self-rising or salt-rising bread.

Abnormal Fermentations of Bread

Undesirable microbial activities may occur in dough or bread. If the dough is kept too long before baking, lactic acid and butyric acid bacteria, which are usually present in flour, may become exceedingly numerous and cause the dough to become sour.

Bread may become "ropy" or slimy if certain capsulated, spore-forming bacteria get into the dough. This defect can be caused by several species, including *Bacillus subtilis* and closely related forms. In the baking process the interior of a loaf of bread usually does not reach a temperature sufficiently high to kill resistant spores. Before the bread is eaten the spores develop into vegetative cells which form capsules, causing the bread to become slimy or ropy. When such bread is broken apart, the slime can be drawn out into threads. By adding calcium or sodium propionate to the dough, ropiness can be prevented. This is now common practice in commercial bakeries. Ropiness can also be prevented by adding lactic, acetic or propionic acid to the dough. These various chemicals added to the dough prevent the spores that survive the baking temperature from germinating into vegetative cells. They also keep bread from becoming moldy.

So-called "bloody bread" results from the presence of *Serratia marcescens,* a chromogenic rod-shaped bacterium that produces a red pigment. This organism may enter bread after it has been baked, causing red spots or areas in the bread. The red discoloration has the appearance of blood. As mentioned in a previous chapter, this organism has an interesting historical background.

BUTTER

Butter consists chiefly of the fat of milk and is obtained from cream by a process of churning. Fat occurs in milk in the form of exceedingly small globules. When cream is churned, the globules become matted together to form butter. Butter may be made from cream that has been soured naturally by bacteria ordinarily present in cream. Most of the butter now used is made from sweet cream that has been pasteurized and then inoculated with a starter culture which usually contains *Streptococcus lactis, Streptococcus cremoris, Leuconostoc citrovorum* and *Leuconostoc dextranicum.* The streptococci produce lactic acid from the lactose in the cream and thus cause the cream to sour. The other two organisms produce chemical compounds which contribute flavor and aroma to the butter. These compounds become adsorbed on the fat particles and consist principally of diacetyl, acetic acid, propionic acid and acetylmethylcarbinol. The most important of these compounds is diacetyl, since it contributes most of the flavor and aroma to butter.

The use of pasteurized cream in the making of butter assures the absence of pathogenic organisms such as typhoid fever bacilli, hemolytic streptococci, tubercle bacilli, diphtheria bacilli, the organisms of undulant fever (brucellosis) and others.

Butter contains approximately 82 per cent fat, 14 per cent water dispersed in the form of small droplets, 2.5 per cent salt dissolved in the water and traces of casein, lactose and other substances. Butter keeps well because the salt concentration in the water droplets is sufficiently high to inhibit the growth of most bacteria. However, fat-splitting bacteria occasionally become active in butter and cause rancidity.

CHEESE

Cheese has been used as a food as far back as history records. It is made from the curd obtained by coagulation of whole milk, skimmed milk or milk enriched with cream. In curd formation, milk is converted to a solid or gel state by precipitation of *casein,* the major protein of milk. Curd formation is accomplished either by the action of acid produced by the fermentation of lactose by bacteria, or by means of *rennet* obtained from the stomachs of calves, or by a combination of the two. The active principle of rennet is the enzyme *rennin,* which is able to curdle milk.

In the production of most cheeses, rennet is used to curdle the milk. In many cases, however, bacteria are added to produce acid to aid the rennet in curdling the milk. Cottage cheese may be made solely from acid curd. In this process, skim milk is inoculated with a starter culture which contains *Streptococcus lactis,* or some other lactic streptococcus, and aroma-producing bacteria. The lactic acid produced induces curdling. The curd is separated from the whey, and the cheese thus obtained is ready for consumption. This type of cheese does not need to undergo a curing or ripening process. Cottage cheese is frequently made from curd formed by both acid-producing bacteria and rennet.

Cream cheese is made by a method similar to that of making cottage cheese. Cream containing 12 to 20 per cent fat is pasteurized and inoculated with a starter culture containing *Str. lactis* and aroma bacteria. A small amount of rennet is usually added to produce a firm curd. The curd is drained, pressed, salted and packaged and is then ready for use. Like cottage cheese, it is not subjected to a curing or ripening process.

Figure 115. Cheddar cheese manufacture. Mechanical mixers thoroughly combine the rennet and coloring matter with the milk. (Courtesy of The Borden Company.)

Most cheeses must undergo a ripening process. These cheeses may be divided into two main groups, hard and soft, according to the amount of water left in the curd. The curd is salted, wrapped in cheesecloth and pressed to remove the excess of whey. If the curd is to be made into a hard cheese, it is subjected to considerable pressure to remove as much whey as possible. The curd is then molded into various forms according to the type of cheese desired. In making the soft type of cheese less water is removed from the curd. Curd that is ready for the ripening process is referred to as "green cheese." Bacteria of the lactobacillus type as well as propionic acid-producing bacteria are usually active in the ripening process. In some cheeses proteolytic and lipolytic forms play an active role. The soft cheeses are ripened chiefly by microorganisms growing in a so-called smear on the outer surface. The enzymes produced diffuse into the cheese and aid in the ripening.

Cheddar cheese is the commonest type of hard cheese consumed in the United States. It originated in Cheddar, England. In the United States it is often called American cheese. Other hard cheeses are Swiss, Roquefort (semihard), Edam and Gorgonzola (semihard). Camembert, Limburger, Brie and Liederkranz are examples of soft cheeses.

Cheddar cheese is usually made from whole milk. A starter culture containing either *Str. lactis* or *Str. cremoris* and a species of *Leuconostoc* is added. After the milk has become slightly acid, rennet is added. A curd soon forms. The milk is then warmed slowly to about 86° F. (30° C.). The curd is drained, salted and pressed into the desired form. The next

Figure 116. The drained curds are cut into blocks. The half of each block toward the center is turned over on the outside half so that the last of the whey may drain off. This step is called "cheddaring the curd." (Courtesy of The Borden Company.)

step is the ripening process, which is carried out under definite conditions of temperature and moisture. Cheddar cheese is usually ripened at 10° C. (50° F.). The length of the ripening period depends upon the amount of ripeness desired. The changes that occur during ripening are brought about by the combined activities of various types of bacteria and the pepsin (proteinase) which were added with the rennet. The hydrolysis of casein, owing largely to the action of pepsin, gives rise to soluble nitrogen-containing substances, including proteoses, peptones and amino acids. Bacterial activities bring about the development of characteristic flavors and aromas. Defects in the ripening process may occur due to the presence of undesirable organisms. Figures 115 and 116 show some of the steps in the manufacture of cheddar cheese.

In the production of Swiss cheese fresh milk is inoculated with starter, and later rennet is added. The curd that forms is cut into small pieces and warmed to the temperature of 90° F. (32.2° C.). The starter usually contains *Streptococcus thermophilus* and various species of lactobacilli. Some cheese makers add *Propionibacterium freudenreichii* or *P. shermanii* to encourage the formation of holes or "eyes." The holes form because the bacteria produce carbon dioxide. These bacteria also form propionic acid, which contributes a desired flavor to the cheese.

In making Roquefort cheese the curd is inoculated with a pure culture of a blue-green mold, *Penicillium roqueforti*. This mold, as well as the bacteria present in the curd, carries on the ripening process. Roquefort cheese had its origin in France and was originally made from sheep's milk. The temperature and moisture conditions of the air in certain natural caves in France in the region of the village of Roquefort are especially favorable for the ripening of this type of cheese. Since molds require air for growth, the cheese is punctured in many places with needles to supply air to the interior. The molds utilize lactic acid as food and secrete proteolytic enzymes. Roquefort cheese is characterized by the mottled or marbled appearance of the interior, due to the presence of the mold. This type of cheese made in the United States is usually called blue cheese.

Blue-green molds are used also in the ripening of Gorgonzola, an Italian cheese, and Stilton, an English cheese. Camembert cheese is ripened chiefly by the growth of a special mold, *Penicillium camemberti* on the outer surface. In this case the ripening proceeds inward, gradually softening the cheese.

Limburger cheese is a soft cheese ripened chiefly by microorganisms growing on the surface in the surface "smear." In Limburger cheese the ripening process is carried further than in most of the other cheeses; a considerable amount of proteolytic decomposition is involved.

FERMENTED MILKS

Many kinds of fermented milks are consumed daily throughout the world. In the United States so-called buttermilk is the common fermented milk produced. Natural buttermilk is the liquid left over when soured cream is churned into butter. Most of the so-called buttermilk is not obtained in this way but is prepared by adding *Streptococcus lactis* or *Streptococcus cremoris* and aroma-producing bacteria to pasteurized skim or whole milk. It is sometimes referred to as "cultured buttermilk."

In Bulgaria and other Balkan countries a fermented milk known as yogurt is popular. The chief fermenting organisms are *Lactobacillus bulgaricus* and *Streptococcus thermophilus*. In Egypt a fermented milk known as leben is used. It is cow's or goat's milk fermented by both yeasts and bacteria. The yeasts produce small amounts of alcohol and considerable amounts of carbon dioxide, while the bacteria give rise to lactic acid. Other fermented milks made by a combined lactic acid and yeast fermentation are koumis and kefir. Koumis originated in southern Russia and is usually prepared from mare's milk. Kefir, originated by the natives of the Caucasus Mountains, is made from the milk of sheep, goats, mares or cows. The microorganisms in kefir exist in masses known as kefir grains, which vary in diameter from ¼ to ¾ inch. These grains form in the fermenting milk and may be removed and used for starting fresh batches of kefir.

Acidophilus milk is a fermented milk prepared by inoculating sterilized milk with a culture of *Lactobacillus acidophilus.* The inoculated milk is incubated at body temperature for twenty-four to forty-eight hours. This milk has therapeutic value in disorders of the gastrointestinal tract due to the activities of certain microorganisms, particularly putrefactive bacteria.

SAUERKRAUT

Sauerkraut is made industrially by finely shredding cabbage and placing it in layers in large wooden tanks, some of which have a capacity of 80 tons. Salt is sprinkled over each layer. The layers are packed closely together by placing a weighted cover over them. The salt extracts the juice from the cabbage by osmosis, resulting in the formation of a brine having a salt concentration of about 2.5 per cent. This brine contains sugar, since cabbage normally has from 3 to 5 per cent sugar by weight.

The bacteria normally present on cabbage leaves begin to multiply in the brine and act upon the sugar and other soluble substances that have been withdrawn from the cabbage. The oxygen present is soon exhausted, owing largely to the respiration carried on by the cabbage cells. Thus anaerobic conditions are quickly established. Owing to the presence of various species of acid-producing bacteria, acids (chiefly lactic, but some acetic) are formed from the sugar in the cabbage juice. In the early stages of sauerkraut fermentation, gas-forming cocci (usually *Leuconostoc mesenteroides*) predominate. These bacteria produce lactic and acetic acids, alcohol and carbon dioxide. Being relatively sensitive to acid, they are inhibited and destroyed as the acid content increases. Nongas-forming lactobacilli (*Lactobacillus plantarum*) then become the predominating organisms. Through their activity the lactic acid content of the kraut is greatly increased. When the acid content reaches about 2 per cent, the growth of these organisms is inhibited. The fermentation is completed by gas-forming lactobacilli (*Lactobacillus brevis*, or related forms) which can tolerate a higher acid content than the other organisms involved in sauerkraut production.

The salt added to the kraut inhibits the growth of bacteria other than acid producers. Aerobic microorganisms are unable to grow because of lack of oxygen. The acids act as a preservative for the finished kraut. Besides acids, other substances are produced during the fermentation which contribute to the flavor and aroma of sauerkraut. When fermentation is completed, the sauerkraut may be canned. The American public consumes about 150,000 tons of sauerkraut annually.

FERMENTED FODDER

Green fodder, such as corn stalks and leaves, leguminous plants, grasses, beet tops and other forage crops, may be preserved by fermentation. To accomplish this they are cut into short pieces and packed in tall cylindrical containers known as silos. In the silo the fodder undergoes a type of fermentation similar to that of cabbage in sauerkraut production. The fermented fodder, known as silage or ensilage, is an excellent food for cattle and other animals during the winter months. Legumes and grasses contain too little fermentable carbohydrate to allow for the production of enough acid to act as a preservative. When they are used in making ensilage, the addition of suitable carbohydrate material, such as molasses, will bring about a normal acid fermentation. Phosphoric acid may be used in place of molasses.

The plant cells continue to respire for some time after being placed in the silo. Because of this, the oxygen supply is soon depleted and anaerobic conditions then prevail. Enough juice oozes from the plant material to form a culture medium for bacteria. The sugars present are attacked by acid-producing bacteria, principally members of the lactobacillus group which are normally present on plant materials. Lactic acid is the principal acid produced, but other organic acids, chiefly acetic and propionic, are formed also, and a small amount of alcohol is produced. The fermentation gives rise to a characteristic flavor and aroma relished by cattle. The fermentation process continues for three to four weeks and then gradually comes to a halt. The acids formed serve as preservatives. Properly prepared ensilage will keep for many months and even years.

PICKLES

The preparation of cucumber pickles is essentially similar to the production of sauerkraut. The two principal types of pickles ordinarily prepared are dill pickles and brine pickles. In the preparation of dill pickles, cucumbers are placed in a 5 per cent salt solution. Dill is added to contribute flavor. Some sugar and other soluble constituents diffuse into the salt solution from the cucumbers. A temporary growth of aerobic bacteria sets in, but soon comes to a halt, owing to the development of anaerobic conditions. Anaerobic lactic acid-producing bacteria soon become the predominating organisms. The resulting lactic acid serves as a preservative.

In the production of brine pickles a stronger salt solution, 10 to 15 per cent, is used. Not many bacteria are capable of growing in a brine of this concentration. Some lactic acid-producing bacteria, however, are able to do so. After the fermentation has proceeded for six to eight weeks, enough lactic acid will be present to preserve the cucumbers. They will then keep as long as the acidity is maintained. After being placed in fresh water for several days to leach out the excess salt the cucumbers have absorbed, brine pickles may be converted into sweet pickles, sour pickles and relishes such as spread relish and piccalilli.

MICROBIOLOGICAL ASSAY OF VITAMINS

Microorganisms can be used as reagents in the qualitative or quantitative determination of certain chemical compounds. This branch of the science of microbiology is known as *microbiological assay* or *analytical microbiology*. Microbiological assay is frequently used for the quantitative determination of vitamins and other growth factors in foods used by man. Microorganisms can be used for this purpose because they themselves require vitamins, particularly those of the B group. Particular species or, in some instances, certain strains of microorganisms have been selected for use in these microbiological assays. Some microorganisms can synthesize some or all of the vitamins they require; others need an exogenous source of at least some of the vitamins. A relatively large number of bacteria that require the presence of certain vitamins in their food can be used as analytical agents to assess the vitamin content of foods and other natural materials. Bacteria belonging to the genera *Lactobacillus*, *Streptococcus* and *Leuconostoc* are frequently used in microbiological assays.

Animal assay procedures for vitamins were in use before the possibility of utilizing microorganisms for this purpose was discovered. Microbiological methods are relatively easy to carry out and much more rapid and less expensive than animal assays. They have the additional advantage of sensitivity to small quantities of vitamins and thus can be used to determine the vitamin content of minute samples. Physical and chemical methods are also available for the assay of some of the vitamins. Except for a few vitamins, these methods are unsatisfactory because of the difficulty of separating vitamins from the compounds with which they are naturally associated. Ascorbic acid (vitamin C) is an example of a vitamin that is assayed chemically. Riboflavin (vitamin B_2) is usually measured optically because it fluoresces, but it can be assayed also by microbiological methods.

In the use of a microorganism as an assay agent it is necessary to have available a culture medium that contains all the nutrients required for the growth of the test microorganisms with the exception of the vitamin to be assayed. This is usually achieved by making the medium from chemically defined ingredients.

Assay of Thiamine by Use of Lactobacilli

A basic medium devoid of thiamine is used in this assay. Since lactobacilli require the presence of thiamine as an accessory growth factor, they are unable to grow in this basic medium. A series of tubes of this medium is inoculated with the lactobacilli. Thiamine is then added in graded amounts to the tubes, each tube receiving a different amount. One tube receives 0.1, another 0.2 and a third 0.5 microgram (one microgram equals one millionth of a gram), or other suitable quantities may be used. In a test of this kind the first tube may show a small amount of growth; the second one, a sufficient amount to make the culture somewhat turbid;

and, in the third tube, the culture may be very turbid, indicating a heavy growth of the bacteria. The growth of the bacteria will be proportional to the amount of thiamine added. The turbidity is measured accurately by means of a photoelectric cell.

The next step involves the use of a parallel set of tubes of the thiamine-free medium. Instead of thiamine, measured amounts of the food being assayed are added, each tube receiving a different amount. The tubes are then inoculated with lactobacilli. The growth in these tubes will depend upon the amount of thiamine present in the food. If one tube in the series

Figure 117.   Fermentometer for use in thiamine assay by yeast. (Courtesy of The Fleischmann Laboratories of Standard Brands Incorporated.)

is as turbid as the second tube in the preceding series, the quantity of food in the tube contains 0.2 microgram of thiamine. By this method the thiamine content of the food can be determined with a high degree of accuracy and sensitivity. This procedure is known as a turbidimetric assay.

Assay of Thiamine by Yeast Fermentation

If the food (milk, for example) is such that it will cause turbidity when added to a medium, the turbidity test cannot be used. The yeast fermentation test may then be used. The quantity of carbon dioxide produced by yeast (*Saccharomyces cerevisiae*) growing in tubes of glucose medium containing different known amounts of thiamine can be determined by experiment. The rate of fermentation of glucose to carbon dioxide and alcohol by yeast depends chiefly upon the amount of thiamine available. If graded amounts of certain foods are added to a parallel set of tubes, the amounts of carbon dioxide produced will indicate the amount of thiamine the foods contain. This assay procedure may be performed with the aid of a fermentometer (Figure 117).

Assay of Other Vitamins

The microbiological assay for niacin, riboflavin, pantothenic acid and biotin is performed in a somewhat similar manner as that for thiamine but is based upon the amount of acid formed from glucose by lactobacilli. The amount of acid produced is dependent upon the concentration of the limiting vitamin.

A few examples of specific bacteria that have been used successfully in vitamin assay work are *Lactobacillus casei* for the estimation of riboflavin, pyridoxine and pantothenic acid, *Lactobacillus arabinosus* for niacin (nicotinic acid or its amide), and *Clostridium acetobutylicum* for the assay of *para*-aminobenzoic acid.

ASSAY OF AMINO ACIDS

The technique for the assay of amino acids is modeled after the vitamin assay. Some bacteria can make the amino acids they need from ammonium salts, nitrate, sugar, and so forth, and require none from the medium in which they are growing; whereas others need only a particular amino acid but can synthesize all others. Still other bacteria require many amino acids ready made. In the quantitative determination of amino acids in foods or in particular proteins, microorganisms that require the presence of certain amino acids in their food are used. If in a certain food material, for example, the amount of the amino acid known as lysine is to be determined, an organism which needs, but cannot synthesize, this amino acid is used in the test. By comparing the growth of the organism in tubes of basic medium containing measured amounts of lysine with the growth in tubes of basic medium devoid of lysine but to which measured graded amounts of the food under test have been added, the amount of lysine present in the food can be determined with a high degree of accuracy. Bacterial species used in amino acid assays include *Lactobacillus delbruekii, Lactobacillus casei, Lactobacillus arabinosus, Lactobacillus fermenti, Streptococcus faecalis* and *Leuconostoc mesenteroides*.

QUESTIONS

1. Explain the production of leavened bread through the agency of yeasts. Indicate some abnormal fermentations of bread.

2. How is butter produced? Which microorganisms are used in the process?

3. Explain the role played by microorganisms in the making of cheese.

4. What is (1) buttermilk, (2) yogurt, (3) koumis, (4) acidophilus milk?

5. How is sauerkraut made? What kind of bacteria take part in the process?

6. Explain the production of (1) ensilage, and (2) pickles. What prevents ensilage from decaying?

7. Discuss the microbiological assay of (1) thiamine by the use of lactobacilli, (2) thiamine by yeast fermentation, (3) amino acids.

REFERENCES

Association of Vitamin Chemists: Method of Vitamin Assay. 2nd ed. New York, Interscience Publishers, Inc., 1951.

Barnett, A. J. G.: Silage Fermentation. New York, Academic Press, Inc., 1954.

Barton-Wright, E. C.: The Microbiological Assay of the Vitamin B-complex and Amino Acids. New York, Pitman Publishing Corporation, 1952.

Elliker, P. R.: Practical Dairy Bacteriology. New York, McGraw-Hill Book Company, Inc., 1949.

Foster, E. M., et al.: Dairy Microbiology. Englewood Cliffs, N. J., Prentice-Hall, Inc., 1957.

Frazier, W. C.: Food Microbiology. New York, McGraw-Hill Book Company, Inc., 1958.

Hammer, B. W., and Babel, F. J.: Dairy Bacteriology. 4th ed. New York, John Wiley & Sons, Inc., 1957.

Prescott, S. C., and Dunn, C. C.: Industrial Microbiology. 3rd ed. New York, McGraw-Hill Book Company, Inc., 1959.

Rahn, O.: Microbes of Merit. New York, The Ronald Press, 1945.

U. S. Department of Agriculture: Cheese Varieties and Descriptions. Handbook No. 54. Washington, D. C., Superintendent of Documents, 1953.

VI · Microbiology of Sewage
and Water

21 • Sewage Treatment

The proper treatment and disposal of sewage are important factors in the maintenance of a sanitary environment. Since infectious agents may be present in sewage, it is potentially dangerous, especially if it is allowed to pollute water supplies. Man learned long ago that keeping his environment clean would help to preserve human life. Fear for his well-being has led him to develop sanitary procedures of various kinds. It has been definitely established that the maintenance of a sanitary environment is of paramount importance in holding communicable diseases in check. Diseases now controlled by sanitation took an enormous toll of human life in former years. The gradual perfection of sanitary techniques has made possible modern urban life and has enabled man to develop his present civilization and culture. Sanitation is a mark of modern civilization; it has become a way of life for modern man.

Among other measures, modern sanitation includes the maintenance of a safe food supply (discussed in Chapter 25), a water supply free from pollution and harmful microorganisms (considered in Chapter 22) and the treatment of sewage so that it will not become a health hazard. The proper disposal of sewage in modern life is transcended in importance by no other activity from the standpoint of health protection.

COMPONENTS OF SEWAGE

Sewage is the used water supply of a community and, as such, is a liquid containing human excreta and the water-borne wastes of the kitchen, laundry and bath. These may be supplemented in some instances by certain industrial wastes. Although sewage contains a variety of waste materials, it is chiefly water. Because of the large amount of water present, average sewage contains less than one-tenth of 1 per cent of total solid matter, and only a small fraction of this is in the form of visible suspended solids. Sewage solids are a mixture of urea, various proteins, carbohydrates (sugars, starches and cellulose) and fats, as well as soaps and other compounds. These are, for the most part, unstable organic substances which, when acted upon by microorganisms, readily undergo decomposition.

Sewage contains a wealth of microscopic life. A large variety of saprophytic microorganisms is represented, including forms capable of decomposing cellulose, starch, sugars, proteins and fats, as well as sulfur-oxidizing, sulfate-splitting, nitrate-reducing and many other forms. The total number may be as high as two million organisms per milliliter. *Escherichia coli,* one of the common intestinal bacteria, is always present in abundance. Inevitably, pathogens will be found, especially those that are discharged from the body with the feces. Examples of pathogens that may be constituents of sewage are *Salmonella typhosa, Salmonella paratyphi, Salmonella schottmuelleri, Shigella dysenteriae, Endamoeba histolytica, Giardia lamblia* and the virus of poliomyelitis. The pathogens present in sewage are of significance if the sewage gets into the water supply of a community, into swimming pools, or if food becomes contaminated with it. When improperly disposed of, sewage represents a danger to the health of the community.

GENERAL PRINCIPLES OF SEWAGE TREATMENT

The important problem in sewage treatment is to convert the solid matter into stabilized innocuous substances. This is brought about through the activities of various kinds of microorganisms naturally present and is controlled so that it is accomplished in the shortest possible time. Sewage undergoes the same processes of biochemical decomposition characteristic of other nonliving organic matter in nature. These processes are a part of the cycle of elements, such as nitrogen, carbon, sulfur and phosphorus. Proper treatment of sewage is simple in principle but represents a complex problem in practice.

Most of the early decomposition that occurs in sewage is hydrolytic. Both aerobic and anaerobic bacteria are engaged in this process. Anaerobic bacteria are particularly involved in the hydrolysis of urea, proteins, cellulose and fats. The breakdown of urea and proteins yields hydrogen sulfide, ammonia, mercaptans and other compounds, some of which have decidedly objectionable odors. Sewage contains paper, fragments of cotton and other cellulose-containing substances. These, together with starches and sugars, may yield carbon dioxide, methane and hydrogen when broken down anaerobically. Fats are decomposed slowly and tend to accumulate. They rise to the surface, where anaerobic bacteria do not readily act upon them. Those that are hydrolyzed yield fatty acids and glycerol. The fatty acids are hydrolyzed to methane, carbon dioxide and hydrogen. Fat is usually removed by skimming it from the surface to prevent it from accumulating around solid objects and forming "grease balls" which may clog pipes.

The products of hydrolytic cleavage are broken down to simpler compounds by oxidative action of microorganisms. This yields such compounds as acids, carbon dioxide, water, nitrites and nitrates. Since these are oxidative processes, oxygen is consumed. The amount of oxygen required by the indigenous flora of the sewage to oxidize the organic and reduced inorganic matter is known as the *biochemical oxygen demand* (B. O. D.). Domestic sewage demands approximately 215 parts of oxygen per million parts of sewage. Because of this oxygen demand, if large quantities of untreated sewage are emptied into a stream, the oxygen tension of the water may fall below the threshold of tolerance of fish and other aquatic animals, thus causing their suffocation.

SEWAGE DISPOSAL BY DILUTION

In the past most communities emptied their raw sewage into the rivers upon which they were dependent for their drinking water. Cities in the Great Lakes area emptied their untreated sewage into the lake which was also the source of their water. Epidemics of water-borne diseases were a natural consequence. Although we are now fully cognizant of the danger of polluting drinking water with sewage, adequate measures for its prevention are not always instituted.

Since sewage discharged into a river or lake becomes diluted with water, this method of sewage disposal is called the dilution method. The organic matter of the sewage undergoes the same kind of hydrolytic and oxidative changes that take place in a modern sewage treatment plant. Eventually, no trace of organic matter remains.

Emptying untreated sewage into natural bodies of water is still practiced in some places. This method was usually harmless in the early history of our country, since the amount of sewage was usually small in relation to the watercourse into which it was emptied; but, owing to the increase in the density of our population, it is no longer an adequate method of sewage disposal. A community which discharges raw sewage into a stream may endanger a neighboring community by contaminating its water supply.

SANITARY SEWAGE TREATMENT IN RURAL AREAS

For a single family or a small community the sewage may be run into a septic tank to undergo decomposition. A septic tank is a closed underground tank which may be of various designs. Sewage is allowed to flow into it slowly to permit the suspended matter to settle to the bottom, forming a sludge. The flow of sewage through the tank is baffled to keep the sludge from being disturbed and to prevent solids from leaving the tank. As the microorganisms in the sewage start decomposing it, they soon use up the small amount of oxygen present, and then anaerobic decom-

position sets in. A microbial flora develops, consisting of common facultative and strict anaerobes which are capable of attacking many of the
compounds ordinarily present in sewage. The sludge gradually decreases
in volume by being hydrolyzed by anaerobic microorganisms. This is
commonly spoken of as "sludge digestion."

Decomposition in a septic tank is chiefly anaerobic. A surface scum of
aerobic bacteria and fungi assists in maintaining anaerobic conditions in
the fluid beneath. The anaerobic activity gives rise to foul-smelling and
offensive compounds. Gases are liberated, causing a bubbling which stirs
up the solids. This is an undesirable feature of the septic tank, since some
of the solids flow out in the outflow or *effluent*. In a septic tank the effluent
is always equal to the influent. The run-off for the effluent is underground

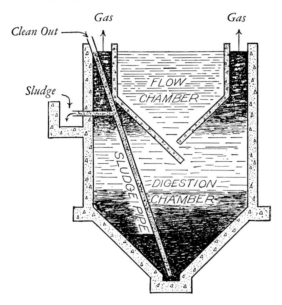

Figure 118. Section
through one type of Imhoff
tank. (From D. B. Swingle
and W. G. Walter: General
Bacteriology, second edition.
Copyright, 1947. D. Van
Nostrand Company, Inc.,
Princeton, New Jersey.)

through drainage tile. The final stages of sewage decomposition take
place in the soil.

An improvement over the septic tank is the Imhoff tank (Figure 118).
It has an upper and a lower chamber and is designed to hasten the decomposition of organic matter. The sewage passes through the upper
chamber (flow chamber), which is in the form of a V-shaped trough, at
such a low velocity that a large proportion of the settleable solids fall
through a slot into the lower chamber, called the digestion chamber. Here
anaerobic microbial activity takes place through the activity of obligate
and facultative anaerobes. A scum consisting of aerobic bacteria, molds
and yeasts forms at the surface. This shuts out the air and helps to produce anaerobic conditions. Various gases, chiefly methane, hydrogen and
carbon dioxide, are produced in this process. The Imhoff tank is so con-

structed that the gases are deflected through a vent into the atmosphere and thus do not disturb the scum. The gases produced may be collected and used for heating purposes and for operating the treatment plant. The material not readily digested forms the sludge, which requires separate treatment. The tank contains a draw-off pipe for the removal of accumulated sludge. The effluent needs to be further purified by filtration, as explained in a subsequent paragraph. For the treatment of the sewage of a community the Imhoff tank is preferable to the septic tank.

URBAN SEWAGE TREATMENT

The treatment of the sewage of a large city is a more difficult problem than that of the rural home or village. In a large sewage treatment plant the sewage is subjected to a number of treatments. The combination of treatments used varies with different communities. The procedure usually involves screening to remove the larger particles, sedimentation to remove the smaller suspended particles, aeration to bring about oxidation, and filtration through sand.

In the screening process the sewage is passed through screens of various sizes to remove the coarse material. After screening the sewage enters grit chambers which are designed to reduce the velocity of the flow sufficiently so that grit and heavier solids (sand, stones, etc.) will settle out. After passing through the grit chamber the sewage flows either to a sedimentation tank, such as an Imhoff tank, or to an activated sludge chamber, depending upon the particular method of treatment being used.

Trickling Filter

If the sedimentation tank method is used, the effluent is usually subjected to some form of filtration. Several kinds of filters are in use. A type of filter frequently used is the trickling filter, which is composed of crushed stone (or similar material). The porous filter bed has a depth of 5 to 10 feet and is provided with under drains. The sewage is sprayed over the bed from fixed or movable nozzles. Being sprayed through the air, it becomes saturated with oxygen. It then trickles slowly down over the surface of the stone, entering the under drains, from which it is discharged into an effluent pipe. Oxidation goes on continuously as the sewage trickles down through the crushed stone. The stones of the filter become covered with a slimy growth consisting of a rich flora of aerobic bacteria and an abundant protozoan fauna (*Vorticella, Opercularia* and other ciliates), as well as some molds. This biological film holds back suspended matter, which the microorganisms oxidize into stable end products. Thus ammonia, for example, is converted into nitrates. The filter beds require periodic cleaning. The effluent from the filter beds is usually sufficiently decomposed to permit its being discharged into a nearby river without dangerous pollution of its waters.

Although the process of sewage treatment is not directed toward the

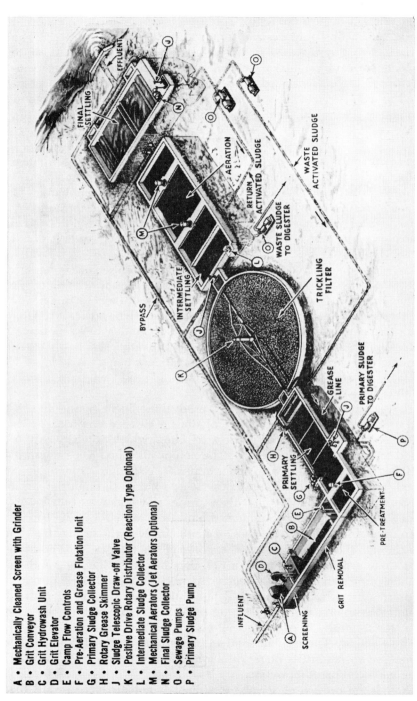

A • Mechanically Cleaned Screen with Grinder
B • Grit Conveyor
C • Grit Hydrowash Unit
D • Grit Elevator
E • Camp Flow Controls
F • Pre-Aeration and Grease Flotation Unit
G • Primary Sludge Collector
H • Rotary Grease Skimmer
J • Sludge Telescopic Draw-off Valve
K • Positive Drive Rotary Distributor (Reaction Type Optional)
L • Intermediate Sludge Collector
M • Mechanical Aerators (Jet Aerators Optional)
N • Final Sludge Collector
O • Sewage Pumps
P • Primary Sludge Pump

Figure 119. A typical sewage treatment plant illustrating all phases of sewage treatment, including both the biological trickling filter and the activated sludge process. The combination of the two is called bio-activation. (Courtesy of The American Well Works.)

destruction of pathogens that might be present, the final effluent is usually free from such organisms, since they do not survive the intense activity of the saprophytic organisms that thrive in sewage.

Activated Sludge Treatment

In many of the large cities the activated sludge process is now used. This relatively recent development is a strictly aerobic method of decomposition. No septic or Imhoff tanks are used in this method of sewage treatment. The process is started by forcing compressed air through a tank (aeration tank) containing sludge. After the sludge develops a heavy growth of microorganisms, i.e., becomes activated, sewage is run into the tank and the mixture is aerated. Finely divided solids which ordinarily would not settle out become adsorbed on the surface of the activated sludge particles. Each particle becomes enmeshed in a slimy matrix which is produced by slime-forming bacteria and contains many actively growing microorganisms. In consequence, a rapid attack upon the organic matter of the sewage is made by oxidizing bacteria. Large amounts of sewage are rapidly oxidized. Not all the organic matter, however, is decomposed. Figure 119 shows the layout of an urban sewage treatment plant, including both the trickling filter and the activated sludge process.

From the aeration tank the sewage is run into settling basins and the sludge is removed and dried. Part of the sludge, however, is returned to activate fresh sludge. A larger amount of sludge is obtained by the activated sludge method than when sewage decomposes in Imhoff tanks. Although the operating costs are high, sludge obtained by this method has a much higher fertilizer value than that obtained by other methods, and its sale may partly defray the cost of operating the sewage treatment plant. Sludge obtained by other methods has little value as fertilizer and is usually dried and burned. The effluent usually needs no further treatment and no trickling filters are required.

Sludge Digestion

When the sludge is not to be used as fertilizer, it must be disposed of in some other way. The volume of the sludge may be reduced by running it into special sludge-digestion tanks where it is acted upon by anaerobic bacteria. Much of the organic matter is digested in these tanks, some of it being converted into gas. To hasten decomposition, the sludge tanks are heated to a temperature of about 80° F. The gas (sewer gas) which forms in the early stage of the process is used to heat the sludge tanks and, if sufficient in amount, may be used to heat the buildings of the sewage treatment plant. The sludge that remains after the completion of the process is a dark brown, carbonaceous mass which has little value as a fertilizer. It is usually dried and burned.

QUESTIONS

1. What is sewage? How much total solid matter does sewage ordinarily contain? Which compounds are normal constituents of sewage?

2. What kinds of bacteria are normally present in sewage?

3. Under what conditions may sewage represent a danger to the health of a community? Which pathogens may be present in sewage?

4. The aim in the treatment of sewage is to convert the solid matter into what kind of substances?

5. Explain the main types of microbial decomposition that go on in sewage. Do these differ essentially from the decomposition of organic matter in the soil or in bodies of water?

6. Explain briefly the type of sanitary sewage treatment generally used in rural areas. In what ways is the Imhoff tank superior to the septic tank?

7. (a) Which types of treatment are included in a large urban sewage treatment plant?

(b) Give a brief explanation of (1) the trickling filter, (2) the activated sludge treatment, (3) sludge digestion.

REFERENCES

Babbitt, H. E.: Sewerage and Sewage Treatment. 8th ed. New York, John Wiley & Sons, Inc., 1958.

Ehlers, V. M., and Steel, E. W.: Municipal and Rural Sanitation. 5th ed. New York, McGraw-Hill Book Company, Inc., 1958.

Fair, G. M., and Geyer, J. C.: Water Supply and Waste-Water Disposal. New York, John Wiley & Sons, Inc., 1954.

Gainey, P. L., and Lord, T. H.: Microbiology of Water and Sewage. New York, Prentice-Hall, Inc., 1952.

Hardenbergh, W. A.: Sewerage and Sewage Treatment. 3rd ed. Scranton, Pa., International Textbook Co., 1950.

Hopkins, E. S., and Schulze, W. H.: The Practice of Sanitation. 3rd ed. Baltimore, The Williams & Wilkins Company, 1958.

Imhoff, K., and Fair, G. M.: Sewage Treatment. 2nd ed. New York, John Wiley & Sons, Inc., 1956.

Maxcy, K. F., ed.: Rosenau Preventive Medicine and Public Health. 8th ed. New York, Appleton-Century-Crofts, Inc., 1956.

Standard Methods for the Examination of Water, Sewage and Industrial Wastes. 10th ed. New York, American Public Health Association, 1955.

22 • The Microbiology and Purification of Water

Public water supplies are derived from two primary sources: (1) surface waters, such as lakes and streams; and (2) ground waters, normally found under the surface of the soil, which may reach the surface in the form of natural springs or through man-made wells. Because of the large volume required, surface waters constitute the only adequate sources for most cities. Rivers are often impounded to form artificial lakes or reservoirs to serve as the source of urban water supplies.

MICROSCOPIC LIFE OF WATERS

Ground waters and the waters of lakes and streams have their origin in atmospheric water which reaches the surface of the earth in the form of rain and snow. Some of this water runs off into brooks, streams and lakes; some of it seeps down into the soil to become a part of the reservoir of ground water. When water comes in contact with the soil, it becomes contaminated with the microorganisms normally present in the soil. However, ground waters at considerable depths are relatively free of microorganisms, which have been removed by filtration through the deeper layers of the soil. Water from a well of considerable depth is usually satisfactory for drinking purposes if the well is so constructed that surface water cannot flow into it. In certain kinds of soil, such as clay soils, pollution from a nearby latrine may find its way into a well through underground fissures. Intestinal pathogens may thus gain access to the water. Spring waters, although not necessarily free of microorganisms, are usually safe for drinking purposes, unless polluted with soil or sewage. It may be noted here that spring waters contain minerals such as sulfur and iron and may therefore contain so-called "sulfur bacteria," or "iron bacteria," which are autotrophic in their nutrition.

Lakes and rivers furnish an environment favorable for microscopic life and contain a mixed population of bacteria and other microorganisms. Microorganisms indigenous to water are adapted to live in a medium relatively low in nutrient matter. Like many of the microorganisms of the soil, they take part in the decomposition of organic residues and in the oxidation of ammonia to nitrates, sulfur to sulfates, as well as other similar processes. They thus play an indispensable role in keeping in motion the cycle of matter through its organic and inorganic stages. These transformations are as necessary in an aquatic habitat for the continued existence of plant and animal life as they are in the soil.

The nature and abundance of microorganisms in bodies of water depend chiefly upon the amount and availability of essential mineral and organic constituents, the supply of oxygen, the temperature and the reaction. Among the indigenous water microorganisms, some are floating forms and some live in the bottom deposits, whereas others live attached to submerged surfaces, being found on inanimate objects and aquatic vegetation. Included in these forms are numerous representatives of the orders Pseudomonadales, Eubacteriales, Chlamydobacteriales, Actinomycetales and Beggiatoales, as well as molds, yeasts, protozoa and algae.

Both autotrophic and heterotrophic bacteria are present. Among the autotrophic forms are nitrifying bacteria (*Nitrosomonas* and *Nitrobacter*) and those that oxidize iron, sulfur and hydrogen. The vast majority of the bacteria are heterotrophic; they decompose the organic residues in suspension and solution in the water, or present in the bottom sediment. The microbial population of the bottom deposits is extensive and consists largely of anaerobes. The activities of these organisms yield organic acids, hydrogen and methane, which are oxidized by other microorganisms in the overlying water. Many of the aquatic bacteria serve as food for protozoa, various species of which are usually present.

Filamentous forms, members of the order Chlamydobacteriales, including the so-called "sulfur" and "iron" bacteria, are frequently present. The most common of the sulfur bacteria is *Beggiatoa alba*. It is found in both fresh and marine waters containing sulfur. Other sulfur bacteria that may be present are members of the genus *Thiothrix*. Among the iron bacteria, *Leptothrix ochracea* is the best known species.

Certain molds, particularly members of the class Phycomycetes, are aquatic. The commonest of the water molds belong to the genus *Saprolegnia*. They live on dead organic matter of various kinds and may grow on living fish or other aquatic animals that have been bruised or otherwise injured.

Besides the indigenous forms, many kinds of microorganisms are washed into the water from the soil or poured in with sewage. These forms survive for longer or shorter periods of time, depending upon the amount of organic matter available, and other factors. Streams flowing through populated areas are almost certain to be polluted with intestinal microorganisms. These organisms, accustomed to living at body temperature and in a rich food supply, perish in a relatively short time since they are not adapted to an aquatic environment. However, many of the human pathogens which find their way into streams remain alive long enough to make the water dangerous to human health. The presence of certain protozoa and bacteriophages, which prey upon bacteria, also tends to reduce their numbers. In heavily polluted streams, such as the Ganges of India, the activity of bacteriophages may bring about a great reduction in the number of bacteria present.

WATER-BORNE DISEASES

Water may become contaminated with pathogenic microorganisms and thus become a public health hazard of great magnitude. The pathogenic organisms which most frequently find their way into water supplies are those which inhabit the intestinal tract of man. The most common waterborne diseases in the United States are typhoid fever, the etiologic agent of which is *Salmonella typhosa;* paratyphoid fever, caused by *Salmonella paratyphi, Salmonella schottmuelleri, Salmonella hirschfeldii* and other species of *Salmonella;* bacillary dysentery, caused by several species of bacteria of the genus *Shigella,* including *Shigella dysenteriae* (Shiga type), *Shigella sonnei* (Sonne type) and *Shigella paradysenteriae* (Flexner type); amebic dysentery, the causative agent of which is the protozoan, *Endamoeba histolytica;* and gastroenteritis, the etiologic agent of which has not been identified. In other parts of the world, especially India and China, Asiatic cholera, caused by *Vibrio comma,* is a common waterborne infection. In the past, extensive epidemics of diseases due to polluted water supplies were common.

Much progress has been made in eradicating typhoid and the paratyphoid fevers which, for many centuries, have played havoc with mankind. Dysentery and gastroenteritis are still common. Gastroenteritis is a nonspecific disorder which may be mild or severe and may last only a day or two, or several weeks. It may be fatal in infants or the infirm. Numerous and extensive outbreaks have occurred in recent years. The causative organism is not known, but in most outbreaks the disease was clearly attributable to the drinking of contaminated water. It is probable that some of the cases diagnosed as gastroenteritis were mild cases of bacillary dysentery.

MUNICIPAL WATER SUPPLIES

Practically all of the larger and many of the smaller municipalities depend on surface waters for their water supply. A near-by stream usually serves as the source. In some cases a natural or artificial lake may be used. Cities located near the Great Lakes use these bodies of water as the source of their water supply. In many areas streams and lakes are being polluted by sewage and industrial wastes. In recent years stream pollution has increased greatly. Increasing population and industrialization will accelerate the damage to the esthetic and health aspects of one of our most important resources, our streams and lakes, unless pollution abatement programs are put into effect.

A large number of water supplies fail to meet the standards for water used for drinking and culinary purposes laid down by the United States Public Health Service. These standards have been adopted, however, in many communities as official for waters offered to the general public. The official standards require safety in regard to source and protection of the water, bacteriological purity, and freedom from chemical substances that might do harm.

SANITARY SURVEY

To determine whether a water supply is satisfactory to use as a source of drinking water requires a carefully conducted sanitary field survey. This survey comprises a comprehensive investigation of all the factors that may affect a water system from the original source of the water until it reaches the consumer. The survey covers three different aspects: (1) the study of the source of the water supply, including the character and topography of the watershed (the land around the water source), chances of human pollution reaching the water source and the possibility of domestic animals or industrial wastes gaining access to the watershed; (2) the operation of the water-treatment plant to determine its adequacy and efficiency; and (3) the condition of the distributing system which carries the water to the consumer. The sanitary survey furnishes important information about the suitability of the water for human consumption and whether it may be safe to use after being subjected to purification procedures.

PURIFICATION OF WATER

A municipal water supply must usually pass through a purification process to make it safe for human consumption. In some instances the supply may be sufficiently good so that the only treatment necessary is the addition of a disinfectant to render it safe for use. Water obtained from rivers or lakes must usually pass through a three-stage purification process: (1) sedimentation, (2) filtration, and (3) disinfection. Figure 120 is a schematic flow diagram of a water purification system.

1. Sedimentation

In the first stage of the process the water is run into large tanks or basins where it is allowed to stand quietly to permit the settling out of suspended matter. Unaided sedimentation proceeds rather slowly, and large storage basins are necessary if a large amount of water is to be purified. The process may be hastened considerably by the addition of chemical coagulants which form a gelatinous precipitate by reacting with the alkaline salts naturally present in the water or added to it. The coagulant most commonly used is aluminum sulfate, usually called alum. It forms a flocculent precipitate of aluminum hydroxide which adsorbs microorganisms and other particulate matter. The precipitate settles rapidly, carrying with it most of the microorganisms and other suspended particles in the water.

2. Filtration

After sedimentation the water is filtered through sand. Sand filters are of two types, the slow and the rapid sand filters. When the slow filter is

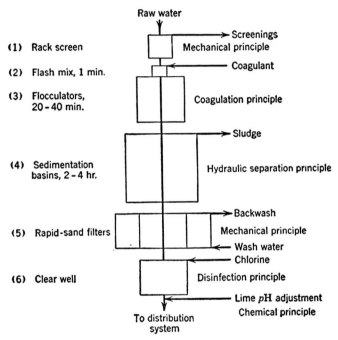

Figure 120. Water purification system flow diagram. (Reproduced by permission from E. B. Phelps: Public Health Engineering, Vol. I, 1948, published by John Wiley & Sons, Inc.)

used, chemical coagulants are usually not added to the water in the sedimentation process. In this filter a slimy or gelatinous film containing many protozoa develops in the upper layers of the sand. As the water slowly passes through the filter, this gelatinous material enmeshes the microorganisms and much of the suspended material. The protozoa present assist in removing bacteria by ingesting them. The slow filter has the disadvantage of requiring a large filtering surface and a high installation cost. Also, it will not effectively purify muddy water. The surface of the filter must be cleaned at intervals.

The rapid sand filter (Figure 121) is used extensively in modern filtration plants. In this filter the precipitate forms a mat of floc on the surface of the sand as the water filters through it. The floc adsorbs the particles that are smaller than the spaces between the sand grains and entangles all suspended matter, preventing it from passing through the filter bed. The surface layer of the filter is retentive and will remove microorganisms and particles of small size. This type of filter can handle much more water per surface area than the slow type. It can be quickly washed by reversing the direction of the flow of water through the sand.

3. Disinfection

Although filtration removes most of the microorganisms from water, a few may pass through. These can be destroyed by minute amounts of

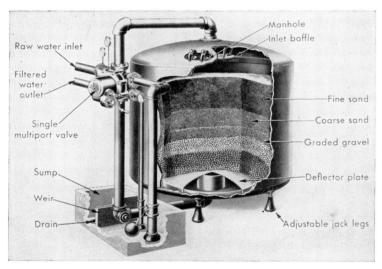

Figure 121. Pressure type rapid sand filter. (Courtesy of the Permutit Company.)

suitable disinfectants. Because of its effectiveness in small quantities, chlorine has become the principal agent for the disinfection of water. Automatic chlorinating machines are available which feed chlorine directly into the water from steel cylinders of liquid chlorine. The liquid vaporizes and the chlorine enters the water as gas. The amount of chlorine required is related directly to the amount of organic matter in the water. Usually the amount added is sufficient to provide a residual of available chlorine equal to one part per million parts of water. Chlorination has the disadvantage of imparting a chlorine taste and odor to the water. If ammonium gas is added with the chlorine, chloramines are formed which are more acceptable from the standpoint of taste and odor.

When the water source is heavily polluted, chlorine may be added at the beginning of the purification (prechlorination) and again at the end of the process (postchlorination).

SANITARY ANALYSIS OF WATER

Bacteriological and chemical tests have been devised to determine the suitability of water for human consumption. Most of the municipal water purification plants have well equipped laboratories to make frequent tests of the water as it undergoes the process of purification. Such tests provide a continuing check on the quality of the water and permit the immediate application of corrective measures when the tests indicate that the water is not meeting the accepted standards. In order that the analyses performed by different workers be more or less comparable, standard procedures have been prescribed by the American Public Health Association in "Standard Methods for the Analysis of Water and Sewage." The United States Health Service has laid down standards (Treasury Department Standards) for the control of water served by common carriers in interstate commerce. Many municipalities, even though their water is not used by common carriers, have adopted these standards for their water supplies.

STANDARD BACTERIOLOGICAL ANALYSIS

The bacteriological analysis of water is designed to disclose evidence of sewage pollution and also to determine the number of bacteria per unit volume of water as indicated by growth on standard culture media. The test for the determination of sewage pollution is a search for the presence of a group of intestinal organisms known as *coliform bacteria.* These organisms are normally present in the large intestine (colon) of warm-blooded animals, including man. The coliform bacteria are aerobic, nonspore-forming, Gram-negative rods which ferment lactose with the formation of both acid and gas. Two genera are represented: *Escherichia* and *Aerobacter.* The coliform group contains some organisms which are not primarily inhabitants of the intestinal tract. The best known of these is *Aerobacter aerogenes,* which, although found in varying degree in the human intestinal tract, is most frequently found on grains and grasses and in the soil. The best known species of the strictly intestinal members of the coliform group is *Escherichia coli.* It is a constant inhabitant of the intestinal tract of man and animals and is ordinarily harmless but may cause infection when some damage to the intestinal wall allows it to pass through it and invade other parts of the body.

Streams and lakes receiving water which has run over top soil are likely to contain some coliform organisms, usually less than 500 per 100 milliliters. Water contaminated with sewage usually contains more than 1000 coliform bacteria per 100 milliliters.

If pathogenic organisms have been introduced into a water supply by sewage contamination, then so have the organisms of the coliform group.

As the latter live longer in water than intestinal pathogens, their absence usually precludes the presence of pathogens, whereas their presence in relatively large numbers indicates possible presence of intestinal pathogens. Intestinal pathogens, even when sufficiently numerous to make water exceedingly dangerous for human consumption, are nevertheless usually present in insufficient numbers to isolate them readily or to detect their presence with certainty. The presence of the coliform group, however, is easily detected by tests which are not prohibitively long or complicated for routine procedures. The search for coliform bacteria has been chosen

Figure 122. Bacteriologist making bacteriological tests in purification plant laboratory. (Courtesy of Virginia State Dept. of Health.)

as the basis for the sanitary bacteriological examination of water because it is the most nearly specific test for the presence of fecal contamination.

The standard tests for the determination of the presence of coliform bacilli, as an index of pollution, are usually classed as presumptive, confirmed and completed tests. Figure 122 shows some of the equipment used in water analysis.

1. The Presumptive Test

To meet the requirements of the United States Public Health Service standards, the test for the presence of the coliform group requires the separate testing of five equal portions of water of either 10 or 100 milliliters each at frequent intervals, the number of samples tested per month depending upon the population served, which varies from one sample per

Table 8.   Most Probable Number of Coliform Bacteria per 100 ml.
of Water

Number of Portions		Most Probable Number of Coliform Bacteria per 100 ml.	
Negative	Positive	When 5–10 ml. Portions Are Examined	When 5–100 ml. Portions Are Examined
5....	0	Less than 2.2	Less than 0.22
4....	1	2.2	0.22
3....	2	5.1	0.51
2....	3	9.2	0.92
1....	4	16.0	1.60
0....	5	More than 16.0	More than 1.60

month for a population of 2500, to 500 samples per month for a population of 500,000. Five 10 milliliter portions or five 100 milliliter portions constitute the "standard sample" for the presumptive test. These portions of the water sample are placed in fermentation tubes containing lactose broth. The tubes are incubated at 37° C. If coliform bacteria are present, gas will be present at the end of twenty-four hours or, at the most, forty-eight hours. To meet safe bacteriological quality standards, the allowable number of tubes showing gas must not exceed 10 per cent of all the 10 milliliter portions, or 60 per cent of all 100 milliliter portions examined per month.

The concentration of coliform bacteria which will most often give a certain number of positive tests out of a total number of tests run has been calculated and tabulated in the form of most probable numbers. The calculations are based on the theory of probability. Table 8 based on a large number of tests, gives an approximation of the most probable number of coliform bacteria per 100 milliliters of water.

The maximum allowable number when a large number of 10 milliliter portions have been examined is one coliform organism per 100 milliliters. This is commonly termed the "coliform index." When a large number of 100 milliliter portions have been examined, the maximum allowable number per 100 milliliters drops to 0.6. A larger number than this is presumptive evidence that the water was contaminated with sewage. The absence of gas formation in all tubes after forty-eight hours constitutes a negative test. No further steps are then necessary.

A few other organisms, besides members of the coliform group, which ferment lactose with gas production are present in water at times. Also, in some cases two different organisms, a Gram-positive and a Gram-negative species, may, through their combined action, produce acid and gas from lactose, although neither one acting alone is capable of doing so. In this synergistic action one species produces acid from lactose and the other utilizes the acid with the formation of gas. Misleading presumptive tests are, therefore, sometimes encountered, and for this reason a confirmatory test is conducted.

2. The Confirmed Test

The confirmation test is carried out by using a solid medium, either Endo's medium or eosin-methylene-blue medium, or the liquid medium, brilliant green bile broth. These media contain inhibiting dyes which discourage the growth of lactose fermenters other than the coliform group. If a solid medium is used, it is streaked with a needle dipped into a tube used in the presumptive test showing gas formation. The liquid medium is inoculated with a loop. After incubation for twenty-four hours the appearance of typical colonies on the solid medium constitutes a positive confirmed test. The colonies are usually recognizable as either *Escherichia coli* or *Aerobacter aerogenes*. If brilliant green bile broth is used, the presence of gas constitutes a positive confirmed test.

3. The Completed Test

To complete the test, transfers are made from typical coliform colonies, on the plates used in the confirmed test, to a lactose broth fermentation tube and to a nutrient agar slant. If typical colonies are absent, the transplants are made from colonies which most closely resemble those of coliform bacteria. If a liquid medium was used in the confirmation test, transplants from those showing gas are made to a lactose broth fermentation tube and an agar slant. The lactose broth tube in either case is incubated at 37° C. for forty-eight hours unless gas appears earlier, and the agar slant is incubated for twenty-four hours at 37° C. Gas formation in the lactose broth and the demonstration of the presence of Gram-negative, nonspore-forming bacilli on the agar slant constitute a positive completed test. In routine laboratory analyses the completed test is often omitted. It is most valuable in the event of doubtful colonies on the selective agar media of the confirmed test.

Total Bacterial Count

Although of little value by itself, the enumeration of the number of bacteria per milliliter of water is a useful supplementary test. Accurately measured amounts of the water sample are added to, and thoroughly mixed with, liquefied nutrient agar in Petri plates. The bacteria thus become separated from one another and become fixed in place when the medium solidifies. Some of the plates are incubated at 20° C. for forty-eight hours and the rest at 37° C. for twenty-four hours. Organisms accustomed to body temperature grow poorly at 20° C., whereas the saprophytes grow poorly at 37° C. The bacteria develop into colonies, and a count of the colonies present gives some indication of the number of bacteria present in the quantity of water added to the medium. By means of a colony counter (Figure 123), an accurate count of the colonies can be made. The count is expressed as the number of bacteria per milliliter.

In this type of test there is always the possibility that some of the bacteria were clumped together into groups, each group giving rise to only one colony. Furthermore, since no one medium is satisfactory for the growth of all kinds of bacteria, the count obtained in this manner gives only a rough estimate of the number of bacteria capable of developing on standard nutrient agar at the temperatures used. This medium, however, is satisfactory for the growth of coliform bacteria. If the ratio of the colony count on the 37° C. plate to that of the 20° C. plate is high, the water may have been contaminated with sewage.

Isolation of Specific Microorganisms

Although the demonstration of the presence of specific pathogens such as *Salmonella typhosa* would constitute direct proof that the water is unfit

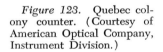
Figure 123. Quebec colony counter. (Courtesy of American Optical Company, Instrument Division.)

for human consumption, it is not used routinely in water analysis because of the technical difficulties of their isolation. To perform the test large amounts of the water are centrifuged at high speed and the sediment is added to certain selective and inhibitory media. *Salmonella typhosa*, for example, can be isolated from water by using a peptone medium to which a small amount of sodium selenite has been added. The selective action of the selenite favors the growth of the typhoid bacillus by inhibiting the growth of the other forms.

MEMBRANE FILTER FOR COLIFORM DETERMINATION

The membrane filter is a recently developed device which can be used to remove microorganisms from large volumes of fluids such as water, milk or urine. The filtering apparatus consists of a glass funnel, filter holder, filter membrane and filter flask (Figure 124). The flask has a side arm for connection to an exhaust pump for the creation of a partial vacuum. The filter membrane is a circular disk approximately 50 mm. in diameter and 0.15 mm. thick and is composed of a cellulose derivative.

It contains millions of regularly spaced pores too small in diameter to permit bacteria to pass through. The size of the pores may be varied in manufacture.

In using this filtering apparatus, all of the equipment must be sterile. By means of sterile forceps the sterile membrane is placed in the filter holder and clamped into position below the funnel. When it is used in the bacteriological analysis of water, a water sample (preferably 100 milliliters) is poured into the funnel and passed through the filter into the filter flask. By reducing the pressure in the flask, the rate of filtration is accelerated. The bacteria in the water sample become trapped on the surface of the filter membrane.

Figure 124. Filtering device for mounting membrane filter. (Courtesy of the Millipore Filter Corporation, Watertown, Mass.)

The next step is to provide the entrapped organisms with a suitable nutrient material so that they will grow and form colonies on the surface of the membrane. To accomplish this, the membrane is removed and placed on an absorbent paper disk previously impregnated with a suitable liquid culture medium and placed in a Petri dish. In water analysis a differential medium (modified Endo medium) that favors the growth of coliform bacteria is generally employed. The Petri dish is then incubated for 15 to 20 hours at body temperature.

During the period of incubation each microbial cell capable of growing on the medium used develops into a visible colony. Colonies of coliform bacteria formed on the Endo-type medium may be recognized by their metallic sheen. Colonies of noncoliform bacteria do not produce a sheen. Each coliform colony is assumed to have developed from a single coliform bacterium. The results of the test are recorded as the number of coliform bacteria per 100 milliliters of water sample.

By means of the membrane filter, relatively large samples of water can be tested at one time for coliform or other kinds of bacteria. The time required is less than that needed for other methods. Compact membrane filter field kits which may be used in making tests at the source of the water supply are available.

With the membrane filter technique it is possible also to determine the presence in water of *Salmonella typhosa,* the typhoid bacillus. For this determination a larger sample (500 milliliters or more) of water is generally used. A suitable medium such as bismuth sulfite broth is employed. On this medium *S. typhosa* forms shiny black colonies with narrow white borders. For other members of the genus *Salmonella,* brilliant green broth may be used as the culture medium.

CHEMICAL ANALYSIS

Chemical tests are of value in determining whether water has been polluted with organic matter. These tests, however, do not distinguish between organic matter of fecal origin and that from other sources. In the chemical analysis it is customary to test the water for the presence of ammonia, nitrites, nitrates and chlorides. The presence of one or more of these compounds indicates pollution with decaying organic matter. The relative proportion of these compounds is also a measure of the time that has elapsed since the organic matter entered the water. If raw sewage is finding its way into the water supply, the nitrogen, at the time of pollution, is largely held in combination by organic molecules. Bacteria immediately begin to attack this organic material and secrete ammonia as waste. The ammonia thus produced is then oxidized to nitrites by other organisms. The nitrites are quickly oxidized to stable nitrates by nitrifying bacteria. The analyst determines the amount of nitrogen in each of these states. If most of it is in organic combination or in the form of free ammonia, fairly recent pollution is indicated. If, on the other hand, most of the nitrogen has reached the nitrate state, the pollution is less recent and potentially less dangerous. In water contaminated with sewage, urea is present in considerable amount and accounts for most of the ammonia, nitrites and nitrates.

As sewage is rich in chlorides, an increase in chloride content of the water may be a danger sign. In order for these tests to have significance it is necessary to know that the water is not receiving chlorides or nitrogen compounds from some mineral source.

INTERPRETATION OF RESULTS

The laboratory procedures, outlined in the previous paragraphs, and the field survey constitute what is generally known as the sanitary examination of water. The data gathered from a complete sanitary examination must be interpreted jointly to arrive at a correct evaluation of the water supply. A single examination should not be depended upon as a criterion of the purity of the water. Data gathered over a prolonged period of time are of most value.

QUESTIONS

1. What are the usual sources of public water supplies?
2. What kinds of microorganisms are indigenous to lakes and streams? Besides these forms, which other kinds may find their way into bodies of water? What are the sources of these organisms?
3. Name the most common water-borne diseases.
4. What is meant by a "sanitary field survey"?
5. Explain the three-stage purification process usually used in a municipal water purification plant.
6. Which bacteria are included in the coliform group?
7. (*a*) In the sanitary bacteriological examination of water, why is the search for coliform bacteria preferable to a search for specific pathogens?

   (*b*) Explain briefly: (1) the presumptive test, (2) the confirmed test, and (3) the completed test for coliform bacteria.

   (*c*) How may the number of bacteria per milliliter be determined? Does the colony count indicate the actual number of bacteria present? Of what value, if any, is the colony count?
8. Explain the membrane filter test as used in the detection and enumeration of coliform bacteria.
9. In what way does a chemical analysis of water aid in indicating pollution with sewage?

REFERENCES

Gainey, P. L., and Lord, T. H.: Microbiology of Water and Sewage. New York, Prentice-Hall, Inc., 1952.

Hopkins, E. S., and Schulze, W. H.: The Practice of Sanitation. 3rd ed. Baltimore, The Williams & Wilkins Company, 1958.

Maxcy, K. F., ed.: Rosenau Preventive Medicine and Public Health. 8th ed. New York, Appleton-Century-Crofts, Inc., 1956.

Prescott, S. C., Winslow, C. E. A., and McCrady, M. H.: Water Bacteriology. 6th ed. New York, John Wiley & Sons, Inc., 1946.

Standard Methods for the Examination of Water, Sewage and Industrial Wastes. 10th ed. New York, American Public Health Association, 1955.

Taylor, E. W.: The Examination of Waters and Water Supplies. 7th ed. Boston, Little Brown and Company, 1958.

ZoBell, C. E.: Marine Microbiology. Waltham, Mass., Chronica Botanica, 1946.

VII · Microbiology of Foods

23 • The Preservation and Spoilage of Food

FOOD PRESERVATION

Methods for the preservation of food came into use long before the cause of decay was understood. As human life increased in complexity it became necessary to preserve certain foods so that an adequate food supply would be available throughout the year. Modern man has added to the methods developed earlier and has introduced many improvements so that at the present time it is possible to preserve and keep, for a relatively long time, almost any kind of food ordinarily used in the human dietary. Knowledge of the role microorganisms play in the spoiling of food has been of great value to man in the development of techniques for food preservation.

The methods used in the preservation of food include drying, cold storage, freezing storage, canning, pickling, smoking and treatment with specific chemicals. In the past, food preservation was carried on chiefly in the home. To meet the needs of modern life, the preservation of food has become a huge industry.

Drying

Some foods obtained from the plant kingdom do not spoil because, in the natural process of ripening, much of the moisture which was present in the green stage is gradually lost. This is true of the various grains (wheat, oats, barley, corn, and the like) and of nuts. Man learned long ago that certain foods could be readily preserved by drying them in the sun. Since microorganisms need moisture to grow, drying is an excellent means of inhibiting their activities. Sun-drying now has been to a large extent replaced by other methods to which the term "dehydration" is usually applied. Dehydration may be accomplished by placing the food in a chamber through which hot air is conducted. For some foods a vacuum drier is used. This operates by the alternate exhaustion and renewal of warm air, thus rapidly removing the moisture from the food.

Many fruits, particularly apricots, peaches, apples, currants, prunes and certain grapes (raisins), are especially suitable for preservation by drying. Meats, fish, milk and eggs are frequently subjected to dehydration. Milk and eggs are converted into a powdered form in this process. One method of preparing powdered milk is to force milk in the form of a fine spray into a large heated chamber. To hasten the evaporation of water from the milk the air in the chamber is partially exhausted. The milk dries into a fine powder which drops to the bottom of the chamber.

Though dehydration reduces the water content of fruits, it at the same time increases the concentration of sugar, acids and salts. The reduction in the water content and the increased concentration of sugar, acids and salts result in a sufficiently high osmotic pressure and acidity to be inimical to the growth of microorganisms. The amount of water permitted to remain depends largely upon the nature of the food. Fruits, which contain considerable quantities of sugar and acid, may be permitted to retain 25 to 30 per cent of their moisture. When milk, meat and eggs are subjected to dehydration, they are allowed to retain only about 2 per cent of their moisture.

Refrigeration

Low temperatures exert a bacteriostatic action, inhibiting the growth of microorganisms without necessarily killing them. They also slow down the action of enzymes normally present in certain foods and thus delay autolysis. Mechanical household refrigerators are usually adjusted to maintain a temperature of about 50° F. (10° C.), but they can be set at lower temperatures. In a household ice refrigerator the temperature is usually somewhat higher. At 50° F. most microorganisms grow slowly. This temperature is effective in preserving foods for a short time. Because microbial activity is not completely halted, the food undergoes slow decomposition that will eventually cause it to become sour or to develop offensive tastes and odors.

At temperatures near the freezing point foods can be kept for a longer period. Certain foods such as fruits, vegetables and eggs are frequently placed in cold storage slightly above their freezing points. Owing to the autolytic enzymes they contain and the presence of microorganisms, eggs gradually deteriorate in cold storage. Eggs that are to be kept for a protracted period of time are removed from the shell and frozen in bulk by subjecting them to temperatures considerably below the freezing point. Meats, when held temporarily at near-freezing temperatures, usually improve in tenderness and flavor, owing to autolytic enzymes which continue to act slowly. If meats are to be kept for a long time, they must be stored at subfreezing temperatures.

The storage of meats, fish and poultry at subfreezing temperatures is a practice of long standing. Meats and poultry are usually held at 10° and fish at 5° F. Stored at such low temperatures, these foods can be kept unchanged for many months.

A comparatively recent development has been the quick-freezing process, which involves the exposure of the food to temperatures considerably below freezing (0° to −25° F.). After the food is thoroughly frozen, it is stored at a temperature well below the freezing point (0° to 30° F.). In this process the food is not materially altered in texture, appearance, flavor or color. Quick freezing, in contrast to slow freezing, gives rise to small ice crystals which do not disrupt the food tissues as do the larger crystals formed in the slow-freezing process. This method is used principally in freezing fruits, vegetables, fish and poultry.

When frozen foods are thawed, they should be used immediately because the microorganisms that have survived the freezing process will cause a rapid decomposition of such foods. In marked contrast to foods preserved by heat, frozen foods are highly perishable when removed from refrigeration. If the food is to be cooked before being eaten, it is advisable that the cooking be begun before the food is completely thawed.

Canning

The process of food preservation by canning originated in France during the first decade of the nineteenth century as the result of a prize of 12,000 francs offered by the French government for an improved method of preserving food without drying, salting or smoking. This offer was made principally to insure an adequate food supply for the military forces. In the year 1810 Nicholas Appert, after many years of persistant trial, succeeded in preserving foods by heating them in tightly corked glass containers. The prize was awarded personally to Appert by Emperor Napoleon Bonaparte. Since Appert's day the canning of foods has become a major industry.

Appert did not understand why foods kept when subjected to his method of heat treatment but was of the opinion that the reason was the exclusion of outside air. He believed that the air remaining in the container was rendered inert by heat and, therefore, could not cause spoilage. Guy Lussac, the foremost chemist of the time, agreed with Appert that air was necessary to initiate the process of spoilage and that the exclusion of outside air kept foods that had been heated in sealed containers from spoiling. It was not until 1860, after Pasteur had demonstrated that microorganisms cause food spoilage and could be killed by heat, that the underlying principles of canning were understood.

Appert's method of processing foods was soon put to work in England and America. After tin cans had come into use in place of glass containers, the canning industry developed rapidly. The industry has been greatly assisted by scientific research. At the present time the National Canners' Association and the larger can manufacturers maintain laboratories where research is constantly in progress. Canned foods are now usually sealed in a vacuum chamber so that most of the air is removed before the cans are heated.

In commercial canning, foods low in acid content, such as meats, poultry, fish and most vegetables, are processed at temperatures above the boiling point. This is accomplished by means of steam pressure cookers (autoclaves) or retorts (Figure 125). Temperatures sufficiently high to sterilize foods can be attained in these cookers. Canned foods, however, are not necessarily sterile. Most of the foods ordinarily canned

Figure 125. A battery of horizontal retorts used in commercial canning. Note the time and temperature controls. (Courtesy of The National Canners' Association.)

deteriorate in texture, palatability and aroma if the processing temperature is high enough to insure sterility. In order to retain as much of the natural flavor and texture as possible, each kind of food is processed at what is considered a safe minimum temperature. The conditions in the finished product are usually such that any bacterial spores that may have survived will be unable to germinate into vegetative cells under ordinary conditions of storage. The major problem in canning is the control of anaerobic spore-forming thermophiles and certain other spore-forming bacteria. The basic operations in commercial canning are illustrated in Figure 126.

The temperature required and the length of time it is to be maintained vary with the nature, consistency and acidity of the food as well as the size of the container in which it is heated. The amount of acid present in foods is an important factor in the processing temperature required. On the basis of their acid content, foods may be classified into two groups:

Figure 126. Basic operations in commercial canning. (Courtesy of American Can Company, Research and Technical Service Laboratories.)

(1) those that have a relatively high acidity (below pH 4.5), and (2) those of medium or low acid content (pH 4.5 to 7.0). Examples of foods high in acid content are tomatoes and most of the common fruits and berries. The low-acid foods include most vegetables, milk, fish, poultry

and meats. Acidity increases the effectiveness of the heat treatment in destroying microorganisms. Furthermore, the acid in the finished product is unfavorable to the germination of bacterial spores which may have survived the processing. Few heat-resistant organisms can grow in an acid medium in the absence of oxygen. For these reasons a processing temperature of 212° F. is usually sufficient to prevent the spoilage of fruits.

The processing of low-acid or neutral foods is a more difficult problem. Higher processing temperatures are required to prevent the spoilage of these foods. As soon as the processing is complete the cans are rapidly cooled by placing them in cold water. This quickly lowers the temperature below that at which the spores of thermophiles will germinate. If, however, cans containing viable spores of thermophiles are allowed to cool slowly, the spores will germinate into vegetative forms which will spoil the food. Spores of certain species of aerobic bacteria are frequently present in canned foods but are unable to germinate, owing to the low oxygen tension.

Canned foods vary in keeping qualities. Some may be kept two or more years without appreciable change. They all keep better when stored in a cool or cold place. The types of spoilage that may occur in commercially canned foods will be discussed in a subsequent section of this chapter.

Home Canning

Proper care should be exercised in canning foods in the home. To secure a high quality product the food selected should be of good grade and in the proper stage of development. If it is fresh and clean, fewer microorganisms will be present, and the processing will be more efficient.

Several methods are in use in canning foods in the home. In the open kettle method food is cooked in an open vessel, and then packed into clean jars and sealed immediately. This procedure is satisfactory for jams and jellies and is frequently used in the canning of tomatoes and fruits. It is disapproved for low-acid vegetables or for such products as meats, poultry and fish chiefly because the heat is insufficient to guard against spoilage. The temperature does not exceed 212° F., which is not high enough, in low-acid foods, to kill the spores of some of the spoilage organisms, including *Clostridium botulinum.*

In the boiling-water-bath method the jars are packed with food, preferably food that has been previously boiled for a short time (hot pack), sealed, and then kept completely covered with boiling water throughout the processing time. This method is satisfactory for the home canning of tomatoes, tomato juice, rhubarb, berries, fruits and fruit juices. It should not be used for canning vegetables other than tomatoes and rhubarb, or for meats, fish and poultry products. It may be noted here that pears occasionally may be too low in acid to be successfully canned by this method.

In the oven method of canning there is danger of underprocessing due to the slow rate of heat transfer through the air to the jars of food and the uneven heat distribution in the oven. The temperature attained by the food is usually not above that of boiling water. There is also danger of the jars exploding. This method, if carefully controlled, is reasonably safe for high-acid foods, but not safe for those of low acid content.

The safest method of home canning is by means of the steam pressure cooker in which temperatures above 212° F. can be attained. If correctly used, it is satisfactory for all low-acid foods and may be used also for foods high in acid content. Pressure cookers are similar in principle to the large processing retorts used in commercial canneries. Authorities agree that all low-acid vegetables and all meats, fish and poultry when canned should be processed in the pressure cooker.

Smoking

Smoking is a process of curing fish and meats, such as pork, beef and sausages, by exposure to smoke. The process has a drying effect plus the germicidal action of certain constituents of smoke, chiefly creosote, acetic acid and formaldehyde. Since these compounds penetrate only partially, uncooked smoked products may be dangerous for consumption, not only because of the presence of harmful microorganisms, but also parasitic macroorganisms such as tapeworms (beef and fish) and trichina worms (pork).

Chemical Preservatives

Certain chemicals, when added to foods in small amounts, have a restraining influence on microorganisms. In the past, various chemicals were widely used as food preservatives. The use of most of these has now been completely abandoned. At the present time sodium benzoate and sulfur dioxide are the only so-called chemical preservatives permitted to be added to foods in the United States. Laws in some states, however, prohibit their use. When these chemicals are used, the container must bear a label stating the amount present. Sodium benzoate is sometimes added to ketchup, chili sauce, apple butter and oleomargarine. One-tenth of 1 per cent is the amount usually used. Sulfur dioxide is at times added to fruit juices. Chemicals formerly used, but no longer permitted in the United States as food preservatives, are boric acid and borates, salicylic acid, salicylates and formaldehyde.

FOOD SPOILAGE

Since organic matter in general constitutes food for microorganisms, organic matter used as human food is subject to spoilage due to its suitability as food for microorganisms. Huge quantities of human food are spoiled annually by bacteria, yeasts and molds. The kinds of microorganisms involved and the changes brought about depend upon the composition of the food and such environmental factors as temperature, moisture and oxygen supply. If conditions are equally favorable for bacteria, yeasts and molds, the bacteria will outgrow the other forms. Different kinds of microorganisms cause different types of spoilage. The rotting of an egg, for example, is not caused by the same kinds of organisms as those that cause the rotting of an apple, and the end products are quite different in these two types of spoilage.

Yeasts require foods that contain sugar and can tolerate a relatively high osmotic pressure and acidity. They grow most rapidly under aerobic conditions. Foods that are acid in reaction—as, for example, fruit juices— are usually spoiled by yeasts. Molds can tolerate still higher osmotic pressures and high acid concentrations. Foods that are too acid for yeast can usually be attacked by molds. Molds also grow well on foods that are neutral or slightly basic in reaction. They can also grow in relatively dry foods such as bread, cheese, stored fruits and vegetables and are strictly aerobic. Yeasts and molds grow best in the temperature range of about 70° to 80° F., although some molds grow slowly at refrigerator temperatures. Bacteria grow best in nitrogenous foods that contain a considerable amount of water and have a pH near the neutral point. Those that give rise to acids are inhibited by the acid they produce when it reaches a certain concentration. Such foods are then usually attacked by molds. Bacteria vary considerably in their optimum temperatures. At high temperatures only thermophilic bacteria will grow. Psychrophiles will grow slowly at refrigerator temperatures if there is sufficient moisture. The vast majority of bacteria, however, grow best at moderate temperatures.

Starch can be utilized by most molds and by some bacteria. Sugars are attacked by bacteria, yeasts and molds. If the concentration of sugar is low, acid fermentation by bacteria usually occurs. The souring of milk is a good example of this type of alteration in food. If a larger amount of sugar is present, and especially if the food is acid, yeasts usually become the predominating organisms. This type of spoilage is characteristic of fruit juices, diluted honey and sirup. Foods in which the sugar concentration is relatively high are subject to attack chiefly by molds, since they are more tolerant of high osmotic pressure than yeasts or bacteria. Molds are frequently found on foods that have been kept under refrigeration for a long time.

Proteinaceous foods, such as meats, which are lacking in carbohydrates are attacked usually by nonacid-forming bacteria. Under anaerobic conditions putrefactive changes occur in these foods with the production of vile odors due to hydrogen sulfide, indole, skatole, mercaptans, ammonia, and so forth.

Fats may be decomposed in the presence of water by certain bacteria and molds, usually under aerobic conditions. Most fats, owing to their low moisture content, are decomposed only slowly. Butter may become rancid under conditions that favor the growth of bacteria in the minute droplets of water which it always contains. In these droplets there are usually small quantities of lactose and proteins which are suitable foods for microorganisms.

Spoilage of Fresh Foods

Some foods can be kept for a long time in their natural stage without spoilage; whereas others, such as milk and meat, will spoil in less than a day unless cooked or refrigerated.

Cereals and Cereal Products. Cereals and most cereal products do not readily undergo decomposition, owing to their low water content. Bread, however, under conditions of high humidity may be attacked by molds. When flour becomes wet, it may become sour, owing to fermentation by lactic acid bacteria. Yeast fermentation may also occur. These fermentations are possible because of the fermentable carbohydrates present in the flour.

Fruits. Because of their dry protective skins or coverings, fruits keep well if they have not been damaged in handling. Bruised fruits may allow microorganisms to enter the internal tissues and, therefore, soon decay unless refrigerated or canned. The microbic spoilage of fruits is due chiefly to molds. A nonmicrobial spoilage is characteristic of fruits. Fruits contain enzymes which bring about ripening. These enzymes produce a softening of the texture of the fruit, form sugars from starches, and produce compounds which contribute flavor and aroma to the fruit. When the fruit has become ripe, certain of these enzymes may continue to act, causing a condition of overripeness in which the fruit becomes soft and dark even though the interior is free of microorganisms. This breakdown of the fruit tissues by enzymes is known as *autolysis*. Bananas and certain pears are examples of fruits which undergo autolysis within a short time after they are thoroughly ripened. Oxidizing enzymes present in certain fruits produce discoloration when the fruits are cut and exposed to the air. As mentioned previously, fruits undergo microbic spoilage chiefly by molds. Fruit juices, however, constitute a medium most suitable for yeasts and thus undergo alcoholic fermentation.

Vegetables. Leafy vegetables such as lettuce and spinach also undergo autolysis; when they are kept moist, bacterial decomposition occurs. The root and tuber vegetables such as potatoes, carrots, beets and turnips do not spoil readily when stored in a cool, well ventilated place. Molds may grow on damaged spots. Spoilage by autolysis is more common in these vegetables than spoilage by microorganisms.

Meats. The spoilage of meat is due chiefly to nonacid-forming bacteria, many species of which are capable of utilizing meat as food. The interior tissues of fresh meat are usually sterile, but the surface quickly becomes contaminated with bacteria of various kinds. Spoilage proceeds on the surface. When meat is ground, the surface bacteria become distributed throughout the meat during the grinding process. The bacteria will then grow throughout the meat and cause rapid spoilage unless the meat is refrigerated. Meats refrigerated a long time at temperatures above freezing may develop a surface growth of molds. If the surface is moist, it may become slimy, owing to the growth of bacteria. Meat also undergoes autolysis or "ripening" due to its own enzymes. When the autolyzing enzymes are permitted to act for a limited time, they exert a tenderizing action on the meat without producing undersirable changes.

Eggs.   Eggs are usually sterile when laid and remain so unless microorganisms enter through the pores of the shell. The shell becomes heavily contaminated as soon as the egg is laid. The shell of a freshly laid egg is covered with a dry, mucilaginous coat which, at least for a time, keeps microorganisms from entering the interior. Molds may grow in this coating if the eggs are stored in a humid atmosphere. Upon long storage this coating disintegrates. If the eggs are washed, the coating is removed. Removal of the coating is followed by a rapid invasion of the egg by various kinds of bacteria. Most of the organisms that spoil the egg are proteolytic.

Milk.   Milk is a good medium for the growth of many kinds of microorganisms. It contains an ample amount of water to meet the needs of bacteria, yeasts and molds. It contains proteins for those organisms that can utilize them. The lactose in milk is an excellent source of energy for many bacteria. Under usual conditions lactic acid bacteria, chiefly *Streptococcus lactis* and lactobacilli, are abundant in milk, causing it to sour quickly unless it is refrigerated. Souring is the most common change that occurs in milk. The acid produced is later utilized by molds which gradually become established in the sour milk. The lactic acid produced in the souring of milk stops the growth of proteolytic bacteria, thus preventing changes in the milk proteins. However, after the acid has been removed by the growth of molds, proteolytic bacteria become active and decompose the proteins.

Milk sometimes becomes ropy, owing chiefly to the growth of *Alcaligenes viscolactis,* a bacterium which produces large slimy capsules. Gassy fermentation may result from the growth of lactose-fermenting yeasts, coliform bacteria or *Clostridium perfringens.* Milk may become discolored by the growth of certain chromogenic bacteria. *Pseudomonas syncyanea* gives milk a faint blue color, and *Serratia marcescens* causes a pink discoloration.

Spoilage of Commercially Canned Foods

As indicated previously, canned foods are not necessarily sterile. The processing temperature varies with the type of food. Foods containing acids are processed at lower temperatures than nonacid foods. The processing temperature is sufficient, however, to prevent spoilage of the food under ordinary conditions of storage.

Spoilage at times occurs in commercially canned foods. Those containing viable spores may undergo spoilage when stored for a long time in a warm place. Under such conditions the spores eventually germinate into vegetative cells, which grow in the food and bring about its spoilage. In "flat sour" spoilage, lactic acid is formed by spore-forming, thermophilic bacilli. Since no gas is produced, the ends of the cans remain flat (not swollen); owing to the formation of acid the food acquires a sour or acid flavor—hence the name "flat sour." This type of spoilage occurs principally in low acid vegetables and sometimes in canned tomato juice. Foods which undergo this type of spoilage are not dangerous to health but may have flavors objectionable to the taste.

In another type of spoilage gaseous fermentation causes the ends of the cans to swell. This is brought about by an anaerobic, spore-forming, obligate thermophilic bacterium known as *Clostridium thermosaccharolyticum*. The gas is produced in considerable amounts and consists chiefly of carbon dioxide and hydrogen. The pressure of the gas may become so great as to cause the can to burst. This type of spoilage has a decided effect on the flavor and texture of the food.

"Sulfide spoilage" is caused by *Clostridium nigrificans,* a spore-forming anaerobic, obligate thermophile. This organism produces hydrogen sulfide, a gas very soluble in water. Because it readily dissolves in the liquid in the can, the production of hydrogen sulfide does not cause the can to swell. Hydrogen sulfide reacts readily with any exposed iron on the inner surface of the tinned iron can, producing black sulfide of iron which causes a darkening of the food. Sulfide spoilage occurs less frequently than the two types previously mentioned.

Spore-forming, mesophilic anaerobes may cause the spoilage of canned meats or other canned proteinaceous foods. In the spoilage carried on by these organisms the food undergoes putrefaction with the formation of gas and foul odors. The gas may produce swelling of the can.

Spoilage of Home-Canned Foods

Home-canned foods frequently spoil, owing to inadequate heat processing permitting the spores of acid-forming anaerobes and putrefactive anaerobes to survive. Another cause of spoilage is improper sealing, allowing molds and aerobic bacteria to grow on the surface of the food. Underprocessing of low-acid foods may result in the growth of *Clostridium botulinum,* a spore-forming, obligate anaerobe which produces a powerful toxin. The eating of food containing this toxin causes the form of food poisoning known as *botulism.* This and other forms of food poisoning will be discussed in Chapter 25.

QUESTIONS

1. Discuss drying as a method of food preservation. Why may the moisture content of dried fruits be much higher than that of dried eggs, meat or milk?

2. In what mays may low temperatures be used for the preservation of foods? What are the advantages of quick freezing over slow freezing?

3. (*a*) Explain the relation of the acidity of the food and the processing temperature used in the commercial canning of foods.

(*b*) Are commercially canned foods necessarily sterile? What properties of the finished product will usually prevent surviving spores from germinating into vegetative cells?

(*c*) What precautions are usually taken to prevent the spores of thermophiles from germinating?

4. Discuss the various methods in use in the home canning of foods. Why should a steam pressure sterilizer be used in the home preservation of low-acid foods?

5. Why does subjecting foods to smoke have a preservative effect? Which kinds of foods may be preserved in this manner?

6. (*a*) In the spoilage of foods in general, which kinds of foods are readily spoiled by (1) yeasts, (2) molds and (3) bacteria?

(*b*) Explain (1) "flat sour" spoilage of canned foods, (2) spoilage causing the swelling of the cans, (3) "sulfide spoilage."

(*c*) Which types of spoilage are frequently encountered in home-canned foods?

REFERENCES

American Can Co.: The Canned Food Reference Manual. 3rd ed. New York, 1947.

Baumgartner, J. G.: Canned Foods—An Introduction to Their Microbiology. 2nd ed. London, Churchill, 1946.

Edelmann, R.: Textbook of Meat Hygiene. 8th ed. Philadelphia, Lea & Febiger, 1943.

Fabian, F. W.: Home Food Preservation: Salting, Canning, Drying, and Freezing. New York, Avi Pub. Co., 1943.

Frazier, W. C.: Food Microbiology. New York, McGraw-Hill Book Company, Inc., 1958.

Hopkins, E. S., and Schulze, W. H.: The Practice of Sanitation. 3rd ed. Baltimore, The Williams & Wilkins Company, 1958.

Jensen, L. B.: Microbiology of Meats. 3rd ed. Champaign, Ill., Gerrard Press, 1954.

Standard Methods for the Microbiological Examination of Foods. New York, American Public Health Association, 1958.

Tanner, F. W.: The Microbiology of Foods. 2nd ed. Champaign, Ill., Gerrard Press, 1944.

24 • The Microbiology of Milk

The suitability of milk as a medium for the growth of many kinds of microorganisms necessitates the exercise of great care in its production and handling if a product of high quality is desired. The fluidity of milk and its composition make it a highly favorable medium for the growth of microorganisms. It contains several kinds of proteins which satisfy the nitrogen requirements of many bacteria. A great many microorganisms can utilize the lactose of milk as a source of energy and find the nearly neutral reaction (approximately pH 6.7) of milk favorable for growth.

Even when milk is obtained and handled under sanitary conditions, microorganisms in small numbers always find their way into it. Unless precautions are taken to inhibit their increase, the milk will, in a comparatively short time, contain an enormously large microbial population. Since certain pathogens are included among the microorganisms capable of growing or surviving in milk, it may become a dangerous food.

CONTAMINATION OF MILK

Milk is secreted as a sterile fluid in the udder of the healthy cow but becomes contaminated as it passes down through the milk ducts of the teats, which always harbor a characteristic bacterial flora. These bacteria are chiefly harmless cocci and small bacilli. Freshly drawn milk is, therefore, never sterile. Unless great care is exercised during the milking process, a great variety of additional bacteria will enter the milk.

Particles of soil and manure adhering to the hair and skin of the cow may drop into the milk pail and thus be an important source of contamination. The milker may contribute microorganisms from his hands and clothing. If dust has been raised in the barn just before milking, dust particles carrying microorganisms may drop into the milk pail. Improperly cleaned milk pails, milk cans and milking machines may be an important source from which microorganisms enter milk. The use of a clean milking machine usually keeps the milk from acquiring contaminants from the hair of the cow and the air of the barn.

If milk is immediately refrigerated after it is drawn, and kept cold, only a gradual increase in the number of microorganisms will occur. Otherwise its microbial content will increase rapidly. When carefully drawn milk is cooled immediately to 40° F., the bacteria will double in number in approximately sixteen hours; when cooled to 50° F., the increase will be five times the original number in this period of time; at 60° F. the increase is fifteen times; at 70° F., 700 times; and at 80° F., 3000 times. The number of microorganisms in milk is an index of the care that has been taken in its production. To keep the count low requires cleanliness in handling, and storage at low temperatures. A high count does not necessarily mean that the milk is dangerous, but excessive numbers of microorganisms produce changes in milk which lower its quality. With proper sanitary precautions the dairy farmer should be able to produce milk with not more than 10,000 bacteria per milliliter.

The organisms that find their way into the milk are chiefly bacteria. Among these are lactic acid producers, coliform bacteria (species of *Escherichia* and *Aerobacter*) and spore-forming anaerobes (chiefly species of *Clostridium*). Other bacteria usually present in milk and dairy products are members of the genera, *Leuconostoc*, *Propionibacterium*, *Bacillus* and *Micrococcus*. Yeasts and the spores of molds may also be present, and occasionally pathogens gain entrance.

Lactic Acid-Producing Bacteria

The chief lactic acid-producing bacteria present in milk belong to the genera *Streptococcus* and *Lactobacillus*. These organisms produce lactic acid from lactose but do not produce gas. *Streptococcus lactis* is the most common and most important species of this group. Plants appear to be its natural habitat. Apparently it gets into milk on dust from dried plant material and from milking utensils. It is the organism chiefly responsible for the souring of raw milk. It has a moderately high acid tolerance. When the acidity reaches about 1 per cent, its growth is checked.

Lactobacilli are slender, nonspore-forming, rod-shaped bacteria which grow more slowly in milk than *Streptococcus lactis*. Some species of this group can tolerate a relatively high acidity and consequently are able to continue the souring of milk after the streptococci have ceased growing, owing to the accumulated acid. The most commonly encountered member of this group in raw milk is *Lactobacillus casei*. Milk usually contains smaller numbers of many other lactic acid rods, including *L. lactis*, *L. helveticus*, *L. bulgaricus* and *L. acidophilus*. Both *Streptococcus lactis* and the lactobacilli produce a smooth curd which usually does not contract to expel the whey.

Coliform Bacteria

This group includes species of the genera *Escherichia* and *Aerobacter*. The coliform bacteria, as mentioned in Chapter 22, are small, Gram-negative, nonspore-forming rods which ferment lactose with the formation of both acid and gas. The most commonly found representatives of this group are *Escherichia coli* and *Aerobacter aerogenes*. *Escherichia coli* is a common intestinal organism in all warm-blooded animals. It gains entrance to milk from manure. *Aerobacter aerogenes* is widely distributed in nature and is normally found on grains and plants. It is also present in limited numbers in the human and animal intestinal tracts. The curd formed in milk by the coliform bacteria is more or less disrupted by gas bubbles; it shrinks, expelling much of the whey. Coliform bacteria may give rise to diagreeable odors and flavors in milk and cheese.

Spore-Forming Anaerobes

These bacteria are chiefly members of the genus *Clostridium* which, under anaerobic conditions, are capable of fermenting lactose with the formation of acid and large amounts of gas. They are widely distributed in nature, occurring abundantly in the soil, and are commonly found in the intestinal tracts of animals. Their presence in milk usually indicates contamination with soil or manure. When anaerobic conditions prevail and the milk is kept at a fairly high temperature, they cause a "stormy" fermentation due to the rapid production of gas in large quantities. The curd that is formed does not remain intact, but is broken up into shreds.

Other Milk Saprophytes

Besides the bacteria mentioned in the preceding paragraphs, a number of other groups of microorganisms may gain entrance to milk. Lactose-fermenting yeasts occasionally are present. Aerobic spore-forming bacteria such as *Bacillus cereus, Bacillus subtilis* and *Bacillus coagulans* may cause sweet curdling. These bacteria produce the enzyme rennin, which causes the milk to curd. They produce little or no acid. At times, considerable protein decomposition may be brought about by this group as well as by other bacteria, causing the milk to acquire undesirable bitter flavors. Under certain conditions of storage, actinomyces may become active, giving the milk a bitter, moldly taste. *Alcaligenes viscolactis* causes slimy or ropy milk. Certain other bacteria may also produce this condition. *Serratia marcescens* colors milk red, and *Pseudomonas syncyanea* produces "blue milk."

Pathogenic Bacteria

Milk may contain pathogens acquired from the cow or contributed by infected persons or healthy carriers engaged in milking or the subsequent handling of milk. Milk from infected cows may contain *Brucella abortus,* the cause of infectious abortion in cattle and one of the organisms causing undulant fever (brucellosis) in man. The bovine type of tubercle bacillus may be present, but, owing to the vigorous campaign that has been waged against tuberculosis in cattle, it is less common now than it was in the past. Cows frequently experience inflammation of the udder (mastitis), which is most commonly caused by *Streptococcus agalactiae* and less often by *Streptococcus pyogenes*. The first of these organisms is not ordinarily pathogenic for man, but *Streptococcus pyogenes* entering milk from an infected udder may cause septic sore throat or some other streptococcal infection in persons who drink raw milk. Mastitis is sometimes caused by *Staphylococcus aureus*. In cows thus infected the organisms enter the milk in large numbers and may multiply rapidly after the milk has been drawn if it is not refrigerated. They produce a toxin which, when the milk is consumed, causes gastroenteritis, an intestinal disturbance characterized by nausea, vomiting and diarrhea. *Coxiella burnetii,* the rickettsia that causes Q fever, may be transmitted through milk from infected cows to man.

Most of the pathogens that find their way into milk are derived from human sources. These include the organisms of typhoid and paratyphoid fevers, the dysenteries (bacillary and amebic), tuberculosis (human type) and scarlet fever. *Streptococcus pyogenes* may enter milk, not only from an infected cow, but also through contamination by infected persons or by persons who are carriers of this organism. Many of these organisms can multiply rapidly in milk if it is not refrigerated.

Milk-borne diseases are due almost exclusively to the consumption of raw milk. Before the days of pasteurization, milk-borne epidemics were common. Although much of the milk now consumed in the United States is pasteurized, raw milk constitutes an appreciable percentage of the milk supply of villages and small cities. The only constantly safe milk is properly pasteurized milk. Disease transmission by milk would almost reach the vanishing point if all milk were pasteurized before being consumed.

PASTEURIZATION

Pasteurization takes its name from Louis Pasteur who, in 1864, devised the process to keep wine and beer from spoiling. The process was not applied to milk until 1886. As applied to milk, pasteurization is a process whereby milk is heated to a sufficiently high temperature to kill harmful microorganisms without impairing its flavor or appreciably reducing its value as a food. There are two recognized methods of commercial pasteurization: the low-temperature, holding method and the high-temperature, short-time or so-called flash method. In the holding method the milk is heated to 143° to 145° F. (61.7° to 62.8° C.) and is held there for thirty minutes. It is then rapidly cooled to 50° F. or below and bottled. In the flash method the milk is quickly heated to 161° F. (71.6° C.) or higher and held there for not less than fifteen seconds and then cooled rapidly and bottled. Either method of pasteurization insures the killing of the

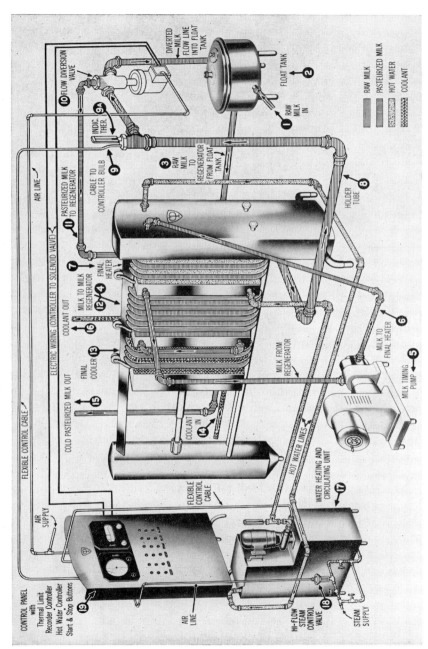

Figure 127. Flow chart illustrating the passage of milk through a high-temperature, short-time pasteurizer. (Courtesy of Creamery Package Manufacturing Company.)

bacteria responsible for milk-borne diseases and between 90 and 99 per cent of all nonpathogenic organisms.

The temperatures used in pasteurization are sufficiently high to kill the tubercle bacillus, *Mycobacterium tuberculosis,* which is the most heat-resistant pathogen likely to be present in raw milk. This organism is killed in six minutes at 145° F. and in ten minutes at 142° F. There is thus a considerable margin of safety between pasteurization requirements and the thermal death time of the tubercle bacillus. Some of the saprophytes, including lactic acid formers, have sufficient thermal resistance to withstand the pasteurization process. Figure 127 shows a high-temperature, short-time pasteurizer. Modern pasteurizing apparatus is equipped with automatic recording thermometers, whereby the heating temperature and holding time are recorded in ink on revolving paper charts which are checked periodically by the milk inspector.

Pasteurization does not alter the milk chemically to an appreciable degree. The most important alteration is a slight reduction in the vitamin C content. By greatly reducing the number of bacteria present, pasteurization improves the quality of the milk and delays spoilage. To obtain milk of high quality it should be produced in accordance with methods and standards that will make it as pure as possible and then be effectively pasteurized in equipment of approved design. Pasteurization should be regarded as a supplement to, rather than a substitute for, the sanitary production of milk.

The Phosphatase Test

A test known as the phosphatase test has been devised to check the completeness of pasteurization. It is a means of determining whether or not a given lot of milk has been properly pasteurized. The test is based upon the fact that the enzyme phosphatase, which is always present in raw milk, is almost completely inactivated when milk is satisfactorily pasteurized. Phosphatase splits phosphates from certain phosphate-bearing compounds.

In performing the test a little disodium phenyl-phosphate is added to a sample of the milk. If the phosphatase in the milk has not been destroyed, it will liberate phenol from the disodium phenyl-phosphate in proportion to the amount of phosphatase present. An indicator is added which, when reacting with phenol, develops a blue color. The quantity of phenol produced is determined colorimetrically, i.e., by the intensity of the blueness, which can be compared with a series of standard colors prepared with known amounts of phenol in a definite volume of milk. Thus the degree of faulty pasteurization can be determined. Underheating by only 1 degree during pasteurization or the addition of as little as 0.5 per cent of raw milk can be detected by the phosphatase test. By means of this test, many cases of underpasteurization have been detected.

DETERMINING THE SANITARY QUALITY OF MILK

The sanitary quality of milk can be determined by the routine application of tests designed for this purpose. These tests are described here to acquaint the reader with the general nature and limitations of these tests, including the method, materials and equipment used.

Standard Plate Count

The extent of bacterial contamination in milk can be determined by the standard plate count. In this procedure a sample of the milk is diluted with sterile water in ratios such as 1:10, 1:100 and 1:1000, and definite portions

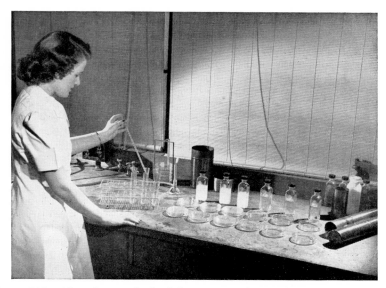

Figure 128. The plate method of determining the number of bacteria in milk. (Courtesy of Corning Glass Works.)

(usually 1 milliliter) of each dilution are transferred to sterile Petri plates. Melted tryptone glucose extract agar is mixed with the dilutions in the plates. As the medium hardens, the bacteria become fixed in position and upon incubation (32° or 35° C. for forty-eight hours) they grow in the form of colonies which become visible to the naked eye. The number of bacterial colonies present on a plate is determined by various counting procedures. By multiplying the number of colonies by the dilution factor, a rough estimate of the degree of bacterial contamination can be made. Since many of the colonies probably develop from clumps of bacteria rather than from single bacterial cells, the results are properly expressed as a standard plate count per milliliter rather than the number of bacteria per milliliter.

It should be noted, also, that some of the bacteria in milk will not grow on the particular medium or at the incubation temperatures used in the test. However, the standard plate count has considerable sanitary significance since it indicates the conditions under which the milk was collected, handled and stored. Also, some idea of the nature of the bacteria in the milk can be obtained from the types of colonies that develop. Figure 128 shows the equipment used in making a standard plate count of the number of bacteria in milk.

Direct Microscopic Count

In this method a small quantity of milk, usually 0.01 milliliter measured in a capillary pipet, is spread out over an area of 1 square cm. on a glass slide. After the fat has been removed by dipping the slide in xylol, the film is fixed in alcohol and stained with methylene blue. To make the microscopic count the microscope is standardized, by using the right combination of ocular and tube length, so that the field will have a diameter of 0.205 mm. A field of this diameter will include the area covered by 1/300,000 milliliter of the milk dried on the slide. The bacteria in a number of fields (usually about thirty) are counted and the average per field obtained. This average multiplied by 300,000 represents the number of bacteria per milliliter of milk. This test makes possible the rapid determination of the approximate number of bacteria in milk.

Methylene Blue Reduction Test

When a small quantity of methylene blue is added to milk, the blue color imparted to it will slowly disappear, owing to the presence of bacteria, the rate of disappearance depending upon the number of bacteria present. Actively growing bacteria in milk consume oxygen and bring about a lowered oxidation-reduction potential. This condition can be detected by the use of methylene blue, which serves as a hydrogen acceptor and becomes reduced to a colorless compound. Methylene blue can thus be used as an oxidation-reduction indicator.

When the number of bacteria in milk is high, the rate of reduction of the dye is rapid; but if the numbers are low, a longer period will be required to reduce the methylene blue. The speed of reduction is an indication of the rate at which oxidation is taking place in the milk. The rate of reduction of the dye, therefore, is proportional to the number of bacteria present.

The test gives a rough index of the degree of contamination the milk was subjected to and is of value in the rapid grading of raw milk supplies on farms and at collecting platforms. Under the standardized conditions devised for the performance of this test, milk of excellent sanitary quality will not decolorize in eight hours, milk of good quality will not decolorize in five and one-half hours, while in milk of fair quality the color disappears in less than five and one-half hours, but not less than two hours. In milk of poor quality the dye is reduced in less than two hours, and in badly contaminated milk the color may disappear in less than twenty minutes.

Membrane Filter for Coliform Determination

The membrane filter described in Chapter 22 may be used for the detection and enumeration of coliform bacteria in milk as well as in water. The procedure for milk is essentially the same as for water.

GRADES OF MILK

Many communities in the United States have established ordinances for the regulation and control of market milk. Regulations for milk vary somewhat in different communities, but many municipalities follow the United States Public Health Service publication "Milk Ordinance and Code," which lists three grades of raw and three grades of pasteurized milk. These are briefly summarized in the following paragraphs.

Grades of Raw Milk

Grade A raw milk for pasteurization must have a bacterial plate count, or a direct microscopic clump count, of not more than 200,000 per milliliter. Grade B raw milk for pasteurization is milk which does not meet the bacterial standards of grade A milk for pasteurization but conforms with all other requirements. The bacterial plate count or direct microscopic clump count must not exceed 1,000,000 per milliliter. Grade C raw milk for pasteurization does not meet the requirements for grade B raw milk for pasteurization.

Grades of Pasteurized Milk

Grade A pasteurized milk is grade A raw milk which has been pasteurized and has a bacterial plate count after pasteurization of not more than 30,000 per milliliter and is phosphatase-negative. Grade B pasteurized milk is obtained by pasteurizing grade B raw milk. The bacterial plate count after pasteurization must not be in excess of 50,000 per milliliter. Grade C pasteurized milk is milk that fails to meet the requirements of grade B pasteurized milk.

In some communities grades of milk lower than A are not permitted to be sold. It is probable that in the future all grades of milk below A will be considered unsatisfactory for human consumption.

Certified Milk

Certified milk is milk produced by dairies operated in accordance with the rules established by the American Association of Medical Milk Commissions. It is produced under direct supervision of agents appointed by local medical milk commissions. The rules are strict regarding cleanliness and health of the cows and the milkers, and also regarding the sanitary condition of the cow stable. The cows are examined frequently for tuberculosis, brucellosis and other diseases. The milk must be collected in sterilized containers and, if sold raw, the standard plate count must not exceed 10,000 bacteria per milliliter. If the rules are observed and the milk is up to the proper standards, it is certified by the commission—hence the name "certified milk." The rules permit the pasteurization of certified milk. Such milk must not have a bacterial plate count in excess of 10,000 before and 500 after pasteurization. Pasteurized certified milk is the highest possible quality of milk from a sanitary standpoint and meets a standard greatly to be desired. Certified milk is usually produced only in areas where a large city market is close at hand.

QUESTIONS

1. What properties of milk make it a suitable medium for the growth of microorganisms?

2. What are the sources of the microorganisms that enter milk?

3. By what procedures can the microbial count of milk be kept down to a low point?

4. (*a*) What kinds of bacteria are usually found in milk?

   (*b*) Name the lactic acid-producing bacteria that milk usually contains.

   (*c*) What is the source of the coliform bacteria found in milk?

   (*d*) Name other kinds of microorganisms commonly present in milk.

5. (*a*) Name diseases transmitted to man by the milk of infected cows.

   (*b*) Name diseases transmitted to man by milk contaminated with pathogens by persons handling the milk.

6. (*a*) Explain the process and importance of pasteurizing milk. Differentiate between the "holding" and "flash" methods.

   (*b*) What is the phosphatase test?

7. Explain briefly: (1) the standard plate count, (2) the direct microscopic count, (3) the methylene blue reduction test.

8. On what basis is market milk graded? What is the usual standard for grade A pasteurized milk? What is certified milk?

REFERENCES

Elliker, P. R.: Practical Dairy Bacteriology. New York, McGraw-Hill Book Company, Inc., 1949.

Facts about the Pasteurization of Milk. Leaflet No. 408, U. S. Department of Agriculture. Washington, D.C., Superintendent of Documents, 1956.

Foster, E. M., et al.: Dairy Microbiology. Englewood Cliffs, N. J., Prentice-Hall, Inc., 1957.

Grant, F. M.: Cleaning and Sanitizing Farm Milk Utensils. Farmers' Bulletin No. 2078. Washington, D. C., Superintendent of Documents, 1955.

Hammer, B. W., and Babel, F. J.: Dairy Bacteriology. 4th ed. New York, John Wiley & Sons, Inc., 1957.

Methods and Standards for the Production of Certified Milk. New York, American Association of Medical Milk Commissions, 1957.

Standard Methods for the Examination of Dairy Products. 10th ed. New York, American Public Health Association, 1953.

U. S. Public Health Service: Milk Ordinance and Code. Washington, D. C., Superintendent of Documents, Public Health Service Publication 229, 1953.

25 • Food Poisoning and Food-Borne Infection

Foods may be deleterious to health, owing to (1) poisons naturally present, as in some mushrooms and clams at certain seasons; (2) chemicals inadvertently or purposely added to food; (3) the presence of toxic substances produced by bacteria capable of growing in foods; or (4) the presence of microorganisms capable of causing infection of the gastrointestinal tract or other parts of the body. In the last case, the resulting symptoms are usually referred to as "food-borne infection." The term "food poisoning" is commonly applied to illness resulting from the ingestion of food containing poisons or bacterial toxins as well as to food-borne infection causing sudden gastrointestinal disturbances. The former may be referred to as the toxic type and the latter as the infectious type of food poisoning. In the infectious type the causative organisms are usually bacteria belonging to the genus *Salmonella* and, infrequently, certain streptococci.

Bacterial food poisoning is popularly, but erroneously, referred to as "ptomaine poisoning." Ptomaines constitute an ill-defined group of amines (organic, basic, nitrogenous compounds) which result from the putrefaction of protein. There is no evidence that ptomaines are involved in food poisoning. They have never been found in foods responsible for food poisoning.

The foods involved in food poisoning are usually those that have been subjected to unsanitary care or have been improperly canned. The contamination may come from unclean hands and utensils, flies, rodents or other sources. Foods prepared several hours before serving and allowed to stand at room temperature become good culture media for bacteria. Among foods frequently responsible for bacterial food poisoning are custard-filled bakery products, ham and other cured meats, creamed salmon, chicken a la king, creamed shrimp, powdered eggs, salads of

373

various kinds and underprocessed home-canned foods, especially string beans, corn and beets.

Bacteria which have been implicated as definitely responsible for outbreaks of food poisoning are (1) certain staphylococci, (2) several members of the genus *Salmonella,* (3) *Clostridium botulinum,* and (4) certain alpha-type streptococci. Less definitely implicated, but believed by some investigators to be responsible for some of the outbreaks of food poisoning, are coliform bacteria, members of the genus *Proteus* and certain spore-bearing aerobes and anaerobes, especially when the food is grossly contaminated with these organisms.

STAPHYLOCOCCAL FOOD POISONING

Staphylococcal poisoning is the most common type of bacterial food poisoning. It is caused by staphylococci which secrete a soluble toxin in the food before it is eaten. The toxin has a strong irritating effect on the gastrointestinal tract. Because of its action on the intestinal tract it is known as *enterotoxin* (entero meaning "intestine"). The bacteria producing this type of toxin are certain strains of *Staphylococcus aureus.* Enterotoxin-producing strains cannot be distinguished from other strains by cultural, biochemical or serological tests. The total number of strains producing enterotoxin is not known. Staphylococcus enterotoxin is heat-resistant, being able to withstand boiling temperatures for more than thirty minutes. It may, therefore, be present in food after the staphylococci have been killed by boiling. The symptoms of staphylococcal food poisoning are due solely to the enterotoxin since the organisms, although pathogenic, are incapable of causing infection in the intestinal tract.

A characteristic feature of staphylococcal food poisoning is the short incubation period, which varies from one to six hours, but is usually about three hours. The chief symptoms are nausea and vomiting accompanied by abdominal cramps, severe diarrhea and prostration. In mild cases there may be abdominal cramps and diarrhea without vomiting. It is usually not fatal. The symptoms are of short duration, recovery occurring within twenty-four to forty-eight hours.

Staphylococcal poisoning is encountered in connection with the eating of (1) certain bakery products, particularly those containing a custard or cream filling, such as eclairs, cream puffs, custard-filled doughnuts, and cream or custard pies; (2) meat products, especially precooked ham and tongue, leftover roast turkey improperly refrigerated, sausages, meat sandwiches and chicken and meat salads; and (3) milk, cream, cheese and ice cream. Frozen foods may cause staphylococcal poisoning if they become contaminated before being frozen and if they are not immediately frozen after contamination has occurred. If they are immediately frozen after contamination has taken place, they may cause poisoning if errors in processing occur or if they are kept at room temperature for a number of hours after thawing, giving the staphylococci an opportunity to grow.

In most cases of staphylococcal food poisoning the responsible food has been allowed to stand at room temperature for several hours before being eaten, during which time the enterotoxin was formed. Unrefrigerated custard-filled bakery products apparently are responsible for the greatest number of outbreaks. Enterotoxin is not formed at temperatures below 45° F. Outbreaks caused by milk are usually due to the consumption of raw milk which may have become contaminated from infected cow's udders or from a person who has handled the milk. The presence of enterotoxin in food does not produce an odor of spoilage or alter its normal taste.

Staphylococcal food poisoning can usually be traced to specific food handlers who harbor enterotoxin-producing strains of staphylococci in the nose and throat or who have purulent skin lesions caused by these organisms. No definite information is available concerning the number of cases of staphylococcal food poisoning occurring annually in the United States since it is usually only the larger outbreaks, such as those occurring at luncheon clubs, picnics, church suppers and military camps, that are reported. It is known, however, that the incidence is high.

SALMONELLA GASTROENTERITIS

The salmonella group of bacteria is composed of many species. The organisms are short, Gram-negative, nonsporulating, motile bacilli. Many kinds of salmonella organisms have been isolated from cases of food poisoning, but there is much uncertainty as to their identity and classification. Some appear to be strictly human pathogens, whereas others are pathogenic for animals or for both man and animals. Certain species cause specific infections in man, such as typhoid fever (S. *typhosa*) and paratyphoid fever (S. *paratyphi*, S. *schottmuelleri* and S. *hirschfeldii*). A wide variety of animals, including cattle, swine, sheep, poultry, rats and mice, are susceptible to infection by species of *Salmonella*. Many of the species normally pathogenic for animals may cause gastroenteritis in man. In some cases, the source of infection may be a human carrier.

Salmonella gastroenteritis is an infection rather than a poisoning due to preformed toxins, as in staphylococcal food poisoning. However, because these organisms are capable of multiplying in great numbers in foods before they are consumed by man, and produce symptoms in a short time, *Salmonella* gastroenteritis is usually classified as a form of food poisoning. Toxins are formed as the organisms grow in the intestinal tract.

Salmonella enteritidis was the first organism of this group to be identified as a human pathogen. It was isolated in 1888 by Gaertner in a meat poisoning outbreak in Germany. The organism most frequently isolated from cases of Salmonella infection in the United States is S. *typhimurium*.

Salmonella food poisoning has an incubation period of twelve to twenty-four hours in the majority of cases. The onset is usually sudden. The illness may start with a headache and chills. These symptoms are followed by vomiting, abdominal pain, diarrhea, fever and prostration. The disease affects infants and young children more severely than adults. With proper medical care the disease seldom lasts longer than a week. The number of cases occurring annually in the United States is relatively small.

The infection is transmitted by means of foods which have become contaminated with animal fecal matter, especially that of rodents such as rats and mice. It is probably more commonly transmitted through food contaminated by food handlers who are carriers of salmonellae. A carrier is a person who harbors and excretes pathogens without exhibiting symptoms of illness. Animal products such as meats, poultry, milk, cheese and eggs, particularly those that have received considerable handling in their preparation, are often the vehicles involved in transmission to man. Salads and pastries are also frequently responsible. The bacteria are capable of rapid multiplication in food that is not refrigerated. Meat obtained from infected animals, if eaten in an undercooked condition, may be a source of infection. The salmonella organisms are destroyed by thorough cooking. Milk and cheese may become contaminated from infected cows. Eggs, particularly duck eggs, may contain bacteria of the salmonella group.

BOTULISM

Botulism is not an infection but an acute toxemia resulting from the ingestion of foods containing the toxin *botulin.* The botulin-producing bacteria are classified in Bergey's *Manual of Determinative Bacteriology* as *Clostridium botulinum* (Figure 129), and *Clostridium parabotulinum.* The name botulism (Latin, *botulus,* sausage) originated from the fact that the ailment was first encountered in Europe as a manifestation of sausage poisoning. In the United States, however, sausage is seldom responsible for botulism.

Both organisms are relatively large, spore-forming, rod-shaped, obligate anaerobes. They may occur singly or in the form of very short chains. They are saprophytic and are ordinarily incapable of living as parasites in the human body. The spores are oval and are situated near one end of the organism. The spores are highly resistant to heat, being able to withstand ordinary boiling, but are destroyed at 120° C. in about ten minutes.

The toxin secreted by these organisms is a globulinlike protein which is not destroyed by the proteolytic enzymes of the digestive tract but is readily absorbed into the blood stream. Due to its high potency, an extremely minute quantity can cause illness and death. Because it has a specific affinity for the nervous system, it is referred to as a *neurotoxin.* It acts upon the motor nerve endings in body muscles, interfering with the transmission of impulses over the nervous system to the muscles of the body. Being susceptible to heat, the toxin can be destroyed in foods that contain it by heating them to the boiling point.

There are five specific types of toxins produced by the botulinum group of organisms. They are designated A, B, C, D and E. Human cases of botulism are due chiefly to types A and B, but a small number of cases are caused by type E toxin. Type C chiefly affects domestic fowls and wild ducks. Strains producing type D toxin are found in South Africa and cause botulism chiefly in cattle, horses and sheep. Types A and B have been obtained in crystalline form. Per unit of weight, they are the most potent poisons known. For human beings 1 gram of the crystals would be a sufficient amount for about 8,000,000 lethal doses.

The normal habitat of the botulinum organisms is the soil, where they

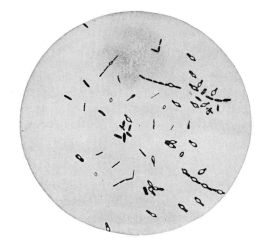

Figure 129. Clostridium botulinum, × 900. (From Frobisher: Fundamentals of Bacteriology.)

are more or less widely distributed. The soils of the western states, including the Great Plains area, contain mainly type A organisms, whereas in the Mississippi Valley and Great Lakes region and most of the Atlantic states, type B is the predominant form.

The organisms gain entrance to food from the soil. Most cases of botulism in the United States arise from inadequately processed home-canned foods, consumed without adequate heating after removal from the jar. The botulinum organisms can grow in canned foods if the *p*H is favorable, i.e., weakly acidic to basic. Canned foods especially favorable for the growth of these organisms are string beans, corn, beets, spinach and asparagus. Pears, apricots and tomatoes are sometimes sufficiently low in acid to constitute a good medium. Canned string beans are more often responsible for botulism than any other food. Canned corn holds second place. Owing to the extreme potency of botulism toxin, it is dangerous to merely taste foods that contain it. In the past, commercially canned foods were often at fault, but the necessary precautions are now taken by canning establishments so that their products are not likely to give rise to botulism.

Foods in which *Cl. botulinum* or *Cl. parabotulinum* have grown usually have a rancid odor, which, however, may not be very noticeable in some cases. It is advisable to thoroughly boil all home-canned vegetables before they are consumed in order to destroy the botulinum toxin should it be present. Foods suspected of being spoiled should never be tasted until they have been boiled. There is no danger of botulism from fresh foods, cooked or raw, since the spores themselves are harmless when present on food and the toxin is formed only under anaerobic conditions such as prevail in sealed containers.

The incubation period of botulism may vary from less than twenty-four hours to several days, depending upon the amount of toxin ingested. Lassitude, fatigue and muscular weakness constitute the first symptoms in the majority of cases. There may be headache and dizziness. These symptoms are followed by such disturbances as double vision (diplopia), drooping of the upper eyelids, dilated pupils, persistent constipation, dryness of the mouth, swelling of the tongue, and difficulty in swallowing and in speaking. There is seldom any pain or fever. The mentality of the patient usually remains clear until a short time before death. There are seldom any gastrointestinal disturbances as witnessed with other types of food poisoning. Death is due to paralysis of the muscles of respiration. In fatal cases the duration of the illness is usually from three to six days after partaking of the poisonous food. Botulism is not of frequent occurrence. In the United States there are only about ten to fifteen small outbreaks annually. The case fatality rate, however, is high, being approximately 65 per cent. In some outbreaks it may be 100 per cent.

Antitoxin is available for treatment, but once the symptoms of botulism have appeared it is not very effective. When administered before the symptoms become noticeable, antitoxin appears to have considerable therapeutic value. Since determination of the type of toxin concerned is time-consuming, resulting in delay, it is customary to administer bivalent antitoxin offering protection against types A and B.

Toxoid, prepared by inactivating the toxin with formaldehyde, is an effective antigen in producing active immunity to botulism. Under normal conditions, however, immunization is not justified, owing to the rarity of botulism. It conceivably would be of value in bacteriological warfare.

STREPTOCOCCAL GASTROENTERITIS

Alpha-type streptococci have been responsible for some cases of gastroenteritis following the eating of contaminated food. This type of gastroenteritis appears to be an infection and not due to preformed toxins. The responsible organism is *Streptococcus faecalis*. This organism is a normal inhabitant of the human intestinal tract, but only a few strains have the property of causing gastrointestinal disturbances. Symptoms arise when large numbers of the organisms are ingested with the contaminated food. The symptoms, which develop within two to eighteen hours, include nausea, colicky pains, diarrhea and sometimes vomiting. They are usually not severe.

SPREAD OF COMMUNICABLE DISEASE THROUGH FOOD

One of the most common means by which communicable diseases are spread is through contaminated food. A number of pathogens can remain alive in food long enough to be conveyed to a new host. Some can actually grow and multiply in certain foods at ordinary room temperatures. Only those pathogens that can cause disease when they gain entrance to the body by way of the mouth are dangerous to man when they are present in food.

Intestinal infections such as typhoid fever and the dysenteries (bacillary and amebic) are readily transmitted through foods contaminated with the intestinal discharges of infected persons or carriers. A carrier is a person who harbors and excretes pathogens without exhibiting symptoms of illness. Milk and dairy products, as mentioned in the preceding chapter, may be the vehicles of transfer for a variety of pathogens, some coming from diseased cows, others from infected human beings or carriers who handle the milk before it reaches the consumer. Infected cows may contribute such organisms as streptococci capable of causing septic sore throat, tubercle bacilli (bovine type) and the causative agents of brucellosis (undulant fever). From human sources milk may acquire the organisms of scarlet fever, tuberculosis (human type), typhoid fever and the dysenteries. Shellfish such as oysters and clams obtained from bays and estuaries polluted with raw sewage may convey typhoid fever to man when eaten raw.

Foods unprotected from flies, cockroaches, mice, rats, cats and dogs, or handled by persons careless in their personal hygiene, may become contaminated with dangerous microbes of various kinds. It is to the advantage of the consumer to be aware of the potential danger that lurks in foods so that he may take proper precautions to safeguard himself against harm.

SANITARY HANDLING OF FOOD

The persons engaged in producing, preparing, selling and serving food constitute a large group which includes farmers, gardeners, dairy workers, grocerymen, butchers, bakers, cooks, waiters and waitresses. Many food handlers are employed in food markets, bakeries, restaurants, tearooms, clubs, lunchrooms and soda bars. These persons constitute a large and important group in our present-day social and economic order. They have the serious obligation of guarding the health of the people by handling food in a sanitary manner. This obligation is not always fulfilled since, all too frequently, the most elementary rules of hygiene and sanitation are violated. Any food handling establishment which violates the principles of sanitation is a source of danger to those who patronize it.

Many communities have ordinances dealing with the sanitary handling of food, provide inspection service and maintain laboratories to guard the public against spoiled or contaminated food. Routine precautions in establishments where foods are sold or served should include protection from flies, cockroaches, rats, mice, cats and dogs, avoidance of promiscuous handling of food, exclusion of carriers of pathogens as food handlers, proper refrigeration of all perishable foods, sanitary washing of restaurant utensils and soda fountain glassware, and adequate clean toilet and hand-washing facilities with individual towels for those engaged in the handling and preparation of food.

Medical Examination of Food Handlers

The routine examination of all persons engaged in the handling and preparation of food is of considerable importance as a safeguard against food contamination. Its purpose is to detect active cases or carriers of disease which might be spread through food. The role of the human carrier in the transmission of disease has become increasingly important. Some of the bacterial flora of a person is generally always transferred to food carelessly handled, or handled by a person who soils his hands with body discharges. Thus, germs of communicable disease which are present in the nose, mouth, throat, urinary tract and intestinal tract, and which leave the body with the excretions of these parts, may be transferred to food. Most cases of typhoid fever at the present time come from carriers by way of contaminated food.

The carrier condition and the presence of infection usually can be detected by a thorough medical examination. It is advisable that the examination include a roentgenogram of the chest; sputum test for tubercle bacilli; a search for diphtheria bacilli and hemolytic streptococci in the nose and throat; a test of the feces for typhoid, paratyphoid, dysentery bacilli and dysentery amebae; a test of the urine for typhoid, paratyphoid and dysentery bacilli; and a blood test for syphilis. Compulsory inspection of food handlers at regular intervals is of considerable importance as a preventive of food-borne infection and food poisoning.

Schools for Food Handlers

In many communities short courses of instruction in food sanitation and personal cleanliness are offered to restaurant personnel, industrial and institutional food service employes, and bakery, meat market and grocery personnel. Such training offers opportunity to explain and emphasize (1) the danger of spreading disease through foods; (2) the importance of good personal habits, particularly the habit of keeping the hands clean; (3) the reasons for keeping the hands away from the nose and mouth and also why they should be washed after visits to the toilet; (4) the importance of refrigerating perishable foods at temperatures below 50° F.; and (5) the reasons for adopting proper dishwashing techniques in places where food and drink are served to the public.

SANITATION OF EATING AND DRINKING UTENSILS

Microorganisms in saliva and sputum may be transferred from the mouth of one person to another by means of eating and drinking utensils that have been inadequately washed. Dishes, knives, forks, spoons and glasses thus may be contaminated with the virus of the common cold, the influenza virus, diphtheria bacillus, the tubercle bacillus, streptococci capable of causing septic sore throat or scarlet fever, the spirochete of syphilis and other pathogens.

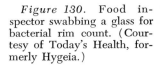
Figure 130. Food inspector swabbing a glass for bacterial rim count. (Courtesy of Today's Health, formerly Hygeia.)

The ordinary washing of eating utensils does not necessarily rid them of infective matter. In many establishments where food and drink are served the provisions for washing dishes and utensils are woefully inadequate. Often the washing is done in lukewarm soapy water, and in many taverns the glasses are washed in hot soapy water only once a day or a few times a week. Between customers they get but a perfunctory dip in cold water.

A highly recommended method of dishwashing requires the use of a three-compartment sink. In the first compartment the dishes are washed in hot water (115° to 120° F.) containing a suitable soap or other detergent. They are then transferred in a wire basket to the second compartment, where they are submerged, for at least two minutes, in clean water at a temperature of not less than 170° F. (77° C.). In the third compartment they are immersed for not less than two minutes in a chlorine bath containing not less than fifty parts per million of available chlorine. In place of chlorine, one of the new quaternary ammonium compounds may be used. These compounds leave a nontoxic film on the utensils which prevents the growth of bacteria. The utensils are not wiped with a towel but are allowed to drain and dry. Dish towels accumulate filth and germs which are passed on to the clean dishes and, therefore, should not be used. Mechanical dishwashers have come into use and, when properly operated, are quite satisfactory.

Bacteriological Examination of Washed Utensils

Bacteriological examination of washed eating and drinking utensils will reveal whether or not the washing methods used are satisfactory. A test frequently used consists in wiping a fork, spoon or glass rim with a sterile swab moistened with sterile water. The organisms picked up by the swab are then suspended in a small, measured volume of water which is plated in agar or a special medium for a count of colonies. A count of 100 bacteria or less is regarded as being within the margin of safety. Counts running into the thousands are not unusual. Figure 130 shows a food inspector swabbing the rim of a glass for a bacterial count.

QUESTIONS

1. Which kinds of foods are frequently responsible for bacterial food poisoning?
2. Which kinds of bacteria are responsible for outbreaks of food poisoning?
3. Discuss staphylococcal food poisoning?
4. How does *Salmonella* gastroenteritis differ from staphylococcal food poisoning?
5. (a) What is botulism? Name the causative organisms. What is their natural habitat?
    (b) Which foods are chiefly responsible for botulism?
    (c) What are the chief symptoms?
    (d) How does botulinum neurotoxin differ from staphylococcal enterotoxin in heat resistance?
6. Explain briefly streptococcal gastroenteritis.
7. Which communicable diseases are frequently spread through contaminated foods?
8. (a) State the precautionary measures that should be practiced by food handlers to prevent food poisoning and food-borne infections.
    (b) Of what importance is the proper washing of eating and drinking utensils?

REFERENCES

Adams, H. S.: Milk and Food Sanitation Practices. New York, The Commonwealth Fund, 1947.
Dack, G. M.: Food Poisoning. 3rd ed. Chicago, University of Chicago Press, 1956.
Ordinance and Code Relative to Eating and Drinking Establishments. U. S. Public Health Service, Publication No. 37. Washington, D. C., Government Printing Office, 1950.
Standard Methods for the Microbiological Examination of Foods. New York, American Public Health Association, 1958.
Tanner, F. W., and Tanner, L. P.: Food-borne Infections and Intoxications. 2nd ed. Champaign, Ill., Gerrard Press, 1953.

VIII · Infection and Body Defenses

26 • Disease Production by Microorganisms

The discovery that microorganisms are the etiological agents of many diseases of man, animals and plants has been one of the great achievements of modern times. The work of Louis Pasteur in France and Robert Koch in Germany laid the foundation for our present-day understanding of the role of microorganisms in the production of disease.

The human race has had a long and arduous struggle to survive against infectious disease. From the remotest periods of antiquity to the present time man has been ravaged by disease. Plagues and pestilences have stalked the earth, have scarred human history and altered its course. For untold centuries man was helpless against his death-dealing microbial foes. Although he now has some defenses against them, they still jeopardize human life and well-being. It should be understood, however, that although microorganisms loom large as the cause of human disease, only a small minority are disease producers.

Infectious disease is one manifestation of the biological phenomenon of parasitism. Gaining a livelihood by parasitism is common in the living world. A parasite must be adapted to live within the tissues of the host and be able to withstand the efforts of the host to destroy it. The parasite is without malicious intent toward the host, and the fact that injury and even death may result is only incidental to the habits of living of the parasite. Besides microorganisms, there are many species of multicellular animals that have taken up life as parasites. Among these are mites, ticks, flukes, tapeworms, trichina worms and hookworms. Most parasitic species have a limited range of hosts. Practically every animal species is parasitized by various types of organisms. The human species serves as host for innumerable parasites.

Parasites, however, do not necessarily injure their hosts. It will be recalled that in the association between parasite and host known as commensalism the host is not harmed, and that the host is actually benefited in the association known as symbiosis. It may be assumed that those parasites that do no appreciable harm or that actually benefit the host have adjusted themselves more adequately to the parasitic mode of life than those that cause disease, since it is to the advantage of the parasite not to jeopardize the survival of the host. If the parasite kills the host, it perishes with the host. Those parasites that injure the host are called *pathogens.* Pathogenic microorganisms are found among the bacteria, protozoa, yeasts, molds, rickettsiae and viruses.

Some microorganisms are *obligate parasites,* not being able to live, ordinarily, apart from the host species; others can live as saprophytes but become parasitic when the opportunity to do so presents itself. The latter are known as *facultative parasites.* Some microorganisms are capable of producing disease without being parasitic. An outstanding example is *Clostridium botulinum* which, although never parasitic, belongs nevertheless in the category of pathogens in that it produces powerful toxins in foods, which, when consumed by human beings, produce severe illness and frequently death.

MICROORGANISMS INDIGENOUS TO THE BODY

Besides those microorganisms which are capable of producing disease, there are many which use the human body as their host without inflicting injury. They are parasitic without being pathogenic. Some of these are closely related to pathogenic forms, and some are potential pathogens. Since a large number of bacteria and, frequently, various protozoa and fungi make the human body their permanent abode, it is appropriate that they be given some consideration before discussing the production of disease by microorganisms. These organisms live on the skin and the various mucous membranes, obtaining their sustenance from the local organic debris and secretions. They do not usually grow within the living tissues but in immediate contact with them. It is probable that disease-producing microorganisms evolved from harmless parasitic species. Many of the pathogenic bacteria closely resemble forms which are a part of the normal flora* of the human body. The typhoid fever bacillus, for example, resembles certain organisms normally present in the intestinal tract, not only in its morphology, but also in many of its physiological character-istics. Some persons harbor virulent pathogens which they are capable of resisting sufficiently to prevent the development of infection but which, when transmitted to others, may cause serious disease.

The indigenous microorganisms of the body may be referred to as the "resident flora," to distinguish them from transient (exogenous) forms whose presence is temporary and, in many cases, merely accidental. The

---

* Since most of the microorganisms indigenous to the human body are classified as members of the plant kingdom, they may, for convenience, be referred to by the col-lective term "flora," even when protozoa are included.

resident organisms have adjusted themselves to each other as well as to the environmental factors prevailing on the tissues of the body.

Body tissues inhabited by microorganisms include chiefly the skin, oral cavity, nasal passages, throat, intestines and the genitalia. Each of these areas harbors its own characteristic microbic population. The blood, muscles, glands and closed body cavities, such as the pleural and peritoneal cavities, are normally without microbial inhabitants. Most of the microorganisms that inhabit the body have a localized distribution. Thus *Escherichia coli* lives in the human intestinal tract and does not usually grow elsewhere in the body, although it may occasionally be present on the skin, especially that of the hands.

The resident microbial population of the human body is not absolutely constant but tends to vary from time to time and from place to place. The climate in which a person lives and his particular diet, as well as other factors, influence his microbial occupants. Certain species live in association with the human body in certain regions of the earth, whereas others inhabit the body in all geographic regions.

At birth the various mucous membranes of a newborn child are free from microorganisms. Within a few hours a microbial population begins to develop. It appears that the gradual acquisition of a microbial population causes these membranes to develop sufficient resistance to prevent the organisms from doing damage to them. It has been found that animals reared experimentally under "germ-free" conditions readily become infected with chance contaminants which ordinarily are without pathogenicity. In these animals a bacterium such as *Bacillus subtilis,* which normally is incapable of causing infection, may function as a pathogen. It is probable that at times the indigenous flora may be beneficial by exerting antibiotic effects on invading pathogens. Certain intestinal bacteria may be considered to be beneficial in that they synthesize vitamins which can be absorbed into the blood stream and utilized by the body.

Flora of the Skin

Certain species are normally present on the skin. The predominant forms are *Staphylococcus aureus* and *Staphylococcus epidermidis.* These organisms are present not only on the surface of the skin but are found also in the hair follicles and the ducts of the sweat glands. Having pathogenicity, they are capable of causing wound infections, abscesses, boils and infections following surgical operations. Many other forms such as streptococci, sarcinae and colon bacteria are frequently present. Rod-shaped forms resembling the diphtheria bacillus and accordingly referred to as *diphtheroids* are sometimes found. In the region of the genital organs and the anus, an acid-fast organism known as *Mycobacterium smegmatis* is usually present. It is a harmless bacterium closely resembling the tubercle bacillus (*Mycobacterium tuberculosis*) in morphology and may be mistaken for it. Because of their contact with many objects, the hands may acquire a large assortment of transient organisms and may at times become contaminated with pathogens of various kinds.

Microorganisms of the Mouth

A large number of species of microorganisms inhabit the human mouth. Various cocci, including staphylococci, streptococci (particularly *Streptococcus salivarius*), neisseriae and pneumococci, are usually present. These are chiefly nonvirulent varieties. Diphtheroids are sometimes found.

Members of the genus *Lactobacillus* are common mouth bacteria. These organisms ferment various sugars with the production of acid. There is evidence which indicates that the acid produced by these organisms is responsible for tooth decay. The diet of the person has a bearing on the number of these organisms present. They usually become numerous when the diet is high in carbohydrates.

Various species of spirochetes are often found in the human mouth. The largest (7 to 20 microns) of the mouth spirochetes is *Borrelia buccalis*. *Borrelia vincentii* is often present. It is associated with a fusiform bacillus (*Fusobacterium fusiforme*) in Vincent's angina (trench mouth). *Treponema microdentium* is another spirochete frequently present in the normal mouth.

Yeasts can often be isolated from the human mouth. A small coccus, *Veillonella parvula,* and a small rod, *Bacteroides melaninogenicus,* are frequently present. A large percentage of persons harbor the mouth ameba *Endamoeba gingivalis*. It is found about the gums and in the tartar of the teeth.

Flora of the Nose and Throat

The nose and throat have a more limited microbial population than the mouth. Staphylococci, streptococci and diphtheroids are commonly found. Some persons harbor meningococci, pneumococci, *Neisseria catarrhalis* and *Haemophilus haemolyticus* in the nasopharynx. A variety of microbes may lurk in the crypts of the tonsils. The trachea, bronchi and lung tissues, however, are practically free from microorganisms.

Intestinal Microorganisms

The majority of the microorganisms that are swallowed with food and saliva are quickly destroyed by the hydrochloric acid of the gastric juice. The healthy stomach is usually free from living microbes. In cases of hypoacidity, however, microorganisms may be abundant in the stomach. Analyses have revealed that the intestinal contents of many animals contain millions of microorganisms per cubic centimeter.

The intestinal population of breast-fed infants is composed almost entirely of *Lactobacillus bifidus*. The intestinal bacteria of infants fed on cow's milk are quite different, consisting largely of *Lactobacillus acidophilus,* with relatively large numbers of cocci, Gram-negative rods, and Gram-positive, aerobic and anaerobic spore-bearing bacilli. As the child's diet becomes more varied, the intestinal population changes.

In the adult the upper part of the small intestine contains few microorganisms. *Streptococcus faecalis* and staphylococci are usually the only ones found. Lower down the species and individual organisms become more numerous. In the large intestine they are exceedingly abundant. Of considerable importance is the coliform group of bacteria. As mentioned in a previous chapter, the coliform bacteria are nonspore-bearing, Gram-negative rods which ferment lactose with the production of gas and acid. Two genera are represented, *Escherichia* and *Aerobacter*. The most important species of this group is *Escherichia coli*, which is a constant inhabitant of the intestinal tract of man and warm-blooded animals and is present in large numbers. It is ordinarily harmless but may cause infection when some damage to the intestinal wall allows it to invade other parts of the body. It may also cause infection of the genitourinary tract. In agonal stages of disease it may invade the blood stream. It is probable that the coliform bacteria constitute the parent group from which many of the intestinal pathogens have been derived. Other organisms often present are anaerobic spore-bearing bacteria such as *Clostridium lentoputrescens, Cl. perfringens* and *Cl. tetani;* acid-producing bacteria, including *Lactobacillus acidophilus;* aerobic spore-bearers, such as *Bacillus subtilis;* a Gram-negative rod, *Alcaligenes faecalis;* protozoa such as *Endamoeba coli* and, less frequently, *Endolimax nana, Iodamoeba bütchlii* and *Dientamoeba fragilis;* and many other kinds, among which may be mentioned streptococci, staphylococci, spirochetes, yeasts, molds and thermophilic bacteria. It has been estimated that from one-fourth to one-third of the dry weight of human feces consists of microorganisms.

The relative proportions of the different kinds of microorganisms present is influenced to a considerable extent by the diet. Experiments on rats, as well as on human subjects, have indicated that the nature of the intestinal flora and fauna can be altered by the regulation of the diet. The growth of certain microorganisms can be increased, and of others diminished, by selective food material. A high carbohydrate intake favors the growth of acid-producing bacteria and, at the same time, decreases the number of proteolytic forms. Lactose (milk sugar) is especially effective in encouraging the development of acid-producing bacteria, particularly *L. acidophilus*. Because lactose digests slowly, a large percentage of the amount taken reaches the large intestine, where it serves as food for acid-producing bacteria. In utilizing lactose, these bacteria produce large amounts of lactic acid, which inhibits the development of proteolytic bacteria.

Flora of the Urogenital Tract

The urethra of males has a few staphylococci, diphtheroids, and a short Gram-positive diplobacillus. The female urethra is either sterile or contains a few cocci. In the secretions about the external genitals of both males and females, as previously mentioned, a characteristic acid-fast bacillus known as *Mycobacterium smegmatis* is common. A spirochete, *Treponema genitalis,* is often found on both male and female genitalia.

The human vulva contains a varied flora. In children up to the age of puberty the reaction of the vaginal secretion is alkaline. The organisms present are chiefly streptococci, staphylococci, diphtheroids and yeasts. At puberty, glycogen is deposited in the cells of the vaginal epithelium and the reaction becomes acid, owing largely to the growth of acid-producing rods (lactobacilli) which ferment glycogen, giving rise to lactic acid. The flora remains mixed, including diphtheroids, tetracocci, sarcinae, staphylococci, streptococci, coliforms and yeasts. At menopause the flora reverts to that which prevailed before puberty.

INFECTION

The invasion of body tissues by microorganisms which multiply there and disturb the normal performance of body functions is termed *infection.* In general, diseases are of two kinds, *infectious* and *noninfectious.* A functional disturbance caused by the growth and activity of biological agents in the body is called an infectious disease, whereas noninfectious diseases are due to various other factors such as deficiencies in essential food materials, as in scurvy; deranged metabolism due to endocrine disturbances, as in diabetes; as well as to chemical poisons, mechanical injury, radiations and degeneration of organs due to age.

A pathogen is usually restricted to one or a few host species. A few are more promiscuous. There are many species of pathogens which, when they invade the body, become lodged in the intercellular spaces of the tissues. They do not enter tissue cells. Certain microorganisms, however, must enter tissue cells in order to grow and multiply in the body of the host. These *intracellular parasites* include the rickettsiae, viruses and the protozoa which cause malaria. The branch of medical science which deals with the nature of disease, particularly with the structural and functional changes caused by disease, is known as *pathology.*

Infectious disease implies not only injury to the body but also the response the body makes to counteract the pathogens that have gained entrance to the tissues. Disease is a process involving the interplay of pathogen and host, each seeking to maintain itself in a competitive world. The functional disturbances caused by the presence of pathogens is manifested by physical signs known as *symptoms.* Usually an infection is accompanied by an alteration in anatomical structure at the site of the infection, which is known as a *lesion.* After pathogens have invaded body tissues, they increase in number and give rise to chemical products which may injure the cells in the immediate area as well as cells in remote areas to which they may be carried by the circulating blood and lymph. This action on the part of pathogens evokes an immediate response on the part of the body by a process which, in its main lines of strategy, includes both the attempt to destroy the invading organisms and to neutralize the toxic substances produced by them. These responses by the host will check or modify the infection.

TYPES OF INFECTION

Most of the infectious diseases are transmitted by natural means from one person to another; i.e., they are *communicable.* Tetanus is an example of an infectious disease that is not communicable, since it is not transmitted from one person to another either directly or indirectly. Communicable diseases which spread readily by direct or indirect contact from one person to another are sometimes called *contagious diseases.* The term is applied especially to diseases such as measles, scarlet fever, whooping cough and smallpox, which spread mainly through direct association between sick and well persons. When a disease runs a short course followed by death or recovery, it is said to be *acute.* The term *chronic* is applied to a disease characterized by a gradual development of symptoms and prolonged illness. A disease which has a low incidence, but is always present in a community or within certain geographical limits, is referred to as being *endemic.* Malaria, for example, is endemic in certain parts of the United States. The term *epidemic* is applied when a disease spreads rapidly through a community, affects a relatively large number of inhabitants, and then subsides. When an epidemic spreads over a large part of the world, it is called a *pandemic.* The branch of medical science which deals with epidemic diseases is known as *epidemiology.*

Certain pathogenic organisms remain at, or close to, the site of invasion, producing a *local infection,* whereas others become distributed through the body, resulting in a *systemic infection.* Although some organisms remain localized, the body as a whole may experience the effects of their presence, owing to soluble toxic substances which they liberate and which become distributed through the body by the blood and lymph, doing harm to susceptible tissues such as the heart, nervous system, kidneys or other structures. A local abscess, for example, may give rise to fever, accelerate the heart beat and cause other symptoms.

In some cases, certain pathogens may become transient invaders of the blood stream, entering it from one or more infected areas. This may enable them to become established in new locations in the tissues of the body. The temporary presence of bacteria in the blood stream is known as *bacteremia.* When the pathogens remain in the blood stream and proliferate there, the condition is known as *septicemia.* The term *toxemia* applies to an infection in which the localized organisms produce a toxin which enters the blood stream from the site of localization and causes damage to tissues for which it has a special affinity. Tetanus and diphtheria are examples of toxemias. An infectious disease which is characterized by a skin eruption is known as an *exanthem* or *exanthema* (plural, *exanthems* or *exanthemata*). Scarlet fever and measles are examples.

Most infections are caused by the presence of one kind of microorganism. Some infections require the cooperative action of two or more species. Vincent's infection (trench mouth) is caused by the combined attack of a spirochete (*Borrelia vincentii*), a fusiform bacillus (*Fusobacterium fusiforme*) a streptococcus and a vibrio.

FACTORS INFLUENCING INFECTION

Not all persons invaded by a given pathogen will become infected. There are four principal factors which determine whether an invading organism can establish a pathological state in a given host: (1) the virulence of the organim, (2) resistance of the individual, (3) the numerical strength of the invading organisms, and (4) the portal or route of invasion.

Virulence denotes the degree of pathogenicity of a disease-producing microorganism. Virulence is a relative condition; it differs among different species and among the different strains of a particular species. Some pathogens are only slightly virulent, whereas others are moderately or highly virulent. The virulence of some pathogens is due chiefly to their invasive capacity and their ability to produce chemical substances injurious to the tissues of the host. Highly virulent microorganisms are well equipped to withstand the defenses mobilized by the host.

Virulence may be altered. The virulence of some organisms may be enhanced for a certain host species by inoculation and frequent transfer from one individual of the species to another. Certain pathogens lose their virulence when cultivated on artificial media, whereas others retain their virulence even after many years of cultivation on laboratory media. In capsulated pathogenic bacteria there is a close relationship between the presence of the capsule and virulence. Such organisms usually lose their virulence when they lose their capsules. Loss of capsules occurs when these organisms are cultivated in the laboratory. This is true particularly of the pneumococcus (*Diplococcus pneumoniae*). Reduction in virulence is called *attenuation*. An organism which has experienced reduction in virulence is said to be *attenuated*. Attenuated microorganisms are frequently used in the preparation of vaccines to immunize people against disease. This will be given consideration in a later chapter.

Some persons have greater resistance to a given pathogen than do others. The body of some persons contains specific defensive agents capable of destroying certain pathogens. Susceptible persons lack these defenses, or have them in insufficient amount to prevent infection with organisms of high virulence. A given person may be susceptible to one disease and resistant to another. With some diseases the state of health of the person is a factor in resistance to infection. In some cases, normal resistance to infection may be reduced by dietary deficiencies of proteins or vitamins. In general, poor health lowers resistance, while good health helps the body to ward off and cope with invading organisms. Good health, however, offers no protection against the etiological agents of such diseases as smallpox, syphilis and gonorrhea.

Whether or not infection occurs depends also upon the numerical strength of the invading pathogens. A small number of invaders may be quickly subdued by the first onslaught of the defensive forces of the host, whereas a larger number might be able to establish a base of operations within the tissues of the host. The greater the virulence, the smaller the number needed to cause infection.

The portal of entry or invasion is of great importance in determining whether or not disease will occur. A number of portals of invasion are available; among these are the skin, the respiratory tract, the alimentary canal and the genitourinary system. To establish itself in the tissues, a given pathogen must gain entrance to the body by the route to which it is adapted. As a rule, there is but one favorable portal for a particular organism, but for a few species several invasion routes are available. To produce typhoid fever the etiological agents of this infection must enter the body via the mouth to reach the intestines. The tetanus bacillus may be swallowed with impunity; but when it enters a wound, it is capable of establishing itself there and causing disease. The genital tract is the usual portal of invasion of the gonococcus, and the pneumococcus ordinarily uses the respiratory tract as the portal of entrance. The various portals of invasion will be discussed more fully in the chapter that follows.

HARMFUL MICROBIAL PRODUCTS

The harmful effects of infection are due chiefly to chemical products resulting from the activity of pathogens in the body. In some instances these substances, though not highly potent, nevertheless alter the course of events of normal tissue metabolism. In many cases, however, they are endowed with great potency and seriously disturb the functioning of the body. They injure the body in characteristic ways: some damage ed blood cells, others injure nerve cells, whereas still others destroy leukocytes. They are absorbed by, and do damage to, the cells for which they have an affinity.

Most of the harmful substances produced by pathogens not only harm the body but also stimulate it to form definite defensive substances and are, therefore, *antigenic*. An *antigen* by definition is an agent which, by its presence in the body, stimulates body tissues to produce defensive chemical substances referred to collectively as *antibodies*. An antibody is capable of neutralizing or inactivating the antigen that stimulated its production.

Included among the injurious substances, elaborated by pathogens are exotoxins, endotoxins, leukocidins, hemolysins, lecithinase, fibrinolysin and hyaluronidase.

Exotoxins

A few species of bacteria exert their pathogenic action by producing and liberating soluble compounds of high toxicity known as *exotoxins*. Exotoxins are water-soluble products of bacterial metabolism which, upon being secreted from the cells, enter the blood stream. They are carried to distant parts of the body and may exert their toxic effects on tissues or organs remote from the site of infection. Exotoxins are not only produced in the body of the host but also appear in culture media during the growth of bacteria in the laboratory. By injecting experimental animals with a specific exotoxin, the essential symptoms of the disease in which these exotoxins play a role can be reproduced. Thus, the injection of diphtheria exotoxin produces symptoms similar to those of clinical diphtheria.

Chemically, exotoxins have the characteristics of proteins. Like proteins, they can be precipitated by ammonium sulfate. Purification, in some instances, has been accomplished by chemical methods similar to those for the purification of proteins. Some exotoxins have been crystallized and obtained in a highly pure state. Analysis of the crystals has confirmed the protein nature of exotoxins. Some, but not all, exotoxins are inactivated by proteolytic enzymes such as pepsin and trypsin.

Exotoxins are endowed with a number of unique properties which differentiate them from other toxic substances. As a group they have the following properties in common:

1. They are compounds of high toxicity. The potency of some is so great that exceedingly minute quantities are deadly when injected into the animal body.

2. They are highly specific; the exotoxin produced by one species is different in its action on the body from that produced by another species. Each kind has characteristic affinities for particular host tissues.

3. Exotoxins are highly antigenic, inciting body tissues to produce specific counteracting antibodies known as *antitoxins*. Each antitoxin will neutralize only the type of toxin which incited its production.

4. Most exotoxins are readily destroyed by heat; i.e., they are *thermolabile*. Heating to 60° C. for ten minutes usually inactivates exotoxins. A few are more heat stable, requiring higher temperatures for inactivation. Certain staphylococci produce an exotoxin (enterotoxin) which can withstand 100° C.

5. When introduced into experimental animals, they do not produce toxic effects immediately. They differ from common poisons in that there is a delay of several hours (sometimes twenty-four hours or more) before their harmful effects are manifested. In other words, they require an incubation in the body of the host. Even when introduced into experimental animals in large doses, the period of incubation is not completely abolished. It is not known why there is a delay in action. One explanation

is that, owing to the large size of the exotoxin molecule, they diffuse rather slowly into susceptible cells. A poison must enter a cell before it can do it harm. Another explanation is that exotoxins must be activated before they become poisonous.

6. Treatment of exotoxins with dilute formaldehyde or certain other chemicals results in loss of toxicity without loss of antigenicity. The resulting detoxified exotoxin is known as *toxoid.* By injecting the body with toxoid, immunity can be artificially induced against such diseases as diphtheria and tetanus. The various methods for inducing immunity to disease will be discussed in Chapter 29.

Among the small number of pathogens producing exotoxins the more important ones are *Corynebacterium diphtheriae,* the diphtheria bacillus; *Clostridium tetani,* the causative organism of tetanus or lockjaw; *Cl. botulinum,* the cause of one form of food poisoning; *Cl. perfringens,* the cause of gas gangrene; certain strains of *Staphylococcus aureus* and *Streptococcus pyogenes;* and *Shigella dysenteriae,* one of the organisms responsible for bacillary dysentery.

Toxins similar to bacterial exotoxins, but of a lower degree of potency, are found in the venom of snakes, the poison of scorpions and some spiders, and certain plant poisons (phytotoxins) such as ricin (from the castor bean) and abrin (from the seed of Indian licorice).

Endotoxins

Endotoxins differ from exotoxins in that they are less toxic and do not diffuse out of the bacterial cells. They are intimately bound to protoplasmic constituents and are liberated only after the death and disintegration of the bacterial cells. They can be obtained when bacterial cells are disrupted by grinding or by repeated freezing and thawing and also by allowing the dead cells to undergo autolysis. They are present in many saprophytes as well as pathogens and appear to be lipid-carbohydrate complexes in association with protein or protein degradation products. Endotoxins lack the definite specificity of exotoxins. They cannot be converted into toxoids upon treatment with formaldehyde or other chemicals and are relatively thermostable. They have little antigenicity and do not ordinarily elicit antitoxin production. Although their toxicity is relatively low, endotoxins play an important role in the production of disease by microorganisms.

Leukocidins

Certain pathogens, through the agency of *leukocidins,* exert a destructive action on those white blood cells (leukocytes) that are known as phagocytes. One of the important functions of phagocytes is to engulf and destroy invading microorganisms. They are wandering cells capable of passing through the walls of the smallest blood vessels and congregating at the site of infection. They thus constitute an important part of the defense mechanism of the body. Their role in this connection will be discussed in greater detail in Chapter 28. Leukocidins are species-specific and antigenic. They elicit the production of specific antileukocidins on the part of the host. They are produced by a number of pathogens, particularly the pus-producing cocci (staphylococci, streptococci and pneumococci).

Hemolysins

Hemolysins, or *hemolytic toxins,* cause the disintegration or lysis of the red blood corpuscles (erythrocytes) of the host. The red corpuscles serve chiefly as oxygen carriers. When they are hemolyzed in considerable numbers, the process of oxidation (energy production) is greatly decreased. Although all hemolysins act in the same way on red corpuscles, those produced by one species are not identical with those of another. Hemolysins are species-specific and are frequently named after the species producing them. Hemolysins* are antigenic in that, during the course of infection, they evoke the production of counteractive substances known as antihemolysins on the part of the host. Antihemolysins are specific; those formed against hemolysins produced by one species will not inactivate those produced by another species. It is due to the lysis of red blood corpuscles that anemia is one of the common results of infection.

Hemolysin production may be demonstrated by growing certain pathogens (streptococci or staphylococci) on agar containing whole blood. The bacterial colonies that develop will be surrounded by either a greenish zone of discolored red blood corpuscles or a clear, colorless zone. Those that produce a green zone are *alpha hemolytic,* whereas those that give rise to a clear, colorless zone are *beta hemolytic.*

Hyaluronidase

A number of pathogenic bacteria such as *Clostridium perfringens, Streptococcus pyogenes, Staphylococcus aureus* and *Diplococcus pneumoniae* produce *hyaluronidase,* an enzyme that catalyzes the hydrolysis of hyaluronic acid. This acid is an essential component of the intercellular cementing material that binds tissues together. The hydrolysis of hyaluronic acid causes a dissolution of the cementing substance and thus increases the invasiveness of pathogenic organisms. Hyaluronidase is referred to as a *spreading factor* since it facilitates the dissemination of bacteria through body tissues.

Lecithinase

A few pathogenic bacteria produce the enzyme *lecithinase,* which hydrolyzes the lecithin present in tissues. This enzyme is destructive to

---

* Hemolysins produced by pathogens should not be confounded with the hemolysins produced when red corpuscles of one species are injected into the blood stream of another species. Those produced by the animal body belong to the category of antibodies, whereas those produced by pathogens are antigens.

many types of cells and facilitates the penetration and spread of pathogens through body tissues. Its action is rapid. *Clostridium perfringens* is an example of a pathogen that elaborates this enzyme.

Fibrinolysin

In some infections the body forms blood clots around the site of infection as a defense measure to prevent spread of the organisms. A blood clot consists of blood corpuscles enmeshed in interlacing strands of a substance known as fibrin. Some pathogens, streptococci in particular, produce an enzyme, *fibrinolysin,* which is capable of dissolving the fibrin of blood clots. This action on the part of pathogens favors their invasion and spread through body tissues.

PROOF OF PATHOGENICITY

It is not a simple matter to obtain positive proof of the etiological or causal relationship of an organism to a particular disease. Infected body tissues frequently contain secondary invaders as well as saprophytic organisms which live in the damaged tissues. Unless great care is exercised in the search for the causative organism of a particular disease, erroneous conclusions may be reached. This happened frequently in the past. To keep investigators from committing such errors, Robert Koch, one of the early leaders in the field of microbiology, outlined a set of conditions that must be fulfilled before an organism can be accepted as the etiological agent of a particular disease. These criteria or rules, known as "Koch's Postulates," were mentioned in Chapter 2, and are repeated here:

1. The suspected organism must be present invariably in all cases of the disease.

2. It must be isolated from an infected individual and grown in pure culture.

3. The organism in pure culture when inoculated into a susceptible animal must produce the disease in question.

4. The suspected organism must be recovered from the inoculated animal.

In some cases it has not been possible to carry out these postulates, owing largely to the fact that some pathogens cannot be cultivated on artificial media. In such cases lesser evidence must be relied upon. This is true of leprosy. Circumstantial evidence suggests that *Mycobacterium leprae* is the etiological agent of leprosy, yet the postulates of Koch have not been fulfilled for this organism. In some instances the presence of specific antibodies, such as agglutinins or bacteriolysins (see Chapter 28), in the blood of a person or animal recovering from an infection may indicate the etiological agent of the disease. The techniques utilized in determining the presence of such antibodies are referred to as immunological or serological tests.

COURSE OF AN INFECTION

Infectious disease is a dynamic process; from a slow or sudden beginning it progresses, reaching in many cases a peak, and finally ending in an acute disease, in recovery or in death. The course of an acute infectious disease may be divided into three distinct stages as follows: (1) incubation period, (2) period of active disease, and (3) convalescence.

The incubation period represents the time lag between the invasion of the body by the pathogenic agents and the first manifestations of the symptoms of the disease. During this period the invaders must overcome the defenses of the body to a sufficient degree so that they may increase in numbers and establish themselves in the tissues of the host. The incubation period varies considerably in length in different diseases, being short in some (one to two days) and long in others (three months or more). In typhoid fever the incubation period is from seven to fourteen days; in smallpox, from five to seven days; in influenza, from one to four days; in syphilis, from three to four weeks; and in rabies, from one to three months or longer.

The period of active disease follows the incubation period. During this period the symptoms manifest themselves, and the strife between the invaders and the invaded host continues until the invaders or the host has won the struggle. In acute diseases this period is short, usually a week or two, but in chronic diseases, such as tuberculosis, leprosy and malaria, it may last for months or years.

If the defensive forces of the host gain the ascendancy, convalescence sets in, during which the invaders are gradually eliminated, damaged tissue repaired and bodily functions returned to their normal state. In some cases the pathogens are not completely eliminated, and the person then becomes a so-called carrier of the disease.

QUESTIONS

1. Give a brief account of the microorganisms normally present (1) on the skin, (2) in the mouth, (3) in the nose and throat, (4) in the intestinal tract, (5) in the genital organs.

2. (*a*) What is meant by the term "infection"?

(*b*) Define the following terms as they apply to disease: (1) communicable, (2) contagious, (3) acute, (4) chronic, (5) endemic, (6) epidemic, (7) epidemiology, (8) bacteremia, (9) septicemia, (10) toxemia.

3. Name and discuss the four principal factors which determine whether or not an invading organism will cause infection.

4. (*a*) What is an antigen? An antibody?

(*b*) What are exotoxins? What unique characteristics do they have? Name some pathogens that produce exotoxins.

5. Explain briefly: (1) endotoxins, (2) leukocidins, (3) hemolysins, (4) hyaluronidase, (5) lecithinase, (6) fibrinolysin.

6. State Koch's postulates.

7. What is meant by the "incubation period" of an infectious disease?

REFERENCES

Burnet, Sir M.: The Natural History of Infectious Disease. 2nd ed. New York, Cambridge University Press, 1953.

Burrows, W.: Textbook of Microbiology. 17th ed. Philadelphia, W. B. Saunders Company, 1959.

Dubos, R. J., ed.: Bacterial and Mycotic Infections of Man. 3rd ed. Philadelphia, J. B. Lippincott Company, 1958.

Dubos, R. J.: Biochemical Determinants of Microbial Disease. Cambridge, Harvard University Press, 1954.

Howie, J. W., and O'Hea, A. J., ed.: Mechanism of Microbial Pathogenicity. New York, Cambridge University Press, 1955.

Most, H., ed.: Parasitic Infections in Man. New York, Columbia University Press, 1951.

Rivers, T. M., ed.: Viral and Rickettsial Infections of Man. 3rd ed. Philadelphia, J. B. Lippincott Company, 1959.

Smith, D. T., et al.: Zinsser's Textbook of Bacteriology. 11th ed. New York, Appleton-Century-Crofts, Inc., 1957.

Smith, T.: Parasitism and Disease. Princeton, N. J., Princeton University Press, 1934.

Wilson, G. S., and Miles, A. A.: Topley and Wilson's Principles of Bacteriology and Immunity. 2 vols. 4th ed. Baltimore, The Williams & Wilkins Company, 1955.

27 • The Sources and Transmission of Infection

For each communicable disease there is (1) a source or reservoir of the specific causal agent, (2) a mode of transfer to and ingress into the body of a susceptible host, and (3) an escape route from the infected host. The existence of infection thus involves a chain of events. If one of the links is eliminated, the chain is broken and infection is blocked. The scientific approach to the prevention of infectious diseases is through investigations that reveal the sources of infectious agents; the modes of transfer to new hosts, including the portals of entry; and the avenues of exit from the host.

Knowledge concerning these points has been obtained for many of the infectious diseases and has had a profound effect on the development of preventive measures. In numerous cases it has enabled man to interrupt, at its most vulnerable point, the cycle of events involved in infection and its dissemination. The knowledge, for example, that drinking water may play a role in the spread of typhoid fever and other diseases has enabled man to nullify it as a vehicle of infection by developing methods of water purification.

SOURCES OF INFECTIOUS AGENTS

Most pathogens are incapable of growth and multiplication, under natural conditions, outside the body of the host. Microorganisms that cause disease in man are, in most cases, strictly human pathogens which cannot ordinarily live apart from the human body. The body of man, therefore, is the reservoir of the agents of these diseases.

But man is also susceptible to a number of diseases which occur primarily in animals. The causal agents of these diseases thus have more than one natural habitat, but the animal hosts as a rule constitute their

400

chief reservoir. Rabies may be cited as an example. Various species of animals are the reservoirs of this disease, and although man is susceptible, he does not serve as the source or reservoir of the causative organisms.

Human reservoirs are not only those persons who exhibit the symptoms of the disease but also those who are carriers. Not only those who exhibit typical symptoms, but also those whose infection is so mild or vague that it may escape recognition (subclinical cases), are reservoirs of pathogens and constitute a hazard to others. Infected persons and carriers more or less continually extrude microbes into their environment in secretions and excretions from the respiratory tract, gastrointestinal and urinary tracts, as well as the skin and wounds.

Carriers of Infection

A *carrier* is a person who harbors and discharges pathogens but does not exhibit the symptoms of disease. The carrier state can be recognized only through bacteriological methods. There are a number of classifications of carriers. *Convalescent carriers* are temporary carriers who, after recovering from an infection, continue to harbor the causative organisms for a variable time. The carrier state may be a temporary condition, lasting not more than ten weeks, or it may be more or less permanent, persisting for months or years or for the remainder of the person's life, in which case the person is referred to as a *chronic carrier*. Among those who recover from diphtheria and typhoid fever there are always some who become chronic carriers. A *contact carrier* is one who harbors a pathogen which he acquired through close contact with an infected person without acquiring the disease. This is usually a temporary condition. In epidemics of cerebrospinal meningitis many persons become contact carriers without acquiring the disease.

Carriers are a source of great danger to others and add to the difficulties of man's fight against disease. Attention is now being focused on carriers, for they are the most important reservoirs of the causal agents of many diseases. Since it is generally not known which persons are carriers, it is practically impossible to avoid associating with them. The sick person is usually confined, coming in contact with few people, but the carrier is at large, mingling freely with others, a condition which makes him an effective disseminator of the germs of disease. During the intervals between epidemics, the infective agents are kept alive in the bodies of carriers. Carriers serve as reservoirs for the organisms causing typhoid fever, dysentery (bacillary and amebic), diphtheria, scarlet fever, meningococcal meningitis, pneumonia and numerous other diseases.

The significance of carriers in the transmission of disease was first appreciated and established in the case of typhoid fever. The classic example of a carrier is Mary Mallon, better known as "Typhoid Mary," who was the first person discovered to be a chronic carrier of typhoid bacilli. Being a cook, she spread typhoid wherever she worked. She is known to have been the cause of at least fifty cases of typhoid fever between the years of 1900 and 1915. It was definitely confirmed in 1907 that Mary Mallon was a typhoid carrier. She was taken into custody at that time and released on parole in 1910, promising not to engage in cooking. She broke her parole and in 1915 was engaged as a cook in a maternity hospital where she became the source of an epidemic involving twenty-five cases. After this she was isolated for about ten years and later housed in a country cottage at the expense of the state of New York.

Animal Sources

Diseases that man can contract from animals are anthrax from cattle and sheep; glanders from horses; brucellosis (undulant fever) from cattle, goats and swine; plague from rats; psittacosis from parrots and related birds; tularemia from rabbits; and rabies from various animals. These diseases are primarily animal infections that occur in man only because of the existence of animal reservoirs. They are not ordinarily transmitted from man to man but are transmitted from animal to man and from animal to animal. Most of the pathogens to which animals are susceptible have their reservoir in animal species.

Contaminated Materials

Some infectious agents can survive for a more or less extended period of time in an environment other than their natural habitat. Being cast off from the body of the host through natural avenues of exit, they frequently find their way into foods, water, soil, debris, dust and air and may become attached to various inanimate objects. They do not ordinarily multiply in this environment, diminishing rather than increasing in numbers, but may remain alive long enough to be transferred to a new host. Staphylococci, streptococci and diphtheria bacilli may remain alive suspended in the air for several days. Typhoid bacilli die within a few hours when exposed to the drying action of air but can remain alive in water for days or weeks and, when frozen in ice, will survive for several months. In milk and certain other foods some pathogenic species may grow and actually increase in numbers. This is true of typhoid and diphtheria bacilli and some of the streptococci. Inanimate vehicles of infectious agents may be responsible for the dissemination of typhoid fever, dysentery, Asiatic cholera and other diseases. Some pathogens die almost instantly in the environment outside the body of the host. This is true of the spirochetes of syphilis, gonococci and meningococci.

A few human diseases are caused by organisms which normally live as saprophytes. When accidentally introduced into wounds, they are capable of producing infection. This is true of *Clostridium tetani,* the organism that causes tetanus, and *Cl. perfringens,* the chief cause of gas gangrene. These organisms live habitually in the soil or in the intestinal tract of animals.

DISCHARGE OF PATHOGENS FROM THE HOST

During the course of an infectious disease, the causative organisms are expelled from the body, often in enormous numbers, through various avenues of excretion. Escape is essential for the perpetuation of the organisms. If there were no way for some of the infecting agents to leave the body of the host during the course of infection and enter a second host, the continued existence of pathogenic agents could not be maintained.

The avenue of escape is dependent upon the region of the body in which the organisms are active. Pathogens that cause disease in the respiratory tract are expelled from the body in droplets of moisture coughed or sneezed into the air. Droplets from the mouth may also enter the air in the act of speaking. Examples of organisms eliminated in the discharges from the nose and mouth are diphtheria bacilli, the streptococci of scarlet fever and septic sore throat, pneumococci, tubercle bacilli and the viruses of influenza, smallpox, mumps and measles. In cerebrospinal meningitis the infection is in the meninges (the membranes enveloping the brain and spinal cord), but the exit of the meningococci is through the nasal discharges. The virus of rabies is eliminated in the saliva of rabid animals, although the seat of infection is in the central nervous system.

Intestinal discharges (feces) serve as pathways of exit for the organisms causing the enteric infections of man, the more noteworthy examples being typhoid, paratyphoid, dysentery bacilli, dysentery amebae and cholera vibrios. Typhoid and paratyphoid bacilli leave the body also in the urine, which serves also as an avenue of exit for the organisms causing brucellosis and for tubercle bacilli when the kidneys are infected by these bacteria.

In diseases such as malaria and yellow fever the causative agents are confined to the blood stream, from which escape would be impossible were it not for the fact that mosquitoes, by sucking blood from the host, may transfer the germs to another host. Pus from the urethra is the mode of exit of gonococci, while the secretions of lesions of the skin and mucous membranes serve as exits for a number of different kinds of pathogens. The causative agents of brucellosis and mastitis are excreted in the milk of infected cows.

TRANSMISSION OF INFECTION

The etiological agents of disease travel in various ways from one host to another. Conveyance may be through feces, urine, sputum, droplets of saliva or mucus emitted from the mouth or nose; by matter from skin lesions and wounds; or by blood transfer from one person to another through the agency of certain insects. In some cases, transmission occurs by means of direct contact with infected persons or carriers. In other instances, transmission is by indirect methods or through the agency of living *vectors*, such as insects, ticks and mites.

Direct Transmission

Most infectious diseases can be spread by direct transfer of the germs from the patient or carrier to another person through close contact. A large variety of diseases may be transmitted in this manner, including diphtheria, scarlet fever, influenza, pneumonia, smallpox, tuberculosis, typhoid fever, dysentery and the venereal diseases.

Transmission by droplets extruded from the nose and mouth is the chief mode of conveyance of diseases of the respiratory tract. During the course of talking, sneezing, laughing or coughing, human beings spray the air with microbe-containing droplets of moisture which originate from the secretions of the nose, throat and mouth. The spray is expelled at high speed for a distance of several feet and may be inhaled into the respira-

Figure 131. Photograph of a violent unstifled sneeze, showing droplets extruded from the nose and mouth. The droplets were photographed by reflected light with an intense flash of short duration. (1/30,000 second) against a dark background. (Courtesy of Dr. M. W. Jennison, Syracuse University, Dept. of Plant Sciences.)

tory tract of persons nearby who thus may become infected. By means of electric-flash photography, photographs of such droplets (Figure 131) have been obtained. The larger droplets settle out of the air and lodge on the floor, furniture or clothing, where they quickly dry. The microbes they contained thus become components of dust. The smaller droplets remain suspended, but dry rapidly, and the microorganisms present may float about in the air on dry residual matter for an indefinite period of time. Figure 132 shows the numerous colonies which developed on medium exposed to a sneeze.

Air serves as an agency in conveying infections only through relatively short distances, probably up to 15 feet. At greater distances the infectious agent is subject to an enormous dilution factor which reduces the hazard of infection through inspired air. The air in rooms where many people congregate may contain a large number of microorganisms of respiratory origin, the microbial content being roughly proportional to the number of persons present. Examples of diseases transmitted through infective droplets are the common cold, pneumococcal and streptococcal pneumonias, influenza, pulmonary tuberculosis, diphtheria, scarlet fever, measles and whooping cough.

In some instances, infection may be conveyed from mother to child (fetus) before birth. Such prenatal or congenital infection is due to the transfer of pathogens from the maternal to the fetal circulation, the tissues separating these being very thin. A child born of a syphilitic mother is likely to have congenital syphilis.

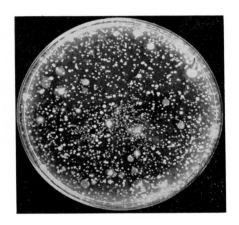

Figure 132. Colonies of bacteria developed during the incubation of a culture plate held in the path of sneeze droplets. (Courtesy of Dr. M. W. Jennison, Syracuse University, Dept. of Plant Sciences.)

A baby's eyes may become infected at birth from organisms present in the vagina of the mother. The pathogen usually responsible is the gonococcus (*Neisseria gonorrhoeae*), and the infection is known as *ophthalmia neonatorum*.

Indirect Transmission through Inanimate Vehicles

Some pathogens have sufficient viability outside the body of the human host to survive long enough to be transferred indirectly from one host to another through inanimate objects or materials. Transfer of such organisms may occur through vehicles such as contaminated objects, water, food and soil. Inanimate objects other than food capable of transmitting infection are known as *fomites*. Examples of such objects are doorknobs, pencils, books, toilet room fittings, towels, handkerchiefs, bed linen, articles of clothing and eating utensils. Diseases that may be spread through the agency of fomites are chiefly those of the intestinal and respiratory tracts such as typhoid fever, dysentery, diphtheria, scarlet fever, pneumonia and others. The human hand may transfer infectious material from fomites to the mouth, nose, eyes or genitalia.

Water may become a vehicle of infection if it has become contaminated with human wastes. As mentioned in Chapter 22, surface waters, such as lakes and streams, as well as ground waters (wells and springs) in populated areas are subject to pollution with the intestinal and urinary discharges of man. Water-borne epidemics of enteric infections such as typhoid fever and dysentery were common in the past and are still a constant threat to health and life in many parts of the world.

Foods readily become vehicles of infection. The most dangerous food from the point of view of disease transmission is raw or unpasteurized milk. Many kinds of pathogens may find their way into milk, some coming from diseased cows, others being derived directly or indirectly from infected human beings or persons who are carriers of infection. Infected cows may contribute such organisms as streptococci, tubercle bacilli (bovine type) and those that cause brucellosis. Milk is frequently contaminated by human beings who handle it before it reaches the consumer. From this source it may acquire the organisms of diphtheria, scarlet fever, dysentery, typhoid fever and others.

Oysters, clams and mussels, when eaten raw or in a partially cooked condition, may convey typhoid fever to man. These shellfish are ordinarily free from dangerous microbes, but those obtained from bays and estuaries polluted with raw sewage are frequently contaminated with human pathogens. Eating and drinking utensils may become contaminated with pathogens and convey them to food and drink or directly to those using the utensils. Diseases that can be transferred in this manner include the common cold, influenza, diphtheria, tuberculosis, scarlet fever, septic sore throat and syphilis.

Food handlers who are carriers of infectious organisms may transfer them from their mouths, noses, skin or bowels to food and thus serve as agents in the dissemination of disease. In some communities persons whose occupation necessitates the handling of food must submit to a special medical examination for the purpose of ascertaining whether or not they are carriers of pathogenic organisms.

Two diseases which man may acquire from the soil are tetanus and gas gangrene. Tetanus is caused by *Clostridium tetani,* and the chief organism responsible for gas gangrene is *Cl. perfringens.* The mode of life of these spore-bearing anaerobes is not ordinarily that of pathogens. Their normal habitat is the intestines of horses and other domestic animals, where they live as harmless commensals. When the spores reach the soil in excrement, they may remain viable indefinitely and, if they gain access to a wound, may germinate into vegetative cells on dead or injured tissue. Here they produce potent exotoxins which are responsible for the symptoms of these diseases.

Transmission by Animals

A large number of diseases may be transmitted to man by the agency of various animals, including chiefly certain arthropods (insects, ticks and

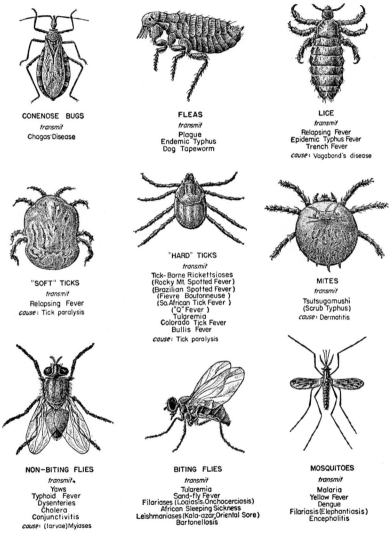

CONENOSE BUGS
transmit
Chagas'Disease

FLEAS
transmit
Plague
Endemic Typhus
Dog Tapeworm

LICE
transmit
Relapsing Fever
Epidemic Typhus Fever
Trench Fever
cause: Vagabond's disease

"SOFT" TICKS
transmit
Relapsing Fever
cause: Tick paralysis

"HARD" TICKS
transmit
Tick-Borne Rickettsioses
(Rocky Mt. Spotted Fever)
(Brazilian Spotted Fever)
(Fievre Boutonneuse)
(So.African Tick Fever)
("Q" Fever)
Tularemia
Colorado Tick Fever
Bullis Fever
cause: Tick paralysis

MITES
transmit
Tsutsugamushi
(Scrub Typhus)
cause: Dermatitis

NON–BITING FLIES
transmit
Yaws
Typhoid Fever
Dysenteries
Cholera
Conjunctivitis
cause: (larvae)Myiases

BITING FLIES
transmit
Tularemia
Sand-fly Fever
Filariases (Loaiasis,Onchocerciasis)
African Sleeping Sickness
Leishmaniases(Kala-azar,Oriental Sore)
Bartonellosis

MOSQUITOES
transmit
Malaria
Yellow Fever
Dengue
Filariasis(Elephantiasis)
Encephalitis

Figure 133. Types of arthropods transmitting human diseases. (Reproduced by permission from Practical Bacteriology, Hematology and Parasitology, by E. Stitt, P. Clough and S. Branham, The Blakiston Company, Publishers.)

mites), birds and mammals. In some cases, the transmission occurs by means of direct contact between man and the animal reservoir of the disease, as when rabies is acquired from the bite of a rabid dog. In other instances, the mode of transmission is through an intermediate animal vector, as when malaria is acquired from the bite of a mosquito. The transmission of disease by means of vectors is accomplished chiefly by lice, fleas, mosquitoes and ticks (Figure 133). These arthropods play an important role in the transmission of disease. If the vector itself is a host in whose body the infecting organism multiplies and develops, it is referred to as a biological vector. Included among biological vectors are ticks, mosquitoes, fleas and lice.

The wood tick and dog tick transmit Rocky Mountain spotted fever to man. The rickettsiae responsible for this disease have a natural reservoir in various wild rodents. Malaria is transmitted to man by a number of species of mosquitoes belonging to the genus *Anopheles,* while yellow fever is conveyed by a single species of mosquito known as *Aëdes aegypti.* Plague (bubonic form) is conveyed to man from rats by the bite of rat fleas. The blood-sucking tsetse fly transports the trypanosomes of African sleeping sickness from native African mammals to man. Typhus, an ever-present menace to world health, may be spread by two kinds of vectors. Old world typhus (epidemic typhus) is louse-borne, while American or murine typhus (endemic typhus) is carried by rat fleas. Equine encephalomyelitis—an inflammation of the brain occurring chiefly in horses, cattle and sheep—is usually carried from infected animals to human beings by mosquitoes.

In some instances, disease is spread by insects which are not capable of biting, but which may carry germs on their feet and mouth parts or in their digestive tracts. They are called *mechanical vectors.* The housefly (*Musca domestica*) is a good example of this kind of vector. It spreads disease by conveying infecting organisms from body discharges to human food. The infections that it transmits are chiefly intestinal diseases, such as typhoid fever and dysentery. Its sticky feet and mouth parts make it an efficient mechanical vector for conveying disease-producing organisms from human excreta to human food. It is particularly dangerous in rural communities, where it may have ready access to human excrement.

A disease of historic importance, but not of frequent occurrence in the United States, is anthrax, which is transmitted to man from cattle and sheep. It was the first disease of mammals shown to be caused by microorganisms. It occurs primarily among industrial workers who handle the hides, hair and wool obtained from infected animals.

Tularemia, commonly called rabbit fever, is found chiefly in rabbits but may be harbored by squirrels, chipmunks, woodchucks, muskrats, ticks and deer flies. It is conveyed to man chiefly by handling infected wild rabbits.

Brucellosis is transmitted to man by cattle, swine and goats. Those who come in contact with infected animals, handle the carcasses of such animals or drink raw milk from infected cows or goats are in danger of acquiring the infection.

The virus of psittacosis, or parrot fever, a disease introduced into the

United States from South America, is transmitted to man by infected psittacine birds such as parrots, parakeets, lovebirds, macaws, cockatoos and Mexican doubleheads.

PORTALS OF ENTRY TO THE HOST

To produce infection it is necessary that the pathogens gain entrance to body tissues through a portal to which they have become adjusted in their evolutionary adaptation. Each pathogen, as a rule, is more or less dependent on a particular channel by which it is capable of entering the body. The typhoid fever bacillus, for example, can cause disease when it enters the body through the mouth but is incapable of establishing itself in the body when introduced through the skin. The etiological agent of malaria must be introduced directly into the blood by the bite of an infected mosquito to produce disease in man. A few species are capable of invading the body through more than one pathway. Pathogenic streptococci are capable of causing disease by invading the skin or entering the body through the nose or mouth.

There are four main portals that may be used as invasion routes by the microscopic agents of disease: (1) the respiratory tract, (2) the alimentary canal, (3) the skin, and (4) the urogenital apparatus. Whichever portal is used, the organisms must enter or pass through epithelial tissue, for this is the tissue that covers the body and lines body cavities. The epithelial tissues that line the body cavities that open to the exterior are commonly called mucous membranes.

Respiratory Tract

Entrance by way of the respiratory tract is utilized by a wide variety of pathogens. This part of the body includes the nasal passages, pharynx, trachea, bronchi and lungs. Numerous kinds of microbes, when inspired with air, can establish themselves in various parts of the respiratory system and produce pathological conditions there. Infections of the respiratory tract are among the most common human infections. Included in this category are the common cold, influenza, the various pneumonias, pulmonary tuberculosis, diphtheria, scarlet fever, pneumonic plague and whooping cough.

Alimentary Canal

Water and food may serve as vehicles bringing pathogens into contact with the epithelium of the alimentary tract, where they may lodge and produce disease or pass through the lining membrane into the lymph and blood streams and produce disease elsewhere in the body. The alimentary tract is the invasion route for the organisms causing typhoid fever, paratyphoid fever, dysentery (bacillary and amebic), Asiatic cholera and some types of tuberculosis.

The Skin

Pathogenic microorganisms, such as staphylococci and streptococci, are usually present on the skin without causing infection; but when a break or cut occurs, infection may ensue. The causative agents of most insect-borne diseases gain entrance through the skin by the bite of the insect host. In some instances, pathogens may invade the intact skin through the hair follicles and the ducts of sweat glands. Wounds furnish a suitable portal of entry, particularly for staphylococci, streptococci, tetanus bacilli and the bacilli of gas gangrene. The more important infections caused by organisms that utilize the skin as an avenue of entrance are acne, boils, carbuncles, erysipelas, impetigo, septicemia, athletes foot, tetanus, gas gangrene, rabies, tularemia, Rocky Mountain spotted fever, typhus fever, malaria and yellow fever.

Urogenital Tract

The urogenital tract affords the usual portal of entry for the causal agents of the venereal diseases. Occasionally other pathogens invade this part of the body and set up infection.

QUESTIONS

1. (*a*) Describe briefly the sources of infection.
   (*b*) What is the significance of disease carriers in the transmission of disease? Name diseases often transmitted by carriers.
2. What are the principal animal sources of pathogens capable of infecting man?
3. What are the chief avenues of escape of infective agents from the body? Of what significance is the fact that pathogens have escape routes? Of what importance is this knowledge in the prevention of disease?
4. Explain direct transmission of disease from person to person. Name diseases transmitted in this manner. What is meant by congenital infection?
5. Discuss transmission by droplets from the nose and mouth. Give examples of diseases transmitted in this manner.
6. (*a*) Which inanimate materials may serve as vehicles of transmission?
   (*b*) Which diseases may be transmitted through (1) water, (2) foods, (3) soil?
7. Which animals may serve as agencies in the transmission of disease to man?
8. What are the portals of invasion by which infective agents enter the body? Give examples of pathogens using the various portals.

REFERENCES

Anderson, G. W., and Arnstein, M. G.: Communicable Disease Control. 3rd ed. New York, The Macmillan Company, 1953.

Burrows, W.: Textbook of Microbiology. 17th ed. Philadelphia, W. B. Saunders Company, 1959.

Dubos, R. J., ed.: Bacterial and Mycotic Infections of Man. 3rd ed. Philadelphia, J. B. Lippincott Company, 1958.

Faust, E. C.: Animal Agents and Vectors of Human Disease. Philadelphia, Lea & Febiger, 1955.

Hull, T. G.: Diseases Transmitted from Animals to Man. 4th ed. Springfield, Ill., Charles C Thomas, 1955.

Maxcy, K. F., ed.: Rosenau Preventive Medicine and Public Health. 8th ed. New York, Appleton-Century-Crofts, Inc., 1956.

Rivers, T. M., ed.: Viral and Rickettsial Infections of Man. 3rd ed. Philadelphia, J. B. Lippincott Company, 1959.

Smith, D. T., et al.: Zinsser's Textbook of Bacteriology. 11th ed. New York, Appleton-Century-Crofts, Inc., 1957.

Stitt, E. R., et al.: Practical Bacteriology, Hematology and Parasitology. 10th ed. New York, McGraw-Hill Book Co., Inc., 1948.

Taylor, I., and Knoweldon, J.: Principles of Epidemiology. Boston, Little, Brown and Company, 1957.

Wilson, G. S., and Miles, A. A.: Topley and Wilson's Principles of Bacteriology and Immunity. 2 vols. 4th ed. Baltimore, The Williams & Wilkins Company, 1955.

28 • The Natural Defenses of the Body

Although microorganisms of various kinds constantly inhabit the human skin and body cavities that open to the exterior, they do not usually invade the tissues of the body. The normal human and animal organism has reasonably effective barriers to keep microorganisms from invading its tissues. If these barriers fail, so that microbes gain access to the underlying tissues, the body's internal defenses enable it to wage counterattacks against the invaders. Every animal, by virtue of the fact that it is alive, has defenses which keep it from being vanquished by microorganisms. This is a fundamental biological property. The capacity for defense is a natural physiological function evolved over the ages by selective adaptation. It is an important adaptation to environment, as necessary for survival as the process of digestion or respiration. It represents the heritage by which man and animals survive despite the presence of microscopic parasites. After death this defense is gone; all the tissues are then promptly invaded by a wide variety of microorganisms.

As just indicated, the human body has both external and internal defenses. The external defenses constitute the outer barriers which guard the tissues against microbic invasion. The internal defenses become active after invasion has occurred.

EXTERNAL DEFENSES

The external defenses consist of the skin and mucous membranes. These two structures belong to the category of epithelial tissues, which are tissues that cover surfaces and line cavities. The skin forms a protective covering for the body, and the mucous membranes line the cavities which open to the exterior, such as the entire alimentary tract from mouth to anus, the respiratory tract and the urogenital system. These epithelial tissues and their secretions constitute the first line of defense, i.e., the

412

primary defense of the body. They ordinarily function as an effective barrier to invasion.

The Skin

Although microorganisms are numerous on the skin, they rarely penetrate it. The skin offers mechanical, as well as chemical, protection. Its outermost layers consist of flat, more or less hard cells, the hardness being due to an insoluble protein known as keratin, which replaces the protoplasm of the cells. These cells are no longer alive. Because of their hardness, the skin is ordinarily impermeable to microorganisms. The skin contains hair follicles and sweat glands which open on the surface. It is through the hair follicles and ducts of the sweat glands that microbes may, at times, invade the intact skin and cause infection; this is particularly true of staphylococci, which are usually always present on the body surface. A slight scratch, even if it is only microscopic in its dimensions, provides an opening for invasion.

Besides acting as a physical armor, the skin also functions in a chemical manner. The secretions of the normal skin exert bacteriostatic or germicidal activity on microorganisms that are not members of its normal microbial inhabitants. When such microorganisms are transferred to it, they usually disappear rapidly from its surface. This self-disinfecting action of the skin has been demonstrated with *Escherichia coli, Proteus vulgaris,* hemolytic streptococci and other bacteria. If one of these organisms is transferred to a certain area of the skin and a sterile swab immediately rubbed over this area and then over the surface of a suitable sterile solid culture medium, a heavy growth of the bacteria will be obtained. If, however, an interval of ten to twenty minutes is permitted to elapse before the transfer from the skin to the culture medium is made, the number of the bacteria will be small or there may be none at all. If the demonstration is repeated on the skin of a cadaver, the bacteria will remain alive a long time. When death occurs, the skin loses its germicidal action. People vary greatly in the ability of their skin to kill adventitious organisms, and the skin of any person may vary from time to time in its germicidal properties. The nature of this germicidal secretion is not understood.

Certain pathogens, particulary staphylococci, are included among the normal microbial flora of the skin. They are not usually destroyed by the germicidal secretions of the skin and cannot be entirely removed by thorough washing.

The Mucous Membranes

Microorganisms present in body cavities that open to the exterior are not within body tissues and, thus, are not in the physiological interior of the body. The mucous membranes which line these cavities, therefore, are a part of the external defenses of the body. These membranes, found in such structures as the gastrointestinal, respiratory and urogenital tracts, ordinarily resist the invasion of most microorganisms. They secrete *mucus,* a thin, highly viscid substance in which microorganisms readily become enmeshed. Besides mucus, some of these membranes give off or receive other secretions.

Inhaled microorganisms and dust particles which become trapped in the mucus of the respiratory tract, are swept by cilia, along with the mucus, into the throat (pharynx) and swallowed. Those which get beyond the trachea into the bronchi and the lungs are usually destroyed by wandering leukocytes (white blood corpuscles), or are propelled upward toward the pharynx by ciliary action.

Saliva, which is constantly being secreted into the mouth by the salivary glands, has slight germicidal powers and exerts a flushing effect, mechanically carrying microorganisms into the throat, from which area they are swallowed. Microorganisms that are not normal inhabitants of the mouth are usually unable to gain a footing among the resident mouth organisms.

Many microorganisms enter the stomach with food and drink, where they encounter the hydrochloric acid of the gastric juice. This acid is destructive to a large variety of microorganisms. However, they may escape its action when the acid is neutralized by food. The normal intestinal bacteria, together with the intestinal secretions, ordinarily prevent the growth of microorganisms which are not part of the normal intestinal flora and fauna.

Lysozyme

Some mucous membranes secrete an enzyme known as *lysozyme* which is capable of catalyzing the disintegration of the cell walls of certain bacteria and thus causing the lysis of the cells. Bacteria sensitive to lysozyme include certain saprophytes and a few pathogens. Lysozyme is present in the nasal secretions, the secretions of the mouth and in the tears produced by the lacrimal glands associated with the eyes.

Penetration of the Outer Defenses

Although the outer defenses of the body constitute an effectual barrier, they are not an absolute safeguard. Microbes occasionally penetrate these bulwarks and enter body tissues or the blood stream. They may enter the skin by way of the ducts of the sweat glands, the orifices of hair follicles, scratches, cuts, abrasions or through the bites of insects. Also, they may gain a foothold on mucous surfaces, causing sufficient damage by toxic secretions to enable them to invade the tissues. The body, therefore, in order to survive, requires further defenses against those organisms which occasionally penetrate its primary defenses.

DEFENSES AFTER INVASION

When microbes succeed in getting through the first line of defense and enter the tissues of the body, they encounter the second line of defense. The strategy of this secondary defense is to destroy the invaders and thus keep them from establishing a base of operations. This defense operates: (1) through the agency of certain cells known as *phagocytes,* which are capable of engulfing invading microbes; (2) through the production of counteracting chemical substances called *antibodies,* which are capable of destroying infectious agents or neutralizing their toxins; and (3) through natural blood constituents, chiefly *complement* and *properdin.*

The power to successfully combat pathogenic microorganisms after they have invaded the tissues is referred to as resistance to infection, or *immunity.* Although this term literally implies complete protection, it must not, when used in connection with disease, be interpreted as indi-

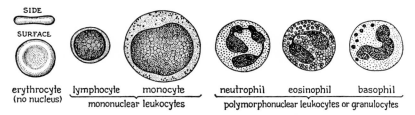

SIDE						
SURFACE						
erythrocyte (no nucleus)	lymphocyte	monocyte	neutrophil	eosinophil	basophil	
	mononuclear leukocytes		polymorphonuclear leukocytes or granulocytes			

Figure 134. Human blood corpuscles. (By permission from General Zoology by T. Storer, Copyright 1943, McGraw-Hill Book Company, Inc.)

cating complete resistance to infection. Being the resultant of two varia- bles, the individual and the invading pathogens, immunity is of necessity a relative condition rather than an absolute one. It may range from a low degree to complete resistance. Individuals vary from time to time in the degree of immunity against, or *susceptibility* toward, a given infection. The phenomena associated with the production of immunity comprise the science of *immunology.*

BLOOD AND LYMPH

Since blood and lymph play a role in the internal defenses of the body, some acquaintance with these two circulating fluids is essential to a proper understanding of the defense mechanism of the human body. Blood is composed of a straw-colored fluid matrix called *plasma,* which constitutes about 55 per cent of its volume, in which are suspended several kinds of structural components known as *corpuscles,* comprising about 45 per cent of the blood volume.

Plasma is a complex aqueous solution containing a large variety of substances in solution. The corpuscles include (1) erythrocytes, or red blood corpuscles; (2) leukocytes, or white blood corpuscles; and (3) thrombocytes, or blood platelets. Certain leukocytes play a role in body defense; the erythrocytes and thrombocytes perform other functions.

Leukocytes are of various kinds, as indicated in Table 9 and illustrated

Table 9.   Types of Leukocytes

A. *Granular leukocytes: cytoplasm with distinct granules; polymorphous nucleus sub-divided into lobes*
   1. Neutrophils: highly motile and phagocytic; about 12 microns in diameter; granules stain with neutral dyes; nucleus has 3 to 5 lobes; comprise about 67 per cent of total leukocyte count.
   2. Basophils: nonphagocytic; about 10 microns in diameter; granules stain with basic dyes; constitute about 0.5 per cent of total white blood cell count.
   3. Eosinophils: nonphagocytic; diameter about 12 microns; granules stain with acid dyes (e.g., eosin); bilobed nucleus; comprise 3 per cent of total leukocyte count.

B. *Nongranular leukocytes: cytoplasm without granules; large spherical nucleus*
   1. Small lymphocytes: nonphagocytic; about 8 microns in diameter; comprise about 25 per cent of total leukocyte count.
   2. Large lymphocytes: nonphagocytic; about 11 microns in diameter; constitute about 3 per cent of total white blood cell count.
   3. Monocytes: actively phagocytic; large nucleus usually indented; about 15 microns in diameter; comprise about 1.5 per cent of total leukocyte count.

Figure 135.   Schematic representation of the passage of phagocytes through the wall of a capillary. *A*, Neutrophil; *B*, capillary wall; *C*, red blood corpuscle.

in Figure 134. They vary in size from 8 to 15 microns in diameter and may be divided into two general types, phagocytes and nonphagocytes.

Phagocytes (from the Greek, meaning "eating cells") are ameboid cells which are spherical in shape in the circulating blood but which, under the influence of adequate stimuli, emit pseudopodia and thus become irregular in form. They are capable of engulfing and digesting infectious agents and other foreign particulate matter as well as dead body cells and tissue debris. A phagocytic leukocyte is capable of passing through the thin walls of the capillaries. It accomplishes this feat by thrusting a delicate pseudopodium between cells of the capillary wall (Figure 135), thus making a minute temporary opening through which it escapes from the capillary. This action on the part of phagocytes, known as *diapedesis*, enables them to enter the minute spaces between the tissue cells and wander about through most of the body tissues.

The blood contains two kinds of phagocytes: (1) neutrophils and (2) monocytes. The *neutrophils* make up the great majority (about 67 per cent) of leukocytes. They have nuclei consisting of three to five lobes connected by narrow strands. The cytoplasm of these cells contains a large number of fine granules which are stainable with neutral dyes. The *monocytes* are relatively large and have large indented nuclei and non-granular cytoplasm. Certain other body cells, which will be considered later, are also actively phagocytic.

The function of the nonphagocytic leukocytes (basophils, eosinophils and lymphocytes) is not well understood.

The blood, as it passes through the capillaries, loses a small proportion of its fluid volume by filtration through the capillary walls. This fluid, after it has seeped through the capillary walls, is called *lymph*. The tissue spaces occupied by lymph communicate with lymph vessels which carry the lymph away from the tissues of the body. This system of vessels, known as the *lymphatic system,* returns the lymph to the blood. The lymph vessels converge, forming larger and larger vessels, and ultimately give rise to two main lymph ducts which deliver the lymph to veins in the thoracic region. Thus the lymph, which continuously filters from the blood in all the capillary networks of the body, is returned to the blood.

In certain places along the lymph vessels, especially where the smaller vessels converge to form larger ones, oval bodies known as *lymph nodes* (glands) are found. They are usually arranged in groups or clusters. A number of groups of relatively large nodes are located at strategic points along the sides of the neck, in the groin and armpits, and in the knee and elbow joints. Each node is permeated by numerous narrow channels through which the lymph flows. The channels are lined with stationary phagocytic cells. Each node has several vessels entering it and a smaller number leaving it. Certain other body cells besides those in the blood and lymphatic systems function as phagocytes, as will be explained later.

THE ROLE OF PHAGOCYTES IN BODY DEFENSE

Phagocytes constitute the body's prime agency for destroying parasites that have passed its external barriers. They are continuously on guard to protect the body and are stationed at many strategic points. This type of defense is known as *phagocytosis*. Figure 136 shows phagocytes which have engulfed bacteria. In most diseases recovery would probably be impossible without the process of phagocytosis. The importance of phago-cytic activity was first recognized by Elie Metchnikoff and described by him in the year 1883. He observed the process under the microscope in the transparent larva of the starfish. He devoted many years of his life to the study of phagocytosis; much of his work was carried on at the Pasteur Institute in Paris.

Types of Phagocytic Cells

On the basis of size, phagocytes may be divided into two groups, microphages and macrophages. The *microphages* are the neutrophils of the blood. They constitute about 67 per cent of the total number of leukocytes. The *macrophages* include the monocytes of the blood, which constitute about 1.5 per cent of the total leukocyte number, and certain cells located in what is known as the reticulo-endothelial system.

Reticulo-endothelial System

The *reticulo-endothelial system* (RES) consists of cells that are located in various parts of the body and which function as a physiologic unit since they all are macrophages. Because they are parts of various tissues, they are known also as *histiocytes* (*histio,* tissue; *cyte,* cell). The endothelial portion of this system consists of sessile macrophages located among the endothelial cells (lining cells) of the small blood channels of the liver, spleen, bone marrow and certain endocrine glands (adrenal

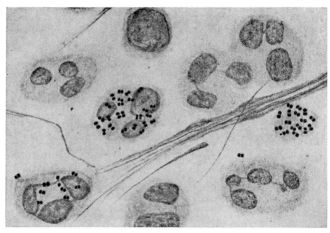

Figure 136. Stained film from pus, showing diplococci phagocytized by white corpuscles (polymorphonuclear leukocytes). (From Ford: Textbook of Bacteriology.)

and thymus); and the lymph channels of the various lymph nodes of the body. The small blood channels of the liver, spleen and bone marrow correspond to the capillaries of the other organs but are somewhat larger and irregular in form. The reticular portion of this system is a form of loose connective tissue consisting of interlacing networks of cells connected by thin protoplasmic strands located chiefly in the spleen, lymph nodes and the thymus gland. Some of the cells in this network are sessile macrophages. Wandering macrophages are also present.

The stationary macrophages are capable of snatching microorganisms, and also other foreign particulate matter, from the circulating blood and lymph by means of their pseudopodia. The macrophages of the blood channels of the liver can become wandering cells when necessity demands. The reticulo-endothelial system offers a large surface expanse for the removal of extraneous particulate matter from the circulating fluids.

It can be demonstrated experimentally that cells of the reticulo-endothelial system take up foreign particles. When insoluble carbon particles are injected intravenously into an animal, they do not remain in the circulation. In a short time most of them can be found deposited in the phagocytic endothelial cells of the liver, spleen, bone marrow, adrenal and thymus glands, and in the monocytes and neutrophils of the blood. When bacteria are injected into the blood or lymph, they also quickly disappear from these circulating fluids because they are taken up by the macrophages of the reticulo-endothelial system and the wandering phagocytes of the blood.

The Process of Phagocytosis

As mentioned previously, the destruction of infectious agents by phagocytic cells is known as phagocytosis. This process plays an important role in the mechanism of recovery in acute infectious diseases. It frequently determines the outcome of such diseases.

The wandering phagocytes form a mobile defense unit capable of engaging in combat microorganisms that have invaded the body. In some mysterious manner they are directed to the area of infection. They are transported in large numbers by the blood stream to the site of infection, pass through the capillary walls (diapedesis) by active ameboid motion and move through the tissue spaces toward the focus of infection, where they engulf the invaders by means of pseudopodia and destroy them by the process of digestion. At any site of infection the neutrophils arrive first and are followed, later, by the monocytes, which ingest not only the microorganisms but also many of the neutrophils and the engulfed bacteria they contain.

Many of the phagocytes are killed in the process of phagocytosis by toxic substances (leukocidins) produced by the invading organisms, but enough ordinarily survive to accomplish the destruction of the pathogens. The pus in a pimple, boil or wound consists largely of phagocytes which have been killed by the action of microorganisms. Phagocytized staphylococci usually can be observed in the stained smear of pus obtained from a boil. In gonorrheal pus, gonococci can be readily demonstrated within the cytoplasm of phagocytes.

The blood phagocytes ordinarily increase in numbers during an infection, the increase being roughly proportional to the severity of the infection. This temporary increase is known as *leukocytosis*. The percentage of the different kinds of leukocytes may vary in different infections. Thus a differential count of the types of leukocytes may be of diagnostic value in certain infections.

The engulfing of pathogens by phagocytes does not necessarily mean their destruction, since some microorganisms are resistant to the digestive enzymes of phagocytes. The surviving pathogens may even multiply within the phagocytes and later make their escape after the phagocytes have wandered away from the site of infection. In such rather uncommon instances the phagocytes actually serve to distribute the infectious agents.

Highly virulent bacteria may survive in the invaded tissues and establish a base of operations in which they may hold forth for some time. Some may be carried away by the lymph and reach the lymphatics. In that case, the endothelial phagocytes in the lymph nodes become active to remove them. Because of the role that lymph nodes play in combating pathogens, they are frequently swollen during an infection. The position of the swollen glands may indicate the site of the infection. If large numbers should enter the lymphatics, some may escape into the blood stream, where they will be prey to the phagocytic cells of the capillary endothelium in such structures as the liver, spleen and bone marrow.

In diseases in which the infection is intracellular, as in those caused by viruses, rickettsiae, some bacteria and certain protozoa, phagocytosis appears to be of little importance. The destruction of such parasites depends upon processes at present not understood which operate within the cytoplasm of the invaded cells.

Opsonins

Phagocytosis is not simply a cellular activity but is one in which certain chemical components of the blood participate. If phagocytes are removed from the blood by centrifuging, washed free of all traces of blood, and then placed in a physiological salt solution (0.85 per cent sodium chloride) along with certain bacteria, they remain indifferent to the bacteria. If, however, the bacteria are first brought in contact with blood, the washed phagocytes will readily attack them. The blood components that play a role in phagocytosis have been called *opsonins*. Opsonins make invading bacteria susceptible to ingestion by phagocytes.

Opsonins act on microorganisms and not on the phagocytes. They become adsorbed on the cell surface and alter it in such a way that they render the microbes amenable to attack by the phagocytes. Microbes coated with opsonins are said to be *opsonized*.

Some opsonins are *antibodies,* which constitute a specific defense of the body against infectious disease.

Opsonins are of two kinds. One kind is *thermolabile* (inactivated at 56° C.), relatively nonspecific, normally present in blood and reacts with antigens in general. The thermolabile opsonins comprise a group of blood proteins called *complement* (cf. p. 425). In addition to these there are *thermostable* opsonins that are formed only in response to the presence of microorganisms in the body and effective only against specific organisms or antigen whose presence incited their production. These type-specific opsonins, more potent than the normal opsonins, are also known as *bacteriotropins,* a type of antibody.

The ratio of the number of microorganisms engulfed by the phagocytes of a patient to the number engulfed by the phagocytes of normal blood, i.e., blood of a person not infected by the organism involved, is known as the *opsonic index*. Determining the opsonic index is of some value in the diagnosis of brucellosis and tularemia.

HUMORAL IMMUNITY

The process of phagocytosis is only part of the battle the body wages against pathogenic intruders. Besides opsonins, the body mobilizes other substances, the part of its protective machinery called *humoral immunity*. The chemical defensive substances present in the body, or produced by it in response to invading organisms (in some cases foreign proteins or other substances foreign to the body), are: (1) specific substances known as *antibodies*, and (2) normal blood constituents, chiefly *complement* and *properdin*, which are nonspecific in their reactions. The foreign substance that stimulates the body to produce antibodies is termed *antigen*.

An *antibody* may be defined as a specifically reacting protein produced by the body in response to the presence of an antigen. An antibody produced in response to a given antigenic substance reacts only (with a few exceptions) with that substance. Specificity is common to all immunological phenomena.

In addition to the opsonic and bacteriotropic reactions considered in the preceding pages, there are other antigen-antibody reactions. Before discussing these it will be helpful to consider the nature of the components of humoral immunity.

ANTIGENS

An *antigen*, as previously indicated, is any substance which, when introducd into animal tissues, has the property of inciting body cells to produce a counteracting substance known as *antibody*. Each antibody reacts ordinarily only with the antigen that evoked it; in some cases it may react also with certain compounds closely related chemically to the antigen. An antigen is usually a substance consisting of large molecules and is always a substance that is foreign to the animal organism.

Almost any protein and a few carbohydrates can function as antigens. A bacterial cell may contain a number of different antigenic components; some are localized in the cell body, whereas others may be in the flagella of motile bacteria or in the capsules of capsulated bacteria. All antigens are not necessarily harmful to the body, although antigens contribute to the virulence of a pathogen.

Certain substances, though not antigenic in themselves, have the power, when linked to proteins, to confer on the proteins specific antigenic properties. Such substances are known as partial antigens or *haptens*. The specificity of the reaction depends upon the hapten and not the protein. Polysaccharides and lipids frequently serve as haptens.

Flagellar and Somatic Antigens

Motile bacteria, such as members of the genus *Salmonella*, usually have one or more antigens located in their flagella, known as *flagellar antigens* (H antigens), in addition to those present in the cell wall or interior of the cell, which are referred to as *somatic antigens* (O antigens).* When flagellated bacterial cells invade the body, both the H antigens and the O antigens incite body tissues to produce specific antibodies. The antigenic properties of the flagella of different species are usually distinct. Toxic somatic antigens of bacteria are called *endotoxins*.

Capsular Antigens

The chief constituents of bacterial capsules are polysaccharides. In certain capsulated bacteria the capsular substance is antigenic. The capsular polysaccharides of the pneumococcus are complete antigens. They differ for each pneumococcus type. The pneumococcus can be divided into more than seventy distinct types on the basis of the presence of polysaccharides which are antigenically distinct for each type. When pneumococci are introduced into body tissues, the body responds by producing type-specific antibodies against the capsular antigen. The capsular antigens are essential not only for type specificity but also for the virulence of the organisms. Thus type specificity and virulence are lost when the capsules are removed. A number of other species of bacteria show similar series of capsular types.

Soluble Antigens

Certain substances excreted by microorganisms are antigenic. Among them are extracellular antigens called *exotoxins* and *enzymes*.

Heterophile Antigens

Most antigens are species-specific, but in a few instances related species, or even unrelated forms, have one or more identical antigens which are known as *heterophile antigens*. The typhus fever rickettsia produces a heterophile antigen which brings about the formation of antibodies effective, not only against itself, but also against the "X" strain of *Proteus vulgaris*. For this reason, the blood serum of typhus fever patients causes X strain *Proteus vulgaris* organisms to clump (agglutinate) together. Certain yeast cells have a common antigenic factor with dysentery bacilli.

Many substances besides those found in microorganisms are antigenic. Antigens are present in certain foods, plant pollens, snake venom, blood plasma, red blood corpuscles and many other substances.

ANTIBODIES

After the invasion of the body by pathogens, or after immunization with

* Flagellar antigens are frequently represented by the letter H, which is the first letter of the German word *Hauch* describing the thin-spreading growth on nutrient agar of *Proteus vulgaris* in which the difference between flagellar and somatic antigens has been studied in considerable detail. Nonflagellated variants of this species do not produce this thin-spreading growth and, therefore, in the German language are *ohne Hauch*. These variants have somatic or O antigens but are without H antigens.

antigen, the presence of antibodies can usually be demonstrated in the blood and tissue fluids. Antibodies are proteins (*gamma*-globulins) produced as a result of the presence of antigen in the body. Antibody globulins differ from other serum globulins in that they have the property of combining with the antigen that induced their production. The union of antibody with antigen is the basic process in immunological reactions. When antigenic material is injected into the body, the presence of specific antibody in the blood can be demonstrated after a lapse of time. Appreciable amounts, however, do not appear for several days. The amount of antibody per volume of blood (antibody titer) reaches its maximum after about ten to fifteen days. The antibody titer can be increased further by a second injection of the same antigen given about seven days after the first injection and can be increased still further by a third administration of the same antigen.

Experimental evidence indicates that antibody production is a function of the reticulo-endothelial system. It is likely that the lymphocytes of the blood are also producers of antibodies. Antibodies produced by different species of mammals in response to the same antigen are alike in their specific affinity for the antigen which evoked their production. Antibodies obtained from immunized animals can be used in the prevention and treatment of certain diseases. This phase of immunology will be explained in a subsequent chapter.

ANTIGEN-ANTIBODY REACTIONS

Antigen-antibody reactions can be demonstrated in blood serum obtained from either man or animals. Because of this the study of these reactions is known as *serology,* and the reactions are referred to as *serological reactions.* Serological tests play an important role in the diagnosis of infectious diseases and the identification of certain biological materials. Examples of such tests are the agglutination, precipitation and complement-fixation tests.

Antibodies are named according to their reaction, *in vitro* or *in vivo,* when allowed to act on homologous antigen. An antibody that neutralizes bacterial exotoxin is an *antitoxin;* if it causes bacteria to clump together, it is an *agglutinin;* one that acts on soluble microbial antigens by precipitating them is a *precipitin;* if it causes the dissolution or lysis of bacterial cells, it is a *lysin* or, more specifically, *bacteriolysin;* and, as previously indicated, it is an *opsonin* if it sensitizes bacterial cells in such a way that they become susceptible to ingestion by phagocytes. Since these various reactions increase specific resistance to disease-producing agents, or produce immunity, they are frequently referred to as *immunological reactions.*

Although it has been generally held that the different types of antigen-antibody reactions exhibited in disease are due to separate and distinct antibodies, evidence has accumulated indicating that each antigen gives rise to a specific antibody (modified *gamma*-globulin) which is capable of functioning in more than one way, the nature of the reaction depending upon the existing conditions. In a certain infection the antibody globulin may cause agglutination of the pathogens and precipitation of the soluble proteins released from disintegrated microbes, and also induce phagocytic activity against the invading organisms. In some infections the antibody may cause the dissolution or lysis of the pathogens or neutralize microbial toxins. In an infection by pneumococci the antibody globulin combines with the specific capsular polysaccharide, agglutinates the bacteria, and sensitizes them to the action of phagocytes. The concept that there is in infectious disease the formation from each antigen of a specific antibody, each of which is capable of producing more than one kind of reaction against the invading organism, is known as the *unitarian hypothesis* of antibody action.

Whether or not the unitarian hypothesis represents a correct interpretation of antibodies is not of primary importance in the present discussion. To assist the student in obtaining a clear understanding of the various antibody activities, the discussion that follows treats them as though each type of activity were produced by a specific antibody.

Antitoxins

An antibody produced by body cells in response to a stimulus by an exotoxin is known as an *antitoxin*. Each antitoxin is specific for the toxin which stimulated its production. Antitoxin becomes fixed to the toxin, thus forming a nontoxic toxin-antitoxin complex. This reaction is known as neutralization of the toxin. Neutralization does not destroy the toxin but merely inactivates it. Under certain conditions the toxin-antitoxin linkage may dissociate, liberating potent toxin.

The presence of a toxin-neutralizing substance in the body of infected animals was first demonstrated by von Behring and Kitasato in 1890 in experiments with tetanus. They named this substance "antitoxin." The damage wrought in diseases such as tetanus, diphtheria, scarlet fever, gas gangrene, bacillary dysentery (Shiga type) and botulism is due to exotoxins released by the invading pathogens. The body combats these infections by producing specific antitoxins. Snake venom is similar to bacterial exotoxin in that it elicits the production of antitoxin. Specific antitoxins produced in the bodies of animals such as horses or goats are used in the treatment of certain human diseases. This will be discussed in another chapter.

Lysins

These antibodies cause the lysis, or dissolution, of cells foreign to the body by disrupting their cell walls, allowing the dispersal of their protoplasm. The lysis of bacterial cells is termed *bacteriolysis,* and the corresponding term for the antibody involved is *bacteriolysin.* A more general term for the dissolution of cells by antibody action is *cytolysis,* the corresponding antibody being called *cytolysin.* Lysins are highly specific but cannot by themselves cause the dissolution of foreign cells. A second substance, *complement,* which is not an antigen, is required. Complement is a nonspecific substance normally present in the blood of mammals. It is needed to complete, i.e., to complement, the lytic action. The mode of action of lysins is not clearly understood, but presumably the foreign cells are sensitized by the antibody, which renders them susceptible to lysis by the complement. Only cells which have been sensitized can be lysed by complement.

The phenomenon of lysis is not restricted to bacterial cells. The injection of red blood corpuscles of an animal into the blood stream of an animal of another species usually results in the lysis of the introduced cells; thus—the red blood corpuscles of a rabbit are lysed by the blood of a sheep which received injections of rabbit red blood cells. This reaction can be observed *in vitro.* A cytolysin that destroys red blood corpuscles is known as a *hemolysin.* In some instances, blood cells from one animal introduced into the blood stream of another animal of the same species will result in the lysis of the introduced cells. This is known as *iso-hemolysis.*

Certain diseases can be accurately diagnosed by tests known as complement fixation tests. These tests are used to determine whether the blood of the patient contains a specific antibody capable of fixing the complement. The outstanding example of a complement fixation diagnostic procedure is the Wassermann test, used in the diagnosis of syphilis. This test is briefly described in Chapter 32.

Agglutinins

Agglutinins are antibodies which cause the clumping together, or *agglutination,* of microorganisms or other foreign cells that have entered body tissues. Agglutinins presumably produce chemical changes at the surface of the cells which cause the cells to stick together, forming irregular masses. The microbes are thus immobilized and can then be readily engulfed by phagocytic cells. Most foreign cells, which may enter body tissues by natural means or be injected artificially, provoke agglutinin production.

The antigenic substances that stimulate the production of agglutinins are called *agglutinogens,* which form part of the structure of the inciting cell, usually a part of its surface. A bacterial cell ordinarily has a number of agglutinogens in different parts of the cell. Flagellated bacteria may have one or more agglutinogens in their flagella and several in their cell bodies. Those in the flagella are termed *flagellar agglutinogens,* whereas the term *somatic agglutinogens* applies to those in the cell body.

Although agglutinins are ordinarily specific, in some instances an antiserum specific for a certain bacterium will also agglutinate, but to a lesser degree, certain other species, usually closely related forms. This is because some bacteria are characterized by a multiplicity of agglutinogens, some of which are not specific but are common to a group of closely related species. Cross agglutination of several species may therefore be brought about by the same antiserum. Identical agglutinins possessed by several kinds of bacteria are known as *group agglutinins,* and their homologous antigens are said to be group-specific. Cross agglutination occurs especially among the Gram-negative intestinal pathogenic and nonpathogenic bacilli such as the coliform bacilli, dysentery bacilli and typhoid bacilli.

Agglutination may be demonstrated either microscopically or macroscopically. The microscopic method involves the use of the hanging-drop preparation. A drop of a bacterial suspension is brought into contact with a drop of serum containing homologous agglutinins. The clumping of the bacteria can then be observed under the microscope. In the macroscopic method larger quantities are used and the process is observed *in vitro.* If a suspension of bacteria is placed in a test tube containing homologous agglutinins, the bacterial suspension will lose its turbidity and become clear, owing to the settling of the agglutinated bacteria at the bottom of the tube.

The phenomenon of agglutination has a number of practical applications. It can be used in identifying and differentiating certain bacteria that are similar in morphology, staining characteristics and other traits. For this purpose it is necessary to prepare agglutinating serums by inoculating a series of animals, each with a different bacterial species. If one of these serums, in proper dilution, causes agglutination when applied to the organism in question, it indicates the species to which the organism belongs.

The agglutination reaction is used extensively in the diagnosis of certain infectious diseases. When used for this purpose, serum from the suspected case is tested with suitable bacterial suspensions to determine the presence of specific agglutinins; or some of the pathogens are isolated from the body of the patient and tested with antiserums containing specific agglutinins. Among the diseases that can be diagnosed by agglutination reactions are typhoid fever, paratyphoid fever, brucellosis, tularemia, typhus fever and Rocky Mountain spotted fever.

As previously indicated, the phenomenon of agglutination is not restricted to the cells of microorganisms. The animal and human body can produce agglutinins against cells that are foreign to it, if such cells should enter the blood stream. When red blood corpuscles are artificially introduced into the blood stream of an animal of another species, specific agglutinins (hemagglutinins) are formed which are capable of agglutinating the foreign corpuscles. In some cases hemagglutinins can be formed against the red blood corpuscles of another individual of the same species. Such agglutinins are known as *isohemagglutinins.* The human body is capable of producing isohemagglutinins. The incompatibility of human blood groups is due to such agglutinins. This is of considerable significance since it endangers persons requiring blood transfusions if the blood of the recipient will agglutinate the red blood corpuscles of the donor. For this reason preliminary tests are made to determine whether or not the bloods of the donor and recipient are compatible. As regards natural isohemagglutinins, human bloods fall into four main groups, designated as AB, A, B and O. The bloods of persons in any given group are compatible, but certain blood groups are not compatible with others.

Precipitins

During infection many bacterial cells are killed by the defensive forces of the body. These cells undergo disintegration, and their constituents go into solution. The proteins and polysaccharides of disintegrated bacteria cause the body to produce antibodies which react with them to form an insoluble precipitate. The antibody in this type of reaction is known as *precipitin,* the antigen as *precipitinogen,* and the reaction is termed *precipitation.* The exact role of the precipitation phenomenon in the body's combat with pathogens is not definitely known.

The mechanism of the precipitation reaction appears to be analogous to that of agglutination. The chief difference in these two reactions is that in agglutination the antigen is attached to individual microbial cells, while in precipitation the antigen is in the form of colloid particles suspended in the blood or lymph. In the precipitation reaction the particles constituting the precipitinogen are coated with the precipitin globulins, resulting in the aggregation and flocculation of the antigen-antibody compound and thus forming a precipitate. It is believed that the precipitate is disposed of by phagocytes or, possibly, by enzymes present in the blood.

It is possible to use the precipitin reaction in the diagnosis of certain diseases, but in most of these the agglutination test also can be used and is preferable because it is simpler to perform. For the diagnosis of syphilis several precipitin tests have been developed, the best known of these being the Kahn and Kline tests (Chapter 32).

Most proteins of both plants and animals will act as precipitinogens on injection into animals. Precipitins can be readily built up in the blood of animals by repeated injections of some specific foreign protein. If, for example, blood serum from a dog is repeatedly injected into the blood stream of a rabbit at intervals of a few days, a precipitin against the proteins of dog serum will be formed in the blood of the rabbit. If blood serum obtained from the rabbit is added to some dog serum in a test tube, a precipitate will be formed. Not only dog serum, but also serum of animals closely related to dogs (wolves and coyotes) will be precipitated by the serum of the rabbit. The closer the relationship, the more marked the precipitin reaction. Serum that contains precipitins against human blood will produce a precipitate, not only in human serum, but also to a lesser degree in the serum of anthropoid apes and to a still smaller degree in that of monkeys. It shows no reaction with the serum of other animals. The precipitin reaction thus may be used as an aid in determining zoological relationships.

The precipitin reaction can be used in medicolegal cases to determine whether a particular blood stain on clothing, paper, knife blade or other article is of human or animal origin. To carry out the test, laboratory animals such as rabbits are immunized against human blood by repeated injections of human serum at intervals of a few days. The blood of such an animal will precipitate human serum but not that of other animals (except anthropoid apes and monkeys). The blood stain in question is dissolved out in a weak salt solution. This solution is then tested with the serum of the laboratory animal. The formation of an intense precipitate definitely indicates that the blood stain is of human origin. This test may be used even though the blood stain has been dried for many years. The test is recognized as reliable in many courts.

The precipitin test may be used also in detecting adulteration of protein foodstuffs. The presence of horse meat in sausage, for example, can be detected by the precipitin reaction.

COMPLEMENT AND PROPERDIN

Blood has bactericidal components which cannot be placed in the category of antibodies. One of these is complement, a protein complex normally present in the blood of all mammals. Although not a true antibody, complement plays a role in antigen-antibody reactions. It is more important in some of these reactions than in others. As mentioned earlier in this chapter, complement is a necessary component in cytolysis, for in its absence this reaction does not occur.

Unlike an antibody, complement is not specific for a particular antigen and is not increased in amount during an infection or artificial immunization. It can enter into almost any antigen-antibody reaction and thus aid the body in inactivating the antigen. It is active only when antigen and its specific antibody unite. In these reactions complement becomes bound by the antigen-antibody combination and is said to be fixed.

Complement is inactivated by a short exposure to a temperature of 56° C. The complement used in laboratory tests, such as complement-fixation tests, is usually obtained from guinea pig serum.

A recently discovered blood constituent, which is a globulin protein that has been named properdin (Latin, "to destroy"), appears to play an important role in man's resistance to disease. It is not yet clear just how it functions. It is nonspecific and inactive by itself, but in the presence of complement and magnesium ions it exhibits high bactericidal activity against a large variety of pathogenic microbes. The degree of resistance of the human body to numerous pathogenic microorganisms is directly related to the amount of properdin in the blood.

It was discovered experimentally that when rats are exposed to atomic radiation, properdin disappears from the blood stream, leaving the animals susceptible to infection by many kinds of infective agents. It was found that resistance could be restored, at least in part, by injecting properdin into the blood stream.

INFLAMMATION

A common response to the invasion of tissues by microorganisms is a local reaction known as *inflammation,* in which the blood supply to the site of infection is increased. The blood brings phagocytes and antibodies to combat the invading organisms. Inflammation is an important defense reaction since it is directed toward localizing, destroying and removing the infectious agents.

In the first stage of the process the capillaries in the area become engorged with blood. The increased amount of blood in the region causes redness (hyperemia), which can be observed if the inflammation is near the surface. Histamine, or a histamine-like substance (see Chapter 30), is released by the invaded tissues. It exerts an irritating effect on blood vessels, causing an increase in the permeability of the capillary walls, which permits a relatively large amount of modified blood plasma (inflammatory exudate), including fibrinogen, to seep into the tissues of the infected area. Microphages increase in numbers and are attracted to the site of inflammation. Besides redness and swelling there are two other symptoms, heat and pain. Heat is due to the increased supply of blood, while the pain is the result of irritation of the sensory nerve endings, brought about by increased pressure due to the swelling.

The fibrinogen which has diffused into the region around the inflamed area coagulates into fibrin, resulting in the formation of a fibrinous network around the affected part. The fibrinous material also forms in the local lymphatics, causing a lymphatic blockade and thus preventing passage of the germs into the lymph stream. In this manner the infected area is walled off from the surrounding tissues and the dissemination of the germs to other parts of the body prevented. The forming of a fibrin wall around the infected area is known as *inflammatory fixation.*

Simultaneously with the increased flow of blood to the infected area, phagocytes in large numbers pass through the capillary walls and enter the fibrin network. If some of the microorganisms succeed in getting out of the walled area and entering the lymphatic capillaries, they will be engulfed by the sessile phagocytes (macrophages) when they reach the lymph nodes. Those that succeed in evading these phagocytes will be exposed to the phagocytic activity of the sessile phagocytes in the blood vessels of that portion of the reticulo-endothelial system located in the liver, spleen, bone marrow and other structures.

QUESTIONS

1. (*a*) Which body structures constitute the external defense against invasion by microorganisms?
   (*b*) Why is the skin a good barrier to invasion?
   (*c*) What enables mucous membranes to resist invasion? What is lysozyme?
2. What internal defenses against pathogens does the body have?
3. What are phagocytes? Which types of body cells have phagocytic properties? Differentiate between microphages and macrophages.
4. What is the reticulo-endothelial system? Which structures make up the endothelial portion? Of what does the reticular part consist? What are histiocytes?
5. Of what importance is the reticulo-endothelial system in body defense?
6. Explain the process of phagocytosis. What role do opsonins play in the process?
7. (*a*) Define the term "antibody."
   (*b*) What are antigens? What is a hapten? Which cellular parts may serve as antigen? What are group-specific antigens?
8. (*a*) What is known concerning the chemical nature of antibodies? By which part of the body is it believed that antibodies are produced?
   (*b*) Explain: (1) antitoxins, (2) lysins, (3) agglutinins, (4) precipitins.
   (*c*) Against which diseases does the body produce antitoxins?
   (*d*) Differentiate between bacteriolysin and hemolysin. What is complement?
   (*e*) Explain the use of the agglutination reaction for diagnostic purposes.
   (*f*) How may precipitation tests be used in medicolegal work?
9. What is the unitarian hypothesis of antibodies?
10. What role does inflammation play as a defense reaction?

REFERENCES

Burrows, W.: Textbook of Microbiology. 17th ed. Philadelphia, W. B. Saunders Company, 1959.

Dubos, R. J., ed.: Bacterial and Mycotic Infections of Man. 3rd ed. Philadelphia, J. B. Lippincott Company, 1958.

Raffel, S.: Immunity, Hypersensitivity, Serology. New York, Appleton-Century-Crofts, Inc., 1953.

Smith, D. T., et al.: Zinsser's Textbook of Bacteriology. 11th ed. New York, Appleton-Century-Crofts, Inc., 1957.

St. Whitlock, O., and Furness, F. N., ed.: Natural Resistance to Infections. Annals of the New York Academy of Sciences. Vol. 66, p. 233. New York Academy of Sciences, 1956.

Wilson, G. S., and Miles, A. A.: Topley and Wilson's Principles of Bacteriology and Immunity. 2 vols. 4th ed. Baltimore, The Williams & Wilkins Company, 1955.

29 • Inborn and Acquired Immunity

Immunity to infectious disease refers to the ability to combat pathogens after they have invaded the body and, thus, to prevent them from producing disease. Because immunity is of varying degrees, the term is used in a relative sense—it does not necessarily mean absolute resistance to an infection. A person may have a high degree of resistance to a disease but may nevertheless contract the infection if his body is invaded by a highly virulent strain of the infective agent. The degree of resistance depends upon the balance between the defense mechanisms of the person and the virulence of the invading pathogens. Many practical applications of value in the treatment and prevention of disease have resulted from investigations in the field of immunology.

Immunity to disease may be inborn, i.e., inherent, or it may be acquired by recovery from an attack of the disease or by artificial inoculation.

INBORN IMMUNITY

Inborn or genetic immunity is an inherent characteristic possessed from the time of birth. It is part of the biological heritage of organisms. It may be inherent in a species or a subdivision of a species, such as a race or a breed. Every species is genetically insusceptible to many diseases that attack other species. Most pathogens can cause disease in only one or a few species. Man is resistant to many diseases to which animals are susceptible, and animals are resistant to many human pathogens. The human species, for example, is resistant to hog cholera, and hogs are immune to Asiatic cholera, to which man is susceptible. Man readily becomes infected by typhoid fever bacteria, while domestic animals never contract typhoid. Dogs are highly susceptible to distemper, but man has an inherent immunity to this disease.

431

ACQUIRED IMMUNITY

Acquired immunity, as the name implies, is not inherent but develops through some incident, usually after birth. It may be acquired actively as the result of infection or artificial immunization, or passively by the injection of specific antibodies.

Actively Acquired Immunity

If immunity results from a response on the part of the body to the presence of antigen, it is said to be actively acquired. Under such conditions the tissues of the body become active and make specific antibodies to react with the antigen. Active immunity may be acquired (1) naturally, through recovery from an infection, the antigen entering the body by natural means; or (2) artificially, by the deliberate injection of antigen into the body in the form of living or killed microorganisms or toxins (usually toxoids). When antigens first gain entrance to the body, a period of seven to ten days or, in some cases, several weeks may elapse before there is evidence of antibody production. Once actively immunized, however, the antibody-producing cells respond more quickly and in a more pronounced manner when antigen is again injected or when the body is invaded by the corresponding pathogens.

Active Immunity Acquired Naturally.   It has been known for centuries that a high degree of immunity to reinfection follows recovery from certain infectious diseases. The immunity is due to the production by the body of specific antibodies which made the combat against the disease a successful one. The body continues to produce the antibodies for weeks or many years, or even for a lifetime, but at a slowly diminishing rate. The antibody-producing cells have been so modified that they can quickly produce additional antibody if the body is again invaded by the pathogens, and thus ward off infection. It is the ability to quickly produce additional antibody that actually protects the person against reinfection rather than the ability of the tissues to maintain a certain blood level of antibody.

Recovery from certain infections is followed by a relatively permanent immunity, whereas in others the immunity is temporary. Some examples of diseases in which recovery ordinarily confers lasting immunity are typhoid fever, typhus fever, diphtheria, plague, smallpox, scarlet fever, chickenpox, whooping cough, measles, mumps and poliomyelitis. Immunity to these diseases acquired by recovery from an attack is not necessarily absolute, since a second attack may occur in some persons.

Even a mild attack may leave a person immune in some diseases. The attack may be so mild as to go unrecognized. In an epidemic such mild infections may greatly outnumber those severe enough to exhibit typical symptoms of the disease. Repeated exposure over a period of time to very small quantities of certain pathogenic microbes may give rise to long-lasting immunity.

Active Immunity Acquired Artificially. Active immunity against a number of diseases can be conferred on susceptible persons by means other than natural infection. This is accomplished by the introduction into the body of antigenic material which may consist of either killed or living infective agents; or bacterial exotoxins, unaltered or detoxified (toxoids). The body reacts to these antigenic substances by the formation of specific counteracting antibodies and thus becomes immune as it would by having the disease itself. Immunity, however, is not immediately established, since body cells respond slowly to the presence of antigen. Two or three inoculations at intervals of several weeks or months are often necessary before antibodies are formed in sufficient concentration to protect the body against infection.

This type of immunity is called artificial immunity because it is artificially induced by the deliberate injection into the body of antigenic material to serve as a stimulus for the production of antibodies. The resulting immunity, however, is basically the same as that evoked when antigen enters the body by natural means.

Artificial active immunization ordinarily is of no value as a therapeutic or curative measure, i.e., in the treatment of disease, but is of value as a preventive or prophylactic procedure in a number of diseases when resorted to before exposure occurs. Two diseases, smallpox and diphtheria, which formerly took a heavy toll of human life, have been practically eliminated from many parts of the world by immunization.

An immunizing preparation containing a suspension of killed or living infective agents is known as a *vaccine*. The name is derived from the Latin word *vacca*, meaning cow, and referred originally to the material used by Jenner to immunize human beings against smallpox. The meaning of the term has been broadened to embrace any immunizing preparation containing microorganisms.* The use of a vaccine for the production of immunity is known as *vaccination*.

Passively Acquired Immunity

Passively acquired immunity is of short duration, lasting usually not longer than four weeks, but in some cases it may last several months. It may arise naturally or be induced by artificial means. Natural passive immunity occurs as the result of the transfer of antibodies from the blood stream of the mother to the fetus during intra-uterine life. The newborn infant thus receives a measure of protection against diseases to which the mother has active immunity. The immunity is transitory, since the antibodies usually disappear from the body of the infant after several months. Artificial passive immunity is produced by injecting (intravenously, subcutaneously or intramuscularly) the blood serum of an animal

---

* The term is used also in a still broader sense by some writers to include toxins used in immunization. Thus, any antigen introduced into the body for the purpose of inducing the production of antibodies is a vaccine.

which has been actively immunized to a high degree against the disease. Such blood serum contains specific antibodies similar to those produced in the human body during disease and is known as *antiserum*. The tissue responses of animals, especially mammals, to the presence of antigen are similar to those of man. In some cases the blood serum of a human being who has recovered from a particular disease is used.

Since no antigen is introduced in this type of immunization, the body is not stimulated to make antibodies but is the passive recipient of antibodies produced in the body of an animal, such as the horse, goat or rabbit, or, in some cases, the body of another person. Because the immunity is immediately effective, this method is used both to treat and to prevent disease.

BACTERIAL VACCINES

Most of the bacterial vaccines contain killed bacteria. If their antigenic molecules have not been too greatly altered by the killing process, killed pathogens can, in some cases, be used to confer immunity. Vaccines of this type are known as *bacterins*. In making these vaccines the bacteria are killed by heat, chemicals or ultraviolet rays. If heat is used, they are subjected to a temperature of 56° to 60° C. for one hour. Temperatures above 60° C. destroy the antigenic properties of the bacteria. When chemicals are used to kill the organisms, phenol or formaldehyde is generally employed. Although less active as immunizing agents than the living bacteria, bacterins are of value for immunization against a number of diseases.

Some bacterial vaccines contain living bacteria which have been treated to reduce their virulence without materially altering their antigenicity. Microorganisms treated in this way are said to be "attenuated." Such organisms are incapable of producing serious disease but, when introduced into the body, are able to bring about an immunity reaction. Attenuation may be accomplished by cultivation at temperatures above the optimum, successive transfer of cultures in artificial culture media over a long period of time, cultivation in media of unfavorable pH or media containing small amounts of injurious substances, or by inoculation of the organism into unnatural animal hosts.

A single injection of an attenuated vaccine confers an effective immunity. Two or more injections of killed vaccines are required at short intervals. Several months may be needed for the development of effective immunity. After active immunity has been established, the antibody level of the blood usually decreases and may drop to a low level. An additional injection of antigen after six months or a year will quickly increase the concentration of antibody. The injection of a dose of antigen into a previously immunized animal or human being in order to maintain a high degree of immunity is referred to as a "booster" injection or "booster shot."

In the manufacture of a bacterial vaccine the organisms are grown in large masses on special culture media, usually solid media such as blood agar, serum agar or, in some cases, plain nutrient agar. The growth is removed and suspended in a physiological salt solution (0.85 per cent sodium chloride). The next step is to kill the bacteria if the vaccine is to consist of killed organisms. The vaccine is then standardized to contain a definite number of bacteria per milliliter. The final preparation is tested for sterility, toxicity and antigenic activity before being released for use.

The best known, and one of the most important, bacterins is the one used against typhoid fever. Vaccines of a similar type are used in immunization against whooping cough (pertussis), plague and Asiatic cholera.

An example of a bacterial vaccine in which the organisms are attenuated is BCG vaccine, which is composed of an attenuated strain of the bovine tubercle bacillus. Attenuation was accomplished at the Pasteur Institute of Paris by Calmette and Guérin by cultivating the bacteria for many years on bile-glycerol-potato medium. This strain of the tubercle bacillus is now known as BCG (Bacillus Calmette-Guérin).

BCG vaccine has been used widely in many European and South American countries. Recent tests carried on in the United States have produced encouraging results.

VIRUS VACCINES

An outstanding example of a vaccine consisting of a virus is smallpox vaccine, the effectiveness of which was first demonstrated by Edward Jenner in 1796. To prepare smallpox vaccine, calves are inoculated with cowpox virus. The inoculation is performed by making parallel scratches in the shaved, washed and disinfected abdominal skin and rubbing virulent virus into the scratches. After six or seven days characteristic skin eruptions (pustules) are formed. The crusts of these are scraped off, and the soft pulp remaining in the lesions is removed and suspended in 50 per cent glycerol. The glycerol acts as a preservative and a mild antiseptic. The vaccine is then stored for several weeks at a low temperature to allow contaminating bacteria, which are invariably present, to die.

Another example of an effective virus vaccine is rabies vaccine. In rabies (hydrophobia) the causative virus becomes localized in the brain and spinal cord. The vaccine is prepared from the spinal cords of rabbits which have been inoculated with the virus. In the rabbit the virulence of the virus is greatly reduced for man and dogs, especially when it is transferred successively from an infected rabbit to a well one in series. The spinal cords of the rabbits are then dried to further attenuate the virus. The vaccine consists of the pulverized spinal cord suspended in sterile salt solution. The original rabies vaccine was prepared by Pasteur. A number of modifications of the Pasteur method have been developed. The vaccine now generally used is prepared from killed virus.

Influenza vaccine is a suspension of inactivated virus prepared from

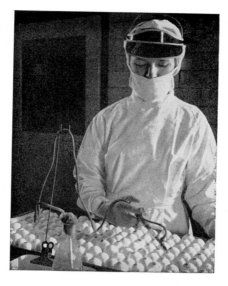

Figure 137. Technician inoculating embryonated hens' eggs with influenza virus. The inoculation is performed with an automatic self-filling syringe through a pin hole in the shell. After inoculation the eggs are returned to the incubator to allow the virus to multiply. (Courtesy of E. R. Squibb & Sons.)

cultures grown in chick embryos. After hens' eggs have been incubated for eleven or twelve days, the virus is inoculated into the fluid of the allantoic sac surrounding the embryo (Figure 137). The eggs are then returned to the incubator for forty-eight hours of additional incubation to allow the virus to multiply. The embryonic fluid is then removed (Figure 138), and the virus is separated from the fluid by centrifugation. The virus is placed in sterile physiological salt solution and inactivated with formaldehyde. Formaldehyde has the property of destroying infectivity without appreciably reducing the antigenicity of the virus. This is true also of certain other viruses. There are at least four different types of

Figure 138. Harvesting the virus. When the virus content is at its height, the shell over the air sac is removed and the virus-containing fluid aspirated aseptically into a collection bottle surrounded with ice. The fluid is used to make influenza vaccine. (Courtesy of E. R. Squibb & Sons.)

influenza viruses, designated as A, B, C and D, and within each type there are a number of different strains. New strains appear to develop from time to time. In 1957 a strain of type A virus caused influenza of epidemic proportions in many parts of the world. To be effective the vaccine must contain the strain responsible for the prevailing infection.

The efficacy of influenza vaccine has not been fully established. It is believed that immunity develops within about a week after injection and that its duration is from four to six months. The vaccine is type-specific and is administered at the time of an outbreak or threatened outbreak of influenza.

Yellow fever vaccine is prepared from chick embryo cultures of the so-called 17D strain of the virus causing yellow fever. The vaccine is placed in ampules, rapidly frozen, desiccated and sealed.

Poliomyelitis vaccine, commonly known as the Salk vaccine, is prepared from poliomyelitis virus that has been grown in a culture of monkey kidney cells. To destroy its infectiousness, the virus is inactivated with formaldehyde. The vaccine contains the three known types of poliomyelitis virus.

TOXINS AND TOXOIDS

In diseases caused by toxin-producing bacteria the chief symptoms result from exotoxins which are formed at the point of infection, absorbed into the blood stream and disseminated through the body. Toxins thus constitute the important antigen in such diseases. It is possible to use toxins in artificial immunization. They are obtained for this purpose from liquid media in which the bacteria have been grown. There are only a few diseases, however, for which immunity can be induced by means of toxin preparations since only a few species of pathogens give rise to exotoxins.

Toxins may be used either unaltered or in modified form. When used unaltered, it is necessary to start with a minute initial dose and to increase the dose gradually through a series of subsequent injections. Because of their high toxicity, toxins are usually modified for immunizing purposes. This destroys their toxicity without impairing their antigenic or immunizing property. Toxin combined with antitoxin, known as *toxin-antitoxin,* was the original method used to modify toxin. Diphtheria toxin-antitoxin was used with considerable success for many years for immunizing children against diphtheria.

The safer method is to modify toxin by means of formaldehyde. Such modified toxins, termed *toxoids,* are now usually purified by being precipitated by alum. The toxoid is adsorbed on the surface of the alum precipitate and is released slowly into the blood stream, thus providing a continuous stimulus for a period of time. Alum-precipitated toxoids are used for immunization against diphtheria and tetanus. The widespread use of diphtheria toxoid in the immunization of young children in recent years has practically abolished diphtheria in many American cities and towns. Some of the equipment used in making alum-precipitated diphtheria toxoid is shown in Figure 139.

ANTISERUMS

Antiserums are of two general types, (1) antitoxic and (2) antibacterial. Antitoxic serums contain antitoxins and are usually referred to as *antitoxins,* whereas antibacterial serums contain antibodies reactive toward one or more components of the bacterial cell. The latter may reveal their presence by agglutination of whole cells, lysis of cells, precipitation of soluble extracts of cells, or by enhancing phagocytosis.

Antiserums are prepared by the injection of antigen into such animals

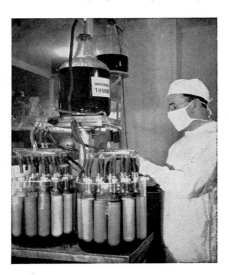

Figure 139. Equipment used in making alum-precipitated diphtheria toxoid. (Reproduced by courtesy of Parke, Davis & Company's Therapeutic Notes.)

as horses, goats or rabbits. In the production of antitoxin the animal is inoculated with a particular bacterial toxin. Since toxin constitutes the antigen, the animal responds by producing antitoxin. Antitoxins are used chiefly in the treatment of diphtheria, tetanus, gas gangrene, botulism and scarlet fever.

In the production of antibacterial serum the animal is inoculated with the pathogens of a particular disease. Since microbial cells constitute the antigen, this kind of antiserum contains antibodies that react with the invading microbes. Not many antiserums of this type are effective. The best examples are those used against the various types of pneumococcal pneumonia. Figure 140 shows the withdrawal of blood from a horse previously inoculated with antigen. The blood is withdrawn aseptically from the jugular vein and is used in the preparation of antiserum.

In some instances, antiserum is obtained from a recovered case of a disease. Such a serum is known as convalescent serum. Human convalescent serum is used when a satisfactory antiserum cannot be obtained by animal immunization.

Table 10 summarizes the ways in which immunity may be acquired.

CONTROL OF MANUFACTURE OF IMMUNIZING SUBSTANCES

Establishments engaged in the manufacture of vaccines, toxins and antiserums must be licensed by, and operate under, the supervision and

Table 10. Types of Acquired Immunity

A. *Actively Acquired Immunity—body stimulated to produce antibodies; resulting immunity of long duration*
   1. Acquired by natural infection and recovery
     a. By typical infection
     b. By a mild or unrecognized infection
   2. Acquired by artificial means
     a. By inoculation with living organisms in a state of attenuated virulence
     b. By inoculation with killed microorganisms
     c. By inoculation with bacterial toxins (usually toxoids)

B. *Passively Acquired Immunity—body not stimulated to produce antibodies; preformed antibodies introduced into the body; resulting immunity of short duration*
   1. Natural passive immunity
     a. Acquired before birth by transfer to the fetus of maternal antibodies during intra-uterine life
     b. Acquired by the suckling infant through the mother's milk
   2. Artificial passive immunity—acquired by the artificial introduction of antibodies developed in the body of another individual

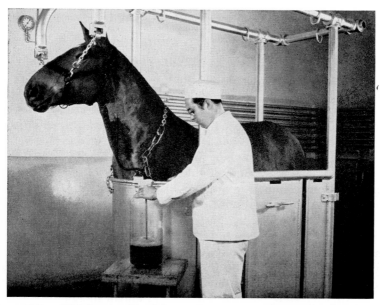

Figure 140. Withdrawing blood from a horse previously inoculated with antigen. The blood is used in the preparation of antiserum. (Reproduced by courtesy of Parke, Davis & Company's Therapeutic Notes.)

control of the United States Public Health Service to insure the preparation of safe and effective products. Samples of the products are tested at regular intervals to determine their purity, potency and freedom from microbial contamination. Establishments engaged in the manufacture of immunizing products for veterinary use must be licensed by the Bureau of Animal Industry.

IMMUNIZATION IN DISEASE CONTROL

Active immunization is one of the principal procedures used in the control of communicable diseases. Because immunity can now be established effectively against a number of infectious diseases, many health departments have made recommendations regarding immunization. The degree of protection by immunization varies for different diseases. A substantial decrease in the incidence of many communicable diseases has occurred during recent years and is attributed to the maintenance of a high level of immunity in the population by mass immunization programs. Mass immunization protects not only the immunized individuals but offers also a measure of protection to the unimmunized by decreasing the number of susceptible persons and thus reducing the chances for the spread of the disease. Immunization has practically eliminated smallpox and diphtheria from many communities. It offers a considerable measure of protection against whooping cough, poliomyelitis, tetanus, typhoid fever, paratyphoid fever, yellow fever, rabies and typhus fever. Immunization is one of the factors that has made life less hazardous than it was in the past.

IMMUNIZATION AND CIVIL DEFENSE

Adequate plans for civil defense in case of war must include a program of defense against disease, including immunization of the civilian population, for any type of major bombing destruction may seriously disrupt our population and cause serious health problems. Consequently, an intensification of all protective measures against disease is in order. Adequate measures taken in advance, such as making full use of our knowledge of immunization and developing new immunizing procedures as well as new methods of mass immunization, might save the lives of many of our people. Investigations along these lines might be of great value to peacetime health as well as to civil defense.

In addition to the problems that would be created by the bombing of our cities, there is the possibility that the enemy may resort to biological warfare by disseminating infective agents or their toxins. How successful this type of warfare would be is problematical. It would probably be directed primarily against the civilian population to cause disease and death and thus interfere with production and impair morale. It could also be directed to the destruction of livestock and agricultural crops. The agents that might be used to spread disease include bacteria, viruses, rickettsiae, protozoa, fungi and botulinus toxin. The mode of attack might be aerial, with specially constructed bombs (aerosol bombs) to release a fine spray or mist of germs over an urban area. Such bombs could be dropped from aircraft or delivered in rockets or guided missiles. The spread of disease also could be attempted by saboteurs in our midst by introducing certain human pathogens or botulinus toxin into water supplies serving a large number of people; or by introducing germs capable of causing disease when inhaled, into the ventilating systems of auditoriums, office buildings and industrial plants. They might also attempt to contaminate certain foods with pathogens or botulinus toxin.

Pathogens that might be possible biological warfare agents include those that cause anthrax, plague, influenza, psittacosis, tularemia, typhus, dysentery, brucellosis, coccidioidomycosis, glanders and cholera.

The capabilities of the artificial production of epidemic disease will not be known until this mode of attack is tried. Research in this field is being carried on to explore its potentialities and to develop protective measures, should an enemy nation attempt biological warfare.

There are defenses against biological warfare, including vaccines, toxoids, antiserums, sulfa drugs and antibiotics. The difficulty of spreading disease among large numbers of people may also be considered a form of defense. It is believed that pathogens as weapons would not be able to destroy a whole community or a large part of it or to induce epidemics that would be self-perpetuating. When epidemics are spread by natural means, only a small percentage of the population is attacked. Many people are immune to various infections as a result of having had these infections or having experienced abortive infections of these diseases. Also, many of our people have been artificially immunized against a number of diseases. The intensification of artificial immunization is an important measure in increasing our defense against biological warfare. A future major war may not be in the offing, but if it is, we cannot be certain that biological warfare will be used. Nevertheless, our plans for defense must take into account all conceivable capabilities of a potential enemy.

QUESTIONS

1. Explain the meaning of the term "immunity" as applied to disease.
2. Differentiate between inborn and acquired immunity, and between actively and passively acquired immunity. Which is of longer duration—active or passive immunity?
3. How may active immunity be acquired naturally? How may it be acquired artificially?
4. (a) What is a vaccine? Give the origin of the word.
   (b) What is a bacterin? Give an example. How are bacterins prepared?
   (c) What is BCG vaccine?
5. Explain the preparation of (1) smallpox vaccine, (2) influenza vaccine, (3) rabies vaccine, (4) poliomyelitis vaccine.
6. Differentiate between toxin and toxoid. What specific effects do vaccines, toxins and toxoids produce in the body by virtue of which they serve as immunizing agents?
7. Differentiate between a serum and a vaccine. Is it proper to call a vaccine a serum?

8. Differentiate between antitoxin and antibacterial serum. What is convalescent serum? How is antitoxin prepared?

9. Should immunization against disease be included in a program of civil defense? Explain.

REFERENCES

Boyd, W.: Fundamentals of Immunology. 3rd ed. New York, Interscience Publishers, Inc., 1956.

Burrows, W.: Textbook of Microbiology. 17th ed. Philadelphia, W. B. Saunders Company, 1959.

Carpenter, P. L.: Immunology and Serology. Philadelphia, W. B. Saunders Company, 1956.

Cushing, J. E., and Campbell, D. H.: Principles of Immunology. New York, McGraw-Hill Book Company, Inc., 1957.

Hare, R.: Bacteriology and Immunity. New York, Longmans, Green & Company, 1956.

Raffel, S.: Immunity, Hypersensitivity, Serology. New York, Appleton-Century-Crofts, Inc., 1953.

Rosebury, T.: Peace or Pestilence. New York, McGraw-Hill Book Company, Inc., 1949.

Smith, D. T. et al.: Zinsser's Textbook of Bacteriology. 11th ed. New York, Appleton-Century-Crofts, Inc., 1957.

Wilson, G. S., and Miles, A. A.: Topley and Wilson's Principles of Bacteriology and Immunity. 2 vols. 4th ed. Baltimore, The Williams & Wilkins Company, 1955.

30 • Hypersensitivity

Hypersensitivity is a condition of a specific sensitivity and reactivity on contact with foreign proteins or other substances which evoke no comparable response in most people. The condition may manifest itself by either local or general disturbances. A relatively large proportion of persons are hypersensitive in varying degree to one or more substances present in the environment. These substances, although harmless to most persons, may cause violent symptoms in sensitive persons whenever they come in intimate contact with them. Even minute amounts may cause violent reactions in susceptible persons. Hay fever, asthma, food allergy, serum sickness and anaphylaxis (limited to animals) are examples of hypersensitivity.

ANAPHYLAXIS

It is possible to artificially induce specific sensitivity in certain animals by injecting them subcutaneously or intravenously with protein substances. If a guinea pig receives an injection of a foreign protein such as egg albumen, it becomes hypersensitive to this protein. The first injection produces no symptoms, but sensitizes the tissues to the foreign protein; in other words, it brings about a reduced tolerance for the foreign substance. In this respect it is the exact reverse of the immunity reaction, in which the introduction of antigen results in an increased resistance. A second injection of the same protein, after a lapse of ten days or more, is followed, often within a few minutes, by symptoms which may range from minor disturbances to difficulty in breathing, convulsions, paralysis and death.

Hypersensitivity artificially induced by the injection of a foreign protein into an animal is known as *anaphylaxis,* meaning "against protection." When the symptoms are severe and occur with remarkable suddenness, the reaction is often referred to as "anaphylactic shock."

Anaphylaxis is precipitated by an antigen-antibody reaction. It is generally regarded that the antibodies become fixed and bound to certain tissues and, consequently, are not circulating in the blood as is the case with antibodies that play a role in infectious diseases. The site of the interaction of antigen and antibody, therefore, is cellular. The injected foreign protein (antigen) combines with the fixed antibody which causes the reacting cells to release *histamine*. Histamine is derived from the amino acid *histidine,* which apparently is present in all cells. It is believed that the liberated histamine causes the anaphylactic symptoms. Similar symptoms can be induced in animals by the injection of histamine. Apparently the anaphylactic reaction is an attempt on the part of the body to defend itself against foreign substances by the production of antibodies to bind these substances—an attempt which miscarries in that the results are detrimental rather than protective.

Anaphylactic reactions can be produced experimentally in a number of species of animals, particularly guinea pigs, rabbits and dogs. An animal made hypersensitive to a certain protein may be desensitized by the repeated injection of the protein in doses too small to produce shock.

COMMON ALLERGIES OF MAN

The term *allergy,* meaning altered reactivity, is commonly used to designate those reactions that are due to natural sensitization of man or animals. Substances capable of giving rise to allergy are called *allergens.*

The present conception of the nature of allergic reactions is a development from the observations of anaphylaxis. Allergy is believed to be fundamentally similar to anaphylaxis in that it is an antigen-antibody reaction resulting in injury to certain body cells with the liberation of histamine from the injured cells. In allergy the reactions tend to be local rather than general. The differences in the symptoms of different types of allergy appear to be due to the localization of the sensitivity in certain cells. The more common sites of allergic reactions are the nasal mucous membranes, bronchial tubes, skin, eyes, brain and gastrointestinal tract. These sites of reaction are referred to as "shock organs."

There appears to be a hereditary tendency to the development of allergy since allergic persons occur more commonly in some families than in others. What is inherited, however, is the tendency to become hypersensitive rather than a tendency to develop a specific hypersensitivity. In cases where several members of a family are allergic, each one is usually sensitive to a different substance, and the allergic manifestation may be hay fever in one individual and hives in another.

The range of substances capable of causing allergy is large. Included among such agents are pollens, animal hair and skin emanations (skin debris), feathers, kapok, glue, wool, sulfonamides, penicillin, streptomycin, poison ivy, mold spores, bacteria, various foods and house dust. In some persons a minute amount of an allergen may cause severe symptoms.

Allergens gain access to the body by inhalation, ingestion and contact with the skin. The most common kinds of allergies are hay fever, asthma, hives, eczema and gastrointestinal disturbances. An allergic person may be sensitive to more than one allergen. It is also true that two persons sensitive to the same allergen may present entirely different symptoms. Allergy may develop during the course of certain infectious diseases. In tuberculosis, brucellosis and some fungal infections, this is of diagnostic significance.

Hay Fever

Many persons have an allergic sensitiveness to the pollens of certain grasses, weeds and trees. These pollens are blown about by the wind and are abundant in the air at certain seasons. Symptoms develop when the pollen grains come in contact with the mucous membranes of the nose and throat or the membrane that lines the eyelids and covers the eyeball (conjunctiva), where they act as allergic excitants. The membranes become irritated and swollen, giving rise to symptoms resembling those of the common cold. Most cases of hay fever occur in the fall of the year and are due chiefly to ragweed pollen. The pollen of trees may cause hay fever early in spring, whereas grass pollen is responsible for late spring and early summer hay fever. Other allergens such as house dust, orris root, mold spores and the emanations of animals may cause hay fever.

Asthma

Asthma is a disorder of the respiratory tract characterized by acute attacks of difficult breathing due to contraction of the muscular fibers in the small air tubes (bronchioles) of the lungs. The attacks are accompanied by coughing and wheezing. Asthmatic symptoms are caused by the inhalation of skin emanations, particularly of the horse; feathers of chickens or ducks; hair particles of various animals; spores of various fungi; house dust; and orris root. Various kinds of foods, particularly eggs, milk, meat, fish and cereals, may also be responsible.

Allergic Skin Reactions

In some allergic reactions the skin is the shock organ. A reaction of this type may be called an *allergic dermatitis*. The condition may be characterized by a skin rash (hives) accompanied by an itchy sensation; or by oozing blisters and the development of scales and crusts, usually called "eczema." The reaction may arise from the surface contact with the exciting agent or may result from the inhalation or ingestion of the allergen.

Gastrointestinal Allergy

Many foods may cause allergic manifestations. Food allergy may express itself in many different ways. In some cases the gastrointestinal tract serves as the "shock organ," the symptoms being nausea, intestinal irritation and vomiting. Food allergy may manifest itself also as asthma, hives, eczema (especially in children) and hay fever.

Allergy of Infection

A person may acquire sensitivity to one or more microbial proteins as a result of having had a particular infection. This is especially true in diseases that are chronic, such as tuberculosis, brucellosis, leprosy and glanders (a disease of horses communicable to man). Many of the rashes and eruptions characteristic of certain infectious diseases are allergic reactions. Bacterial allergy is well illustrated in tuberculosis, in which the infected person acquires a sensitivity to proteins peculiar to the tubercle bacillus. These proteins are present in the preparation known as tuberculin (Chapter 32). Injection of tuberculin into the skin of a tuberculous patient, or one who at some previous time was infected by the tubercle bacillus, gives rise to swelling and redness at the site of application. It may also cause general symptoms consisting chiefly of a rise in body temperature and malaise. A person who was never infected by the tubercle bacillus does not react to tuberculin because he is not hypersensitive to it.

Serum Sickness

Untoward reactions known as "serum sickness" may follow the administration of an antiserum in the treatment of disease. The antibody content is not the responsible factor, since normal serum may cause the reaction. Horse serum is more often responsible for serum sickness than the serum of other animals. Serum sickness is characterized by a skin eruption, joint pains and fever. The duration of the symptoms is usually not longer than two or three days. In some cases the reaction occurs immediately after injection of the antiserum, but in most instances, three to twelve days later. The reactions occur because the person has either a natural or an acquired hypersensitivity to certain proteins normally present in serum. The incidence of serum sickness is much greater in those persons who received horse serum for the treatment of a previous infection. It also occurs frequently in those who have asthma due to horse proteins. In these cases the symptoms usually develop earlier and are more severe. Infrequently, the symptoms are severe and then closely resemble those of anaphylaxis in the lower animals. In a few cases, collapse and death have occurred. The purified concentrated antiserums used at present are less likely to give rise to untoward reactions than older types, which contained relatively large quantities of proteins.

IDENTIFICATION OF THE ALLERGEN

In an allergic person the skin is usually sensitive to the exciting agent. This is made use of in determining the allergen responsible for the allergy. A small amount of an extract of the suspected allergen is applied to a superficial scratch in the skin or injected into the skin. Hypersensitivity to the allergen is indicated by the formation within a few minutes of a raised wheal at the area of application. To determine the agent responsible for allergic contact dermatitis, which, as previously stated, is caused by substances coming in direct contact with the skin, the material is applied to the skin on a small square of cloth or paper. This is known as the "patch test." A positive reaction produces a skin lesion similar to the lesions present in the skin of the patient. After the allergen has been identified, the patient may take steps to avoid it or, if he cannot do so, may in some cases be desensitized to it.

Desensitization

Treatment of allergies is carried out in some cases by desensitization, which is accomplished by a long series of injections of an extract of the allergen in increasing amounts, beginning with a dose too small to cause reactions. This treatment, if successful, gradually depresses sensitivity to the allergen. Desensitization is not always successful and, in most cases, it is partial rather than complete. In many cases it is of short duration, lasting only a few months. It is assumed that desensitization of an allergic person is due to the production of large amounts of circulating antibody which is capable of binding allergens that may enter the body, thus preventing the allergen from coming in contact with sensitized cells.

SYMPTOMATIC TREATMENT

Certain drugs are of value in the temporary alleviation of the symptoms of allergy. Such drugs, known as antihistamines, produce satisfactory results in the palliative treatment of certain allergic conditions. They act by neutralizing the action of histamine. The action of these drugs is transitory. They have no remedial effect on the basic allergic condition or in reducing the person's hypersensitivity. They are more useful in the treatment of hay fever and hives than in the treatment of asthma or eczema. The undesirable side effects these drugs are capable of producing limit their usefulness.

QUESTIONS

1. What is hypersensitivity? Give examples.
2. Explain the term "anaphylaxis."
3. What is the nature of the anaphylaxis reaction? What is histamine?
4. Explain the term "allergy." What is an allergen? Name some common allergens.
5. What are the common sites of allergic reaction? What are "shock organs"?
6. Discuss briefly: (1) hay fever, (2) asthma, (3) allergic skin reactions, (4) gastrointestinal allergy, (5) serum sickness.
7. Explain the tuberculin reaction on the basis of allergy.
8. How may the specific allergen responsible for an allergic condition be determined? How can a hypersensitive person be desensitized to an allergen? What are antihistamines?

REFERENCES

All references cited for Chapters 28 and 29 plus:

Cooke, R. A. et al.: Allergy in Theory and Practice. Philadelphia, W. B. Saunders Company, 1947.

Ratner, B.: Allergy, Anaphylaxis and Immunity. Baltimore, The Williams & Wilkins Company, 1943.

IX · Infectious Diseases

31 • Diseases Caused by Cocci

The spherical shaped bacteria are ubiquitous, the pathogenic species being prevalent on the skin and mucous membranes of man and other animals. The variety of diseases they cause are truly tremendous. No organ or tissue is entirely refractory to infection by the pathogenic cocci. Some of them produce rather potent toxins and enzymes, while others are highly invasive and weakly toxigenic. The Gram-positive pathogenic cocci of significance are the staphylococcus, the streptococcus and the pneumococcus. The Gram-negative pathogenic cocci, classified in the family Neisseriaceae, are the meningococcus and the gonococcus.

THE GENUS STAPHYLOCOCCUS

In the seventh edition (1957) of Bergey's *Manual of Determinative Bacteriology* the genus *Staphylococcus** (family Micrococcaceae) comprises two species, *Staphylococcus aureus* and *Staphylococcus epidermidis*. The species *Staphylococcus aureus* consists of a number of strains which differ from one another in regard to certain traits. The most commonly encountered pathogenic cocci belong to the staphylococcus group. It is chiefly the aureus species that is pathogenic; the epidermidis group is parasitic rather than pathogenic.

Staphylococci are spherical organisms, usually less than a micron in diameter, occurring singly, in pairs and in irregular clusters (Figure 141). Many of the strains form an orange or yellow pigment, whereas others are unpigmented. Staphylococci are nonspore-forming, nonmotile, aerobic and facultatively anaerobic organisms. The normal habitat of staphylococci is the skin and mucous membranes of the nose and mouth. They are

* In the sixth edition (1948) of Bergey's *Manual of Determinative Bacteriology,* the term "staphylococcus" was not used as the name of a taxonomic group. The bacteria now included in the genus *Staphylococcus* were placed, along with certain other cocci, in the genus *Micrococcus.*

present almost constantly on the skin, not only on the surface, but also in hair follicles and the ducts of sweat glands. Staphylococci have a high degree of resistance to desiccation and, consequently, are often present in the dust that accumulates in houses, stables and hospitals. A temperature of 60° C. maintained for half an hour usually destroys them. These cocci are more resistant to the ordinary disinfectants than most other nonspore-forming bacteria. This is of importance to the surgeon since it is these organisms which are likely to invade surgical incisions and cause what are known as stitch abscesses. Staphylococci develop resistance to antibiotics and other chemotherapeutic agents more readily than do most other pathogenic bacteria.

Various toxic or harmful metabolic products are formed during growth in culture media, but individual strains vary in their ability to form these

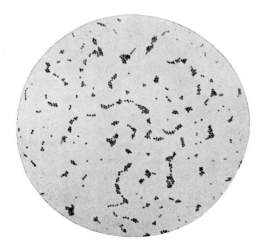

Figure 141. Staphylococcus aureus × 1000. (Reproduced by permission from Principles of Bacteriology and Immunity by W. Topley and G. Wilson, Edward Arnold & Company, London, publishers.)

products. Filtrates of broth cultures contain leukocidin, which disintegrates leukocytes. Certain strains produce a potent enterotoxin (Chapter 25) which, when ingested, is responsible for staphylococcal food poisoning. Many strains are hemolytic in that they cause the lysis of red blood corpuscles. On blood agar these strains form colonies surrounded by a zone of hemolysis. Most strains of pathogenic staphylococci produce coagulase, which causes the clotting of plasma in the immediate vicinity of the bacteria. It is probable that the coagulated plasma serves to protect the staphylococci from phagocytosis.

INFECTIONS CAUSED BY STAPHYLOCOCCI

Staphylococci are the etiological agents of a variety of infections or lesions. They usually gain entrance to body tissues by invading hair follicles and ducts of sweat glands, and by passive introduction through the skin by way of abrasions, cuts and punctures caused by penetrating objects. Infections by staphylococci of small cuts and scratches in the skin are common. Staphylococci are associated with most cases of suppurative wound infections, pustular infections of the skin and subcutaneous tissues, and abscesses in the deeper tissues of the body. Included in these infections are boils, carbuncles, impetigo, otitis media, sinusitis, osteomyelitis, pyemia, septicemia and stitch abscesses.

A *boil* (furuncle) is a localized, tumor-like inflammation of the skin and subcutaneous tissues inclosing a core of dead tissue and pus. Necrosis of the overlying skin eventually forms an opening for the escape of the pus and the organisms. A *carbuncle* is an inflammation of the skin and subcutaneous tissues which terminates in perforations to the exterior through which pus is discharged. The dead tissue finally sloughs away, leaving an ulcerated excavation. The infection has a tendency to spread. A carbuncle is somewhat like a boil but is more serious in its effects and is accompanied by marked constitutional symptoms. The staphylococci responsible for the formation of boils and carbuncles invade the skin most frequently through hair follicles, usually as a result of friction.

Impetigo is a contagious skin infection characterized by the formation of small, purulent, superficial lesions which rupture and then become covered with thick yellowish or brown crusts. The infection most often appears upon the face, neck and hands but may spread over other areas of the skin. It occurs most commonly in young children and is readily transmitted by contact.

Otitis media is an inflammation of the middle ear. The disease is marked by pain radiating over the side of the head. It may be accompanied by ringing sounds in the ears and by dizziness. The infection may be acute or chronic. Besides staphylococci, a number of other organisms may cause otitis media, particularly streptococci and pneumococci.

Another infection in which staphylococci are frequently encountered is *sinusitis*, which is an inflammation of a sinus or sinuses, especially those connected with the nasal passages. It may be acute or chronic. A number of other bacteria may cause sinusitis.

Staphylococci may enter the blood stream from a local infection and be transferred to other parts of the body where they may give rise to secondary foci of infection. They may localize in the bone marrow and cause *osteomyelitis*, which is a purulent inflammation of bone and bone marrow or of the marrow alone. Osteomyelitis occurs most often in children, usually following a blow or trauma. Staphylococci cause about 75 per cent of the cases; the remaining cases are caused by streptococci and a number of other organisms. Blood-borne staphylococci may lodge in the lining membrane (endocardium) of the heart and cause *endocarditis*, or they may cause many abscesses simultaneously in different parts of the body, a condition known as *pyemia*. In some cases they remain in the blood stream, growing and multiplying there, resulting in the condition known as *septicemia*. Streptococci, however, are more often associated with this condition.

THE GENUS STREPTOCOCCUS

The genus *Streptococcus* (family Lactobacteriaceae, tribe Streptococceae) constitutes a large and diverse group of cocci widely distributed in nature. Some are dangerous pathogens associated with a large variety of acute and chronic diseases in both man and animals; others are normal inhabitants of the nose, mouth and intestinal tract of man and animals, without being pathogenic; still others are found in the soil, bodies of water, milk and dairy products. Strains pathogenic for man belong chiefly to the species, *Streptococcus pyogenes*. Individual streptococci are spherical or ovoid in shape and 0.8 to 1.0 micron in diameter. Streptococci have the tendency to form chainlike groups.

HEMOLYTIC AND NONHEMOLYTIC GROUPS

Streptococci may be divided into groups on the basis of their action upon blood when growing on blood agar medium. Three types, designated as *alpha, beta* and *gamma*, may be distinguished. In the *alpha type* of hemolysis there is a narrow greenish zone of partial hemolysis immediately around the colony. Beyond this zone is an outer clear zone in which the blood cells have been completely hemolyzed. Alpha type streptococci are often referred to as "green streptococci." In the *beta type* of hemolysis only a clear zone of complete hemolysis forms around the colony, no greenish zone being present. *Gamma type* streptococci have no effect on red blood corpuscles; consequently no zones of discoloration occur around the colonies growing on blood agar.

Each of these groups is heterogeneous, consisting of a variety of different strains. The beta type is the most important one in regard to pathogenesis since it contains highly virulent forms which are associated with a variety of infections of man and animals. The most important human pathogen in this group is *Streptococcus pyogenes*. The alpha type streptococci are of a lower degree of virulence, and the gamma or nonhemolytic kinds generally lack virulence. Figure 142 shows beta type hemolysis produced by streptococci.

Beta type streptococci give rise to a variety of toxic substances, including hemolysins and leukocidins. A number of strains produce fibrinolysin, which liquefies the fibrin present in blood clots. An erythrogenic ("red-producing") toxin is formed by some strains. This toxin causes the rash in scarlet fever, erysipelas and certain other streptococcal infections. It is antigenic, and an antitoxin can be produced to neutralize it. Some strains produce hyaluronidase, the so-called spreading factor, considered in Chapter 26. It will be recalled that this factor affects the permeability of tissues, thus allowing the organisms to spread through them more readily.

INFECTIONS CAUSED BY STREPTOCOCCI

Beta type streptococci are the etiological agents of a variety of infections in the human species. The virulence exhibited by these organisms varies considerably with different species or strains. The sulfonamides and certain antibiotics are usually effective therapeutic agents in streptococcal infections.

Streptococcal sore throat is a severe type of infection occurring at times in epidemic form. It is characterized by intense local hyperemia, swelling of the tonsils and the lymph nodes in the neck region, fever and prostration. The organisms frequently invade the blood stream, resulting in complications such as acute nephritis, endocarditis, arthritis and bronchopneumonia.

Erysipelas (St. Anthony's fire) is an acute inflammatory infection of the

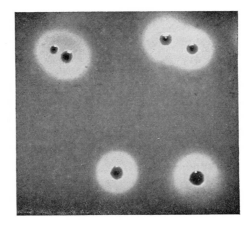

Figure 142. Streptococcus pyogenes showing beta-type hemolysis on blood agar. (From W. Burrows, Textbook of Microbiology.)

skin which, in adults, usually occurs upon the nose or face, although any part of the skin may become involved. It is characterized by rapidly spreading, sharply demarcated red areas which become swollen and painful. It is accompanied by constitutional symptoms, including chills and fever. Serious complications may occur, especially in the young or very old.

Puerperal fever is an infection of the uterus following childbirth in which streptococci are usually the etiologic agents. If it is caused by highly virulent streptococci, serious complications such as peritonitis or septicemia may occur.

Rheumatic fever, which is a widespread disease of childhood and young adults, appears to be an allergic reaction to the cell substance of beta-hemolytic streptococci following recovery from streptococcal infection of the respiratory tract. Apparently rheumatic fever is always preceded (from one to five weeks) by an upper respiratory infection such as sore throat, tonsillitis or scarlet fever. The exact relationship of streptococci to rheumatic fever is not understood. Available evidence suggests that allergy toward streptococci may be the cause of the symptoms of rheumatic fever. The disease gets its name from the fact that the patient usually has a fever and the joints become inflamed as they do in rheumatism (arthritis). The joint inflammation and the fever subside after a short time. The most serious feature of the disease is the fact that it commonly eventuates in chronic valvular heart inflammation known as "rheumatic heart disease." Rheumatic fever and the associated heart disease kill more children of school age than any other disease and make invalids of many they fail to kill. Prompt treatment of beta-hemolytic streptococcal infections of the respiratory tract is an important factor in lowering the incidence of rheumatic fever.

Subacute bacterial endocarditis, an inflammation of the endocardium or epithelial lining membrane of the heart, is caused most frequently by alpha-hemolytic streptococci. It is a relatively rare but serious disease. The streptococci localize on the valves of the heart and multiply there. The valves become damaged, causing them to leak. The disease may last for months or years and in the past was almost invariably fatal. Many cases now yield to prolonged treatment with penicillin and streptomycin.

Scarlet fever is an acute streptococcal infection of childhood and early adolescence, characterized by an abrupt onset, sore throat, a diffuse scarlet rash (from which the disease takes its name) and constitutional disturbances. The streptococci usually remain localized in the throat, where they produce erythrogenic toxin which is responsible for the scarlet rash.

Although the streptococci are localized in the throat, invasion of other parts of the body may occur, resulting in numerous and varied sequelae such as nephritis, otitis media, endocarditis, bronchopneumonia, sinusitis and joint affections. Nephritis and otitis media are by far the most common sequelae.

A useful diagnostic test has been devised which may be resorted to in doubtful cases. It involves the intracutaneous injection of a small amount of scarlet fever antitoxin where the rash appears. If the rash is due to scarlet fever toxin, a blanching of the skin at the site of injection will occur within eight to twelve hours. This is known as the *Schultz-Charlton reaction.*

The presence or absence of immunity to scarlet fever may be determined by a skin test known as the *Dick test.* It involves the intracutaneous injection of a small quantity of streptococcal erythrogenic toxin. In susceptible individuals a reddish discoloration of the skin occurs at the site of inoculation. In individuals who are immune to scarlet fever no reaction occurs due to the presence of sufficient antitoxin to neutralize the injected toxin.

One attack of the disease usually establishes immunity, but second and even third attacks do occur in some persons. An attack may produce resistance to the erythrogenic toxin, but it does not produce immunity to subsequent infections of the throat or other parts of the body by the streptococcus. Active immunity may be conferred on susceptible persons by the administration of scarlet fever toxin. This usually requires about five subcutaneous injections of increasing doses at weekly intervals. Because the reactions are sometimes severe (nausea, vomiting, fever, joint pain, and so forth), active immunization has not come into widespread use. It has been difficult to prepare a satisfactory scarlet fever toxoid. Most adults are immune, apparently from repeated slight exposures to the disease resulting in subclinical or unrecognized infection.

PNEUMONIA, GONORRHEA AND MENINGITIS

Pneumococcal pneumonia, epidemic meningitis and gonorrhea are caused by bacteria which commonly occur as paired cocci.

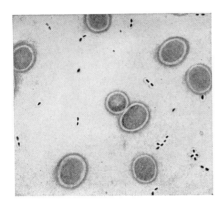

Figure 143. Pneumococci in blood from the heart of a rabbit. × 1000. (From McFarland: Pathogenic Bacteria and Protozoa.)

THE PNEUMOCOCCUS

The most common cause of bacterial pneumonia is *Diplococcus pneumoniae,* commonly known as the *pneumococcus.* The organism is ovoid or spheroid and usually occurs in pairs, but frequently also in short chains. The adjacent sides of each pair are rounded, but the distal ends are somewhat pointed, making the cells lanceolate in form. Upon cultivation the organisms usually become spherical and tend to form short chains. In size the cells vary from 0.5 to 1.2 microns in diameter. A well-defined capsule (Figure 143) is present which, as a rule, surrounds each pair or chain. The capsule disappears upon artificial cultivation unless serum is present in the medium or certain special media are used.

Pneumococci are separable antigenically into more than seventy types on the basis of their type-specific capsular polysaccharide. The various types are indistinguishable by their morphological and cultural characteristics.

Identification of types is usually made directly from the sputum of the patient by a technique known as the Neufeld capsular-swelling reaction (Quellung reaction). This technique is based on the swelling of the capsule when it comes in contact with an antiserum specific for the type. The swelling appears to be due to the precipitation of the polysaccharide-antibody complex within the capsule and the absorption of water by the precipitate. The capsular polysaccharide is the antigenic material of the pneumococcus, and both the type specificity and virulence of the organism are dependent upon this capsular material.

Pneumococci are normal inhabitants of the upper respiratory tract of man and certain animals. Many healthy persons are pneumococcus carriers. Some persons are temporary carriers, whereas others carry the organisms for a long time. In the winter and spring months the number of carriers is greater than during the other seasons. Pneumococci do not ordinarily thrive outside the human body; man, therefore, is the main reservoir of the organisms.

Pneumococcal Pneumonia

The two chief types of pneumonia are *lobar pneumonia* and *bronchopneumonia*. Both types are usually caused by the pneumococcus but may be caused by streptococci, staphylococci and a few other species. Pneumococcal pneumonia occurs in all climates but is more prevalent in the colder areas of the world than in the warmer regions. In the United States more cases occur in the winter and early spring than at any other time of the year.

In lobar pneumonia one or more of the five lobes of the lungs may be involved. The right lung has three, the left lung two lobes. One or both lungs may be affected. The disease usually has a sudden onset with a severe chill followed by a steep rise in temperature. The capillaries in the involved portion of the lungs become congested with blood, and some of the fluid portion of the blood, together with red corpuscles, enters the alveoli (air sacs). This exudate becomes fibrinous and leads to a consolidation of the lung tissue. Thus the functional area of the lung is decreased, and the work of respiration is thrown upon the unaffected part. The temperature hovers around 104 or 105° F. If no specific treatment is administered, the patient remains in this condition for about seven days, when the so-called "crisis" occurs and the patient either dies or undergoes a striking change for the better. Recovery is due to type-specific antibody produced by the defense mechanism of the body.

Most persons are normally resistant to the pneumococcus. It is only when this resistance becomes lowered that the organism can set up infection. Factors that lower resistance are infections of the respiratory tract, such as the common cold, bronchitis and influenza. Fatigue, starvation, chilling of the body and alcoholic intoxication also lower the resistance of the body. Most cases of lobar pneumonia develop after an infection of the upper respiratory tract, chiefly the common cold.

Bronchopneumonia usually follows in the wake of measles, whooping cough, influenza, severe colds and other diseases. It accounts for most of the deaths which occur in these diseases. The onset is gradual and the infection is scattered through the lungs. The inflammation occurs in patches. Both lungs usually are involved. It is usually caused by the pneumococcus but may be caused by streptococci, staphylococci, the rod-shaped organism known as *Klebsiella pneumoniae* (Friedländer's bacillus) and *Haemophilus influenzae*.

Immunity and Immunization. Recovery from an attack of pneumonia does not confer immunity against subsequent attacks. The antibodies produced during an attack of the disease are directed against the capsular polysaccharides. The injection of minute amounts of pneumococcal polysaccharide confers active immunity against the homologous type.

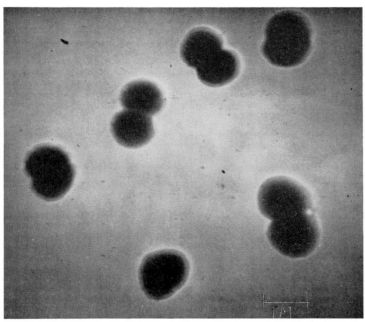

Figure 144. Electron micrograph of *Neisseria gonorrhoeae*, showing the organisms in various stages of division. (Courtesy of Dr. H. E. Morton.)

Treatment. Although type-specific antiserums are available for the treatment of pneumococcal pneumonia, it is treated chiefly with antibiotics and sulfonamides. In some cases, serum therapy is used in conjunction with chemotherapy. Before these therapeutic agents were available, the mortality rate of pneumonia was relatively high.

THE GONOCOCCUS

Gonorrhea and epidemic meningitis are caused by bacteria belonging to the genus *Neisseria*. The name of the genus is derived from the name of the German bacteriologist Albert Neisser, who in 1879 first observed the causative agent of gonorrhea in urethral pus. This organism was later shown to be the etiological agent of gonorrhea and was named *Neisseria gonorrhoeae*. It is commonly known as the *gonococcus*. In pus obtained from human lesions the gonococci are usually arranged in pairs with the adjacent sides flattened, giving them a biscuit-like appearance. In culture media they tend to become spherical or ovoid. They are non-motile and nonspore-forming and sometimes have a capsule. Gonococci are aerobic and facultatively anaerobic. They measure from 0.6 to 1.0 micron in diameter. The gonococcus is shown very much enlarged in Figure 144.

The habitat of the gonococcus is the human body, the organisms being parasitic exclusively for the human species. Laboratory animals cannot be infected with the organisms, and even anthropoid apes are resistant to it. Persons in the age group of twenty to thirty years constitute the chief reservoir of the organism since it is in this age group that most cases of gonorrhea occur. The gonococcus is not a hardy organism and is incapable of long survival in the outside environment.

The gonococcus is fastidious in its growth requirements. It is cultivated with considerable difficulty, particularly when first isolated from human lesions. The gonococcus grows best in an atmosphere of reduced oxygen tension containing from 5 to 10 per cent carbon dioxide.

Gonorrhea

Gonorrhea, being a venereal disease, is transmitted in most cases by direct sexual contact. Transmission may occur, however, by means of contaminated objects (fomites), but the time between contamination and transmission must be very short since the organism survives only a brief period outside the body. Under certain conditions transmission may occur through the agency of toilet seats and toilet accessories.

Gonorrhea is a suppurative infection of the urogenital tract. In both male and female the disease may persist in chronic form. The gonococci may invade the blood stream and localize in the joints, causing arthritis ("gonorrheal rheumatism"). Infection of the conjunctiva, the membrane which lines the eyelids and covers the eyeballs, may result from the use of recently contaminated towels or from contaminated hands. This infection, known as gonorrheal ophthalmia, usually results in blindness unless proper treatment is instituted promptly. *Ophthalmia neonatorum* is a gonococcal infection of the eyes of the newborn. The infection is acquired from the mother as the head of the child passes through the infected maternal genital tract. The instillation of a few drops of a suitable antiseptic solution into the eyes at birth usually destroys the gonococci before they can become established in the tissues of the eyes. In many states this is required by law whether or not the mother is suspected of having gonorrhea. A 1 or 2 per cent solution of silver nitrate is usually used for this purpose.

Although it is difficult to obtain exact data in regard to its incidence, gonorrhea ranks high in prevalence, probably being exceeded only by measles. It has been estimated that a million fresh infections occur annually in the United States.

Immunity and Immunization.   All persons, apparently, are highly susceptible to infection with the gonococcus, there being no inherent immunity to this organism. Recovery from an attack of the disease does not confer immunity to subsequent attacks. Phagocytosis seems to be the chief immunological response to the infection.

Chemotherapy.   Gonorrhea was readily curable with sulfonamides when these therapeutic agents first came into use. Since then many strains of the gonococcus have become sulfonamide-resistant. The disease can now be treated successfully with penicillin.

THE MENINGOCOCCUS

The etiological agent of epidemic meningitis is *Neisseria meningitidis,* commonly known as the *meningococcus.* Morphologically, the meningococcus is indistinguishable from the gonococcus.

Man is the reservoir and the sole natural host of the meningococcus. Meningitis does not occur naturally in animals but can be experimentally induced in monkeys. A large number of normal, healthy persons habitually harbor the organism in the nasopharynx. During epidemics the number of carriers increases; the ratio of carriers to cases is said to be 30 to 1. It is believed that most persons who come in close contact with a carrier or a case will become carriers. They may or may not acquire the disease. The greater the number of carriers, the greater the number of cases that occur. Although many people become carriers, comparatively few acquire the disease, indicating that most people have a rather high natural resistance to the organism.

Meningitis is an acute inflammation of the meninges. The term "meninges" is a collective name for the three membranes that envelop the brain and the spinal cord. Meningococcal meningitis occurs predominantly in epidemic form. The sulfonamides (especially sulfadiazine), penicillin and several other antibiotics are used in the treatment of this disease.

A number of other bacteria are capable of causing inflammation of the meninges. The infection in these cases is usually secondary to some other infection by the same organism. Included in this group are the pneumococcus, streptococcus, staphylococcus, gonococcus, tubercle bacillus and numerous other organisms. It is only the meningococcus, however, that gives rise to the epidemic form of meningitis.

QUESTIONS

1. (*a*) What is the normal habitat of parasitic staphylococci? Name the two species that comprise the genus Staphylococcus.

(*b*) Describe briefly the more important staphylococcal infections encountered in man.

(c) What toxic products may be formed by staphylococci?

2. In the streptococcal group, which species is the most important human pathogen?

3. (a) Explain how streptococci are grouped according to their action on blood agar.

(b) Distinguish between alpha and beta hemolytic streptococci.

(c) Discuss briefly: (1) scarlet fever, (2) rheumatic fever. Name other streptococcal infections.

4. (a) Describe the pneumococcus. On what basis is it divided into types?

(b) What is the normal habitat of this organism?

(c) Describe the course of an attack of lobar pneumonia. Which therapeutic agents are available for the treatment of the disease?

5. (a) Describe the gonococcus. What is its scientific name?

(b) Summarize the chief facts about gonorrhea.

6. What kind of infection is meningitis? Name the etiological agent of epidemic meningitis. How is the infection transmitted?

REFERENCES

Burnett, G. W., and Scherp, H. W.: Oral Microbiology and Infectious Disease. Baltimore, The Williams & Wilkins Company, 1957.

Burrows, W.: Textbook of Microbiology. 17th ed. Philadelphia, W. B. Saunders Company, 1959.

Dubos, R. J., ed.: Bacterial and Mycotic Infections of Man. 3rd ed. Philadelphia, J. B. Lippincott Company, 1958.

McCarty, M., ed.: Streptococcal Infections. New York, Columbia University Press, 1954.

Rogers, D. E., ed.: Staphylococcal Infections. Annals of the New York Academy of Sciences. Vol. 65, p. 57. New York Academy of Sciences, 1956.

Smith, D. T., et al.: Zinsser's Textbook of Bacteriology. 11th ed. New York, Appleton-Century-Crofts, Inc., 1957.

Stimson, P. M., and Hodes, H. L.: A Manual of the Common Contagious Diseases. 5th ed. Philadelphia, Lea & Febiger, 1956.

Wilson, G. S., and Miles, A. A.: Topley and Wilson's Principles of Bacteriology and Immunity. 2 vols. 4th ed. Baltimore, The Williams & Wilkins Company, 1955.

32 • Diseases Caused by
Bacilli and Spirochetes

ENTERIC INFECTIONS

The chief enteric diseases caused by bacteria are typhoid fever, paratyphoid fever, dysentery and cholera. Except for cholera these diseases are caused by members of the family Enterobacteriaceae, which includes a large number of short, Gram-negative, nonsporulating rods whose natural habitat in many instances is the intestinal tract of man and other animals. Some are motile, owing to the presence of peritrichous flagella; others are nonmotile. Typhoid and paratyphoid fever are caused by members of the genus *Salmonella*. This genus comprises a large number of species and types and is very complex antigenically. Some species cause gastroenteritis, which was described in Chapter 25. Many salmonellae are found primarily in animals. The genus *Shigella* includes the causative agents of bacillary dysentery. These pathogenic organisms are closely related to the coliform bacteria.

TYPHOID FEVER

One of the most virulent members of the *salmonella* group is the typhoid bacillus, *Salmonella typhosa*. It is a short, plump rod, 2 to 3 microns in length, with rounded ends and occurs singly, in pairs and, at times, in short chains. It has numerous peritrichous flagella (Figure 23, Chapter 4) and is facultatively anaerobic.

The organism is sufficiently hardy to remain alive outside the body for a relatively long time. It may survive in water for seven days or more. When frozen in ice, it may remain viable for several months. In milk it is capable not only of surviving but also of multiplication. However, it has no natural habitat in the outside world in which it can continue to live indefinitely.

Transmission and Nature of Infection

Typhoid bacilli may gain entrance to the body through food and drinking water contaminated with the body discharges (feces and urine) of patients or carriers. The water supply of a community may become contaminated with human sewage, which frequently contains typhoid bacteria; milk may become contaminated by a carrier; flies that have recently fed on contaminated excreta may convey the organisms to foods of various kinds; oysters from contaminated estuaries may harbor typhoid bacteria and be a source of infection.

Typhoid fever was one of the great infectious diseases of former years. The typhoid epidemics of the past were caused chiefly by polluted water supplies and contaminated milk. The great progress that has been made in the establishment of modern water purification plants and the sanitary disposal of sewage, as well as the increasing attention that has been given to the sanitation of our food supplies, have been the chief factors in the decline of the incidence of typhoid fever and in its practical elimination from many communities. The majority of cases that occur now are in the form of small-scale epidemics in which an unknown carrier is the source of the organism.

Typhoid fever is a generalized, rather complicated type of infection characterized by bacteremia and localized areas of infection in various parts of the body, including the intestinal tract. After the bacteria have gained entrance to the intestinal tract by being swallowed with food or drink, they reach the spleen, liver and mesenteric lymph nodes, probably by way of lymphatic vessels. Here they proliferate and enter the blood stream, producing a bacteremia. During the first week or ten days of illness the bacteria usually can be isolated from the blood. Later they disappear from the circulation and become restricted to certain areas, chiefly the gallbladder, spleen, bone marrow, liver, urinary bladder and the intestinal tract. The spleen is almost always enlarged. The mucous membrane of the intestine becomes inflamed, and the lymph nodes known as "Peyer's patches," which are located on the internal surface of the lower third of the small intestine (ileum), become enlarged and ulcerated. The ulceration may become so deep as to cause perforations of the intestinal wall, leading to peritonitis.

Most patients continue to harbor typhoid bacteria in the gallbladder or urinary bladder and excrete typhoid bacilli in the feces and urine for three weeks to three months after the symptoms of the disease have disappeared. During this period they are convalescent carriers. A small percentage of these patients become chronic carriers, harboring and discharging the bacteria in some cases for a period of six months, but in many cases, for years or even for life. It has been estimated that about 2 per cent of those who recover from the disease become chronic carriers. In these individuals the organisms usually become sequestered in the gallbladder and biliary passages where they multiply and are discharged more or less intermittently into the intestine, thus contaminating the intestinal contents.

Owing to neglect of strict personal cleanliness, carriers frequently contribute typhoid bacteria to food through the agency of their fingers, which become contaminated with their body discharges (feces and urine). Most of the typhoid fever cases now reported are traced directly to carriers. The carrier state in some cases can be remedied by the surgical removal of the gallbladder. As mentioned in Chapter 27, the classic example of a carrier is "Typhoid Mary," who was the first person discovered to be a chronic carrier of typhoid bacilli.

Immunity and Immunization

Recovery from an attack of typhoid fever is usually followed by permanent immunity. The immunity, however, is not absolute and may be overcome by a massive invasion of the body by typhoid bacilli. The immune state can be induced by inoculation with typhoid vaccine. Vaccination generally confers a high degree of immunity but does not protect all persons equally against the occurrence of typhoid fever. The vaccine is given in three injections five to seven days apart. Vaccination is especially indicated for military personnel, those engaged in nursing the sick, workers in clinical laboratories and those who live or travel in places where sanitation is not well maintained. The widespread use of typhoid vaccine for immunization of military personnel has practically eliminated typhoid fever from the list of war diseases. For centuries typhoid fever was the scourge of armies all over the world; more men died of the disease than were killed in battle, but in modern warfare the case rate of typhoid fever has become a negligible quantity.

The duration of immunity conferred by vaccination is limited to about three years. Immunity may be maintained, however, by a repeat injection of vaccine once each year after the initial series of three inoculations. This "booster shot" brings about a rapid rise of the antibody titer to a relatively high level.

The vaccine now widely used in the United States is made from a highly virulent strain of the organism. A triple vaccine is frequently used. This is composed of *Salmonella typhosa* along with highly virulent strains of *Salmonella paratyphi* (paratyphoid A) and *Salmonella schottmuelleri* (paratyphoid B), two related species which are the causative organisms of paratyphoid fever.

The antibiotics chloramphenicol and chlortetracycline are of definite value in the treatment of typhoid fever.

PARATYPHOID FEVER

The organisms most commonly responsible for paratyphoid fever are *Salmonella paratyphi*, *Salmonella schottmuelleri* and *Salmonella hirschfeldii*. Morphologically, these organisms are indistinguishable from *Sal-*

monella typhosa. They can be differentiated from *S. typhosa* and from each other by fermentation reactions and serological (agglutination) tests.

Paratyphoid fever is clinically similar to typhoid fever. The disease varies from a slight enteric disorder to a severe fever indistinguishable from typhoid fever. It is usually milder than typhoid fever. The incidence and the case mortality rate are low in the United States. The carrier state is not common.

BACILLARY DYSENTERY

Bacillary dysentery is caused by a number of species of bacteria included in the genus *Shigella.* Dysentery caused by bacteria is referred to as bacillary dysentery, to distinguish it from the dysentery that is of protozoan etiology, and is known as amebic dysentery (see Chapter 33). The bacteria are short, nonmotile rods. The type species of the genus *Shigella* is *Shigella dysenteriae,* which was isolated by Shiga of Japan in 1898 and is commonly called the Shiga type dysentery bacillus. It is found chiefly in Japan, China and other oriental countries and is by far the most virulent member of the genus, differing from the other species by producing a potent neurotropic exotoxin which has an affinity for the nervous system, causing paralysis and other neurological symptoms. It also produces an endotoxin, in common with the other dysentery bacilli, which acts chiefly on the intestinal tract.

The other dysentery bacilli usually cause a much milder type of disease and are found in most areas of the world. Species commonly encountered in the United States are *Shigella flexneri* and *Shigella sonnei.* The Shiga type, however, has been found in some epidemics of dysentery in the United States.

The disease is transmitted by water and food which have become contaminated, directly or indirectly, from the feces of cases or carriers, by dysentery bacteria. Flies may serve as agents in the transfer of the bacteria from feces to food.

Dysentery is an infection of the intestinal tract, the disease being localized chiefly in the large intestine or colon. Extensive ulceration may occur in the mucous membrane of the large intestine.

Immunity and Immunization

Recovery from an attack of the disease confers a relative, but not a permanent, immunity. An antitoxic serum has been used with encouraging results in the treatment of dysentery caused by the Shiga type of dysentery bacillus.

Chemotherapy

Sulfonamides, chloramphenicol, chlortetracycline and oxytetracycline are effective in the treatment of bacillary dysentery.

ASIATIC CHOLERA

Cholera is caused by a small, curved bacterium, *Vibrio comma*, classified in the family Spirillaceae of the order Pseudomonadales. It is motile, nonencapsulated, nonspore-forming, aerobic and Gram-negative. It was first isolated by Robert Koch from Egyptian patients during a pandemic in 1883. Since cholera is an enteric disease, and thus spread by polluted water and foods, the rigid application of sanitation has practically eliminated the disease in many parts of the world. The endemic center of this disease is the Orient, particularly in the regions around the Yangtze and Ganges rivers of China and India.

The disease, in its severest form, is sudden, resulting in semi-continuous vomiting and diarrhea, induced by liberation of endotoxins from the numerous cholera organisms when they die and autolyze in the small intestine. This results in an alarming loss of body fluids, often great enough to impair circulation and cause death. The watery stools in the acute stage contain bits of intestinal mucosa, imparting a "rice water" appearance to them. The mortality rate is very high, but encouragingly low when the patient receives prompt medical attention. Treatment consists of replacement of fluids, achievement of salt balance and administration of certain antibiotics. Killed vaccines are available and should be given to any person entering an area where cholera is endemic. Recovery from an attack confers active immunity.

TUBERCULOSIS

The bacteria that cause tuberculosis and leprosy are classified in the genus *Mycobacterium* (order Actinomycetales, family Mycobacteriaceae). This genus contains species that cause tuberculosis in mammals, birds and cold-blooded animals; a species considered to be the cause of leprosy; a species that causes chronic diarrhea (Johne's disease) in cattle and sheep; and numerous saprophytic forms, including *Mycobacterium phlei*, which is widely distributed on grass, hay and in the soil, and *Mycobacterium smegmatis*, found in soil, dust and dairy products.

The species causing tuberculosis include two mammalian varieties: (1) the *human type*, the primary host of which is man; (2) the *bovine type*, which is pathogenic primarily for cattle. In addition to the primary host, each type is capable of invading other hosts. The human type may cause disease in anthropoid apes, monkeys, certain parrots, swine and dogs; the bovine type is capable of infecting goats, sheep, pigs, cats, monkeys and man. Guinea pigs are highly susceptible to both the human and bovine types; when large doses are injected, death results, due to acute peritoneal tuberculosis. This applies also to rabbits when inoculated with the bovine type; but when inoculated with the human type, they rarely succumb to it. The human and bovine types of the tubercle bacillus are very much alike in many of their characteristics. The human type is known as *Mycobacterium tuberculosis*, and the bovine type as *Mycobacterium bovis*.

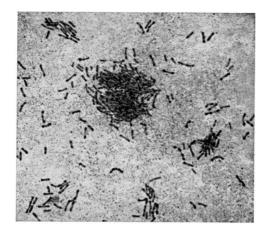

Figure 145. Tubercle bacilli showing beaded appearance. × 1000. (From Ford: Textbook of Bacteriology.)

A species of tubercle bacillus which causes tuberculosis chiefly in birds is known as *Mycobacterium avium.* A number of species of mycobacteria produce tuberculous infections in cold-blooded animals, such as fish, frogs, lizards, snakes and turtles.

The organism considered to be the cause of human leprosy is known as *Mycobacterium leprae.*

TUBERCLE BACILLUS

In 1882 Robert Koch announced that he had isolated the tubercle bacillus. He offered specific proof that it was the etiological agent of tuberculosis. Tubercle bacilli are slender, straight or slightly curved rods with rounded ends, varying in length from 1 to 4 microns. (See Figures 145 and 146.) They usually occur singly, but occasionally form slender filaments, and are acid-fast in their straining characteristics. (See Chapter 14.) The organisms frequently stain unevenly, showing banded or beaded forms. Theobald Smith, an American bacteriologist, differentiated between the human and bovine varieties in 1897. The bovine tubercle bacil-

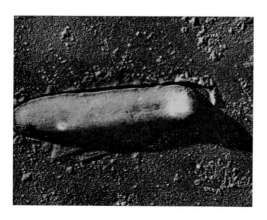

Figure 146. Tubercle bacillus, × 25,000. Reduced approximately one quarter in size from original electron micrograph. (Courtesy of Dept. of Physical Chemistry, The Lilly Research Laboratories.)

lus is shorter and plumper than the human type, but owing to the variations that are characteristic of bacteria, this morphological difference is not always apparent. The human and bovine types differ in their cultural characters and virulence for laboratory animals.

The human tubercle bacillus is widely disseminated through the human population of the world. It does not multiply naturally outside the body but is capable of remaining viable for a considerable time in the outside environment. Because of its waxy cell wall, the organism has a relatively high resistance to desiccation, being able to remain alive in dust at room temperature for many months. It is more resistant than most nonspore-forming bacteria to bactericidal agents, particularly acids and alkalis. This property can be used to facilitate its isolation from sputum by adding strong alkali (4 per cent sodium hydroxide), which will kill many of the other bacteria present but will not kill the tubercle bacillus. A 5 per cent solution of phenol requires about twenty-four hours to kill the organism in sputum. The tubercle bacillus can grow in the presence of dilutions of gentian violet and certain other dyes that prevent the growth of many other organisms. It is readily killed by exposure to direct sunlight.

TUBERCULOSIS IN HUMAN BEINGS

Tuberculosis is a long-drawn-out and treacherous disease which in the early stages is usually symptomless. It may reach an advanced stage without the patient's being aware of having the disease. Since most cases of tuberculosis in man are pulmonary, the disease is spread chiefly by sputum. Droplets of sputum expelled by a patient in talking, sneezing or coughing may remain suspended in the air for a considerable time and may be inhaled by others or may contaminate food. The disease is also spread by the inhalation of dust arising from dried sputum. Thus tubercle bacilli may enter the body through the respiratory or alimentary tracts. The chief portal of entry of the human tubercle bacillus is the respiratory tract, whereas the avenue of entrance of the bovine type is usually the alimentary tract.

At the beginning of the present century the tuberculosis death rate in the United States was in excess of 200 per 100,000 population; at the present time it is about 8 per 100,000. This decline is due to the concentrated attack that has been carried on against the disease for over fifty years. Many nations of the world still have the high tuberculosis death rate that prevailed in the United States fifty years ago. Although the tuberculosis death rate has been forced down drastically in the United States, the disease causes more deaths than all the other infectious diseases combined. Tuberculosis is on the wane, but it is still a great killer. Formerly a disease primarily of adolescents and young adults, tuberculosis is now encountered in many middle-aged and older persons.

Whether or not the tubercle bacillus can establish itself in the body to produce active infection depends very much upon the condition of the individual. A person who maintains a high standard of health, is well nourished, obtains adequate rest and recreation and lives in good surroundings usually has a high degree of resistance to infection by the tubercle bacillus. Any factor that lowers the general level of health may predispose a person to active infection.

The lungs are the common seat of infection, but tubercle bacilli are capable of invading almost any body structure. It is possible to have tuberculosis of the bones, lymph nodes (particularly those of the neck and within the chest at the root of the lungs), larynx, spleen, intestines, liver, urinary bladder, kidneys, skin, spine and the meninges. About 90 per cent of the deaths from tuberculosis, however, are due to the pulmonary type. In children the bones, joints and lymph nodes are more commonly infected than in adults. Because of the frequency of pulmonary tuberculosis, it has received the greatest attention and has been the basis of most investigations concerning the nature of the disease.

Pulmonary tuberculosis is usually always due to the human type of tubercle bacillus. One of the striking peculiarities of pulmonary tuberculosis is that it occurs in two distinct phases: phase one, known as the *primary* or *initial infection type,* and phase two, known as the *reinfection type* or *clinical tuberculosis.* The primary or initial infection type of the disease represents the reaction of body tissues to a first invasion by tubercle bacilli. The human body is remarkably resistant to a first invasion by the germs of tuberculosis. The infection is generally quickly held in check. The bacteria usually grow in only a small area, forming a small lesion. A connective tissue wall is formed around the lesion, imprisoning the organisms. This prevents extension of the infection. Later a deposit of calcium salts is added to the wall around the lesion. The bacteria may remain alive for many years in the calcified lesion. Such lesions are readily visible on x-ray films. The primary infection produces no symptoms but sensitizes the body to the protein products of the tubercle bacillus.

In the past the number of persons who acquired primary tuberculosis was large. It was acquired usually during childhood. As tuberculosis control measures became more effective, the incidence of primary tuberculosis began to decrease in the United States, until today we have communities in which the majority of the people have never been infected by tubercle bacilli. Primary tuberculosis now is more common in adults than in children. In many parts of the world, however, nearly all persons before they attain adulthood acquire primary tuberculosis.

Clinical pulmonary tuberculosis, or the second phase of the infection, may be caused by bacteria released from the person's own primary lesions, which may under certain circumstances break down (endogenous reinfection), or by bacteria from some other person (exogenous reinfection). The bacteria in this second phase of the infection are growing in tissue sensitized to the protein products of the tubercle bacillus. These proteins are poisonous to the tissues, giving rise to inflammatory reactions which may be followed by death of the tissues. Only a small percentage of persons who acquire the primary infection exhibit clinical tuberculosis.

Clinical tuberculosis is characterized by the presence of a large number of lesions in the form of small rounded nodules known as *tubercles,* from which the disease gets its name. As the tubercles become numerous, adjacent ones often fuse into larger masses. Later the accumulation of toxic bacterial products causes necrosis (death) of the central portion of these lesions, which undergoes caseation, i.e., becomes cheeselike in consistency. As the caseated masses become softened, this material is coughed up as sputum, leaving cavities in the lungs. The necrosis may include blood capillaries, resulting in hemorrhage of the lungs.

Nonpulmonary tuberculosis, such as tuberculosis of the bones and joints, lymph nodes of the neck (scrofula), alimentary tract, liver, spleen and kidneys, is usually active primary tuberculosis. A rapidly developing, generalized form of the disease is known as miliary tuberculosis. In this form of the disease thousands of tubercles are formed throughout the body. Most of the nonpulmonary types of tuberculosis are encountered in children more often than in adults and appear to result from the ingestion of food-borne bovine tubercle bacilli.

BOVINE TUBERCULOSIS

Bovine tuberculosis occurs chiefly in cattle but is transmissible to man. Swine are susceptible to both the bovine and avian bacilli; most cases of tuberculosis, however, in these animals are caused by the avian type. Chickens are susceptible only to the avian type. Horses, dogs, cats, sheep and goats are not highly susceptible but occasionally contract tuberculosis caused by the bovine type of tubercle bacillus. Cases of avian tuberculosis have been reported in man but in most instances definite proof was not produced.

Human infection by bovine bacilli results chiefly from the consumption of contaminated milk and milk products. The bovine tubercle bacillus has for centuries been the cause of tuberculosis in young children. Although it may occur in the lungs, this type of tuberculosis is usually nonpulmonary. It frequently involves the bones and lymph nodes. Generalized infection, called miliary tuberculosis, often occurs. In the United States the danger from bovine tuberculosis has been almost completely eliminated, owing largely to the periodic tuberculin testing of cattle which was initiated in 1917 and has been carried on in every county. The test is followed by the slaughter of positive reactors. It has been estimated that at the present time less than 0.5 per cent of the cattle of the United States are tuberculous. No other country has been so successful in the eradication of bovine tuberculosis. The widespread pasteurization of milk is also important in the prevention of tuberculosis as well as other diseases.

DETECTION OF INFECTED PERSONS

Since the early symptoms of tuberculosis are usually vague or absent, a diagnosis of early tuberculosis cannot be made on the basis of symptoms. Tuberculosis may be present two years or more without causing symptoms that would suggest its presence. An important factor in the control of the disease is to find cases in the early stages before symptoms are present. The proper treatment of such patients may cure their infection and will prevent them from spreading the disease to others. Early cases can be detected by the tuberculin skin test and the chest roentgenogram.

The Tuberculin Test

The term "tuberculin" is applied to any one of a number of preparations which, when introduced into the skin of a tuberculous person, will cause a reaction at the site of application. The reaction is due to hypersensitivity (allergy) to certain proteins of the tubercle bacillus. Persons who have never been infected by the tubercle bacillus are not allergic to these proteins. The test thus is based on an allergy induced by the tubercle bacillus.

Tuberculin was originally prepared by Robert Koch in 1890. He prepared it by growing tubercle bacilli on glycerinated veal broth. After a good growth had been obtained the bacteria were killed by heat, removed from the broth by filtration, and the filtrate concentrated by evaporation on a water bath to one-tenth of its original volume. Tuberculin prepared in this manner was used for many years and is known as Koch's old tuberculin (OT). Most of the tuberculin now used is prepared by growing the bacteria in a synthetic, protein-free medium. The growth of the bacteria gives rise to the production of specific proteins which become a part of the medium, presumably as a result of the partial disintegration of tubercle bacilli during the course of growth, rather than as a product of excretion or secretion. The proteins can be precipitated from the filtrate of the medium with trichloracetic acid and can be obtained in a purified but denatured form. This purified product is known as purified protein derivative (PPD).

The characteristic response when tuberculin is introduced into the skin is made use of in the detection of infected persons. A positive response is indicated by an area of redness and swelling at the point of application. This is called the *tuberculin reaction.*

A positive reaction to tuberculin is not necessarily indicative of active tuberculosis; it indicates only the existence of an allergic state to tuberculin, which may be due to active infection or to quiescent lesions in which tubercle bacilli are no longer active. A negative reaction is more specific than one that is positive. In a child, however, a positive tuberculin reaction usually indicates active infection. To evaluate a positive reactor requires additional investigation to complete the diagnosis.

The tuberculin test in cattle is of great diagnostic importance and is widely used in the United States. Tuberculin-positive cattle usually have tuberculosis and are slaughtered as a public health measure.

Roentgenogram of the Lungs

Positive reactions to the tuberculin test call for roentgenograms, by means of which the extent and severity of the lung lesions can be determined. The interpretation of the chest roentgenogram is based upon the nature of the shadows cast on the x-ray film. From the roentgenogram the presence of the reinfection type of tuberculosis can be determined before any outward signs of the disease are apparent.

Case-finding by means of the tuberculin test and the roentgenogram has become the front-line weapon against tuberculosis in many communities. Mass surveys are now being conducted on a large scale throughout the United States for the detection of tuberculosis in its early stages. Mobile units are frequently used for this purpose.

Demonstration of Tubercle Bacilli

A positive tuberculin reaction and x-ray report constitute a presumptive, but not a conclusive, diagnosis of tuberculosis. To complete the diagnosis it is necessary to demonstrate the presence of tubercle bacilli in the body of the patient. Since tubercle bacilli are coughed up into the mouth and are swallowed, stained smears of sputum or stomach contents may show the presence of acid-fast bacteria. The results may be confirmed by inoculating guinea pigs with sputum or stomach washings. If tubercle bacilli are present, these animals will quickly acquire a rapidly spreading form of tuberculosis, usually ending fatally in three to five weeks. The inoculation of appropriate culture media with material obtained from the patient may also be resorted to. Identification of the tubercle bacillus confirms the diagnosis of tuberculosis in suspected cases.

IMMUNITY AND IMMUNIZATION

The healthy human body has a high degree of resistance to tuberculosis, but there is no evidence that anyone is endowed with complete inherent or acquired immunity to the disease. Recovery from infection by the tubercle bacillus does not confer a high degree of immunity to reinfection. A widely used immunizing agent for the prevention of tuberculosis is BCG vaccine (described in Chapter 29), prepared from an attenuated strain of the bovine type of tubercle bacillus. Mass vaccination campaigns have been carried on in many European countries and in South America. It has been estimated that the vaccine has been given to approximately 10 million children and adults. The results obtained indicate that the vaccine is of value in the prevention of tuberculosis. The World Health Organization, an agency of United Nations, has supervised the vaccination of several million children in Europe. In recent years a number of projects for the use of the vaccine have been started in the United States and Canada. It is being administered to young children in areas having unusually high tuberculosis mortality rates, and to sanitorium and hospital employees who are unavoidably exposed to tuberculosis.

TREATMENT

Adequate treatment of recognized cases is an important part of the tuberculosis control program. In the majority of cases the disease can be cured if detected in its early stages; in more advanced cases it usually can be arrested by proper treatment. The most important factor in treatment is complete rest in bed. This reduces lung activity to a minimum and promotes healing of the affected areas. An abundance of fresh air is beneficial in that it acts as a stimulus to metabolism and to appetite. Adequate nutrition is also important.

In advanced cases of the disease, collapse of the affected lung may be necessary. One way of accomplishing this is to introduce air through a small needle into the thoracic cavity between the lung and the chest wall. This procedure, known as *pneumothorax*, immobilizes the lung temporarily and holds it at rest. The lung thus is not involved in the breathing movements but remains in a state of rest which expedites healing. The degree of immobilization can be adjusted by varying the amount of air introduced. In cases in which both lungs are infected, both can be held partially at rest. As the air is gradually absorbed, periodic refills are made.

Ever since the discovery of the tubercle bacillus, an intensive search has gone on for drugs with which to effectively combat tuberculosis. In recent years, drug therapy has been of aid as an adjunct to the accepted methods of treatment. The drugs now used are streptomycin, isoniazid (isonicotinic acid hydrazide) and *para*-aminosalicylic acid (PAS). The use of these drugs has reduced the time patients are required to spend in a hospital and has greatly reduced the number of patients resident in tuberculosis hospitals.

TETANUS

THE ORGANISM

The causative organism of tetanus, *Clostridium tetani* (tetanus bacillus), was first described in 1884 by Nicolaier of Germany. He produced tetanus in rabbits by inoculating them with garden soil and observed long slender bacilli, along with other bacteria, in the lesions which developed at the site of injection. Efforts to cultivate the bacillus were unsuccessful until Kitasato, a Japanese bacteriologist, applied anaerobic methods (1889). He produced tetanus in laboratory animals by inoculating them with his pure culture.

The tetanus bacillus is a slender, round-ended rod, 4 to 8 microns in length. It occurs singly, in pairs and, at times, in chains and filaments. It is motile, owing to peritrichously arranged flagella, and forms spores. The spore is spherical and two to four times the diameter of the cell. It is situated terminally, thus giving the spore-containing rod the appearance of a drumstick. The tetanus bacillus is an obligate anaerobe.

Clostridium tetani has a wide distribution in nature. Its normal habitat appears to be the intestinal tract of herbivorous animals, particularly the horse. It lives on the intestinal contents and does not attack the tissues of the intestine. It has been found also in some cases in the human intestinal tract. The spores of the tetanus bacillus are present in soil fertilized with barnyard manure. From the soil the spores may enter the air along with dust particles and may be conveyed to clothing, the human skin and common objects of various kinds.

THE DISEASE

Tetanus is a toxemia due to infection of wounds caused by objects which carry tetanus spores into the deeper tissues. A wound contaminated with soil is likely to contain spores of the tetanus bacillus. Deeply lacerated wounds, deep puncture wounds and compound fractures of bones in which there has been considerable tissue damage afford a suitable environment for the organism. In normal tissue the spores will not germinate because of the high oxygen tension. In damaged or necrotic tissue the oxygen tension is greatly reduced. In most cases a wound contaminated with *Clostridium tetani* contains a mixture of bacteria, many of which are aerobes. The presence of these bacteria reduces the oxygen tension in the wound and thus favors the germination of tetanus spores and the growth of the vegetative cells. War wounds and those resulting from automobile accidents in which the wounds become fouled with soil or road dirt are particularly likely to become infected with tetanus.

Tetanus is primarily a toxemia caused by an extremely potent, soluble exotoxin produced by the bacteria at the local site of growth. The organisms do not invade the tissues beyond the point of entry but remain localized in the damaged tissue. The toxin, however, becomes distributed throughout the body. Tetanus toxin is one of the most powerful poisons known to man. Incredibly small quantities, such as the amount present in 0.0000002 milliliter of a culture filtrate, when injected into guinea pigs will cause their death. It has been estimated that 0.0002 gm. of the purified toxin would be fatal to man.

The toxin is active in the motor nerve centers, giving rise to violent spasms and rigidity of many or all of the voluntary muscles. The spasms usually begin in the muscles of the neck and lower jaw. The jaw becomes set so that the patient is unable to open his mouth. It is for this reason that the disease is commonly called "lockjaw." The spasms are associated with violent pain, labored breathing and difficulty in swallowing. The disease is often fatal.

IMMUNIZATION AND TREATMENT

Recovery from an attack of tetanus apparently does not confer an immunity adequate to prevent future attacks. Numerous cases are on record in which repeated attacks occurred in man and animals. An effective degree of active immunity may be achieved artificially by the injection of tetanus toxoid. Alum-precipitated toxoid is now generally used. The first injection is followed by a second one after three months. Immunity requires several months to develop. After an injury a "booster" dose is given to increase the antitoxin titer of the blood. This protection was administered to our military personnel in World War II with the result that tetanus was an extremely rare disease in our armed forces. Tetanus toxoid is combined with diphtheria toxoid and pertussis vaccine for immunizing children.

When a person who has not been actively immunized against tetanus receives an injury from which tetanus might develop, he may be protected by a large dose of tetanus antitoxin. The immunity thus produced is not lasting, owing to the rapid elimination of the introduced antitoxin, but, if administered shortly after the occurrence of the wound, it will usually prevent the development of the symptoms of tetanus. It is advisable that such persons receive a prophylactic inoculation of tetanus toxoid at the same time, since tetanus sometimes has a long incubation period and the immunity conferred by the antitoxin may not be of sufficient duration to prevent the development of the disease.

Although tetanus antitoxin is used chiefly prophylactically, it is administered also after the clinical symptoms of tetanus have set in, but its efficacy as a curative agent is questionable.

DIPHTHERIA

In the past diphtheria was one of the great scourges of humanity; devastating epidemics were common throughout the world. The death rate was appallingly high. In 1900 the diphtheria death rate in the United States was forty-three per 100,000 population; at present it is less than one per 100,000 population. Because of the development of an effective immunization procedure, the disease has been virtually eliminated from many communities.

THE ORGANISM

The causative organism of diphtheria, *Corynebacterium diphtheriae* (Figures 147 and 148), is a straight or slightly curved, nonmotile rod, varying in length from 1 to 8 microns. The rods frequently have swollen ends giving them a club-shaped appearance. When only one end is swollen, the cells are wedge-shaped. The typical clubbed appearance of these organisms accounts for the genus name, *Corynebacterium,* which means club-shaped bacterium. They do not stain uniformly with methylene blue but show alternate bands of stained and unstained areas. One or more

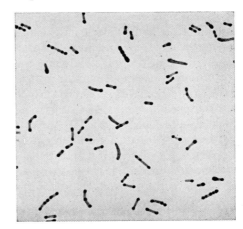

*Figure 147. Corynebac-
terium diphtheriae,* showing
deeply stained granules situated at the poles and also
in the central part of the
rods. × 1000. (From Ford:
Textbook of Bacteriology.)

volutin granules can usually be demonstrated by use of special stains. The
diphtheria bacillus produces a very potent exotoxin.

THE DISEASE

Diphtheria is disseminated by personal contact with infected persons
or carriers and also, in some instances, by fomites such as eating utensils,
toys, pencils and handkerchiefs that have been handled by infected persons or carriers. Raw milk contaminated by a human carrier may convey
the infection. The organisms enter the body via the mouth or nose.

Diphtheria is an acute infectious disease characterized by the formation
of patches of false membrane (pseudomembrane) in the throat or on
some other mucous surface. The membrane is formed from a fibrinous
exudate which coagulates into a membrane-like structure. The pseudomembrane has a tendency to spread. Constitutional symptoms are caused
by the absorption of exotoxin at the site of infection. Besides the throat
the infection may involve the larynx (voice box), upper trachea and,
less frequently, the nasal passages. Since the throat is most commonly
affected, the first symptom of the disease is usually a moderately severe
sore throat.

The absorption of diphtheria exotoxin from the local lesion into the

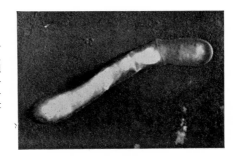

Figure 148. Electron micrograph of *C. diphtheriae.*
(× 35,000 and reduced
about two thirds.) (Cour-
tesy of Division of Laboratories, Michigan Department
of Health.)

blood stream may cause damage to many tissues and organs of the body. It may affect the heart muscle and damage it severely. It may do damage to the nervous system and to the kidneys. Paralysis of certain muscles, especially those of the soft palate and the eyes, may result. The disease is a good example of a toxemia, since it is the toxin that causes the chief damage to the body. The bacteria usually remain localized. The formation of the pseudomembrane in the respiratory passages may completely block these passages in the laryngeal form of diphtheria (diphtheritic croup) and cause death by suffocation. The disease has a duration of one to two weeks; death, when it follows, occurs usually within a week from the onset of the infection. Highly virulent strains of the bacteria may kill their victims within twenty-four to forty-eight hours.

IMMUNITY AND IMMUNIZATION

Recovery from an attack of diphtheria results in immunity which is usually permanent. The immune state is due to the presence of an adequate level of diphtheria antitoxin in the body. Artificial immunization can be accomplished by inoculation with diphtheria toxoid. The alum-precipitated toxoid is now generally used. It is usually given in two doses a month apart. It is advised that every infant between the ages of six and twelve months be immunized against diphtheria. To maintain the immunity, a "booster" dose of toxoid should be administered at the age of two years and again just prior to entering school and at the age of twelve to fourteen years. Continued widespread immunization is necessary to keep the disease under control.

In the past, owing to the wide distribution of diphtheria bacilli in the human population, many persons became immune to diphtheria, presumably through repeated encounters with diphtheria bacilli of low virulence, without exhibiting any symptoms of the disease. As the prevalence of diphtheria declines, such encounters are less likely to occur; consequently, a susceptible adult population will gradually develop if artificial immunization is limited to the period of infancy. It is, therefore, necessary that two or more "booster" injections of toxoid be administered after the childhood immunizations to maintain an adequate level of immunity during adult life.

Diphtheria can be effectively treated by the early administration of diphtheria antitoxin. Antitoxin came into use before methods of active immunization were developed. The introduction of antitoxin dramatically reduced the death rate but had no appreciable effect on the incidence of the disease. The incidence, however, began to decline with the introduction of active immunization. It may be noted here that diphtheria was the first disease in which an antitoxin was used therapeutically. Although antitoxin is the important therapeutic agent in diphtheria, under certain circumstances antibiotics such as penicillin, chloramphenicol and the tetracyclines are now used as adjuncts in the treatment. They cannot neutralize the exotoxin produced, but exert a bactericidal action against the diphtheria bacilli.

The Schick Test

The Schick test is a method of testing for the presence of diphtheria antitoxin in the blood and is used to determine susceptibility to diphtheria. The test was devised in 1913 by Bela Schick, a physician in Vienna. In this test a carefully controlled amount of diphtheria exotoxin is injected into the skin. If the person is susceptible to diphtheria, a local inflammatory reaction will occur within forty-eight hours at the site of injection. Those who show this reaction are said to be Schick positive. Adults as well as children who are Schick positive are vulnerable to diphtheria. A person immune to diphtheria does not react to the Schick test because his body contains antitoxin which promptly neutralizes the exotoxin injected into the skin.

From the Schick test it has been learned that most newborn infants have sufficient antitoxin, derived from the mother, to protect them against contracting diphtheria but that they lose enough of this to become susceptible during the first year of life. The greatest susceptibility occurs between the second and fifth years.

BRUCELLOSIS

Brucellosis is a disease which primarily attacks certain farm animals, chiefly cattle, swine and goats, from which it is readily transmitted to man. When the disease occurs in man, it is often called undulant fever; in cattle it is commonly known as contagious abortion or Bang's disease, whereas in goats the infection is called Malta fever. While cattle, swine and goats are the animals usually infected, other animals may also carry the infection.

THE ORGANISM

Three closely related species of bacteria, *Brucella abortus, Br. suis* (Figure 149) and *Br. melitensis,* are capable of causing the infection. The chief host of *Br. abortus* is the cow, of *Br. suis* the hog, and of *Br. melitensis* the goat. Any one of these three species may cause brucellosis in man. Although all three species are capable of infecting cattle, only *Br. abortus* is highly infectious for these animals. The following table indicates susceptibilities to brucellosis on the part of man and those domestic animals in which the disease is widespread.

Species	Primary Host	Secondary Hosts
Br. abortus	Cattle	Man, horse
Br. suis	Swine	Man, cattle
Br. melitensis	Goats	Man, cattle, swine

The first of these organisms discovered was *Br. melitensis.* In 1887 David Bruce, an English army surgeon working on the island of Malta, isolated this organism from British troops affected with fever. A thorough study made later by Bruce and other investigators revealed that the disease was contracted by drinking goat's milk. *Brucella abortus* was isolated in 1897 by Bernard Bang, a Danish veterinarian and research worker. *Brucella suis* was isolated from swine in 1914 by Jacob Traum of the United States. The generic name *Brucella* was chosen for these organisms in honor of Bruce for his pioneer work with these pathogens.

The etiological agents of brucellosis are minute rods or coccobacilli measuring 0.3 to 0.4 micron in length. They occur singly or in pairs, are

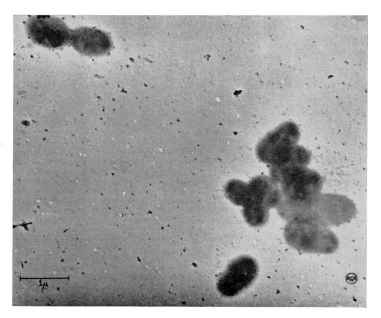

Figure 149. Electron micrograph of *Brucella suis.* Note the very small coccobacillary cells. (Courtesy of Drs. T. F. Anderson and K. Polevitsky-Zworykin.)

nonmotile and nonspore-bearing. They stain readily with the ordinary dyes and are Gram-negative.

Although these organisms ordinarily live as parasites, they can survive for a long time in dairy products such as ice cream and cheese and also in the soil and stable dust. They are readily killed by the common disinfectants and by the temperature of pasteurization.

BRUCELLOSIS IN ANIMALS

Brucellosis in cattle is difficult to detect since the symptoms are inconstant and indefinite. The most noted symptom is abortion, which occurs frequently among the infected females of a herd. Not all cows, however, that are infected abort, and cows not infected abort at times. Many other symptoms and manifestations are seen in bovine brucellosis, including sterility, enlarged joints, lameness and inflammation of the testes. The organisms become localized chiefly in the uterus, mammary glands and testes. At the present time brucellosis is the most serious disease affecting cattle. It is more common in some localities than others. The incidence averages about 5 per cent of the cattle in the United States. It causes tremendous economic losses in milk production and in the loss of aborted fetuses.

Brucella infection affects swine in much the same way as cattle, causing abortion in some instances, breeding failures and weak offspring. The disease is even more difficult to detect in swine than in cattle, but recovery occurs more frequently in hogs than in cattle. In swine the organisms are found in many body structures, including the uterus, mammary glands, ovaries, testes, bones, joints, liver, spleen and lungs. From 1 to 3 per cent of the swine of the middle western states are infected.

Brucellosis in goats is important in the United States chiefly in the southwest (Colorado, New Mexico, Texas and Arizona), where goat-raising is an important industry.

Through the activities of the World Health Organization and the Food and Agricultural Organization, brucellosis centers have been established in a number of countries to carry on regional surveys on the prevalence of brucellosis in livestock and to work out methods of controlling the disease.

BRUCELLOSIS IN MAN

Man contracts brucellosis through contact with infected livestock, by handling infected meat, by eating inadequately cooked meat contaminated with *Brucella* organisms, or by consuming contaminated raw milk or dairy products made from such milk. The majority of cases are contracted through direct contact with infected animals and the handling of infected meat. Farmers, veterinarians and slaughterhouse workers are most often affected. The *Brucella* organisms are capable of passing through mucous membranes and may enter the body through breaks in the skin and, probably, also through the unbroken skin. Thousands of our people are sticken each year by brucellosis. The chief victims of the disease are farmers, veterinarians who come in contact with infected animals, and meat packers who handle the carcasses of infected animals.

Of the three *Brucella* species, *Br. suis* causes the most severe attacks of the disease in man. It is an important cause of human brucellosis in the hog-raising regions of the United States. *Brucella abortus* is the common cause of human brucellosis in the areas where cattle are abundant. In the United States *Br. melitensis* is only infrequently the cause of brucellosis in man.

The disease is characterized by an intermittent, undulating fever, headache, rheumatic joint pains, profuse sweating and lassitude. The symptoms usually continue for three to five days and then abate. This is followed by a recurrence; hence the name "undulant fever," as the malady is sometimes called. During the course of the acute phase of the disease, there are usually from two to seven undulatory relapses. The patient loses weight and becomes greatly prostrated and extremely weak. The average duration of the infection is three months. There is considerable variation, however, in the character, severity and duration of the symptoms. Many persons are only mildly affected. In such cases the disease is usually not diagnosed as brucellosis until after many years of poor health for which no other cause was found to be responsible.

The disease frequently becomes chronic and thus may have a long duration, in some cases as long as five years. In the chronic form the symptoms are indefinite. The patient becomes mentally depressed, owing to worry and concern over his ill health and incapacity for work. Because these symptoms are suggestive of a mental disorder, the chronic form of brucellosis is frequently erroneously diagnosed as neurasthenia.

PREVENTION AND TREATMENT

The control of brucellosis in livestock presents a difficult problem. *Brucella* vaccines have been prepared, some of which appear to decrease the incidence of abortion in cattle, indicating that they create some degree of resistance, but they do not necessarily prevent infection. Various measures for treating brucellosis have been tried. Antiserums have not been effective, and no drug has been discovered that will overcome brucellosis in either animals or man with any degree of certainty. Recently, chloramphenicol, chlortetracycline and oxytetracycline have given promising results.

The best method of control is the detection of all infected animals by periodic testing and the elimination of the infected animals from the herds by segregation or slaughter. Since animals serve as the reservoirs of *Brucella* organisms, the eradication of human brucellosis depends basically upon the complete elimination of animal sources of the disease. Transmission of the disease to man through milk and dairy products can be prevented by the pasteurization of milk. It is more difficult to prevent the disease in farmers and packing house workers, whose occupation brings them in close contact with infected animals or the carcasses of such animals.

PLAGUE AND TULAREMIA

The causative organisms of plague and tularemia belong to the genus *Pasteurella*, which was named in honor of Pasteur. This genus comprises a group of short rod-shaped bacteria, some of which are ellipsoidal in form. Bacteria of the *Pasteurella* group are pathogenic primarily for animals. A few, notably *Pasteurella pestis*, the cause of plague, and *Pasteurella tularensis*, the etiological agent of tularemia, are pathogenic for man as well as for certain animals.

PLAGUE

Plague is primarily a disease of rats and other rodents and secondarily a human infection. The disease is transmitted from rodents to man by infected fleas. No other infectious disease has wiped out so many human lives within the period of recorded history as the plague. During the early centuries of the Christian era the disease invaded Europe from the Orient. The first extensive outbreak of the plague in Europe took place in the sixth century A.D. It devastated the Roman Empire, killing almost 50 per cent of the population. The disease continued to ravage northern and western Europe with unfettered violence up to the seventeenth century. In the Middle Ages repeated waves of the disease killed millions of people. In the fourteenth century the greatest pandemic of plague in-

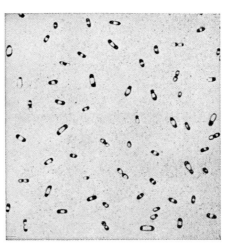

Figure 150. Pasteurella pestis, showing bipolar staining. × 1500. (From Ford: Textbook of Bacteriology.)

vaded the continent of Europe from Asia. This visitation, commonly called the "Black Death," wiped out large sections of the population in the course of a few years. Europe lost an estimated 25,000,000 persons, which represented a quarter to a third of its entire population. Wave after wave of plague swept over Europe until the close of the seventeenth century.

Plague made its first appearance in the United States in San Francisco in 1900, being introduced, presumably, by infected rats from the Orient. The infection spread to ground squirrels and other rodents which now serve as reservoirs of the infection in a number of western states. Plague in wild rodents is called *sylvatic plague*. The number of human cases contracted from ground squirrels is not great, since they do not live in close association with man. The cases are sporadic rather than epidemic.

At the present time plague is limited to certain areas of the world where the disease is endemic. The plague centers include India, China, Burma, Manchuria, Russia, Hawaii, Brazil, Peru, Bolivia, Argentina and the western portion of the United States. Plague in the United States is of infrequent occurrence.

The Causative Organism

Pasteurella pestis (Figure 150) is a short, plump, ovoid rod with rounded ends, measuring approximately 2 microns in length. It is without

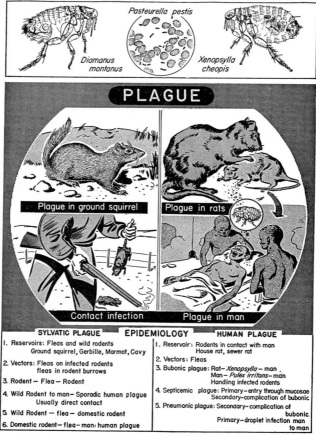

Figure 151. Epidemiology of plague. (From Mackie et al.: A Manual of Tropical Medicine.)

flagella and does not form spores. When stained with dilute dyes, it has a tendency to show bipolar staining; the center of the cell remains uncolored, whereas the ends or poles are deeply colored. In liquid media it grows mainly in chains.

The Disease

Plague is transmitted from rat to rat and from rat to man through the bite of rat fleas. However, one form of the disease (pneumonic plague) may be transmitted directly from man to man. Plague in rats is similar to that in man, and the death rate is about as great.

Plague in man occurs in two well-recognized forms, (1) bubonic plague and (2) pneumonic plague. Of these the former is by far the more common type. When epidemics of bubonic plague occur, the disease first develops in the rat population and then is transmitted to man through the bites of rat fleas (Figure 151).

Bubonic plague takes its name from the fact that certain lymph nodes become enlarged. An inflammatory swelling of a lymph node is known as a *bubo* (plural *buboes*). The plague bacilli enter lymph nodes in the region where the flea-bite occurred. Buboes usually appear between the second and fifth days but may appear earlier. The bacteria may escape from the lymph nodes and enter the blood stream. The disease may then take an acute septicemic form which is rapidly fatal. The bubonic form of plague is usually not transmissible from man to man. The occurrence of hemorrhages in the skin, resulting in dark or black areas, is responsible for the term "Black Death" applied to plague of medieval times. Sulfonamides and antibiotics are now used in the treatment of plague.

In the pneumonic type of plague the incubation period is short, one to three days. The plague bacilli are localized chiefly in the lungs, and the symptoms are those of a rapidly developing primary pneumonia. Pneumonic plague may be spread from man to man by droplets discharged from the mouth in coughing or sneezing. The mortality rate is usually 100 per cent.

TULAREMIA

Tularemia is primarily a disease of wild rodents and secondarily a disease of man. It was first recognized in ground squirrels in California as a disease characterized by lesions similar to those of plague. Because the infection was first observed in Tulare county, California, it was named "tularemia." Besides ground squirrels, the disease affects rabbits and, occasionally, sheep and certain birds. The wild rabbit population is the greatest reservoir of tularemia in the United States. Man acquires the infection through direct contact with the carcasses of infected animals or through the agency of ticks, deer flies or other blood-sucking insects. Since most human cases originate from the handling of the carcasses of rabbits, the disease is commonly called "rabbit fever."

The Causative Organism

The tularemia bacillus, *Pasteurella tularensis*, is a minute, Gram-negative, pleomorphic, nonmotile bacterium. It does not produce spores. Because of their small size, the individual cells are difficult to distinguish. Bacillary, ovoid and coccoid forms are usually present. The coccoid forms may be as small as 0.2 micron in diameter. Bacillary and ovoid forms are usually not more than 0.7 micron in length. Bipolar staining may occur.

The Disease

Tularemia is spread from animal to animal through the bite of ticks, deer flies and other blood-sucking flies. The disease may be transmitted to man by direct contact with infected animals or through the bite of blood-sucking flies or ticks which have fed on infected animals. The principal source of tularemia is the wild rabbit. The disease may be transmitted also through drinking water contaminated by infected animals.

When the disease is contracted through the handling of infected carcasses of wild rabbits, the organisms enter the body through an abrasion or even through the apparently unbroken skin. It is possible also to contract the disease through the intestinal tract by eating inadequately cooked infected rabbit meat. Some cases are contracted by rubbing the eyes with the hands while handling diseased animals.

Several types of the disease occur, depending upon the mode of entry of the infective agent. In its most common form the organisms gain entrance through the skin. In a typical case the onset is sudden and is accompanied by aching pains in the back and extremities, severe headache, fever, sweats, vomiting and marked prostration. An ulcer usually appears at the site of infection. The near-by lymph nodes become swollen and painful, resembling the buboes of plague. They frequently become suppurating wounds. The fever may last three to six weeks and is followed by a slow convalescence. The disease is debilitating, often incapacitating the patient for several months or even longer than a year.

Another form of the disease is the typhoidal or intestinal type. It is characterized by a prolonged intermittent fever. Because the symptoms resemble those of typhoid fever, it is sometimes mistaken for this disease. There are no skin lesions or swollen lymph nodes in this form of tularemia. Infections acquired in the laboratory are usually of this type.

When the organisms gain entrance to the body through the conjunctiva, a severe conjunctivitis results, accompanied by enlargement of the regional lymph nodes. In some cases of tularemia the lungs become involved.

Recovery from an attack of the disease confers immunity in man. Persons who have recovered from the disease have specific agglutinins in their blood which persist for long periods. Tularemia vaccine confers a measure of protection against infection. An antiserum has been developed for the treatment of the disease. It must be given early to be of value. Streptomycin is the most effective therapeutic agent at the present time. It shortens the course of the disease from months to weeks. The results are best when it is given early in the disease.

SYPHILIS

THE CAUSATIVE ORGANISM

The causative organism of syphilis, *Treponema pallidum*, is a spirochete which was discovered in 1905 by Schaudinn and Hoffmann in material taken from a syphilitic person. It is an exceedingly slender, tightly coiled organism 6 to 14 microns long with six to fourteen regular turns, each occupying about 1 micron. The diameter is not more than 0.3 micron. A spiral filament is present at each pole. Motility takes the form of rotation about the long axis and flexion of the entire body, accompanied by rela-

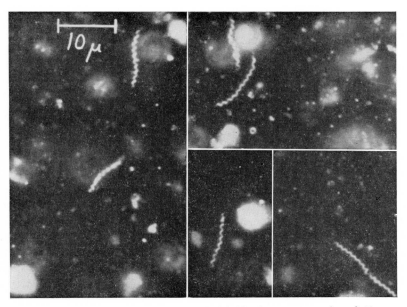

Figure 152. Composite picture of four darkfield photomicrographs of *Treponema pallidum.* (Courtesy of Dr. T. Rosebury, Washington University, St. Louis, Mo.)

tively slow progressive movement. The organism does not form spores. Unstained microscopic preparations are readily visible by darkfield microscope (Figure 152). Smears can be stained by Giemsa's method. Silver impregnation methods are commonly used to stain the organism in tissue sections. This procedure stains the spirochetes a dense black. *Treponema pallidum* can be cultivated under strict anaerobic conditions in ascitic fluid to which fresh rabbit kidney has been added.

The spirochete of syphilis is a frail organism which cannot survive for more than a brief period in the outside environment. It is particularly sensitive to the drying action of the air and is readily destroyed by heat and chemical agents.

Treponema pallidum has a wide distribution throughout the civilized world in the bodies of syphilitic human beings, since syphilis is one of the most widespread communicable diseases. Being essentially a disease of mankind, there are no animal reservoirs of the organism. Under natural conditions syphilis is an exclusively human disease but is transmissible experimentally to anthropoid apes and rabbits.

THE DISEASE

Primarily a venereal disease, syphilis infection is usually acquired by intimate contact, such as coitus or kissing. Promiscuous sexual intercourse is the chief factor in the spread of the disease; if it could be halted, the incidence of syphilis would sharply decline. In rare instances it may be transmitted through the medium of contaminated towels, drinking cups or other utensils, if used shortly after their use by a syphilitic. It may be transmitted also from a syphilitic woman to her unborn child. Syphilis acquired in this manner is known as congenital syphilis.

Syphilis is one of the most dangerous diseases with which mankind has to contend. It is acquired primarily between the ages of fifteen and thirty years. The disease runs a chronic course and is divided into three stages, primary, secondary and tertiary.

Primary Stage

After an incubation period of two to four weeks, the disease manifests itself by the appearance of a lesion known as a *chancre,* which is always located at the point where the spirochetes gained entrance to the tissues of the body. The syphilitic chancre is a small vesicle which soon ruptures, forming an ulcer. It then enlarges and becomes hard and flat. It occurs most frequently on the genital organs. It may go undetected in the female because of its location within the folds of the mucous membranes of the vagina or on the cervix of the uterus. If the infectious agent was transmitted by the act of kissing, the chancre will appear on the lips, tongue or tonsils. The chancre is highly infectious, since the exudate from its surface teems with syphilitic spirochetes. The primary stage is attended by little or no discomfort. After about six weeks the chancre disappears.

Secondary Stage

The secondary stage manifests itself six to twelve weeks after the appearance of the chancre. The spirochetes are now no longer localized but have entered the blood stream and accomplished a general invasion of the body. A characteristic of the secondary stage is the multiplicity of symptoms and the great variation in their intensity. Not any of the symptoms are distinctive. The patient may experience headache, sore throat, pain in the joints, fever, enlargement of the lymph nodes and eye lesions. Usually a rash appears on the face, neck, trunk and limbs. The rash may be so faint as to be scarcely discernible, or it may be very pronounced. Mucous patches in the mouth and throat and on the genital organs are characteristic of this stage. Spirochetes are abundant in these lesions. The infection takes a malignant course in some persons and is very mild in others. The secondary stage lasts from a few months to several years.

After the symptoms of the secondary stage have subsided, the disease passes into a latent period, in which there are no visible signs of infection, before entering the tertiary stage. The period of latency may continue for many years, the average being six to eight years. In some cases there is a brief revival of the secondary symptoms before the appearance of tertiary or late syphilis.

Tertiary Stage

In the tertiary stage the course the disease takes depends on the particular tissues or organs in which the spirochetes become localized. They show a predilection in this stage for certain body structures, and in any given case there is usually a localization of the organisms in one or several tissues or organs. The localization may be in the skin, bones, heart, blood vessels, brain or spinal cord. Progressive ulcerative and destructive lesions known as *gummata* are formed. A gumma is a soft, gummy enlargement enclosing a mass of necrotic tissue. It may be as small as a pinhead but more often attains the size of a cherry or walnut. The gummata finally ulcerate and, when they heal, leave deep radiating scars.

Degenerative lesions of the heart, wall of the aorta and other blood vessels are common (cardiovascular syphilis). The wall of the aorta, the large artery by which the blood from the left ventricle leaves the heart, is frequently involved. The wall becomes weakened, bulges appear, and, when the vessel bursts, death ensues. A gumma may be formed in the roof of the mouth, resulting in a perforation of the bony palate.

The brain may be attacked, giving rise to *paresis*, which involves progressive loss of mental capacity and loss of motor control of the muscles, thus resulting in what is known as general paralysis of the insane. In some patients the lower portion of the spinal cord is attacked, bringing about the condition known as *locomotor ataxia*, or *tabes dorsalis*, which is characterized by a peculiar gait and the inability to control the lower limbs in a normal manner. Syphilis of the nervous system is referred to as *neurosyphilis*.

Congenital Syphilis

Syphilis may be transmitted to the fetus (unborn child) from the syphilitic mother by way of her blood stream during the period of gestation. Syphilitic infection acquired in this manner is called *congenital syphilis*. The spirochetes frequently multiply in enormous numbers in the unborn child and may penetrate all parts of the body. Syphilis may result in the death and expulsion of the fetus (stillbirth). In some cases the newborn child may show no signs of the disease but may exhibit symptoms later.

Laboratory Diagnosis

In the primary stage the disease may be diagnosed by a microscopic examination (darkfield technique) of material from the lesion suspected of being a syphilitic chancre. The presence of spirochetes indicates syphilis. After the disease has entered the secondary or tertiary stages the diagnosis is made by blood tests (serological tests). In these procedures the blood serum of the patient is tested for the presence of an antigen peculiar to syphilis, known as *reagin.* The first of these to be used was the complement fixation test originally devised by Wassermann. A number of other tests, called precipitation or flocculation tests, have been developed.

Wassermann Test. In this test the blood serum of the patient is tested for the presence of *reagin,* an antibody peculiar to syphilis. In the performance of the test, complement, a nonspecific antigen* and serum from the patient are mixed in a test tube in suitable proportions. If the serum is from a syphilitic person, the reagin it contains will combine with the antigen and this antigen-antibody complex will adsorb the complement. The complement thus becomes bound or fixed. The test is then positive. In the absence of reagin, and therefore of syphilis, the complement does not become fixed. The test is then negative. There is no noticeable change, however, in the appearance of the contents of the test tube to indicate whether or not the complement has become fixed. To determine whether any unfixed or free complement is present requires the addition of two other reagents, namely, red blood cells of a suitable animal (sheep) and a specific antibody, hemolytic amboceptor, capable of bringing about the lysis of the red blood cells. Measured amounts of these are added to the tube. If any free complement is present, it will cause hemolysis of the red blood cells. This produces a visible change in the tube. If all the complement becomes fixed in the first reaction, the red blood cells will remain intact. Complete hemolysis indicates the absence of syphilitic antibody (reagin); i.e., the reaction is negative. No hemolysis indicates a strongly positive reaction. Partial hemolysis indicates a weakly positive reaction. Because the antigen is nonspecific, the Wassermann test occasionally gives false positive reactions.

Precipitation or Flocculation Tests. A number of precipitation or flocculation tests have been devised. They have the advantage of being less complex than the Wassermann test. Some of these, such as the Kahn, Hinton and Eagle tests, are performed in a test tube; others, such as the Kline and Mazzini tests, are done on a slide. In the Kahn test, which is widely used, blood serum of the patient is mixed with antigen (alcoholic extract of beef heart muscle to which cholesterol has been added) in the presence of a suitable salt solution. If a visible precipitate occurs, the test

---

* The antigen now generally used, called *cardiolipin,* consists of an alcoholic extract of beef heart muscle to which cholesterol and lecithin have been added.

is positive, indicating that the patient is syphilitic; if no precipitate forms, the test is negative.

Treponema Pallidum Immobilization Test. The *Treponema pallidum* immobilization test, commonly referred to as the TPI test, is a recent development. It is a highly specific test for determining the presence of syphilitic infection. The serum of patients with syphilis contains antibodies which, when added to living syphilis spirochetes, will promptly immobilize them and eventually kill them. The spirochetes used in the test are grown in the testes of rabbits. Compliment must be present for the immobilization action to take place. The immobilization can be observed with a darkfield microscope. This test is a very important new development since it is the first serological test for syphilis using a specific antigen in place of an "artificial" one used in older diagnostic tests.

Treponema Pallidum Complement Fixation Test. Another recently developed test for the diagnosis of syphilis is known as the *Treponema pallidum* complement fixation test (TPCF). In this test a specific antigen in the form of an extract of *Treponema pallidum* is employed. It thus differs fundamentally from the Wassermann test, which is also a complement fixation test. The TPCF test is now used in many state health departments.

Immunity

No person apparently has natural resistance to syphilis, and no method for producing immunity artificially is available. An infected person, however, is resistant to primary reinfection. Recovery from the disease by the aid of chemical agents does not confer immunity, for reinfection may then occur.

Treatment

All the former methods of treatment have now been largely replaced by the use of penicillin. Treatment with large doses cures about 90 per cent of the cases that have not reached the tertiary stage. It is sometimes used in conjunction with arsenicals or bismuth compounds.

When the disease has reached the tertiary stage, treatment is less effective than in the earlier stages. Artificially induced fever is beneficial in cases in which the central nervous system is involved (neurosyphilis). The fever is produced either by inoculating the patient with malaria germs or by placing the patient in a special apparatus known as a fever cabinet. Drug therapy is used in conjunction with the fever treatment.

QUESTIONS

1. (*a*) Describe the organism that causes typhoid fever. What is its scientific name?

(*b*) Give a brief description of typhoid fever. How is the disease most commonly conveyed from one person to another?

(*c*) Discuss the value of typhoid immunization. How is typhoid vaccine prepared?

(*d*) Account for the decline of the incidence of typhoid fever.

2. (*a*) Name and describe the two mammalian types of tubercle bacilli.

(*b*) Discuss pulmonary tuberculosis. Differentiate between primary tuberculosis and clinical tuberculosis.

(*c*) What is tuberculin? What is PPD? Of what value is the tuberculin test? Of what value is the chest roentgenogram?

(*d*) Discuss the prevention and treatment of tuberculosis.

3. What is BCG vaccine? To what extent is it used at present?

4. Explain the following points in regard to tetanus: (1) name and natural habitat of the etiological agent, (2) portal of invasion, (3) symptoms, (4) immunization and treatment.

5. (*a*) Name and describe the causative organism of diphtheria.

(*b*) Point out the chief characteristics of diphtheria.

(*c*) What procedure should be followed to immunize a child effectively against the disease? What is the Schick test?

(*d*) What specific treatment is available for diphtheria?

6. (*a*) Which organisms constitute the *Brucella* group?

(*b*) How is brucellosis transmitted to man?

(*c*) Describe the course of the disease in man.

7. Explain the following points in regard to plague: (1) causative organism, (2) chief animal reservoirs of the organism, (3) the two forms of the disease in man, (4) present geographic distribution.

8. Of what historic interest is plague?

9. Discuss tularemia, including (1) the animal reservoirs of the etiological agent, (2) the mode of transmission from animals to man, (3) the nature of the disease.

10. (*a*) Which organism causes syphilis? To which order of bacteria does it belong?

(*b*) Describe the three stages of syphilis.

(*c*) What is congenital syphilis.

(*d*) What procedures are available for the diagnosis of syphilis?

REFERENCES

Burnett, G. W., and Scherp, H. W.: Oral Microbiology and Infectious Disease. Baltimore, The Williams & Wilkins Company, 1957.

Burrows, W.: Textbook of Microbiology. 17th ed. Philadelphia, W. B. Saunders Company, 1959.

Darzins, E.: The Bacteriology of Tuberculosis. Minneapolis, University of Minnesota Press, 1958.

Dubos, R. J., ed.: Bacterial and Mycotic Infections of Man. 3rd ed. Philadelphia, J. B. Lippincott Company, 1958.

Hagen, W. A., and Bruner, D. W.: The Infectious Diseases of Domestic Animals. 3rd ed. Ithaca, N. Y., Cornell University Press, 1957.

Hirst, L. F.: The Conquest of Plague. Oxford, Clarendon Press, 1953.

Koch, R.: The Aetiology of Tuberculosis. (Translation of Koch's original paper.) New York, National Tuberculosis Association, 1932.

Pollitzer, R.: Plague, WHO Monograph Series, No. 22. New York, Columbia University Press, 1954.

Rosenthal, S. R.: BCG Vaccination against Tuberculosis. Boston, Little, Brown & Company, 1957.

Smith, D. T., et al.: Zinsser's Textbook of Bacteriology. 11th ed. New York, Appleton-Century-Crofts, Inc., 1957.

Spink, W. W.: The Nature of Brucellosis. Minneapolis, University of Minnesota Press, 1956.

Stefferud, A., ed.: Animal Diseases: The Yearbook of Agriculture. Washington, D. C., Government Printing Office, 1956.

Wilson, G. S., and Miles, A. A.: Topley and Wilson's Principles of Bacteriology and Immunity. 2 vols. 4th ed. Baltimore, The Williams & Wilkins Company, 1955.

33 • Diseases Caused by Organisms Other than Bacteria

FUNGOUS DISEASES

The pathogenic fungi constitute a large and diverse group of organisms producing a variety of diseases in man, animals and plants. They include certain molds and moldlike forms as well as a number of yeasts and yeast-like organisms. Most of the pathogenic fungi are members of the Fungi Imperfecti. Diseases caused by fungi are known as *mycoses* (singular, *mycosis*) or *mycotic infections*. Some of the mycoses have a limited geographic distribution, others are of world-wide occurrence.

Many mycotic infections are superficial lesions of the skin or mucous membranes and are relatively benign and restricted to certain areas of the body. Those limited to the skin are termed *dermatomycoses* and are commonly known as "ringworm" infections. These are the most common of all the fungous diseases. Less common among fungous infections are those in which extensive, deep-seated lesions occur. Most of the mycoses are chronic diseases which develop slowly and inconspicuously. They have a tendency to be resistant to treatment.

Fungi are responsible for such diseases as ringworm, blastomycosis, candidiasis, sporotrichosis, cryptococcosis, histoplasmosis and coccidioidomycosis. In this chapter the first three of these diseases are briefly considered.

RINGWORM INFECTION

Ringworm infections are extremely common and are of various types. They are caused by a number of different species of moldlike organisms. Some species cause infections in animals as well as in man. The organisms are capable of invading only the keratinized areas of the body, i.e., the outer layer of the skin, the hair and nails. They are capable of utilizing the insoluble protein keratin, which is present in the outermost cells of the skin as well as in the hair and the fingernails and toenails. They are incapable of invading the deeper tissues or internal organs. The infections caused by these organisms are commonly referred to as "ringworm" because they have the characteristic feature of giving rise to lesions which take the form of concentric rings.

A wide variety of ringworm infections are recognized; although the lesions vary according to the site and species of fungus, the general pathological changes produced are essentially the same in all types. Blisters are frequently formed, and scaling of the skin occurs. The infection

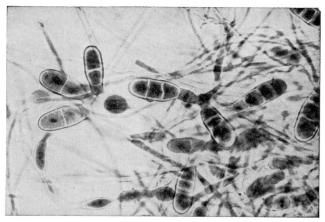

Figure 153.   Epidermophyton floccosum, showing mycelium and spores. × 600. (From Conant et al.: Manual of Clinical Mycology.)

tends to heal in the center of the concentric rings and to spread at the periphery. Thus, advancing rings of inflamed tissue are formed. Itching of varying severity may accompany the infection. Not only the skin, but also the hair and nails, may become infected. Some species grow only within the hair substance.

The infection is transmitted by means of spores formed in or on the skin. Transmission may be from man to man or from animals (cats, dogs, cattle, horses) to man, and also by various articles such as combs, brushes and towels contaminated with the spores of the fungus. Ringworm infections usually increase in prevalence during the summer months since heat and moisture favor the growth of the fungi.

The most common of all fungous diseases is ringworm of the feet, commonly known as "athlete's foot." It is an infection of the skin of the feet. The infection usually begins between the toes as a series of small blisters which tend to coalesce and may spread to the sole of the foot. The blisters later dry up, desquamate and expose a smooth, red area with upturned scales. Fissures and cracks may form. In most instances the disease is mild, but it may become painful and annoying. Pyogenic cocci may gain entrance through the cracks and crevices formed in the skin, giving rise to secondary bacterial infection. A number of different fungi may cause the infection, but it is most commonly caused by various spe-

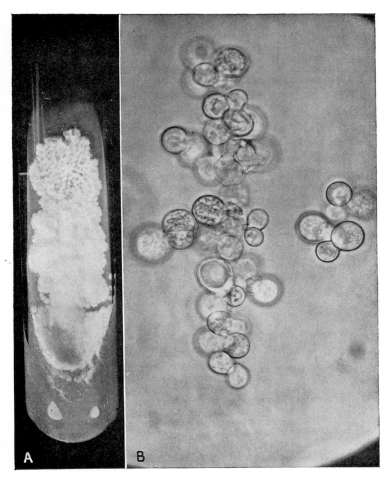

Figure 154. Blastomyces dermatitidis. A, Yeastlike, agar-slant culture; B, budding yeastlike cells. × 700. (From Conant et al.: Manual of Clinical Mycology.)

cies of *Trichophyton,* or by *Epidermophyton floccosum* (Figure 153). Microscopic examination of a piece of skin usually reveals mycelial threads and chains of spores.

The infection is frequently contracted in gymnasiums, dressing rooms, shower rooms and swimming pools where persons go about barefooted. Although the disease is somewhat resistant to treatment, it usually can be cured readily unless the causative organism is *Trichophyton rubrum,* which is extremely resistant.

BLASTOMYCOSIS

Blastomycosis (Gilchrist's disease) is a fungous infection of man and animals caused by *Blastomyces dermatitidis.* It is often referred to as North American blastomycosis to distinguish it from the South American type, which is caused by a related species of fungus. Blastomycosis exists in two forms: (1) cutaneous, and (2) systemic. The cutaneous type is the common form of the disease. It starts as a small, circumscribed elevation (papule) on the face, hands, forearms or forelegs. Secondary lesions develop in the surrounding skin. The lesions enlarge, coalesce and break

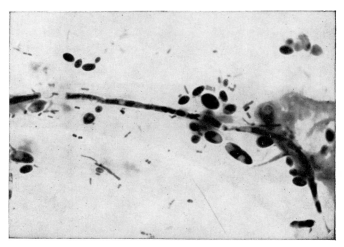

Figure 155.   Candida albicans in sputum. × 1350. (From Conant et al.: Manual of Clinical Mycology.)

down into granulating ulcerated patches, giving rise to a large mass of tissue with an irregular ulcerated surface. The disease may remain localized in the skin for months or years and then spread to the internal organs.

Systemic blastomycosis may be a primary infection or may be secondary to the cutaneous type. In a large percentage of cases the lungs become infected. The bones and other internal structures are frequently involved.

The fungus is a budding, yeastlike organism (Figure 154) but is not a true yeast since, when it is cultured on Sabouraud's glucose agar, it gives rise to a filamentous growth which produces conidia. On blood agar, however, it produces yeastlike forms.

CANDIDIASIS

Candidiasis, also known as moniliasis, is an acute or subacute infection which may involve the mouth, skin, nails, lungs or vagina. The most common type of candidiasis is known as "thrush," which is a mouth infection characterized by the presence of whitish spots on the tongue, gums, cheeks, lips and throat. It is usually mild and is encountered more frequently in nursing infants and in children than in adults. In adults, thrush may follow a debilitating illness such as typhoid fever, tuberculosis or cancer. Other less common types of candidiasis involve the skin, nails, vagina and lungs.

The infection is caused by species of *Candida,* usually *C. albicans* (Figure 155). The organism is an oval, budding yeastlike fungus which is capable of producing a mycelium. Many normal persons harbor the fungus in the mouth, throat, intestines, vagina or skin.

PROTOZOAN DISEASES

The majority of protozoa are free-living, but a number of species have become adapted to live as parasites in the bodies of animals and man. Practically every type of vertebrate animal is parasitized by one or more species of protozoa. Among the parasitic protozoa there are species that live as commensals and thus do no harm to the host. Others cause severe infections in man and animals. Although relatively few species of protozoa are pathogenic, some of the most devastating diseases of man and animals are of protozoal causation. In some cases an intermediate host, such as a blood-sucking insect, is necessary for the transmission of pathogenic protozoa to man or other vertebrates.

All major groups of protozoa—Sarcodina, Mastigophora, Sporozoa and Ciliata—contain parasitic species. In some the life histories are simple, an active stage, *trophozoite* (Greek, "nourishing animal"), alternating with an inactive one, *cystic stage;* in others the life cycles are complex, often involving an alternation of asexual and sexual generations in different host species.

Protozoan diseases differ from the majority of bacterial diseases in that the organisms are not attacked by leukocytes. In many cases the symptoms subside after an initial flare-up; the pathogens, however, are not destroyed but remain to become active when the resistance of the host is weakened. Treatment with vaccines or antiserums is not very effective in diseases caused by protozoa.

Of outstanding importance among protozoan diseases are amebiasis (amebic dysentery) and malaria. These are discussed in this chapter. Other diseases caused by protozoa are Chagas' disease, kala-azar, Oriental sore, espundia, giardiasis, balantidiasis and African sleeping sickness.

AMEBIASIS

Amebiasis, also known as amebic dysentery, is primarily an intestinal infection. It is world-wide in distribution and is of frequent occurrence in the United States. The incidence of the disease is higher, however, in tropical and subtropical areas of the earth. In World War II it was one of the disease scourges of the South Pacific area as well as of some of the European fronts.

Causative Organism

The causative organism, *Endamoeba histolytica,* occurs in two forms or stages: (1) the motile vegetative stage or trophozoite, and (2) the cystic

Figure 156. Epidemiology of amebiasis. (From Mackie, Hunter and Worth: Manual of Tropical Medicine.)

stage. The trophozoite has a typical ameboid shape with usually one blunt pseudopodium. It averages about 20 to 30 microns in diameter. Several ingested red corpuscles usually can be observed in the cytosome of the cell. The nucleus is ringlike with a central granule (karyosome). The inner portion of the nuclear membrane contains a thin layer of chromatin.

The cyst, which is derived from the trophozoite, is spherical in form and smaller than the trophozoite. It is surrounded by an impervious, elastic wall and has four nuclei. An immature cyst may contain one or two nuclei. One or more rodlike bodies with rounded ends (chromatoid bodies) are often seen in the stained cysts. These, however, disappear as the cyst grows older. *Endamoeba histolytica* reproduces by binary fission of the trophozoite and by nuclear division in the cyst.

Pathogenesis

The organisms live primarily in the large intestine, where they invade the mucous membrane. Here they ingest red blood corpuscles and fragments of tissue. The protozoa are aided in penetrating the mucous membrane by producing a histolytic substance (tissue dissolving) which produces small areas of necrosis (death of tissue). This accounts for the name *histolytica,* which means tissue dissolving.

It has been estimated that between 5 and 10 per cent of the population of the United States harbor *E. histolytica.* In areas where sanitation is poor the incidence is much higher. In many of these cases, symptoms are absent or are so mild that a physician is not consulted. In most cases the infection is chronic with indefinite symptoms. Males are more often infected than females. (See Figure 156.)

Transmission

The disease is spread through fecally contaminated drinking water or food. The symptomless carrier and the patient with mild symptoms are the most important agents in the spread of the disease, since they are constantly eliminating cysts in their stools, often in enormous numbers.

MALARIA

Malaria is a disease that is transmitted to man by the bite of mosquitoes of the genus *Anopheles.* It is only the female mosquito that is responsible for transmitting the infection; male mosquitoes live entirely on plant juices. The disease has a wide geographic distribution (Figure 157), extending around the world in a great belt which covers the tropics and subtropics as well as numerous temperate regions. Its range lies between 60 degrees north latitude and 40 degrees south latitude and completely encircles the world. In the United States malaria has been virtually eradicated through measures directed at the destruction of the insect vector, the *Anopheles* mosquito. In colonial days it was prevalent as far north as the Canadian border. The reason for the retreat from the northern states is not entirely clear.

Owing largely to the efforts of the World Health Organization, much progress has been made in the elimination of malaria from many areas of the world. It is still, however, one of the leading diseases that afflicts mankind. About 200 million cases occur annually throughout the world.

Malaria is one of the most debilitating of human diseases. By reducing vitality, it impedes industrial development and political progress of the inhabitants of large areas of the world, areas which have great agricultural potentials and could become important food producers and contribute toward increasing the world's food supply. Many historians now believe that malaria played a role in the fall of ancient Greece and Rome by sapping the moral fiber and physical and mental energy of the people.

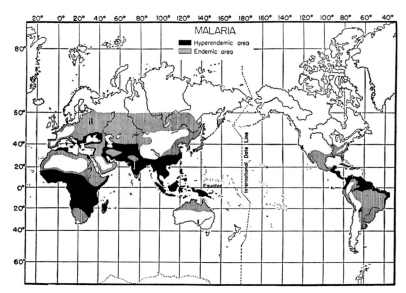

Figure 157. Geographic distribution of malaria. (Reproduced by permission from Practical Bacteriology, Hematology, and Parasitology by E. Stitt, P. Clough and S. Branham, The Blakiston Company, publishers.)

Etiological Agents

There are four kinds of human malaria, each kind caused by a specific species of sporozoan belonging to the genus *Plasmodium*. *Plasmodium vivax*, the most common species, causes so-called "benign, tertian malaria," which has a high tendency to relapse, but has a low death rate. *Plasmodium falciparum* causes a malignant form of malaria known as "malignant tertian" or "estivo-autumnal" malaria, which is extremely dangerous if untreated. It is widely distributed in the tropics but is not found as far north as *vivax*. These two organisms cause more than 90 per cent of all malaria cases. *Plasmodium malariae* causes "quartan malaria." It is found in both tropical and temperate climates in a number of widely separate areas of the world but has a spotty distribution. *Plasmodium ovale* is rare and has not been found in the United States. It produces a tertian type of malaria. Although these species have an essentially similar life cycle, there are minor and diagnostic differences. The infections they produce vary in symptoms, severity, tendency to relapse and response to therapeutic agents.

The various changes malarial parasites undergo in the red blood corpuscles are illustrated in Figure 158.

Vivax Malaria

Vivax malaria occurs throughout the tropics and subtropics, as well as in extensive areas of the temperate zone. It is the type that was common

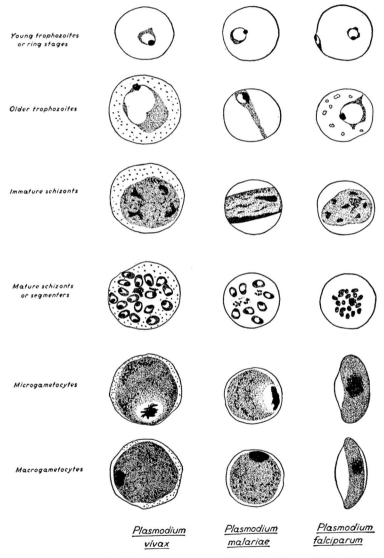

Figure 158. Stages of malarial parasites in red blood cells. × 3000. (From R. M. Cable: Manual of Parasitology. Burgess Publishing Company. Reproduced by permission of Dr. R. M. Cable, Purdue University.)

in the United States in former years. After an incubation period of about two weeks after the bite of an anopheline mosquito, the characteristic recurring paroxysms of chills and fever are experienced for a period of

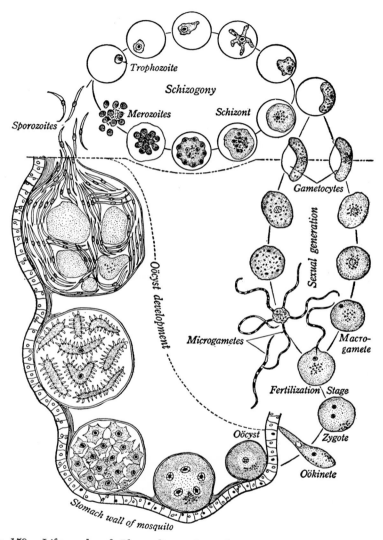

Figure 159. Life cycle of *Plasmodium vivax.* (Reproduced by permission from N. Fasten: Introduction to General Zoology, Ginn & Company.)

several days. The chills last twenty to sixty minutes and are followed by a rise in temperature, in some cases to 105° F. or above, which may last one to four hours. This is followed by profuse perspiration and a drop in temperature to normal or below. After this the patient feels well until the next paroxysm. The chills and fever, although at first somewhat irregular, soon occur at forty-eight hour intervals, or every third day; hence the name "tertian" malaria.

Life Cycle of Plasmodium Vivax. There are two distinct developmental stages in the life cycle of all human malarial parasites: an asexual one, which occurs only in the human body, and a sexual one in the anopheline mosquito. Figure 159 illustrates the life cycle of *Plasmodium vivax.* When a female *Anopheles* mosquito bites a human being, it injects into the body a large number of threadlike organisms known as *sporozoites.* Each sporozoite invades a red blood cell, where it grows and develops into an ameba-like cell known as a *trophozoite.* When fully grown, each trophozoite divides asexually into a number of small bodies known as *merozoites.* The red blood cell then bursts, releasing fifteen to twenty merozoites which at once attack new blood cells, and the cycle is repeated.

After the asexual cycle has become established, some of the trophozoites do not become merozoites but develop into male and female *gametocytes* (Greek, gamete-forming cells). Gametocytes are incapable of further development until taken up by mosquitoes of the genus *Anopheles.* In the stomach of the mosquito they develop into *gametes.* The female gametocytes become eggs, or *macrogametes,* the male gametocytes divide, each producing four to eight elongated sperm cells, or *microgametes.* The union of a microgamete with a macrogamete results in the formation of a *zygote,* which corresponds to a fertilized egg of higher animals. The zygote immediately becomes an active, wormlike cell (oökinete) which bores its way through the stomach and becomes encysted just beneath the covering epithelium of the stomach, forming a wartlike protrusion on the surface of the stomach. Within the *oöcyst* thus formed multiplication is resumed until a large number of spindle-shaped sporozoites are produced. The rupture of the oöcyst liberates the sporozoites into the body fluids of the insect through which they reach the salivary glands, where they are in position to be injected into another human victim to complete the two-host life cycle. The life cycle in the mosquito under optimum temperature conditions requires about ten days.

RICKETTSIAL INFECTIONS

As mentioned in an earlier chapter, the rickettsiae comprise a group of minute bacteria-like organisms which are obligate intracellular parasites. Their primary habitat is in the cells of arthropods, chiefly ticks, mites, fleas and lice, where they live as commensals or, probably in some cases, as symbionts. They live in the intestinal epithelium of the arthropod host. In some arthropods, chiefly ticks, the rickettsiae are transmitted through the egg to succeeding generations. Pathogenic rickettsiae are transmitted to man chiefly through the bites of ticks, lice, fleas and mites. However, for the disease known as "Q fever" transmission is not dependent upon arthropods.

Rickettsiae are responsible for such diseases as typhus fever, Rocky

Mountain spotted fever, tsutsugamushi disease, Q fever and rickettsial-pox. Most of the rickettsial diseases are serious infections with a high mortality rate. Only a small number of the many known species of rickettsiae cause human disease. There are now several antibiotics that are effective against rickettsial diseases.

In this chapter, three rickettsial diseases, typhus fever, Rocky Mountain spotted fever and psittacosis, are briefly considered.

TYPHUS FEVER

There are two kinds of typhus which differ in regard to the arthropod vectors responsible for their dissemination: (1) louse-borne or epidemic typhus, and (2) flea-borne or murine typhus, also known as endemic typhus.

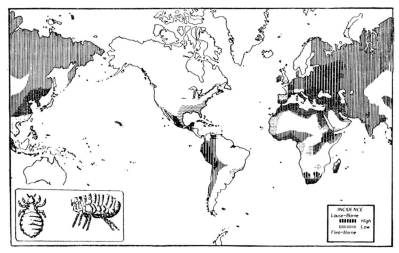

Figure 160. Distribution of typhus fever and vectors (louse and flea). (From Ash and Spitz: Pathology of Tropical Diseases.)

The etiological agent of epidemic typhus is *Rickettsia prowazekii.* It was named to commemorate Howard T. Ricketts and Stanislaus von Prowazek, two investigators who lost their lives in the study of typhus. The disease is transmitted from person to person by the human body louse and the human head louse. It is a severe, acute infection; the case fatality rate in epidemics is about 20 per cent, but may be as high as 70 per cent in some cases.

In former years typhus occurred in great epidemics in Europe and Asia and was one of the world's great scourges. It has killed untold millions of human beings and ranks with plague, cholera, smallpox and yellow fever in historical importance. Its distribution is indicated in Figure 160.

Rickettsia prowazekii (Figure 161) is a minute, pleomorphic coccobacillary form, usually occurring in pairs. It shows considerable variation in size and occasionally forms filaments.

Recovery from typhus leaves the person immune. The use of antityphus vaccine prepared from rickettsiae grown in developing chick embryos has proved effective in immunizing persons against the disease. American troops in World War II going into areas where they might be exposed to epidemic typhus were immunized with this vaccine.

Murine typhus is primarily a disease of rats and is spread from rat to rat and from rat to man by the rat flea. It is world-wide in distribution; in the United States it is found chiefly in the South Atlantic and Gulf

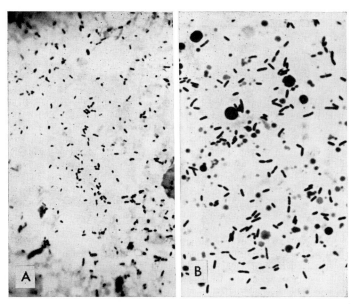

Figure 161. Photomicrographs of rickettsiae. (*A*), *Rickettsia prowazekii;* (*B*), *Rickettsia typhi.* Both were grown in yolk sac. × 1500. (Courtesy of National Microbiological Institute, Rocky Mountain Laboratory, Hamilton, Montana. Photograph by N. J. Kramis.)

states. The etiologic agent of murine typhus is *Rickettsia typhi* (Figure 161), which is morphologically similar to *Rickettsia prowazekii.*

The epidemiology of typhus is illustrated in Figure 162.

ROCKY MOUNTAIN SPOTTED FEVER

Rocky Mountain spotted fever is an acute tick-borne disease first discovered in the state of Montana. Until 1930 it was thought to be confined to the mountainous regions of the Northwest, but it is now known that the disease is widely dispersed, occurring in most parts of the United States.

There are two types of the disease, the western type, transmitted by the wood tick (*Dermacentor andersoni*), and the eastern type, conveyed by the dog tick (*Dermacentor variabilis*). The mortality rate of the western type is approximately 75 per cent, but the eastern type is a milder disease, terminating in death for about 20 per cent of those afflicted.

The infection is caused by *Rickettsia rickettsii* (Figure 163). The rickettsiae are transmitted from generation to generation of the tick

MURINE	EPIDEMIOLOGY	EPIDEMIC
1. Reservoirs: Rats, mice		1. Reservoir: Man
2. Vectors: Fleas, rat louse, rat mite		2. Vector: *Pediculus humanus*
Rat to rat—*Nosopsylla, Xenopsylla,*		3. Louse-infested population
Polyplax, Liponyssus		4. Famine
Rat to man—*Xenopsylla*		5. Crushed lice—abraded skin
3. Rat transportation, migration		6. Louse feces—abraded skin; mucous
4. Infected rat urine, feces, in food, drink		membranes
5. Flea feces—abraded skin, inhalation		7. Dust from infested clothing, bedding

Figure 162. Epidemiology of epidemic and murine typhus. (From Mackie, Hunter and Worth: Manual of Tropical Medicine.)

through the eggs of infected females. The presence of the parasites in the ticks apparently does them no harm.

The disease manifests itself three to fourteen days after the tick bite. A red spotted rash develops which gives the disease the name "spotted fever." Recovery from the infection gives a high degree of immunity. The infection can now be treated with antibiotics. An effective vaccine is produced in the chick embryo.

PSITTACOSIS

Psittacosis is a disease of parrots and many other species of birds including domestic flocks of turkeys, pigeons and chickens. It is readily transmitted to man. The disease is widely distributed among parrots, parakeets, cockatoos and related species, and is commonly called "parrot fever." Although man usually acquires the infection from birds, man to man infection is possible. The infection in man is known as *ornithosis.*

The etiological agent of psittacosis is coccoid in form and has a diameter of about 0.3 to 0.5 micron, making it sufficiently large to be seen

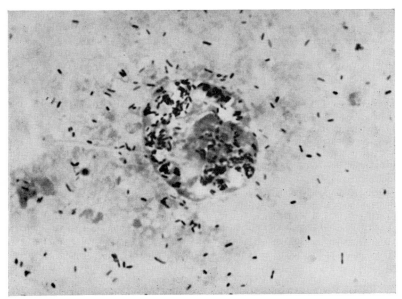

Figure 163. Photomicrograph of *Rickettsia rickettsii,* the causative organism of Rocky Mountain spotted fever. × 1500. (Courtesy of National Microbiological Institute, Rocky Mountain Laboratory, Hamilton, Montana. Photograph by N. J. Kramis.)

under the optical microscope. Although it is sometimes referred to as a virus, it has the dimensions of the smaller rickettsiae and has staining qualities which are essentially the same as those of the rickettsiae. It appears to be a borderline form between the viruses and the rickettsiae. In Bergey's *Manual of Determinative Bacteriology* it is classified with the rickettsiae and has been given the name *Miyagawanella psittaci.*

In man the disease has an incubation period of six to fifteen days and may run a severe course marked by lung involvement and high fever. The disease is often confused with atypical pneumonia, influenza and typhoid fever. It responds to treatment with antibiotics, which has been a factor in lowering the mortality rate.

VIRAL DISEASES

A large number of the communicable diseases of plants, animals and man are caused by viruses. The list includes a considerable number of important human diseases. Most notable of these are smallpox, rabies, poliomyelitis, influenza, measles, yellow fever and the common cold. Dog distemper, foot-and-mouth disease of cattle and hog cholera are also virus diseases. Even bacteria, which themselves are often parasites, may be parasitized by viruses. Such viruses, as mentioned in Chapter 9, are called "bacteriophages."

Some viruses can attack many kinds of hosts. The rabies virus, for example, is capable of infecting most species of mammals, and the smallpox virus will grow, not only in man, but also in the cow and the rabbit. On the other hand, some viruses are highly host-specific. Measles, one of the most common infections of children, occurs only in the human species.

Viruses, like rickettsiae, are intracellular parasites and are capable of reproducing rapidly in the tissue cells of the host. They often produce characteristic "inclusion bodies" in the form of granules or groups of granules in the cells they invade. In some diseases these bodies are located in the cytoplasm, in others in the nuclei of the cells; in a few cases they are either intranuclear or intracytoplasmic. The nature of these intracellular inclusions is obscure, but they are interpreted as being products of cell degeneration or aggregates of virus particles.

The inclusion bodies of different virus diseases are usually sufficiently characteristic so that a postmortem diagnosis of these diseases may be based on their appearance, staining properties and position within the cell. In rabies, inclusion bodies are present in the cytoplasm of brain cells and are known as "Negri bodies."

In most instances viruses stimulate the formation of specific neutralizing antibodies which are capable of inactivating them. Such antibodies are of value in the identification of viruses. Recovery from a viral infection is often followed by a long-lasting, often lifelong immunity. This is true of smallpox, poliomyelitis, measles, mumps, yellow fever, distemper in dogs and hog cholera but is not true of influenza and the common cold. Active immunity to many of the virus diseases can be obtained by the use of vaccines containing the virus in attenuated form. This has been achieved in the case of smallpox, rabies, poliomyelitis, yellow fever and certain other viral infections. It is of historic interest that the first vaccine that came into use was smallpox vaccine.

SMALLPOX

Smallpox, also known as *variola*, is an acute, highly contagious, often fatal disease characterized by a pustular skin eruption which may leave permanent scars or pits. The disease is of great historical significance because, in former centuries, it was one of the most dreaded scourges. It invaded every continent and every community, disrupting the social and

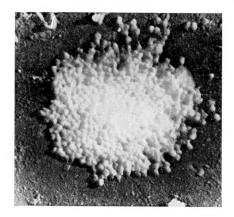

Figure 164. Electron micrograph of a mass of virus particles from a case of smallpox. × 8000. Reduced approximately three quarters in size from original micrograph. (From C. E. van Rooyen and G. E. Scott: Canadian Journal of Public Health, Dec. 1948. Courtesy of the authors.)

economic life of the people and, at times, killing as many as 10 per cent of the population in a single year. During the eighteenth century it killed an estimated 60,000,000 people in Europe. Smallpox was essentially a disease of childhood, most persons having either survived the disease or succumbed to it before reaching adult life. In early Colonial days smallpox became firmly established in America.

Etiology and Mode of Transmission

Smallpox is caused by a virus which is antigenically related to the cowpox (vaccinia) virus, since an attack of cowpox, a benign disease, confers immunity to smallpox. The virus particle (Figure 164) is a spherical body having a diameter of about 200 millimicrons.

The disease is spread mainly by direct personal contact. The virus is present in the skin lesions and the lesions of the mucous membranes. The secretions of the nose and mouth are highly infectious, and particles from the scabs formed on the skin of infected persons may also play a role in

Figure 165. Edward Jenner (1749–1823). From the painting by Sir Thomas Laurence. (From Garrison: History of Medicine. 4th edition.)

the spread of smallpox. The upper respiratory tract serves as the avenue of entrance, but the disease can be produced by artificial introduction of the virus into the skin. Practically every human being is susceptible unless he has immunity from a previous infection or from vaccination.

Vaccination

Vaccination against smallpox, developed by Jenner (Figure 165), is now universally recognized as an efficient protection against smallpox.

Figure 166.   The first vaccination to prevent smallpox. The vaccine was prepared from cowpox vesicles (blisters) on the hands of a milkmaid. (From the Fisher Collection of Alchemical and Historical Pictures. Courtesy of the Fisher Scientific Company.)

It has subjugated smallpox, which now is an uncommon disease in the United States and in many other parts of the world, and has saved the lives of untold millions of human beings.

The immunity conferred lasts on an average at least five years and often longer. It should not be assumed that one vaccination gives lifetime protection. It is recommended that the first vaccination be made during the first year of life and a second one at the age of six years. If an outbreak of smallpox occurs in any community, it is advisable that the entire population be vaccinated or revaccinated. Vaccination within three to four days after exposure to the infection usually protects against the development of the disease. The incidence of smallpox within a community or nation depends upon the extent to which vaccination is practiced. In areas where vaccination is compulsory smallpox is rare.

The vaccine used at the present time is prepared from material obtained from the skin vesicles of inoculated calves (Chapter 29). The lymph and pulp present in the vesicles contain the active virus of cowpox. This material is mixed with an equal amount of glycerin to destroy extraneous organisms. Usually a small amount of carbolic acid is added. In some cases brilliant green (1:10,000) is added to hasten the destruction of any other organisms which may be present. These added substances do not destroy the vaccine virus. The vaccine is thoroughly tested for potency and purity and is dispensed in sealed capillary glass tubes. It must be kept cold to preserve the virus in active form.

RABIES

Rabies is an acute infection of the central nervous system. It is primarily a disease of animals such as dogs, skunks, wolves, foxes and coyotes, but man and all warm-blooded animals are susceptible. In man, and apparently also in animals, the disease always terminates fatally once its symptoms have developed. The incubation period of rabies is relatively long and variable.

Etiology and Mode of Transmission

The causative organism of rabies is one of the larger viruses. It is found in the central nervous system of an infected animal and is present also in the saliva. It can be cultivated in tissue media containing minced brain of mouse embryos and will grow also in chick and duck embryos.

Animals and man become infected through the saliva of a rabid animal. The dog is chiefly responsible for the disease in man. The portal of entry of the virus is usually the wound resulting from a bite. But the virus may also enter the body through a scratch or other break in the skin if contaminated with the saliva of a rabid animal.

The incubation period of human rabies varies from fourteen days to several months but is usually about six weeks. The length of the period of incubation depends largely on the seat of the injury and its distance from the central nervous system. A person bitten about the face and head region or hands by a rabid animal will exhibit symptoms in a shorter period than one whose wound is on the legs. In children the incubation period is shorter than in adults. When introduced into the body, the virus becomes established in nerve tissue and travels along nerve trunks, not through the blood stream, to the spinal cord and brain. This explains the long incubation period of the disease. The virus multiplies and spreads through the entire central nervous system. It enters peripheral nerves and the salivary glands as well as many of the internal organs. Negri bodies form as a specific reaction of the nerve cells to presence of the virus.

Vaccination

The long period of incubation of rabies usually allows sufficient time to immunize a person bitten by a rabid animal and thus prevent the disease from developing. The method of postexposure immunization used for this purpose was introduced by Pasteur. The vaccine is prepared from an attenuated form of virus called "fixed virus." (See Chapters 2 and 29.) A number of modifications of Pasteur's method have been developed. A full course of treatment consists of a daily injection of vaccine for a period of 14 to 21 days.

Dogs can be given advance protection against rabies by a single injection of vaccine, which will ordinarily keep them from developing rabies should they be bitten by a rabid animal. The vaccine for immunizing dogs contains living rabies virus attenuated by cultivation in chick embryos. It is effective for one year.

POLIOMYELITIS

Poliomyelitis, also known as infantile paralysis, is an acute disease which, in most cases, is a mild infection exhibiting upper respiratory and gastrointestinal symptoms but which, occasionally, affects the central nervous system, destroying motor nerve cells in the spinal cord and the

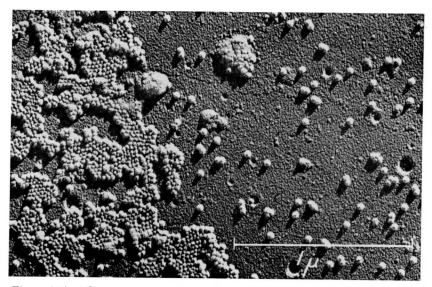

Figure 167.   Electron micrograph of poliomyelitis virus shadowed with chromium. (Courtesy of A. R. Taylor, Virus Laboratories, Research Department, Parke, Davis and Company.)

brain. These cells control the movement of muscles. The disease may occur sporadically, but it usually appears in epidemic form. In the United States it is chiefly a seasonal disease, occurring during the summer and fall. It attacks children with greater frequency than adults, the highest incidence being in children less than five years old.

Etiology and Mode of Transmission

The etiological agent of poliomyelitis is an extremely small, spherical-shaped virus (Figure 167) between 8 and 12 millimicrons in diameter. Three distinct types of the virus are recognized. These types vary in size and antigenic properties. They resist desiccation and can survive for a considerable time in water, feces and sewage.

As far as is known, the only natural host of poliomyelitis virus is man. Human carriers are extremely numerous. They harbor the virus chiefly in the throat and the intestinal tract. Carriers and subclinical cases apparently play a large role in the spread of the disease. Transmission appears to be by droplets of mouth and throat secretions and probably, at times, by food contaminated either by such droplets or by feces. Flies are believed to play a role in the spread of the virus from feces to food. The virus apparently enters the body by way of the mouth. It escapes from the body of an infected person through the secretions of the respiratory tract and through the feces.

Clinical Manifestations

The disease exhibits great variability in symptoms, pathology and severity. Three forms of poliomyelitis are recognized, the abortive, the nonparalytic and paralytic. In the abortive type there are vague symptoms in the upper respiratory or gastrointestinal tract. There is no evidence of involvement of the central nervous system. The symptoms are mild and not distinctive. The diagnosis in such cases is largely presumptive, but in some instances it can be confirmed by the isolation of the virus. Many of these cases go unrecognized.

The nonparalytic type includes those cases in which there is evidence of the presence of the virus in the central nervous system, but the damage done is not sufficient to cause paralysis. The paralytic type is characterized by destruction of motor nerve cells in the spinal cord and, in some instances, in the brain, resulting in more or less extensive paralysis.

Vaccination

An immunizing agent is now available in the form of a vaccine developed by Dr. Jonas Salk. The vaccine is prepared from poliomyelitis virus grown in a culture of monkey kidney tissue. All three types of the virus are included in the vaccine. The virus is inactivated by treatment with formaldehyde to render it harmless. In 1954 a nationwide field trial of the vaccine, conducted by the National Foundation for Infantile Paralysis, indicated that it was an effective immunizing agent. The vaccine is administered in three doses with an interval between the first and second doses of approximately one month and an interval of at least five months between the second and third doses.

Work is now in progress for the production of a live-virus vaccine. It is expected that such a vaccine can be administered by mouth and will offer long-lasting immunity without requiring booster doses.

INFLUENZA

Influenza is an acute, highly contagious disease characterized by a sudden onset, fever, aches and pains in the back and limbs, and general prostration with or without symptoms similar to those of the common cold. It appears in several forms, endemic, epidemic and pandemic, but occurs most commonly in epidemic form at two- to five-year intervals. Sporadic or endemic cases occur in periods when there are no epidemics of the disease. Pandemics are infrequent.

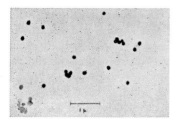

Figure 168. Electron micrograph of influenza virus particles. (From S. Mudd and T. Anderson: J.A.M.A., Vol. 126. Reproduced by permission of the American Medical Association.)

Etiology and Transmission

There are at least four different types of influenza virus, called A, B, C and D. Within each type there are a number of different strains and new strains appear to develop from time to time. In 1957 the so-called Asian strain developed within type A. The different types and strains differ antigenically. The influenza viruses are spherical or nearly spherical and are of medium size, having a diameter of approximately 100 millimicrons. (See Figure 168.)

The virus is present in the mouth and nasal discharges of infected persons. Transfer of infection is by droplets liberated by persons when they cough or sneeze, or by articles soiled with the oral or nasal discharges of a patient. The virus gains entrance to the body through the respiratory tract.

Immunity and Control

Influenza vaccine, prepared from virus grown in chick embryos and inactivated with formaldehyde, appears to have some immunizing power. The vaccine is most useful when administered just before, or at the onset of, an epidemic. To be effective, the vaccine must contain the strain of the virus responsible for the prevailing infection.

A World Influenza Center, with cooperating laboratories in various countries, has been set up by the World Health Organization. Through the facilities of this Center, the virus strains of new outbreaks of influenza are isolated and used in making vaccines in advance of the epidemic spread of the disease.

THE COMMON COLD

It is generally accepted that the etiological agent of the common cold is a virus, but little is known about it. It is probable that several different viruses are capable of causing the infection. The incidence of the common cold in the United States is approximately two attacks per person annually. Children are usually more susceptible than adults. The disease is not dangerous in itself, but it may lower resistance of the mucous membrane of the upper respiratory tract sufficiently to permit other germs to set up secondary complications such as sinusitis, middle ear infection, bronchitis or pneumonia. There is no effective treatment for the common cold, nor are there any effective control measures.

MEASLES

Measles is a highly infectious disease which occurs usually in epidemics at about two or three year intervals. Susceptibility appears to be universal, virtually all persons who have not had the disease being susceptible. It is chiefly a disease of childhood, however, because most adults are immune as a result of childhood infection. In urban communities most children have been infected before they reach the age of ten years. In rural areas epidemics are less regular and many children escape infection, but more cases occur among adolescents and young adults. Hence, in army camps where boys from rural areas are brought together, epidemics of measles frequently occur.

The early symptoms of measles resemble those of the common cold. The initial symptoms are followed by a rise in temperature and grayish specks on the mucous membrane of the mouth. Three or four days after the onset a skin rash appears. Complications may occur, especially in children under five years of age and in adults. The usual ones are middle ear infection with perforation of the drum and bronchopneumonia. These are always due to secondary bacterial infection. Pneumonia causes most of the deaths attributable to measles. In the United States two-thirds of the measles deaths occur in children under the age of five. The incubation period is usually fourteen days.

Measles can be prevented, or the attack can be modified, by the use of *gamma*-globulin prepared from human blood. Since the majority of adult human beings have had measles, their blood contains specific measles antibodies in the *gamma*-globulin fraction of the blood. The *gamma*-globulin fraction can be separated from the other plasma proteins in almost pure form. It is usually obtained from the pooled blood donated by volunteers through the American Red Cross. The administration of *gamma*-globulin within five days after exposure to measles results in complete protection. The immunity is passive, lasting about four weeks. If administered after the eighth or ninth day of exposure, measles is not entirely prevented, but is modified so that the attack is mild. Upon recovery the person is actively immune to measles, usually for life. Modified measles is frequently preferable to complete prevention, since it results in permanent immunity. However, in very young or sick children, prevention is advisable. An attenuated vaccine has been introduced recently.

"German measles" (*rubella*), a relatively mild disease most common in children, is of particular significance to women if contracted during the first few months of pregnancy. This is because a high percentage of infants with congenital defects are born to mothers who had rubella during the first 3 or 4 months of gestation.

Roseola infantum, an acute exanthematous disease of infants or young children, resembles rubella. Its onset is rather alarming to the parent since convulsions and a very high fever (as high as 106° F.), followed by a rash, are the outstanding symptoms.

YELLOW FEVER

Yellow fever is an acute infectious disease caused by a specific virus transmitted to the blood of man chiefly by the bite of infected females of the mosquito, *Aëdes aegypti.* A number of other species of mosquitoes are also vectors of the disease. The role played by mosquitoes as vectors was first demonstrated in 1900 by Walter Reed and his co-workers of the American Army Yellow Fever Commission. The causal agent of yellow fever is a small virus, having a diameter of about 20 millimicrons. It is present in the blood of infected persons during the first three or four days, at which time it can be withdrawn by the mosquito.

The disease is characterized by abrupt onset, fever, headache, backache, pain in the legs, vomiting, severe prostration and jaundice. The jaundice is due to liver involvement and is evidenced by a yellow coloring of the skin and mucous membranes.

The disease is at present limited chiefly to certain areas in Africa and is found in Brazil and a number of other South American countries. In the past, epidemics occurred in other parts of the world. Prior to the present century numerous epidemics occurred in the United States as far north as Boston.

An effective vaccine containing live yellow fever virus (strain 17D) is now available. By long passage through chick embryos this strain has lost most of its virulence while retaining a high degree of antigenicity. Given in a single dose, it confers complete immunity, which develops in ten days and has a duration of about four years. American troops in jungle regions were successfully immunized against yellow fever in World War II.

OTHER VIRAL DISEASES

In recent years a new group of viruses known as "Coxsackie viruses" (Figure 169) were discovered at Coxsackie, New York. Some types of these viruses are very prevalent in children during warm weather, causing fever, sore throat and pain in the neck, arms and legs. Because the symptoms resemble those of nonparalytic poliomyelitis, the illness often has been confused with poliomyelitis. One strain causes meningitis (aseptic).

The *adenoviruses* constitute another group of recently recognized viruses. Many types of these viruses were found to be present in the adenoids of human beings. This group is frequently associated with feverish respiratory tract infections in young children and is responsible for much of the respiratory illness among recruits in the military services. Certain types of the adenoviruses cause virus pneumonia (primary atypical pneumonia). The army has prepared an effective vaccine against adenovirus

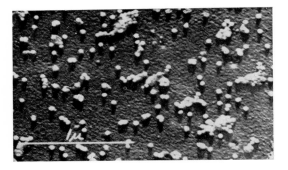

Figure 169. Electron micrograph of Coxsackie virus. (From A. Briefs, S. S. Breese, Jr., J. Warren and R. J. Huebner: J. Bacteriol., Vol. 64. Reproduced by permission of The Williams & Wilkins Company.)

infections. It appears that the great majority of respiratory infections are due to viruses, most of which have not as yet been identified.

Another newly recognized group of viruses, the *orphan viruses,* have many characteristics in common with both the Coxsackie and poliomyelitis viruses. They were found to be present in the intestinal tract of various animals, as well as human beings, especially children. Those found in man are called ECHO* viruses. They may be isolated from stools of healthy people as well as from children mistakenly diagnosed as having nonparalytic poliomyelitis. Their role in the causation of disease is not well understood. These viruses are called "orphans" because they are often found in healthy individuals and cannot be assigned a specific role in the etiology of disease. When injected into laboratory animals the orphan viruses do not cause illness, but they infect certain types of cells in artificial cultures.

* The name ECHO has been derived from the initials of the words "enteric cytopathogenic human orphans." The term "enteric" refers to the intestines where the viruses are found, and "cytopathogenic" means that they infect cells in tissue cultures.

QUESTIONS

1. (*a*) What are some of the common characteristics of fungous diseases?
    (*b*) Describe the ringworm infections.
    (*c*) In what two forms may blastomycosis occur?
    (*d*) What is candidiasis?
2. Describe the nature, causative organism and mode of transmission of amebiasis.
3. Of what importance is malaria as a world disease? Describe vivax malaria. Outline the life cycle of *Plasmodium vivax*. Name the other malarial parasites.
4. (*a*) What is the primary habitat of the rickettsiae pathogenic for man? How are rickettsial diseases usually transmitted to man?
    (*b*) Describe briefly: (1) epidemic and murine typhus, (2) Rocky Mountain spotted fever, (3) psittacosis.
5. (*a*) Compare the prevalence of smallpox in former centuries and at present.
    (*b*) Describe the smallpox virus.
    (*c*) Of what value is vaccination against smallpox? Does one vaccination give lifetime protection? What is the accepted procedure in regard to effective immunization against smallpox? How is smallpox vaccine prepared?
    (*d*) Do you favor compulsory vaccination against this disease? Why?
6. Explain the following points in regard to rabies: (1) chief habitat of the causative virus, (2) mode of transmission, (3) course of the disease in man, (4) prevention, (5) inclusion bodies.
7. Describe briefly the principal features of (1) poliomyelitis, (2) influenza, and (3) yellow fever.
8. What use is made of *gamma*-globulin in measles?

REFERENCES

Bedson, S. P., et al.: Virus and Rickettsial Diseases. 2nd ed. Baltimore, The Williams & Wilkins Company, 1955.

Burnett, G. W., and Scherp, H. W.: Oral Microbiology and Infectious Disease. Baltimore, The Williams & Wilkins Company, 1957.

Burrows, W.: Textbook of Microbiology. 17th ed. Philadelphia, W. B. Saunders Company, 1959.

Cameron, T. W. M.: Parasites and Parasitism. New York, John Wiley & Sons, Inc., 1956.

Chandler, A. C.: Introduction to Parasitology. 9th ed. New York, John Wiley & Sons, Inc., 1955.

Conant, N. F., et al.: Manual of Clinical Mycology. 2nd ed. Philadelphia, W. B. Saunders Company, 1954.

Dubos, R. J., ed.: Bacterial and Mycotic Infections of Man. 3rd ed. Philadelphia, J. B. Lippincott Company, 1958.

Morse, K. T., and Nigrelli, R. F., ed.: Some Protozoan Diseases of Man and Animals: Anaplasmosis, Babesiosis, and Toxoplasmosis. Annals of the New York Academy of Sciences. Vol. 64, p. 25, 1956.

Rabies. WHO Technical Report Series, No. 82. New York, Columbia University Press, 1954.

Rhodes, A. J., and van Rooyen, C. E.: Textbook of Virology. 3rd ed. Baltimore, The Williams & Wilkins Company, 1958.

Rivers, T. M., ed.: Viral and Rickettsial Infections of Man. 3rd ed. Philadelphia, J. B. Lippincott Company, 1959.

Trueta, J., et al.: Handbook of Poliomyelitis. Springfield, Ill., Charles C Thomas, 1957.

Yellow Fever Vaccination. WHO. Monograph Series, No. 30. New York, Columbia University Press, 1956.

Wilson, G. S., and Miles, A. A.: Topley and Wilson's Principles of Bacteriology and Immunity. 2 vols. 4th ed. Baltimore, The Williams & Wilkins Company, 1955.

34 • Plant Diseases Caused by Microorganisms

Plants, like animals, are susceptible to attack by microorganisms of various kinds. Plant diseases inflict severe losses annually on crops such as potatoes, tomatoes, carrots, beets, cabbage, cauliflower, turnips, celery, corn, beans, wheat, alfalfa, tobacco and fruits. The etiological agents of plant diseases are chiefly bacteria, fungi and viruses. Plant pathogens exhibit specificity similar to that of animal pathogens. Some infect only one species, whereas others are pathogenic for a number of species. They have invasive power and the ability to damage plant tissues and structures.

PORTALS OF ENTRY

To invade the plant, pathogens must gain entrance to the plant tissues through natural openings, such as stomata (minute orifices in the epidermis of leaves), lenticels (pores in the stems of some plants), the nectar ducts of flowers, pores for the excretion of water (modified stomata), or through wounds. Among the pathogenic fungi, however, there are species which are capable of penetrating the intact epidermis of plants. Wounds caused by agricultural implements are frequently utilized as avenues of entrance to plant tissues. However, wounds caused by the bite of insects are the most common portals of entry of plant pathogens.

Some pathogens are tissue-specific. They must gain entrance through portals that will allow them to reach tissues in which they can grow.

TRANSMISSION OF PLANT DISEASES

Infected plants are the source of plant pathogens. From such plants the agents of disease may be transported by implements, water, soil, human beings and animals, especially insects. The most common mode of transmission is by the agency of sap-sucking insects (leaf hoppers and plant lice) and winged insects. These insects normally live on the juices

519

of plants and thus serve as vectors of plant pathogens, transmitting them from one plant to another. Their long, sucking mouth parts serve as an injection apparatus when thrust into plant tissues.

PLANT RESISTANCE TO INFECTION

Individual plants or species have resistance or immunity to certain infections. Immunity in plants is not comparable to immunity in animals. Plants do not have cells comparable to the phagocytes of animals and seem to lack the capacity to produce antibodies in response to the presence of pathogens. Not much is known concerning the mechanism of immunity in plants. A plant does not ordinarily acquire immunity to an infection to which it is naturally susceptible. The immunity that certain species or varieties have is inherent to the group, transmitted by hereditary factors from generation to generation. Plant immunity apparently is due to the chemical nature of the cells and the sap and, in some cases, to specific chemicals which are akin to antibiotics in that minute amounts inhibit the growth of microorganisms. In some cases, environmental factors may alter resistance.

Owing to the variations characteristic of all organisms, some individuals of a species are more resistant than others to a given infection. Hence by selecting and breeding such individuals, varieties resistant to specific infections often can be developed.

INJURY TO THE HOST

The injury produced by plant pathogens apparently is not due to specific toxins but presumably in many cases to enzymes which are capable of attacking various plant constituents. In some cases the pathogens liberate acids or alkalis which may be detrimental to the host plant. The harm done usually results in necrosis (tissue destruction), which may be localized in small areas or result in a progressive degeneration of the entire plant. Some of the more common results of plant infections are retarded growth of certain tissues or the entire plant; distortions of leaves, stems or other structures; changes of color; and abnormal overgrowths of certain tissues.

PLANT DISEASES CAUSED BY BACTERIA

The bacterial diseases of plants may be grouped into five types: (1) soft rots, (2) wilts, (3) blights, (4) tumors or galls, and (5) spots. The names indicate the kind of chief lesions produced.

Soft rots are produced by species of bacteria chiefly of the genus *Erwinia*. These bacteria produce pectinase, an enzyme which hydrolyzes pectin, the cementing material that holds plant cells together. This results in the distintegration and death of plant tissues and their conversion into a soft, pulpy mass. Stored vegetables as well as growing vegetables may be affected. The most important organism responsible for this disease is

Erwinia carotovora, which causes soft rot in carrots, cabbage, celery, cucumbers, muskmelons, onions, potatoes, tomatoes, turnips and other vegetables. Another species (*E. atroseptica*) causes a black rot on the stems and tubers of potatoes and other vegetables.

Wilts are diseases in which the plant becomes limp, causing it to droop. The invading organisms multiply and accumulate in large numbers in the sap-conducting vessels of the plant, frequently obstructing the flow of sap. Complete obstruction of the flow of sap causes a rapid wilting of the plant, whereas partial obstruction of the flow results in the growth of a sickly plant. *Bacterium stewartii* causes corn wilt. Sweet corn is very susceptible to this disease, but field corn is only slightly susceptible. *Erwinia tracheiphila* causes cucumber wilt and also affects muskmelons, pumpkins and squashes. *Xanthomonas campestris* is the causative organism of wilt in cabbages, cauliflowers and rutabagas.

Blights are widespread and destructive diseases in which the invading bacteria enter the spaces between the cells and grow in the sap of the plant. Various parts of the plant, including the blossoms, leaves, twigs, fruit, limbs or trunk, may be affected. Discoloration of the affected parts occurs. *Erwinia amylovora* causes fire blight of apples, pears and quinces; *Xanthomonas phaseoli* causes bean blight.

Tumors or *galls* are diseases produced by organisms that cause abnormal growths in the plant. The pathogens irritate the cells in a local area, causing an overgrowth of tissue. The tumors vary in size, some being very small, others growing larger than the original plant. Tumor production in plants is considered by some to be analogous to cancerous growths in animals. There are fundamental differences, however, in the pathology of these two types of diseases. Crown gall, occurring in a variety of plants and caused by *Agrobacterium tumefaciens,* is an example of a tumor disease. Included among the plants affected are the apple, peach, orange, grape, raspberry and many others.

Spots are localized infections, usually in the leaves of plants, and are restricted to relatively small areas of tissue around the portals of entry, which are usually the stomata. The infected areas become discolored and may become dry and fall out, leaving holes in the leaves. *Xanthomonas cucurbitae* is the cause of leaf spot in squash and related plants. Leaf spot of celery is caused by *Pseudomonas apii.* Other examples of leaf spot are angular leaf spot of tobacco, cauliflower spot and angular leaf spot of cotton.

PLANT DISEASES CAUSED BY FUNGI

Fungi are important causal agents of plant diseases. A large number of species are capable of living parasitically, attacking the leaves, stems, flowers or seeds of plants. Some are obligate parasites, but the majority of pathogenic fungi are facultative parasites capable of living on plant debris in the soil as well as on or in the tissues of living plants. Because of this, when a given crop is grown on the land for a number of years, certain fungous diseases may increase to the point where the cultivation of that crop becomes economically impossible.

It will be recalled (Chapter 7) that the fungi are divided into four classes, Phycomycetes, Ascomycetes, Basidiomycetes and Fungi Imperfecti.

DISEASES CAUSED BY PHYCOMYCETES

The most important of the diseases caused by the Phycomycetes are the *downy mildews*. As contrasted with the powdery mildews, which are external parasites and belong to the Ascomycetes, the downy mildews grow in the tissue spaces of the leaves, stems, flowers and fruits of the plants they parasitize. The downy mildews are so called because they give rise to a large number of spore-bearing branches (sporangiophores) which protrude through the stomata of the host plant, producing white, gray or violet downy patches on the leaves. An example of a destructive downy mildew is the one that attacks the grape.

The disease known as *late potato blight* is one of the downy mildews. The fungus, *Phytophthora infestans,* is localized in the leaves and stems. The disease may spread rapidly and kill the entire plant. Potato blight caused a severe famine in Ireland in 1845 and was responsible for an extensive migration of the Irish to America.

DISEASES CAUSED BY ASCOMYCETES

The class Ascomycetes includes the majority of the fungi causing plant diseases, examples of which are apple scab, ergot, powdery mildews and brown rot.

In *apple scab* the fungus affects the leaves, flowers, fruit and twigs of the tree. Spots or diffuse discolorations occur on the leaves, which later develop into scabs. The fruit may also become spotted, and large scab areas may be formed. Scab spots may develop also on fruits in storage. Loss of leaves usually results. The causative organism is *Venturia inaequalis.*

Ergot is a fungous infection of cereals (especially rye) and grasses. *Claviceps purpurea,* which causes ergot of rye, is one of the best known of the ergot fungi. In this disease some or all of the grains of the head are replaced by dark purple, spurlike structures, the so-called "ergot grains." Each of these grains is a dense aggregate of fungus cells which have taken the place of the normal grain. The ergot grains yield a medicinal substance which is of value in the treatment of hemorrhage following childbirth.

The *powdery mildews* are external parasites which cause economically important diseases of grapes, apples, clover and many other plants. The mycelium grows on the surface of the host, producing usually a white, powdery appearance. Some powdery mildews have a dark mycelium which produces a sooty effect. Special branches (haustoria) of the mycelium grow into the tissues of the plant for the absorption of nourishment. The disease has a dwarfing or stunting effect on the plant.

Brown rot is a disease of apples, peaches and other fruits. It causes the blighting of blossoms, the killing of leaves and twigs and the rotting of fruit as it approaches maturity. The causative fungus, *Sclerotinia fructicola,* survives the winter in rotted fruits or "mummies" which fall to the ground or remain clinging to the tree.

DISEASES CAUSED BY BASIDIOMYCETES

Two important groups of diseases caused by Basidiomycetes are the *rusts* and the *smuts*. Both are destructive diseases which affect chiefly the cereal plants.

Rusts are so called because of the characteristic brown or rust-colored spores produced by many of the rust fungi. There are many species of these fungi, all of which are obligate parasites. They attack the foliage of the plant and, in many cases, the stems or fruits. In their annual life cycle many of the rusts parasitize two distinct and unrelated host plants or groups of host plants. Some produce as many as five different kinds of spores in orderly sequence during their life cycle (Figure 170).

Black stem rust of wheat is caused by *Puccinia graminis.* This fungus has a complicated life cycle, including stages in two widely different host plants, wheat and the common barberry. When a spore produced by the fungus growing in the leaf of the barberry is conveyed to the leaf or stem of a young wheat plant, it germinates and produces a mycelium. Within several weeks this mycelium gives rise to a crop of rust-colored, so-called *summer spores* (uredospores) on the infected leaves and stems. Later the spores become black. These spores are blown about by the wind and are capable of infecting other wheat plants, resulting in another crop of summer spores. This can continue indefinitely in climates where the winters are not very cold. Thus it is possible for this fungus to exist only on the wheat plant and related grasses, completely by-passing the barberry part of the cycle. In northern areas, however, these spores do not survive the winter. In the late summer the mycelium that has been producing uredospores gives rise to so-called *winter spores* (teliospores), which can survive cold winter weather. These spores are present in the stubble in the field after the wheat crop has been harvested. They remain attached to the stubble until the following spring when they germinate, forming short hyphae which give rise to another type of spore (basidiospore). These spores are blown about by the wind and are capable of infecting the leaves of the barberry. On the barberry the fungus develops and produces structures in which large numbers of spores (aeciospores) are formed. These dry and powdery spores are capable of infecting wheat as

well as other cereal grains and grasses. Thus, in the northern United
States, the barberry is a necessary host if the fungus is to survive during
the winter months.

The harmful effects of the disease in the wheat plant are seen chiefly
when the grain matures. Because the nutrition of the plant has been impaired by the growth of the fungus within it, the grains are small and
mushy and the yield is greatly reduced.

Resistant varieties of wheat have been produced. Such varieties, however, do not remain permanently resistant. Sooner or later mutations occur
which give rise to new strains of the rust fungus which can attack the

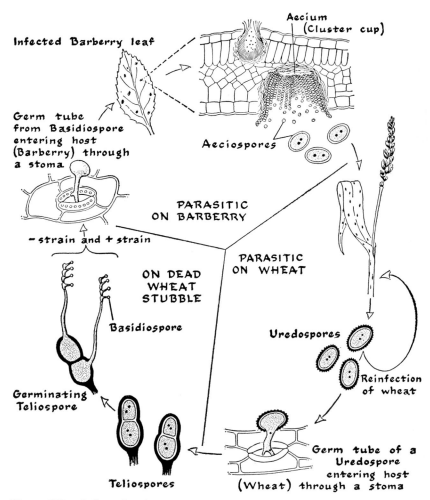

Figure 170. Life cycle of *Puccinia graminis*, the etiological agent of black stem
rust of wheat. (From Hardin, G.: Biology: Its Human Implications, 2nd ed., W. H.
Freeman and Company.)

new varieties of wheat. Geographically new strains may arise since the spores of this fungus are known to carry via air over 500 miles.

Another important rust is *blister rust* of the white pine and other five-needle pines. Besides the pine, the fungus requires a second host to complete its annual life cycle. This host may be either the currant or the gooseberry. The infection starts in pine needles and spreads downward from the smaller to the larger branches and to the trunk of the pine tree. Spindle-shaped swellings are formed on the bark. This disease can be controlled by eradicating currant and gooseberry from white pine areas.

In the diseases known as *smuts,* the causative fungi produce dark spores that have a smutty appearance. The smut fungi parasitize chiefly various cereals and grasses. There are many species of these fungi. The smut fungi produce masses of *chlamydospores,* usually in the floral parts of the host plant. After a short interval these spores germinate and produce short hyphae from the cells of which *basidiospores* arise. Two of these spores fuse and develop a mycelium which invades the tissues of the host, frequently the seeds. Tumor-like swellings made up of masses of hyphae are formed. The chlamydospores survive the winter in soil and corn debris. Corn smut and stinking smut of wheat (bunt) are two common smut diseases.

PLANT DISEASES CAUSED BY VIRUSES

A large variety of plant diseases are due to viruses, which cause some of the most destructive diseases of agricultural crops. The symptoms of viral diseases are highly varied. Virus-infected plants may show changes in the leaves, such as mottling, rolling, crinkling, ringspots, bronzing, yellowing, striping and distortion. Other symptoms include changes in flower color, dwarfing of the plant, splitting of the plant stems, outgrowths, tumors and necrosis.

In most cases the transmission of viral diseases is by the agency of sap-sucking insect vectors such as leaf hoppers and plant lice. Less commonly, transmission occurs by contact with infected plants, by contaminated seed or through contaminated soil. Symptomless carriers may also play a role in the transmission of viral diseases. Certain plants, such as potatoes, raspberries and strawberries, may become carriers of certain viruses. In some cases the carrier shows an initial reaction to the virus after which the symptoms disappear, although the virus remains in the tissues of the plant. In other cases there is no initial reaction to the presence of the virus, the plant exhibiting no signs of any kind due to invasion of the virus.

On the basis of the more common symptoms produced, viral diseases of plants may be grouped into four main types: (1) mosaic diseases, (2) the yellows, (3) distorting diseases, and (4) necrotic diseases.

Mosaic diseases are those in which the main symptom is the appearance of varicolored, mottled areas on the leaves. The leaves acquire spots or blotches of different colors, resembling a mosaic in composition. Changes in the coloring of flowers and the development of ringspots in the leaves may also result. The rings may be concentric or single and usually contain a central spot.

Tobacco mosaic disease is an example of a viral disease in which the leaves become mottled. The virus particles are rod-shaped and are sometimes associated in pairs, end-to-end (Figure 171). It will be recalled that tobacco-mosaic was the first virus to be identified as an etiologic agent of an infectious disease and was also the first virus to be purified and crystallized.

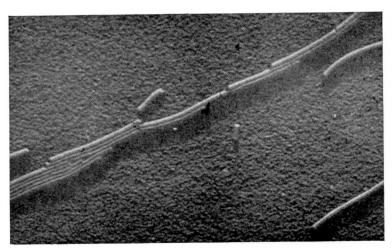

Figure 171.   Electron micrograph showing rods of tobacco mosaic virus. × 76,000. (From Electron Microscopy by Ralph Wyckoff, copyright 1949, Interscience Publishers, Inc.)

Yellows diseases give rise to a uniform yellowing of the leaves. Peach yellows and aster yellows are examples of this type of viral disease. Both are transmitted by leaf hoppers. Sugar-beet yellows, another example, is transmitted by plant lice.

Distorting diseases take various forms. They affect chiefly the leaves of plants. Curling and crinkling are common symptoms. These diseases usually have specific insect vectors. Curly top of sugar-beets, potato leaf roll and tobacco vein-distorting disease are examples of this type of infection.

Necrotic diseases are diseases in which cells are killed. Necrosis may be confined to the leaves or may involve the entire plant. Alfalfa dwarf disease, tobacco yellow dwarf disease and elm necrosis are examples of necrotic virus diseases. Transmission of these diseases is by leaf hoppers.

QUESTIONS

1. (*a*) Which general groups of microorganisms produce diseases in plants?
   (*b*) What are the various portals of entry used by plant pathogens?
2. (*a*) What is the most common mode of transmission of plant diseases?

(*b*) How does immunity in plant diseases differ from that in animals?

(*c*) Is it possible to control plant diseases by the development of resistant varieties?

3. Discuss briefly: (1) soft rots, (2) wilts, (3) blights, (4) tumors, (5) spots.

4. Differentiate between downy mildews and powdery mildews.

5. What is the life cycle of black stem rust of wheat?

6. (*a*) Give a brief description of blister rust of the white pine.

(*b*) What are smut diseases?

7. Characterize briefly the mosaic diseases of plants. Name other plant diseases caused by viruses.

REFERENCES

Bawden, F. C.: Plant Viruses and Virus Diseases. 3rd ed. Waltham, Mass., Chronica Botanica Company, 1950.

Dickson, J. G.: Diseases of Field Crops. 2nd ed. New York, McGraw-Hill Book Company, Inc., 1956.

Elliot, C.: A Manual of Plant Pathogens. 2nd ed. Waltham, Mass., Chronica Botanica Company, 1951.

First International Conference on Antibiotics in Agriculture. Proceedings, Publication 397. National Academy of Sciences-National Research Council, Washington, D. C., 1956.

Leach, J. G.: Insect Transmission of Plant Diseases. New York, McGraw-Hill Book Company, Inc., 1940.

Smith, K. M.: A Textbook of Plant Virus Diseases. 2nd ed. Boston, Little, Brown & Company, 1957.

Stakman, E. C., and Harrar, J. G.: Principles of Plant Pathology. New York, The Ronald Press Company, 1957.

Stefferud, A., ed.: Plant Diseases. Yearbook of Agriculture. Washington, D. C., Government Printing Office, 1953.

Walker, J. C.: Plant Pathology. 2nd ed. New York, McGraw-Hill Book Company, Inc., 1957.

Index

Page numbers in *italic type* refer to illustrations.